635

THE GARDENER'S BUG BOOK

THE
GARDENER'S
BUG BOOK

COMPLETELY REWRITTEN AND RESET

Cynthia Westcott

With Full-Color Illustrations of 102 Pests
by Eva Melady
and 94 Line Drawings
by J. E. Edmonson and Eva Melady

The American Garden Guild
and Doubleday & Company, Inc.
Garden City, New York, 1956

BIBLIOGRAPHICAL NOTE

First Published ....July 25, 1946
Completely Rewritten and Reset ....April, 1956

Typography by Edward Gorey

Library of Congress Catalog Card Number 56-6532

PESTS

The rose-bug on the rose
Is evil—so are those
Who see the rose-bug
Not the rose.

ELLA M. BOULT

PREFACE

When *The Gardener's Bug Book* was published, in 1946, we were on the threshold of an exciting new era of chemical control of plant pests. Since then, synthetic chemicals have come on the market so rapidly it has been difficult to keep them sorted out, to know which one is best for a particular pest. I have been repeatedly asked, in person, by telephone, and by letter, "When are you going to revise the *Bug Book* and put in the modern chemicals?"

It is gratifying to know that the book has proved useful to others as well as myself. Seed dealers tell me they keep it beside the telephone to answer inquiries. Some universities and some tree companies use it for their students. Garden writers, nurserymen, and professional gardeners refer to it, while plain dirt gardeners from every state in the union, as well as a few from abroad, have written that they find it understandable and helpful, though usually this politeness is preliminary to asking for information on some pest *not* included.

So here is the new *Gardener's Bug Book,* rewritten to include a few pests omitted from the first edition, a few pests that have become problems since 1946, many new chemicals, and numerous name changes. One or two new hosts have been added and the listing of pests under hosts has been simplified.

The general format has been retained because the book has proved in practice to be the easy, finger-tip reference we hoped for. At least the layman so considers it. Some scientists have found it difficult to find their way around insects grouped by common names rather than taxonomic relationships, but for them there is always the Index, with its full complement of scientific names.

Two of Eva Melady's exquisite color plates had to be jettisoned for economic reasons, but the rest are here, grouped together in the center

vii

of the book for easier reference. Most of the line drawings have been retained, but the sprayers and dusters have been redrawn to represent apparatus in current favor.

In the Introduction to the first edition I said, "Probably an apology is in order for a book on entomology written by one who is not a trained entomologist" (my academic work was all in plant pathology) "and has learned her insects the hard way, through having to subdue them in her own and in many other people's gardens." I no longer apologize. I now know that no real entomologist would be fool enough to attempt such a large scope—pests of flowers, fruits, vegetables, trees, shrubs, vines, and grasses in home plantings across the country. The scientist is hesitant to publish even in his own special field, for he is all too cognizant of the many gaps in our knowledge and he seldom ventures an opinion in any field outside his own.

But as a plant doctor, spraying over fifty gardens a week in New Jersey and New York from March to November, checking on problems in most other states during lecture trips, answering countless inquiries from every section, I have to take the broad view. This manual is a combination of my own experience—and I have personally met, if not always conquered, over half of the approximately 1100 pests presented here—what I have learned from talking with home gardeners and entomologists in nearly every state, and what I am continually learning from books and pamphlets. My house overflows with books, technical and garden, with bulletins, circulars, periodicals, scientific and otherwise. I have done my best to keep up with, and digest, this continuing flood, but in these swiftly changing times many books are partially out of date before they get off the press and even the information in current periodicals will be somewhat outmoded by the time this book gets into print. Descriptions and life histories of insects are reasonably stable; control measures and names are subject to constant revision.

Of the many people who have helped me with insect problems over the years I can name but a few: Irene Dobroscky Van de Water, who was the entomological half of The Plant Doctor until she married an apple farmer; Dr. C. C. Hamilton, of Rutgers University, who has patiently answered my questions for a quarter of a century; Dr. E. O. Essig of the University of California whose writings on western pests have been so very useful; John C. Schread of the Connecticut Experiment Station; Dr. Louis Pyenson, Long Island Agricultural and Technical Institute; Dr. Floyd Smith, entomologist, Entomology Research Branch, U. S. Department of Agriculture. I particularly thank Dr.

Reece I. Sailer and his colleagues at the U. S. National Museum for help with names of insects, and M. Truman Fossum, Agricultural Marketing Service, for many statistics. I continue to be grateful to Eva Melady and Ellen Edmonson for the fine illustrations, and I hereby express appreciation to Clara Claasen of Doubleday & Company for encouragement in preparing this revision, a task that proved to be somewhat more arduous than the original version.

Cynthia Westcott

Glen Ridge, New Jersey
August, 1955

CONTENTS

LIST OF COLOR PLATES

Following Page 326

xv

LIST OF LINE DRAWINGS

The new *Gardener's Bug Book* is not designed to be swallowed whole. It is not meant to floor you with so many pests that you decide not to garden at all. It is a reference manual to be consulted as problems arise in your own garden. You will never have, in one place, all the pests presented here, but you will have your fair share and after you have gardened long enough to know that insects are facts of life not to be completely ignored you will start trying to identify them and to keep them at a minimum with the least effort.

Before using this book as a manual, before attempting to look up information on any specific pest, please read Chapter I for a general picture of insects in gardens and types of control measures.

Next, read the first part of Chapter II, on Garden Chemicals, carefully and thoroughly. Skim through the Dictionary of Insecticides, Miticides, and Fumigants, starting on page 8, so that you will know the types of chemicals available and their general functions, but plan to return to this list for specific information before using any particular chemical. Be sure and read, most attentively, the words under Stop, Look, and Listen, p. 28, *before* opening any package and *before* using any material on any plant at any time.

Chapter III helps you in choosing, manipulating, and cleaning a sprayer, in making up spray mixtures. If you prefer dusting, check its advantages and disadvantages, the types of dusters available.

Chapter IV orients insects in the animal kingdom, tells how they are made and grow, how they are named, prerequisites to later identification.

With this background information there are two methods by which you can locate the information you need about a plant enemy.

1. If you know the common name of the insect or other pest, look it up directly in Chapter V, Garden Pests (and a Few Friends). Here

groups are in alphabetical order under common names, ANT-LIONS, ANTS, APHID-LIONS, ARMYWORMS, BEES, BEETLES, BIRDS, and so on. Consult the Table of Contents for the complete list of 72 such groups. Under each heading a general discussion of group characteristics is followed by specific insects arranged alphabetically by their common names. For instance, if you want information on the rhododendron lace bug, turn to BUGS for characters common to all true bugs and distinguishing family characteristics and then thumb your way along to R for **Rhododendron Lace Bug** for detailed information. The presently accepted common name is given in boldface type, followed by the scientific name in italics. Other names in rather common use are capitalized. For example, the **Mourning-cloak Butterfly** (*Nymphalis antiopa*) is treated under BUTTERFLIES because that name is now approved by the Committee on Common Names of the Entomological Society of America, but this insect may be more familiar to you as the Spiny Elm Caterpillar, so that name is given as well, both in the description and in the Index.

2. If you do not know the name of the pest, look up, in the alphabetical treatment of Host Plants, Chapter VI, the plant or plants attacked and note the most likely prospects, **Borer** or **Caterpillar, Mealybug** or **Aphid.** There may be only one or two possibilities, so the checking back is simple. There may be several kinds of aphids or borers listed and you may have to read the description of each one to find yours. It may well be that your particular species is not in this book at all for the 1100 species included are only about ten per cent of those that might possibly be damaging, but you should find its type described and you can probably control it without knowing its full name.

The color plates are grouped together, following page 326. The plate number is referred to in the description of the pest and in the Index. The actual size of most insects is shown by a line on the color plate. Line drawings are indicated by boldface in the Index.

THE GARDENER'S BUG BOOK

Chapter I

INSECTS IN THE GARDEN

INSECTS are not new. They have been around for about 300 million years, compared with less than 1,000,000 for man. They were undoubtedly waiting for Adam and Eve in the Garden of Eden and they have been aiding and bedeviling every gardener since that time. There is a lament in the Bible (Joel 1:4) which sounds very modern: "That which the palmerworm hath left hath the locust eaten; and that which the locust hath left hath the cankerworm eaten; and that which the cankerworm hath left hath the caterpillar eaten."

Organized warfare against insects is relatively new. In 1954 we celebrated the Centennial of Professional Entomology in the United States. Our public fight began in May 1854, when the New York State Legislature appropriated funds and Dr. Asa Fitch was employed to study injurious insects and their control. The next month Dr. Townend Glover was appointed as the first federal entomologist.

Today there are about 4500 economic entomologists responsible for protecting our resources from insect damage. Of these, 435 are employed by the United States Department of Agriculture, 476 are in state experiment stations, 80 in public health services, 100 in the Armed Forces, and 1400 concerned with state and federal inspection and quarantines, or acting as private consultants, or running pest-control services. That means that there is not too much individual help available for the more than 30 million gardeners in this country and that each gardener must learn for himself enough about insects to profit from the investigations made by the professionals.

ARE INSECTS INCREASING?

Gardeners are always complaining about the numbers of insects now compared to the good old days. They say our grandfathers did not have to be continually concerned with pests. That is only partially true. Grandfather did not insist so much on unblemished fruits and vege- tables as we do today; he did not worry too much about holes in the leaves of the ornamentals around the house. But he had his problems and so did great-grandfather. Many of the insects we fear today were mentioned in a book, *Insects Injurious to Vegetation,* published in 1841 by T. W. Harris in Massachusetts. Way back in 1833 the plum curculio often totally destroyed the plum, apricot, and nectarine crop. Codling moth, first mentioned by name in 1868, was recorded in 1898 as causing an annual loss of one fourth to one half of our apple crop. Serious inva- sions have been reported in the West since 1922. Our native eastern grape phylloxera became a major pest in California in 1863. The cot- tony-cushion scale from Australia nearly wrecked the citrus industry in the 1870s.

Our habit of introducing new insects along with foreign plants was not checked before 1912 when the Plant Quarantine Act was created to regulate the movement of nursery stock. Two of our worst pests evidently got in just before that date, although they went unnoticed for a few years. The European corn borer is thought to have arrived in shipments of broomcorn from southern Europe, and the Japanese beetle with ornamental shrubs from Japan. Even with rigid quarantines and careful inspection insects sneak in. The European bark beetle, vector of the Dutch elm disease fungus, arrived in elm burls imported by furniture veneer factories and in crates used for transporting dishes.

INSECTS AS FRIENDS OF MAN

No one knows exactly how many kinds of insects there are and figures vary widely even on the number already described. The total number of named insects in the world probably runs between 700,000 and 1,000,000, with upward of 100,000 of these in North America. Not more than a tenth of the latter can be designated as public enemies. The rest are either harmless or decidedly beneficial. Without insects, life as we know it today would not exist. We depend on insects for the pollination of 85 per cent of our fruits and many of our vegetables. They play a large role as scavengers. They provide food for birds and fishes. They give us honey and wax, shellac, cochineal, and silk; they have a minor role in surgery and medicine. Only recently, when so many have been killed by some of our too efficient new chemicals, have we learned what a very large role many insects have had as parasites and predators on harmful insects and mites.

INSECTS AS ENEMIES OF MAN

In 1868 our crop loss due to insects was figured at $300 million. Today the annual figure is around 4 billion, but that includes the cost of control measures as well as direct loss from insects not controlled. In general, we feed about $\frac{1}{10}$ of our crops each year to insects but this can vary with the crop and the location and the season from 0 to 100 per cent. In some cases losses have been drastically reduced in the last few years by new chemicals. Greenhouse operators, who used to average 15 per cent loss, have, with proper methods, cut that to 1 or 2 per cent. Figures are not available for home garden losses, but certainly some of the nurseryman's profit comes from plants sold to replace those killed by insects in home plantings.

Besides their direct effect on plants, insects can be even more injurious as disseminators of plant disease. Leafhoppers spread curly top, aster yellows, peach yellows, cranberry false blossom, elm phloem necrosis. Aphids transmit the virus of potato leaf roll, mosaics of lily, cucurbits, and crucifers. The iris borer and cabbage maggots spread bacterial soft rot. Cucumber beetles transmit the bacteria of cucurbit wilt, and flea beetles those causing Stewart's disease of corn. Bark beetles spread the Dutch elm disease fungus most efficiently. Insects are also, of course, enormously important in causing human misery and disease, but that is outside the scope of this garden manual.

WAYS OF CONTROLLING INSECT PESTS

Control of plant pests is not limited to spraying and dusting operations. First we have natural control, factors influencing the numbers of insects without any effort by man, and then we have biological control, where man tries to aid in natural control. We have legal control, exclusion, to prevent the introduction of pests; we have control by cultural methods; by mechanical and physical measures; and, finally, we have control by chemicals.

Natural control comes from the climate and physical characters of a region and the presence there of natural enemies. Not many insects live in all climatic zones—arctic, temperate, and tropical. Winter temperatures restrict the range of some; summer heat limits others. Some insects prefer a warm, moist climate; others like it warm but dry. Some insects can fly or be carried by the wind long distances; others can crawl only a short distance. Large lakes, rivers, and mountain ranges check the natural spread of insects. The character of the soil limits certain pests, wireworms flourishing in poorly drained soil, nematodes in sandy soil.

Birds, moles, shrews, skunks, snakes, lizards, newts, salamanders, and toads eat many insects. Birds consume enough to more than pay for the cherries, strawberries, grapes, and corn they also eat. Skunks eat a lot of grubs—compensation for the rather conspicuous holes they leave in lawns.

Biological control is a sort of artificial restoration of the balance of nature, bringing in insect predators and parasites, encouraging birds and useful animals, introducing nematodes or bacteria or fungi which will work on the undesirable insects.

Control by exclusion can be either legal or voluntary. The Plant Quarantine Act of 1912 provides that whenever it seems necessary, in order to prevent the introduction of any dangerous insect or plant disease, the federal government has the power, after a public hearing, to prohibit the importation, or shipment interstate, of any class of plants or plant products from any country or locality and from any state or portion of a state or territory in this country. Such specific prohibitions are called *quarantines*. In addition to the federal quarantines there are a number of state quarantines. Domestic quarantines are now in force against gypsy and brown-tail moths, Japanese beetle, pink bollworm, Mexican fruitfly, and white-fringed beetle.

It is not expected that a quarantine can keep out a pest forever, but the expense of the inspection service is justified if the insect is prohibited for a period sufficiently long to enable us to learn its life history, to develop control measures, and to introduce its parasites.

As a home gardener you can make your own voluntary exclusion laws. Why, for instance, borrow trouble by introducing a dephinium crippled by cyclamen mites, or a Norway spruce with aphid galls, or a juniper with scale?

Cultural control, including sanitation, is usually free from expense except for labor costs. Sometimes it does not even require labor, merely a little planning based on knowledge of life histories of particular insects. Crop rotation is a fundamental principle in good culture, although it is not always possible in a small garden. Most insects attack a small group of related plants. Cabbage worms chew members of the cabbage family; the squash vine borer sticks to the cucurbit group; Mexican bean beetles don't like much except beans. By switching locations for crops you can starve out certain pests, or at least keep them from building up huge populations.

Soil cultivation during the season destroys some insects. Spading up the vegetable patch in the fall, leaving the ground rough, exposes some larvae and pupae to death by freezing.

Timing of planting is another cultural measure. In Connecticut snap beans planted in early June often mature between broods of Mexican bean beetles. Early summer squash may come along ahead of the squash vine borer; late corn is less apt to be injured by the European corn borer.

Resistant varieties are often thought of in connection with plant diseases, but the idea works for insects, too. Most native plants have developed some degree of resistance to their pests. European varieties of grapes can be grown in this country only on native root stock resistant to grape phylloxera. Often the character of the foliage keeps off pests. Leafhoppers usually prefer varieties with smooth leaves, but the azalea whitefly restricts operations to varieties with hairy leaves.

Destruction of crop residues, weeds, and trash—in other words, garden sanitation—is tremendously important. It is the cheapest, easiest, most foolproof measure for the amateur gardener. The wrong chemical may injure sensitive plants, but it never does any harm to clean up all old plant parts after harvest, compost some of the material, and burn anything capable of causing trouble another year. Clean up old iris leaves to get rid of borer eggs; make slugs homeless by cutting down hollyhock stalks; get rid of weeds and trash around the garden and so avoid offering winter protection to cucumber, Mexican bean, and Colorado potato beetles, as well as many other pests.

Control by mechanical and physical measures depends on barriers erected between the plant and the pest. A wire fence, or a single electrified wire, is used against rabbits and other animals; flower bulbs are planted in wire baskets for protection from mice and moles; wire guards keep dogs off shrubbery; hardware cloth protects orchard trees from rabbits and mice; a cardboard cylinder keeps cutworms away from young transplants; hotkaps keep cucumber beetles off seedlings.

Control by chemicals makes up the bulk of this book on garden pests. The list of materials available today is given in the next chapter and the application of these chemicals for the control of specific pests in Chapter V.

Chapter II

GARDEN CHEMICALS

THE last 10 years of the first century of economic entomology has had more activity in the development of chemicals to control plant pests than the previous 90. In 1854 tobacco, soap, and sulfur were about the only materials tried as insecticides; pyrethrum came into use for household pests soon after. In 1865 Paris green, brushed onto vines with a broom, began to halt Colorado potato beetles, the first successful use of a stomach poison. About 1880 kerosene emulsion was tried as a contact insecticide and was largely replaced by oil sprays in another quarter of a century. The proprietary miscible oil, Scalecide, which appeared in the market in 1905, is still sold under that brand name. Lead arsenate became available commercially in 1903 and calcium arsenate came into use, chiefly for cotton pests, about 10 years later. Rotenone became popular about 1933.

That was the year I started out as a doctor to gardens. Life was very simple. I used a miscible oil or lime-sulfur as a dormant spray, lead arsenate for chewing insects, nicotine sulfate for sucking insects on ornamentals, and rotenone on fruits and vegetables. Then came World War II and the spectacular debut of DDT. More and more and more synthesized organic chemicals have been put out to share in the glory and the end is not yet in sight. They say it takes a million and a quarter dollars to do the preliminary testing on an acceptable new chemical, but that seems no deterrent. Insecticides have become big business.

In the same chlorinated hydrocarbon group with DDT we have its analogs methoxychlor and TDE; we have benzene hexachloride, with lindane, its purified form; we have chlordane, toxaphene, aldrin, dieldrin, heptachlor and endrin. We have phosphates such as parathion and tetraethyl pyrophosphate, so poisonous that spilling a little on your skin may kill you, and some, like schradan and demeton, that can be absorbed by a plant through roots or foliage and kill the bug when it sucks. We also have a phosphate, malathion, that is not so toxic to humans and acts as a miticide as well as an insecticide. And we have fine safe miticides, such as Aramite and Ovotran, that do a swell job on red spiders and other mites but are useless for other pests. The old distinction between a stomach poison and a contact insecticide has become rather hazy because many of the new compounds act as both.

There are numerous fumigants on the market that kill insects by their poisonous gases. They are used for soil treatment and in enclosed chambers, but in greenhouses fumigation has been replaced to a large extent by treatment with aerosol bombs, which apply the chemicals as extremely fine particles.

All of these new chemicals are marketed under trade names, in many different formulations and combinations. By the terms of the 1947 Federal Insecticide, Fungicide and Rodenticide Act all such economic poisons (which we prefer now to call pesticides) must be registered with the United States Department of Agriculture and have their labels approved. These must give the brand name, name and address of the manufacturer, the approved common name or the chemical name of all active ingredients. Poisons toxic to man must carry the skull and crossbones symbol, or a caution statement for less hazardous material, with the prescribed antidote. As a safety measure it is strongly advised that all gardeners read the label carefully, every word, *before opening the package*. Merely inhaling the chemical may be dangerous; if a respirator or gas mask is advised, don't open the container until all precautions given on the label have been followed.

There are about 32,000 pesticides currently registered. These may change their formulations (and the label) from year to year while keeping the same brand name. To avoid confusion later, the use of proprietary names has been kept at a minimum in this new edition of the *Bug Book* which we hope will be useful for more than the current year. There is, however, a very useful compilation, *Pesticide Handbook,* published each spring, which gives several thousand trade names, with their latest formulations, in alphabetical order. The 1955 edition (price $1.25 paperbound) lists 6204 pesticides. You may order your copy from *Pesticide Handbook,* P. O. Box 798, State College, Pennsylvania.

In July 1954, the Miller Pesticide Residue Amendment to the Federal Food, Drug, and Cosmetic Act became Public Law 518. This provided for the setting up of tolerances for the chemicals necessary for the production of fruits and vegetables. A tolerance is the maximum amount of pesticide residue that may lawfully remain on or in food. It is stated in parts per million by weight. Some chemicals may have zero tolerance, meaning no residue allowed; some have only 0.1 p.p.m. Lead arsenate has a tolerance of 7 on apples but only 1 on citrus fruits. DDT has a tolerance of 7, and relatively non-toxic methoxychlor has a tolerance of 14. Even fungicides, which we customarily think of as non-toxic, are considered poisons with ferbam, zineb, and ziram given the same tolerance as DDT.

Public Law 518 means that the food you buy is safe. The farmer has stopped applying poisons long enough before harvest or else has provided adequate machinery for the removal of poisons. The food you produce in your own back yard may not be safe unless you are careful to use non-poisonous compounds after edible plant parts are formed. Ordinary washing in the kitchen sink will seldom adequately remove poisonous residues.

Most of the new pesticides have long and complicated chemical names and so have been given short common names for everyday use, such names being approved by the Interdepartmental Committee on Pest Control of the United States Department of Agriculture. In writing about chemicals, trade names are capitalized, official common names written in lower case. Sometimes the trade name has been released for use as a common name, in which case it is not capitalized. The common and chemical names of most of the new insecticides in the following list have been taken from that given by the Committee on Insecticide Terminology of the Entomological Society of America in the February 1955 issue of the *Journal of Economic Entomology*.

A DICTIONARY OF INSECTICIDES, MITICIDES, AND FUMIGANTS

Aerosol Sprays. True aerosols are air suspensions of solid or liquid particles of ultramicroscopic size. They remain suspended in air for hours and are very effective in fogging operations for mosquitoes but are not so useful for plant pests. The so-called aerosol sprays have somewhat larger particles, which deposit readily on foliage. The insecticide is dissolved in liquefied gas and held under pressure in a metal container known as a bomb. When a valve is opened the chemical is dispersed in a fine mist spray from which the solvent gas immediately evaporates. Greenhouse aerosols containing TEPP or parathion have to be used with gas masks and other safety measures, but there are small bombs containing pyrethrum and rotenone safe to use indoors on house plants, and others formulated for safe use on garden plants. Do not ever use on plants bombs sold for household pests. Always use the bomb 12 to 18 inches away from the plant. Otherwise the solvent does not evaporate fast enough and may cause severe burning. Always use the bomb in short bursts with a sweeping motion; do not visibly wet the foliage.

Aldrin (not less than 95 per cent of 1,2,3,4,10,10-hexachloro-1,4,4a,-5,8,8a-hexahydro-1,4,5,8-dimethanonaphthalene). A new chlorinated hydrocarbon that has given excellent control of grasshoppers, is used somewhat for ants, grubs, and other lawn pests, controls wireworms, seed-corn and root maggots, and plum curculio when applied to the soil, and kills some leaf miner larvae when applied to foliage. It is stable in the presence of lime and other alkaline materials and is compatible with most other chemicals. It is available as a 25 per cent emulsion, 25 per cent wettable powder, and as a 1 or 2 per cent dust.

Allethrin (dl-2-allyl-4-hydroxy-3-methyl-2-cyclopenten-1-one esterified with a mixture of cis and trans dl-chrysanthemum monocarboxylic acids). Also known as allyl homolog of cinerin 1 and synthetic pyrethrins. This synthetic compound is sometimes used in place of the chemical obtained from ground pyrethrum flowers. See Pyrethrum.

Aramite (product containing 2-[p-tert-butylphenoxy]isopropyl-1-methylethyl 2-chloroethyl-sulfite). An efficient, safe (relatively non-toxic to plants and people) miticide or acaricide for home garden use. Available as a 15 per cent wettable powder (use 1 tablespoon to 1 gallon of water), in emulsions, and in combination dusts. It controls spruce spider mite, two-spotted spider mite and other red spiders but not insects, so it does not kill our beneficial insects. It is incompatible with dinitro compounds, bordeaux mixture, lime-sulfur, and other alkaline materials but can be used with sulfur dust or wettable sulfur and with captan, ferbam, maneb, ziram, and zineb fungicides. It is supposed to be used with caution combined with copper, but I have added it weakly to a combination spray containing ammoniacal copper and have had no trace of injury. Aramite is the trade name used as a common name.

Azobenzene ($C_6H_5NNC_6H_5$). An orange crystalline compound toxic to some beetles, but used more as a fumigant for spider mites in greenhouses. When painted on the heating pipes, it volatilizes.

Baits. Prepared poison baits for the control of ants, earwigs, cutworms, slugs, weevils, etc., are sold under many trade names. A few formulae for home mixtures are given under the specific pests.

BHC; Benzene Hexachloride (1,2,3,4,5,6-hexachlorocyclohexane, consisting of several isomers and containing 12 to 14 per cent of the gamma isomer). First compounded in 1825 but its insecticidal properties were not realized until World War II, in France and England. It has a disagreeable odor and imparts an objectionable flavor to some fruits and vegetables, but it is an efficient contact and stomach poison as well as fumigant. Its purified gamma isomer is used more in gardens. See Lindane.

Bordeaux Mixture. A fungicide—combination of lime and copper sulfate—that also has some repellent properties for leafhoppers, flea beetles, and a few other insects. It is better adapted to potatoes than ornamentals and may be purchased as a ready-mixed dry powder to be diluted with water at the time of use.

Bulan (1,1-bis[*p*-chlorophenyl]-2-nitrobutane).

Butoxy Thiocyanodiethyl Ether; Lethane 384 (2-butoxy-2'-thiocyanodiethyl ether). A contact insecticide good for aphids and houseflies.

Calcium Arsenate. First used extensively about 1919 for dusting cotton, now often applied by airplane to this crop. It is sometimes used on potatoes, beans, tomatoes, and other vegetables, but is not safe on fruits and is seldom applied to ornamentals. It is used at the same rate as lead arsenate, which is safer on many plants. It can be mixed with lime, preferably that with a high magnesium content, as a dust. It is incompatible with soaps and cryolite and of doubtful compatibility with many new insecticides and fungicides. It is sometimes combined with apple pomace in a weevil bait.

Calcium Cyanide. A deadly poison, used in fumigating greenhouses, sometimes blown into wasp nests or animal burrows. Under the trade name of Cyanogas it may be purchased in a mixture resembling sand for ant nests, as a fine dust for nests and burrows of insects and rodents, and in granular form for wireworms in soil. For greenhouse fumigation granules are spread evenly over walks which have been previously wet down. They can be shaken out of a wide-mouth jar with a few holes punched in the lid. The dosage must be exact, too much will injure. For most plants ¼ ounce is used for 1000 cubic feet. Hydrocyanic acid is given off slowly in the moist air of the greenhouse. However, except for slight wetting down of paths, the house should not be watered for 24 hours before fumigation nor immediately afterward. Fumigation should be at night, when it is calm and clear, with temperatures between 60° and 70°F. It is not safe in lean-to greenhouses attached to houses.

Sweet pea, asparagus fern, coleus, marguerite, wandering Jew, and snapdragon are sensitive to cyanide; the dosage should be halved. In many greenhouses cyanide fumigation has been replaced by aerosol sprays.

Calomel (mercurous chloride). Used chiefly for control of cabbage and other root maggots. Dilute 1 part with 19 parts talc, hydrated lime, or pyrophyllite, and dust after transplanting; or mix with half as much cornstarch by weight and dust stems above roots and below leaves before transplanting. Calomel is not a dangerous poison like mercuric chloride.

Carbon Bisulfide. A nearly colorless, vile-smelling liquid which is heavier than air and changes to a highly inflammable gas on exposure to air. It is used as a fumigant for bean and pea weevils and other stored grain pests, at the rate of 1 pound per 100 cubic feet of space. Placed in a machine-oil can, it can be readily squirted into ant nests or into borer holes in trees, the openings plugged with putty to hold in the gas. As a soil fumigant it is injected into holes 18 inches apart, but this is done only in fallow ground, never near living plants. A wad of cotton can be soaked with it and pushed down into the burrow of a ground squirrel, prairie dog, or gopher. Do not smoke in the process; remember that it is *inflammable*.

Chlordane (1,2,4,5,6,7,8,8-octachloro-2,3,3a,4,7,7a-hexahydro-4,7-methanoindene). This is an American chemical, brought out in 1945, that has proved very useful in the control of ants, indoors and in gardens and lawns, grasshoppers, mole crickets, beetle grubs, chinch bugs, black vine and other weevils. It is a complex hydrocarbon acting as both contact and stomach poison and has a slight fumigating action. It is available as a 50 per cent wettable powder (use 2 tablespoons to a gallon of water), as a 5 per cent dust, and in emulsions of various strengths. It is sold under many brand names. It should be used with caution with nicotine, bordeaux, lime-sulfur, and lime.

Chlorobenzilate (ethyl 4,4'-dichlorobenzilate). A new miticide very useful in greenhouses for spider mites resistant to other chemicals and promising for outdoor use, with low toxicity to man. It comes as a 25 per cent wettable powder, a 25 per cent emulsion, and in an aerosol bomb.

Chloropicrin (CCl_3NO_2). Tear gas, sold as Larvacide, a useful soil fumigant for nematodes, weed seeds, some fungi. It is non-inflammable but very irritating and is best used with a special applicator. It injures living plants; treat only fallow soil.

Chlorthion (O[3-chloro-4-nitrophenyl]-O,O-dimethyl thiosphosphate).

Coal-tar Distillates. A fraction from the distillation of coal known as "coal-tar oil" provides a basis for tar washes and fruit-tree carbolineums sold under proprietary names. Some are toxic to plant foliage and are used only as dormant sprays to kill overwintering eggs. Some are used to kill various soil pests.

Cryolite (sodium fluoaluminate). Natural, brought from Greenland, and synthetic, used in the manufacture of aluminum and for insecticides. It has low toxicity to mammals and has been used fairly extensively in the South on vegetables and in the Northwest on fruits. It controls codling moth, walnut husk fly, Mexican bean beetle, western grape leaf skeletonizer, cucumber beetles, flea beetles, and some others. It is occasionally injurious to plants in New Jersey and other humid locations. It is inactivated by lime and alkaline materials. As a dust, 2 parts of talc or sulfur are mixed with 1 of cryolite. As a spray, use $1\frac{1}{2}$ to 3 tablespoons to 1 gallon of water.

Cube. A tropical plant used as a source of rotenone.

Cyanogas. See Calcium Cyanide.

Cyclethrin (dl-2-[2-cyclopentynyl]-4-hydroxy-3-methyl-2-cyclopenten-1-one esterified with a mixture of cis and trans dl-chrysanthemum monocarboxylic acids). Analog of allethrin.

DDD. See TDE.

D-D Mixture (mixture of 1,2-dichloropropane and 1,3-dichloropropene). An excellent soil fumigant controlling root-knot nematodes, wireworms, and some other soil insects, some weeds. It is not so unpleasant to use as chloropicrin but will burn if spilled on the skin and not removed immediately with soap and water. It is applied in holes 6 inches deep, staggered 18 inches apart, at the rate of $\frac{1}{3}$ ounce per hole. For large-scale applications it is used with a special applicator in furrows 18 inches apart at the rate of 200 pounds per acre for nematodes, slightly more for wireworms. It is most effective in sandy soil. Delay planting 10 to 15 days after treatment.

DDT (commercially available dichloro-diphenyl-trichloroethane, the principal constituent of which is 1,1,1-trichloro-2,2,bis[p-chlorophenyl]-ethane). The most publicized insecticide yet produced, first synthesized in 1874 by a German chemist but not put to practical use until 1939 when its value against the Colorado potato beetle was determined in Switzerland. It came into its own as an aid in public health during World War II and it is estimated that it has saved 5,000,000 lives and prevented 100,000,000 illnesses by controlling mosquitoes, lice, flies, and other insects that carry human diseases. It was released for general agricultural and garden use in 1945. Since then it has had many spectacular successes and has introduced some grave problems.

DDT has given remarkable control of codling moth on apple and walnut; leafhoppers; gypsy moth; cankerworms and many other caterpillars defoliating shade trees (but not bagworms) ; bark beetle vectors of Dutch elm disease; boxwood and holly leaf miners; peach tree, iris, lilac, and other borers; gladiolus thrips; rose midge; Japanese, blister, and other beetles on ornamentals; and grubs in lawns. It controls cabbageworms and many other vegetable insects but not Mexican bean beetle. It is not particularly dangerous on warm-blooded animals and is safe on most plants.

On the debit side it may severely stunt squashes and injure other cucurbits; it has killed some camellias (though it is reasonably safe on other varieties) and the house plant kalanchoe; it sometimes gives a yellowish cast to rose foliage; and it is doubtful on tomatoes, at times markedly reducing the yield.

Also, some insects have been building up resistance to DDT and some are markedly increased by it. This has been particularly true with twospotted spider mite and other common red spiders, spruce spider mite on evergreens, European red mite on fruit, mites on oaks, elms and other shade trees wherever DDT has been used directly in sprays or indirectly for mosquito control. This is partly due to killing beneficial insects that ordinarily keep mites under control and apparently also, in some cases, to increasing the susceptibility of the host to mite injury and to irritating the mites so they move around more. DDT has been useful in controlling euonymus and orchid scales but has brought others into prominence. Forbes scale has increased in orchards and we have a rhododendron scale in New Jersey that I find wherever DDT has been applied in the vicinity. Aphids, also, usually build up large populations after DDT, and the red-banded leaf roller becomes so serious in orchards DDT is often omitted in early sprays despite its usefulness for codling moth. In my own work I prefer not to use any spray or dust regularly that contains DDT, but I use it thankfully for special pests on special occasions.

DDT is available under many trade names as a 50 per cent wettable powder, the usual dosage being 2 tablespoons per gallon or 2 pounds per 100 gallons, though this is doubled for control of bark beetles. It is also used as a 12 per cent emulsion in mist blowers. It is sold as a

3, 5 or 10 per cent dust and is included in a great many general-purpose dusts now on the market. For grubproofing lawns it is used at the rate of 6 pounds of 10 per cent dust to 1000 square feet. It is compatible with almost all fungicides and insecticides, though doubtful with lime-sulfur and other compounds with lime, and with some oil sprays. It kills fish and pools should be covered if nearby trees and shrubs are to be sprayed. In excessive dosages it kills birds, but at recommended strengths and by avoiding drenching trees at the height of the nesting season, it is not particularly dangerous. It is only moderately toxic to man and can be used without special precautions.

Demeton (mixture of O,O-diethyl-S-ethylmercaptoethyl thiophosphate and O,O-diethyl-O-ethylmercaptoethyl thiophosphate). Probably better known as Systox, an organic phosphate acting as a systemic insecticide, first synthesized in Germany by Schrader in 1948. The chemical, applied to soil or foliage, is translocated in the plant in the xylem or phloem, or both, and kills aphids and some other insects, and mites, that subsequently feed on the host. Demeton is registered for use on apples, potatoes, walnuts, and ornamentals but must not be used on food crops within 21 days of harvest. It has given good control of pear leaf blister mite, peach silver mite, apple mite, southern red mite on camellias, aphids and whiteflies on gardenias, aphids and mites on roses and chrysanthemums. It is highly poisonous to man and should not be used without special training in safety precautions. In California a permit for use must be obtained from the agricultural commissioner. As an aerosol in combination with chlorobenzilate, demeton is said to be effective against red spiders resistant to parathion and Aramite.

Derris. A plant with insecticidal properties. Two species, *Derris elliptica* and *D. malaccensis* from Malaya and the East Indies, have 4 to 5 per cent rotenone in their dried roots. See Rotenone.

Diazinon (O,O-diethyl O-[2-isopropyl-6-methyl-4-pyrimidinyl] thiophosphate). Another new organic phosphate, promising in control of two-spotted spider and privet mites, clover aphid, apple maggots, and other insects.

Dichloroethyl Ether (beta,beta'-dichloroethyl ether). A soil fumigant sometimes used for sod webworms, also in corn earworm oils.

Dichlorophenyl Benzenesulfonate (2,4-dichlorophenyl benzenesulfonate). Also known as Genite and Genitol.

Dieldrin (not less than 85 per cent of 1,2,3,4,10,10-hexachloro-6,7-epoxy-1,4,4a,5,6,7,8,8a-octahydro-1,4,5,8-dimethanonaphthalene). A chlorinated hydrocarbon similar to aldrin but taking care of more insects and with a longer residual effect. It is a poison but does not present undue hazards to warm-blooded animals and seems destined for wide use in home gardens as well as on farms. It is effective for ants, beetle grubs, mole crickets, chinch bugs, sod webworms, cutworms, army-worms, grasshoppers, earwigs, sowbugs, and pillbugs, and in baits for snails and slugs. It is useful for borers, leaf miners, maggots, thrips, and many other pests. It is marketed in granular form, particularly good for lawns; as a 1½ per cent dust to be applied at the rate of 4½ pounds per 1000 square feet; as a wettable powder, 5, 25, and 50 per cent, to be mixed with water and applied as a spray. It is now available in small packages under various brand names; follow manufacturer's directions for each formulation. It is compatible with most other pesticides.

Diisopropyl Parathion (O,O-diisopropyl O-p-nitrophenyl thiophosphate).

Dilan (mixture of 1 part of Prolan and 2 parts of Bulan). Used in the control of Mexican bean beetles and other truck crop and fruit insects. It is only half as toxic to mammals as DDT.

Dimefox (bis[dimethylamino]fluorophosphine oxide).

Dimethyl Carbate (dimethyl cis-bicyclo[2.2.1]-5-heptene-2,3-dicar-boxylate).

Dimite. See DMC.

Dinitro Compounds. Derivatives of cresol and phenol, used chiefly as dormant sprays for aphids, red mites, and scale insects. They are incompatible with summer oils and many other pesticides.

Dinitrobutyl-phenol (4,6-dinitro-o-sec-butylphenol). A new insecticide and fungicide called DNOSBP.

Dinitrocresol (4,6-dinitro-o-cresol). The sodium salt of this compound is sold as a yellow paste, Elgetol. A wettable powder, DN-Dry Mix No. 2, is also available.

Dinitrocyclohexylphenol (4,6-dinitro-o-cyclohexylphenol). DNO-CHP, formulated as a 20 per cent wettable powder and as a dust for control of mites on apples, citrus fruits, walnuts, beans, and other crops. Sold as DN-Dry Mix No. 1.

Dithiocyanodiethyl Ether (beta,beta'-dithiocyanodiethyl ether). Lethane A-70.

DMC; Dimite (4,4'-dichloro-alpha-methylbenzhydrol). A miticide particularly effective for cyclamen mite on delphinium, African violets, and other plants; also useful for European red mite and privet mite. It is somewhat phytotoxic, injuring trees particularly. Use no more than 1 teaspoon of emulsion to a gallon of water. It is not very toxic to warm-blooded animals and is compatible with most pesticides but not with acid compounds.

Endrin (1,2,3,4,10,10-hexachloro-6,7-epoxy-1,4,4a,5,6,7,8,8a-octahydro-1,4,5,8-endo-endo-dimethanonaphthalene). A very new compound that has given good results on a variety of pests including army cutworm, corn earworm, cranberry fruitworm on blueberries, Japanese beetle grubs, spittlebugs.

EPN (O-ethyl O-*p*-nitrophenyl benzenethiophosphonate). A phosphate not quite so toxic to man as parathion but still to be used with great caution. It controls mites, some aphids; it has given good results with hard-to-control hickory shuckworm on pecan and also the pecan nut casebearer.

Ethylene Dibromide (1,2 dibromoethane)—A fumigant used for stored grain and for treating soil. It is available as a liquid for general use and in measured doses in capsules for easy application to small garden plots. Apply to fallow soil only.

Ethylene Dichloride. A fumigant sometimes used as an emulsion for peach tree borer but not otherwise for living plants. It is inflammable.

Furethrin (*dl*-2-[2-furfuryl]-4-hydroxy-3-methyl-2-cyclopenten-1-one esterified with a mixture of cis and trans *dl*-chrysanthemum monocarboxylic acids). An analog of allethrin.

Hellebore. The ground rhizome of *Veratrum album* and *V. viride*. An insecticide of historical importance, it is little used today except occasionally on currants and gooseberries.

Heptachlor (1[or 3a],4,5,6,7,8,8-heptachloro-3a,4,7,7a-tetrahydro-4,7-methanoindane). A chlorinated hydrocarbon particularly effective for grasshoppers, onion, turnip, and seed-corn maggots, wireworms, beetle and weevil grubs, and other pests. It is available as a 25 per cent wettable powder, in emulsions, and as 1 and 2 per cent dusts; it is compatible with most other pesticides.

HETP (mixture of ethyl polyphosphates containing 12 to 20 per cent of tetraethyl pyrophosphate). See TEPP.

Hydrocyanic Acid Gas (HCN). Originally used to protect insect collections in museums, then, in 1886, to kill scale on citrus trees in California and later for nursery stock and greenhouse insects. It is a deadly poison to be used only by experts. Hydrogen cyanide was formerly obtained by treating sodium cyanide with sulfuric acid and water, but now calcium cyanide, which releases the gas on contact with moist air, is preferred. Citrus trees in California have been fumigated with HCN under tents for many years, but, because so many insects have developed a resistance to cyanide, fumigation is being replaced by spraying.

Isodrin (1,2,3,4,10,10-hexachloro-1,4,4a,5,8,8a-hexahydro-1,4,5,8-endo-endo-dimethanonaphthalene). An isomer of aldrin.

Isolan (dimethyl 5-[1-isopropyl-3-methylpyrazolyl]carbamate). Promising in control of aphids, especially early in the season to prevent leaf curling by the viburnum aphid.

Karathane (dinitrocaprylphenyl crotonate). Originally offered as an acaricide, under the name of Arathane, and then as Iscothan, it is probably used more now as a fungicide, for control of powdery mildew, sold as Mildex.

Lead Arsenate. Up to the advent of DDT this was our best-known and most widely used stomach poison, standard control for chewing insects on fruit trees, shade trees, ornamental shrubs and flowers. It was developed by the Federal Bureau of Entomology for gypsy moth control and first used in Massachusetts in 1892. Even today many arborists and orchardists prefer it to DDT because it does not bring so many other problems. Basic lead arsenate, less toxic to insects but safer on foliage, is used in foggy areas of California and in some eastern peach orchards, but the standard form is acid lead arsenate, safe on most foliage at proper dilutions. Brown spots on leaves of peaches, cherries, plums, and other tender fruits may be arsenical injury, which can be avoided by using the chemical at low strength mixed with an equal quantity of lime.

Dosages vary from 3 to 6 pounds per 100 gallons of water, which is ½ to 1 ounce (3 to 6 tablespoons) for 1 gallon. For grubproofing lawns the rate is 10 pounds per 1000 square feet but lead arsenate has been largely superseded for this purpose by newer insecticides. The good old "Massey dust," consisting of 1 part arsenate of lead to 9 parts of sulfur, which took care of chewing insects and many fungi, is now difficult to buy; you may have to mix your own. Lead arsenate is incompatible with soap but compatible with nicotine sulfate and bordeaux mixture. It is highly toxic if swallowed and is usually colored pink to denote its poisonous character, but it is not dangerous spilled on the skin or inhaled, as are many of the new pesticides.

Lime, Hydrated. Used as a diluent in dusts, in the preparation of bordeaux mixture, and as a safener for arsenical sprays, preventing the formation of arsenic acid on sensitive foliage. Depending on its source, lime has either a high-magnesium or a high-calcium content. It should not be used with cryolite, pyrethrum, rotenone, DDT, or dormant oils.

It is used in nicotine dusts to release nicotine fumes for action against sucking insects. When spread on the ground around plants it is a deterrent for slugs.

Lime-Sulfur. A fungicide used also as a contact insecticide, chiefly as a dormant spray, 1 part to 8 or 9 of water, sometimes in summer for mites, at a 1 to 40 or 1 to 50 dilution. Used first as a sheep dip, it started as an insecticide for plants in 1886 in California, against the San Jose scale; it was not introduced into eastern states until 1900. The liquid form is preferable, being more stable, but it is rather hard to obtain nowadays; a dry mix may have to be substituted. Lime-sulfur is unpleasant to use and will stain paint, but in my own experience it does a better job for juniper and rose scales than oil sprays. It is compatible with nicotine sulfate but should not be mixed with fluo-silicates, rotenone, pyrethrum, fixed nicotine, dormant oils, dormant dinitros, Aramite, captan, or coppers.

Lindane (gamma isomer of BHC of not less than 99 per cent purity). This purified form of benzene hexachloride has lost most of the objectionable odor but can still impart an off flavor to certain root crops. It is a versatile insecticide that gives excellent control of lace bugs, is effective for some aphids, especially woolly aphids, thrips, leaf rollers, many plant bugs, some leaf miners, plum curculio, flea beetles, weevils, cutworms, and wireworms. It is sometimes used with a fungicide for treating seed before planting. It does not control leafhoppers or mites. It is incompatible with alkaline compounds like bordeaux mixture and lime-sulfur and is slightly more toxic than DDT to warm-blooded animals. It is available as a 25 per cent wettable powder (use 1 tablespoon to a gallon of water), as 1 to 5 per cent dusts, and in emulsions.

Magnesium Arsenate. Patented in 1922 and with a limited use. It is safer on bean foliage than lead arsenate but not so safe on fruit trees.

Malathion (O,O-dimethyl-S-[1,2-dicarboxyethyl]dithiophosphate). A phosphate spray with properties similar to parathion but less toxic to warm-blooded animals. It can be safely used in home gardens to control mites, aphids, mealybugs, whiteflies, crawling stages of certain scale insects, leafhoppers, lace bugs, thrips, and other pests of ornamentals. It controls such fruit insects as pear pylla, Oriental fruit moth, eye-spotted bud moth. It is used for pea aphids, lygus bugs, and other vegetable pests but should be applied to spinach and other greens with caution, for it is very difficult to remove with ordinary washing. It is available as a 50 per cent emulsion (usual dosage 1 teaspoon to a gallon, increased to 2 to 4 teaspoons for scales), as a 25 per cent wettable powder, and is included in combination dusts. There is some evidence that it loses potency when combined with the fungicide captan. It is incompatible with bordeaux mixture and is listed as of doubtful compatibility with karathane. It may injure poinsettia.

Mercuric Chloride. Also known as corrosive sublimate and bichloride of mercury. A virulent poison, used as a disinfectant at a 1 to 1000 dilution (one 7-grain tablet to a pint of water). It has been used as a soil treatment for cabbage maggots (but calomel is safer) and as a dip for iris rhizomes to prevent rot following borer attack; it kills earthworms in lawns.

Metacide. (Product containing methyl parathion and parathion.)

Metaldehyde. An attractant in baits for slugs and snails, usually mixed with calcium arsenate. It is available as a dry mix, in convenient pellet form, and as a 10 per cent dust, the latter often used in greenhouses, sometimes combined with chlordane.

Methoxychlor (1,1,1-trichloro-2,2-bis[p-methoxyphenyl]-ethane). DMDT, sold as Marlate. Closely related to DDT, but only $\frac{1}{25}$ as toxic to warm-blooded animals. It is used for Mexican bean beetles and other vegetable pests, for cherry fruitfly, plum curculio, and other fruit insects, and may replace DDT for roses. It acts more rapidly than DDT. It is compatible with most pesticides but not with alkaline or dinitro compounds or dormant oils. It is available as a 24 per cent and a 50 per cent wettable powder and in combination dusts.

Methyl Bromide. A fumigant, originally used in fire extinguishers, then for treatment of dried fruit, and now for fumigation of balled or potted nursery stock in special fumigation chambers.

Methyl Parathion (O,O-dimethyl O-p-nitrophenyl thiophosphate). Methyl homolog of parathion.

Naphthalene. Sold as flakes and as moth balls. The latter are sometimes effective as rabbit repellents and the flakes have been widely used for thrips on gladiolus corms, carrot rust fly, and have been vaporized in greenhouses for mites. Newer chemicals have largely replaced naphthalene.

Neotran (product containing bis[p-chlorophenoxy]-methane). Another miticide or acaricide.

Nicotine. An alkaloid in the tobacco plant, obtained from wastes in cigar and cigarette factories, and an important contact poison. The standard nicotine-sulfate solution (usually purchased as Black Leaf 40) contains 40 per cent nicotine sulfate. For aphids and other soft-bodied insects the usual dilution is 1 to 800, or 1 teaspoon per gallon, or 1 pint to 100 gallons. It may, however, be used at weaker, 1 to 1000, or stronger, 1 to 400, dilutions. Soap, 1 ounce per gallon, is added to increase wetting and spreading qualities and to help liberate the nicotine. Although nicotine sulfate is a deadly poison, there is little residual effect and any residue can be readily washed off. Hence it can be safely applied to vegetables for aphids and other sucking insects almost up to harvest. Nicotine dusts usually have 3 to 5 per cent nicotine diluted with lime.

Free nicotine, 40 or 50 per cent, is more volatile than nicotine sulfate; it is used in greenhouses and in manufacturing dusts. It is painted on steampipes in greenhouses, vaporized on hot plates, or impregnated on papers or punk and sold in a container for convenient use. Holes are punched in the lid and the contents ignited. Violets, astilbe, cyclamen, and maidenhair fern are rather sensitive to nicotine fumigation. Nicotine is also used as a stomach poison in non-volatile "fixed" compounds such as nicotine bentonite. These should not be used with lime, which "unfixes" them. Nicotine is incompatible with cryolite.

NPD (tetrapropyl dithiopyrophosphate).

Oil Sprays. Animal or vegetable oils, as fish oil, lemon oil, coconut oil, but more often petroleum oils, miscible oils, oil emulsions, and emulsifiable oils.

In an *emulsion* the oil is broken up into fine globules in water, varying in amount so that the product is a thin cream or a thick paste. Most dormant oil emulsions are made from red engine oil or pale lubricating oil, with the oil kept suspended by an emulsifier which is chemically active (soap, sulfated alcohol, sulphonated oils, organic acids, or vegetable oils) or chemically inactive (soybean flour, calcium, or ammonium caseinate). They are made with a minimum of water and are diluted at the time of spraying. The percentage of oil in an emulsion is stated on the label; the percentage of oil desirable for a dormant spray varies according to plants and locality. To calculate the dilution multiply the gallons of spray required by the per cent of oil desired and divide by the per cent of oil in the stock emulsion.

Miscible oils are used for dormant sprays in home gardens. They are manufactured from lubricating oils, are transparent, contain 93 to 99 per cent oil, with an emulsifier dissolved in the oil, are somewhat more stable than oil emulsions, and have too little water to freeze when stored. They mix readily with water, turning the creamy white color of an emulsion, and are sold under many brand names. Manufacturer's directions must be followed, but normally a dilution of 1 part to 16 parts of water is used for deciduous trees and 1 to 25 or 1 to 30 for ever-greens. *Emulsifiable oils* are much like miscible oils but they emulsify to the white color only under pressure as the solution leaves the sprayer.

There are many precautions for dormant oil spraying on fruits or ornamentals:

1. Do not use an oil spray when the temperature is below 45° F. or is likely to drop below freezing during the following night.

2. Spray early enough in the day so the spray can dry before night.

3. Spray, if possible, in early spring rather than fall or winter, and close to the time buds are ready to burst.

4. Do not use a dormant spray after buds break and leaves are more than 1/4 inch long.

5. Do not use oil sprays on sugar or Japanese maples, on Japanese or black walnut, on butternut, beech, or magnolia, or on some ever-greens—chamaecyparis, cryptomeria, Douglas-fir, true firs, hemlock, and yews.

6. Never repeat a dormant spray the same season; do not drench trees.

7. Make sure that other spray residues are flushed out of the spray tank before putting in oils.

Summer white oils, such as Volck, are lighter oils, safe, at proper dilutions, for summer sprays on fruit trees and for control of scales, mealybugs, whiteflies on ornamentals in greenhouses or outdoors. Man-ufacturer's cautions for particular plants should be carefully followed. Do not spray when the temperature is above 85°F. or when plants are in bright sun. Greenhouse and house plants should be moved out of the sun for treatment and washed off with water in a few hours. Do not combine summer oils with wettable sulfur, lime-sulfur, quinones, glyo-din, captan, or summer dinitro compounds. Nicotine or rotenone may be added. Allow 2 to 4 weeks between applications of sulfur and summer oils.

Ovotran (product containing p-chlorophenyl p-chlorobenzenesul-fonate). A miticide or acaricide more effective against eggs and young larvae than adult mites. It is relatively non-toxic to man but somewhat phytotoxic, having injured oak, American holly, dogwood, rose, and other trees and shrubs in certain circumstances. It has been quite satisfactory in controlling spruce and other mites on evergreens and is included in some all-purpose dusts for general garden use. It is available as a 50 per cent powder, in 5 and 10 per cent dusts, and in emulsions. It is compatible with most pesticides.

Paradichlorobenzene, PDB. Similar to naphthalene but more volatile. Used principally as a soil fumigant in the control of peach tree borers, being scattered in a ring around the base of the tree in early autumn and the fumes confined with earth. The dosage must be exact. See Peach Tree Borer.

Para-Oxon (diethyl *p*-nitrophenyl phosphate). Oxygen analog of parathion.

Parathion (O,O-diethyl O-*p*-nitrophenyl thiophosphate). A most efficient insecticide and miticide for spider mites, aphids, mealybugs, whiteflies, armored scales (but not soft scale), leaf rollers, thrips, springtails, millipedes, sowbugs, and other pests but extremely toxic to man. It should not be used by amateurs but left to experienced operators willing to take the necessary precautions of special respirator or gas mask, completely protective clothing, laundered after each exposure, and natural rubber gloves. Parathion can kill you if absorbed through the skin, or inhaled, or accidentally swallowed. Atropine is the antidote for acute poisoning. Workers with repeated contacts with parathion should have periodic blood tests. A lowering of cholinesterase in the blood is a sign of phosphate poisoning. Workers should not enter orchards within 2 days of parathion spraying. Fruits and vegetables should not be sprayed within 30 days of marketing. One city in Florida has prohibited the use of parathion within its limits; a permit from the agricultural commissioner is required in California.

Parathion is available as 15 and 25 per cent wettable powders, as 0.25 to 2 per cent dusts, and in aerosol bombs for greenhouses. It is compatible with most pesticides but doubtfully compatible with alkaline materials.

Paris Green (copper acetoarsenite). A stomach poison used for Colorado potato bettles as early as 1865 and later for other pests, but little used now except in grasshopper, cutworm, and sowbug baits and even here being replaced by new chemicals.

Perthane (1,1-dichloro-2,2-bis[*p*-ethylphenyl]ethane).

Piperonyl Butoxide and **Piperonyl Cyclonene.** Very complex organic chemicals used as synergists or activators for pyrethrum, especially in aerosol sprays.

Pirazinon (O,O-diethyl 3-[2-propyl-6-methyl-4-pyrimidinyl]thiophosphate).

Potasan (4-methylumbelliferone O,O-diethyl thiophosphate). A selective stomach and contact poison.

Prolan (1,1-bis[p-chlorophenyl]-2-nitropropane).

Pyrethrum. One of the earliest insecticides, possibly first used by Caucasian tribesmen. Pyrethrum is a plant, one of the chrysanthemums. The use of its flower heads for insecticidal purposes probably originated in Persia, whence it was introduced into Europe early in the nineteenth century and sold as Persian or Dalmatian Insect Powder. Most of the pyrethrum coming into this country has been extracted for household sprays, about 2000 brands being on the market prior to World War II. The active chemical principles, found in the ovaries and achenes of the flowers, are known as pyrethrins I and II, cinerins I and II. Allethrin is a synthetic pyrethrin.

Pyrethrum kills the insect by actual contact, paralyzing the nerve ganglia and being absorbed through the spiracles or breathing pores. Taken internally by chewing insects, it can also act as a stomach poison. Because it is relatively non-poisonous to man and warm-blooded animals it is especially suitable for edible crops, and because it leaves no unsightly residue it is often desirable for ornamentals. Pyrethrum gives a quick kill, or at least a paralysis, particularly at high temperatures, but the residual effect is low. Rotenone works much more slowly but is effective for a longer period and at lower temperatures. Consequently the two are often combined in sprays or dusts.

Pyrethrum is not compatible with lime or bordeaux mixture or lime-sulfur. It decomposes rapidly when diluted with water, so always use a pyrethrum spray *immediately* after diluting to proper strength.

Pyrolan (dimethyl 5-[3-methyl-1-phenylpyrazolyl]carbamate). A carbamate toxic to aphids and some other insects.

Pyrophyllite. A hydrated aluminum silicate very similar to talc in its properties and used as a diluent in various dust mixtures, often seeming to increase the toxicity of the insecticide. It can be used where lime is undesirable.

Red Squill. The ground bulb of a tropical plant, *Urginea maritima*, used as a rat poison and not harmful to humans and pets.

Rotenone. A contact and stomach poison derived from the roots of several species of plants, principally derris (*Derris elliptica* and *D. malaccensis* from Malaya and the East Indies) and cube or timbo (*Lonchocarpus utilis* and *L. urucu* from South America). These plants were used by natives as fish poisons for centuries but rotenone itself, the active principle, was not isolated until 1902. Its great popularity as a "safe" insecticide, relatively non-toxic to man and other warm-blooded animals, began in the 1930s. It is, however, deadly to cold-blooded animals and will kill goldfish in garden pools as readily as food fish in a tropical stream.

The plant roots vary in rotenone content, but they are ground and blended by manufacturers to a uniform 4 or 5 per cent. This powder is then mixed with talc, sulfur, pyrophyllite, or other diluent until the final strength is 0.75 to 1 per cent. For spraying, rotenone is sold as a liquid extract containing also deguelin and other materials with some value as insecticides. Such spray concentrates are labeled as to rotenone content and total extractives.

Rotenone apparently paralyzes the respiratory system as well as acting as a true stomach poison. It gives a slow kill, sometimes taking as much as 48 hours, but it is surer than pyrethrum, particularly in cool weather, and the residue remains effective for nearly a week. It is not compatible with alkalies such as lime, lime-sulfur, calcium arsenate, and bordeaux mixture.

Ryania. A contact and stomach poison derived from the stem and root of a South American plant (*Ryania speciosa*), even less toxic than rotenone to mammals. It is quite effective in controlling European corn borer, cranberry fruitworm, and various pests on food crops. It is used as a dust or spray and seems to be compatible with most other pesticides.

Sabadilla. Ground seeds of a South American plant (*Schoenocaulon officinale*) of the lily family. This contact and stomach poison, available as 5, 10, and 20 per cent dusts, is irritating to the eyes and respiratory tract but otherwise is of low toxicity to man. It is particularly effective against squash bugs, stink bugs, harlequin bugs, tarnished plant bugs, cabbageworms, cranberry insects, and leafhoppers.

Schradan; OMPA (octamethyl pyrophosphoramide). A systemic insecticide that has been known by the trade name of Pestox III. The common name is in honor of the German, Schrader, who developed it about 1940. It is an emulsion used as a spray or soil drench for mites and aphids, one application lasting 3 to 5 weeks in warm weather with short-stemmed plants. It is highly toxic to man and should be used only by experienced growers. A permit is required in California.

Sesamin (2,6-bis[3,4-methylenedioxyphenyl]-3,7-dioxabicyclo[3,3.0]-octane). A synergist for pyrethrum.

Soap. Used as a spreader to break the surface tension between the spray droplet and the waxy surface of plant foliage, thus ensuring the wetting of the entire leaf. Soap is usually added to nicotine sulfate at the time of dilution but many proprietary mixtures already contain soap. There are liquid insecticide soaps, which can be measured easily in a cup marked in ounces and go into solution readily. The usual dosage is 1 ounce to 1 gallon of water. Bar soap can be used, 1 cubic inch to a gallon, or flakes, 1 heaping tablespoon per gallon, but these have to be dissolved in warm water. Soap itself has insecticidal properties and soapy water is often used for bathing ivies and other house plants. Soap should not be used with lead or calcium arsenate, with cryolite, lime-sulfur, or lime.

Sodium Arsenite. A very soluble and poisonous compound used in ant syrups, sometimes in other poison baits, and as a weed killer. It is very toxic to plants and man.

Sodium Fluosilicate. Rather widely used in poison baits for grasshoppers, crickets, cutworms, and weevils.

Sodium Selenate. The first systemic insecticide to come into general use, first tried for mites on carnations in greenhouses. When applied to the soil it is taken up by the plant and is effective for red spiders and cyclamen mites and leaf nematodes in chrysanthemum. It is so poisonous it should never be used on soil that may be planted to vegetables in the next year or two. Handle with caution and measure exactly; use at the rate of ¼ gram for each square foot of soil (dissolve 1 gram in 1 gallon of water and apply to 4 square feet). Do not repeat treatment for 4 to 6 months. For African violets sodium selenate can be used in capsule form, purchased as Kapsulate. One capsule is placed on the soil of a 4-inch pot, which is then watered.

Strobane (a terpene polychlorinate with a chlorine content of approximately 66 per cent).

Sulfotepp (O,O,O,O-tetraethyl dithiopyrophosphate). Also called dithione and used in greenhouses in aerosol bombs or smoke generators for spider mites, thrips, aphids, whiteflies, mealybugs, and scale insects. Several applications are advised at 3- to 4-day intervals with the series repeated in another 3 or 4 weeks. This is highly toxic to man.

Sulfoxide (n-octyl sulfoxide of isosafrole). An organic sulfur.

Sulfur. Usually considered a fungicide or a diluent for insecticidal dusts but itself a contact poison, both as straight sulfur and as lime-sulfur. The Greeks had a word for it, "Theion"; the Romans named it sulfur. Homer mentions it as a disinfectant. In dust form, ground so small it will pass through a 325-mesh sieve, it gives fair control of broad mites and some spider mites (though not as efficient as the specific new miticides), may kill crawling stages of some scale insects and young tent caterpillars. Wettable sulfurs are provided for spray mixtures. Sulfur is not compatible with oils and should not be used on plants which have been recently treated with oil; it should not be mixed with most soaps. It tends to burn foliage in hot weather; use with caution above 80°F. It may injure squash, melon, and other cucurbits, but some varieties are less sensitive. Do not use sulfur as a diluent in any dust meant for cucurbits.

Sulphenone (product containing *p*-chlorophenyl phenyl sulfone and related sulfones). Another miticide.

Systox. See Demeton.

Tartar Emetic (potassium antimonyl tartrate). Formerly used with brown sugar, honey, or corn syrups as a bait spray for thrips on gladiolus, roses, onions, citrus fruits, etc., but now mostly replaced with DDT, lindane, and other insecticides.

TDE; DDD (commercially available dichloro-diphenyl-dichloroethane the principal constituent of which is 1,1-dichloro-2,2-bis[*p*-chlorophenyl]ethane). Sometimes sold as Rhothane, an analog of DDT; less toxic to man, more toxic to Mexican bean beetles, tomato worms, redbanded leaf rollers, and a few other insects, including mosquito larvae. Available as a 50 per cent wettable power and a 25 per cent emulsion.

TEPP (tetraethyl pyrophosphate). A contact insecticide, even more poisonous to man than parathion, but with such slight residual effect it can be used for aphids, mites, etc. on vegetables up to a week or so before harvest. It is sold as a 20 per cent and 40 per cent liquid for sprays and in dusts and aerosols for commercial growers. It is so potent that ½ teaspoon of the 20 per cent solution to 1 gallon of water is sufficient for most soft-bodied insects. A small amount spilled on the skin may, if not immediately washed off, have fatal results. It is also toxic by inhalation; use a respirator as well as protective clothing. TEPP is incompatible with calcium arsenate, Paris green, lime-sulfur, lime, and bordeaux mixture and questionable with lead arsenate, nicotine, and dinitro compounds. It decomposes rapidly after dilution with water; use immediately after mixing.

Thallium Sulfate. Used in ant baits and in poisoning seeds for control of mice, rats, ground squirrels, and the like. It is so poisonous to man baits containing it should not be mixed at home.

Thiocyanoethyl Laurate (beta-thiocyanoethyl laurate). Sold as Lethane 60, one of the organic thiocyanates. A contact poison used for aphids, whiteflies, thrips, mealybugs, and leafhoppers in greenhouses and on truck and garden crops. It is compatible with, and often used with, pyrethrum and rotenone but questionable with lime, lime-sulfur, and sulfur. Use care in handling and applying.

Toxaphene (chlorinated camphene having a chlorine content of 67 to 69 per cent). Formulated as a 25 to 40 per cent wettable powder, a 5 to 20 per cent dust, and in emulsions. It is especially valuable for control of grasshoppers and cotton insects and is used somewhat for thrips and other insects controlled by DDT, but it is more poisonous to mammals. It is incompatible with lime, lime-sulfur, bordeaux mixture, and other alkaline compounds. Use care in handling, especially in oil solutions of toxaphene, which can be readily absorbed through the skin.

CHEMICALS IN COMBINATION

There are thousands of all-purpose sprays and dusts now on the market that combine several different chemicals. A fungicide (sulfur, copper, captan, dichlone, ferbam, karathane, maneb, zineb, or ziram) is usually included to take care of plant diseases along with insect pests and mites. It is seldom possible to solve all problems with one mixture, but usually you can find one that will do fairly well for ornamentals, another for vegetables, and another for fruit trees, with a few supplementary treatments for special pests.

In choosing the right combination you must make sure that both the active ingredients and the diluents used in making up the mixture are safe on the plants you want to protect. Rotenone is non-toxic to most plants but sometimes sulfur is combined with it, both as a diluent and as a fungicide, and sulfur is decidedly toxic to most melon varieties and to some other cucurbits. Figure 1 shows what happened when cantaloupes were dusted in Alabama for pickleworms. The plot shown in A was dusted with 1 part derris (source of rotenone) with 3 parts talc; it averaged 31 melons per 10 hills. But the plot shown in B was dusted with 1 part derris, 1 part sulfur, and 2 parts talc; it averaged only 2.2 melons per 10 hills. That small amount of sulfur, only 25 per cent of the dust mixture, cut the yield 93 per cent.

Dust mixtures containing DDT will markedly reduce squash yields, for some cucurbits are allergic to DDT. Tomatoes are sometimes sensitive to it, although it is recommended for tomato pests in some states. DDT in a mixture can kill or seriously injure some varieties of camellias though others are little affected. DDT used in a rose spray or dust without a miticide added may encourage so many red spiders the re-

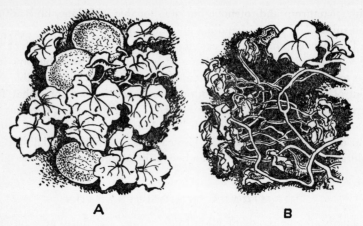

1. Sulfur injury on melon: A, vines dusted with rotenone; B, with rotenone combined with sulfur.

sults may be worse than no treatment. Mixtures with DDT must be formulated for use on plants, not for mosquitoes and household pests. I have seen severe injury to rose foliage when DDT was applied with a mist blower for mosquito control. The injury was not from the DDT itself but from the kerosene or other oil solvent.

A spray containing lead arsenate planned for shade trees is not usually safe on the tender foliage of peaches and other stone fruits, or for flowering cherries or ornamental plums. For these, lead arsenate is used at a weaker strength and lime or zinc sulfate is added as a safener.

The mixing of incompatible chemicals may cause injury to a plant that would be safe with either one alone. One chemical may inactivate another so that the spray loses its potency. Aramite in a dust having a certain kind of clay as a diluent is far less potent than when mixed with pyrophyllite. The fungicide captan seems to reduce the efficiency of malathion.

STOP, LOOK, AND LISTEN!

Before using *any* chemical or combination, in *any* form, at *any* time, on *any* plant, ask yourself these questions:

1. *Is it safe for me?* Before opening any package or bottle read the label. See if you are to take special precautions against inhalation or

skin contact. The very moment of opening a bag or can of toxic dust presents the grave danger of getting poison into your lungs.

2. *Have I safeguarded my neighbor's children and pets?* Children do trespass and they sometimes find discarded containers with a trace of poison left inside. There have been tragic fatal accidents. It is not easy to dispose of leftover poisons and their containers. Some liquids can be flushed down the toilet and the bottles carefully rinsed before being put out for the trash man. Some bags and cardboard cartons can be burned, but with others the burning itself creates a hazard. Some can be buried deeply, but few of us have enough unused land for this. Under no circumstances should a chemical be divided and part given away without the original label.

At the end of any spraying operation there is some unused liquid. This can be poured into a gravel drive where it can be absorbed instantly, or down a drain, but should not stand in gutters or in hollows in a concrete drive long enough for birds or dogs to take a drink.

3. *Do I know the active ingredient in this material and is it formulated for use on plants?* Is there any danger of injuring my plant at the dilution needed to kill the insect?

4. *Is there any diluent in this dust or spreader in this spray that may harm my plant?* Remember the cantaloupe and the sulfur.

5. *Is it specifically recommended for the pest I want to kill?*

6. *Are the weather conditions right for this chemical on this plant at this time?* Oil sprays injure all plants somewhat and evergreens severely if used when it is too cold; copper puts red spots on rose leaves in cold weather; sulfur burns tips of foliage when it is too hot.

7. *Have I used anything on this plant in the recent past that would either inactivate this chemical or be injurious to the plant when mixed with this chemical?* Don't lime your lawn the same spring you use chlordane for grub control; don't follow summer oils with sulfur.

8. *Have I used any other material recently in this sprayer and forgotten to clean it out?* The sprayer should be rinsed between different chemical mixtures and at the end of each day. Weed killers, however, should be used in a separate sprayer, for it is almost impossible to clean a sprayer that has been used for 2,4-D sufficiently for protective spraying.

9. *Have I measured or weighed the amounts correctly?* If you need only 1 teaspoon and spill enough more to make 2, you are doubling the dosage and vastly increasing the chance of plant injury.

10. *Have I compensated for possible harm from this chemical?* Have

you added a miticide to DDT to take care of the red spiders it will encourage; have you safened lead arsenate with lime for fruit trees?

If you can answer these questions, go ahead and spray or dust. If you can't, hesitate. You can do more harm in 10 thoughtless minutes than the bugs can do in a whole season. If you don't know *what* you are doing and *why* you are doing it, don't do anything in the line of chemicals. Stick to sanitary and cultural measures and encourage the beneficial insects and birds to work for you.

Chapter III

SPRAYING AND DUSTING

THE ART OF SPRAYING

SPRAYING is a fine art and one which all too few gardeners ever acquire. It takes a lot of common sense and a modicum of brains; it takes a sense of timing and a sense of responsibility to plants. It takes a little mechanical skill but not necessarily too much brawn, for you may still be able to hire that. To turn a spraying schedule over to a handyman gardener is fatal—to the plants, not the bugs—but to use the handyman to supply power while you do the actual spraying, well, that's different. At least it ought to be, although experience makes me rather skeptical. Lack of common sense in selecting and applying chemicals and inability or unwillingness to keep up regular weekly treatments throughout the growing season seem to be the two chief obstacles.

CHOOSING A SPRAYER

Sprayers vary in size and type from those suitable for a few house plants to large trucks for farmers and shade-tree experts and airplanes for forests or field crops.

The **Atomizer-type Sprayer** works something like a flit gun, averages 1 quart in capacity, and is made of tin, galvanized iron, brass, or copper. The extra expense of brass or copper is repaid with longer life *if* you clean the sprayer after each use. You push a plunger back and forth to get a fine spray and this is a lot harder than it looks; after you have sprayed 2 or 3 rosebushes you are ready to quit. Such a sprayer is fine for house plants and for a *very* few plants outside. It is most effective when you are after aphids on buds and new shoots and can hit them directly. Getting adequate coverage of undersurfaces is difficult.

The **Compressed-air Sprayer** varies in capacity from 1½ to 4 gallons. It is designed to be pumped up, slung over one shoulder with a strap, operated as long as the pressure lasts, then set down, pumped up again, and so on, as long as your breath holds out to pump. Mine doesn't last very long. In this sprayer the air pump is clamped tightly into an airtight tank, not more than two thirds full of solution. Air pumped into the space between the solution and the top of the tank provides the pressure. This sprayer has a short hose and a spray rod with a curved or swivel nozzle which will let the spray reach the underside of foliage. It is hard to clean unless you get one with a large opening at the top, but properly taken care of one should last several seasons. There is no agitator, so the tank must be shaken occasionally to keep the chemicals from settling out. The compressed-air sprayer is also available mounted on wheels for pushing around the garden.

The **Knapsack Sprayer** is fine for a man, rather heavy for a woman to carry on her back, although I used one for several years with a good deal of satisfaction. The pressure is continuous, maintained by an effortless moving up and down of a lever on the right side of the operator while the left hand is free to hold the spray rod which can send spray to the top of fairly tall bushes or underneath low plants. The spray mixture is kept agitated and comes out in fine droplets.

The **Trombone Sprayer** is a slide pump that looks and works something like a trombone. One end of the hose is dropped in a bucket and if the slide works properly (mine often does not) you can send a stream of spray up into small trees. It is a nuisance to keep moving the bucket around, the spray is not kept agitated, and working the slide back and forth is fairly arduous.

Wheelbarrow Sprayers don't have to be literally wheelbarrows, but they are tanks, usually of galvanized iron, which can be mounted on a 1- or 2-wheeled truck and readily moved around the garden. My own opinion is that if you can have but one sprayer this is the type to buy. It will take care of anything from 1 or 2 roses to a good-sized border of shrubs or small fruit and shade trees. Pressure is maintained and the mixture agitated by pushing a handle up and down which operates a plunger cup inside a cylinder. The chief disadvantage of this sprayer is that it takes 2 people to operate it efficiently. Here is where that handyman gardener comes in (or maybe your husband). He does the pumping and pushes the heavy truck around the garden while you concentrate on handling the spray rod, which comes in 3 sections. For trees, all 3 sections are put together; for most garden work

ATOMIZER SPRAYER

COMPRESSED AIR SPRAYERS

KNAPSACK SPRAYER

WHEELBARROW SPRAYER

TROMBONE SPRAYER

2. Sprayers of assorted sizes and types.

POWER SPRAYERS

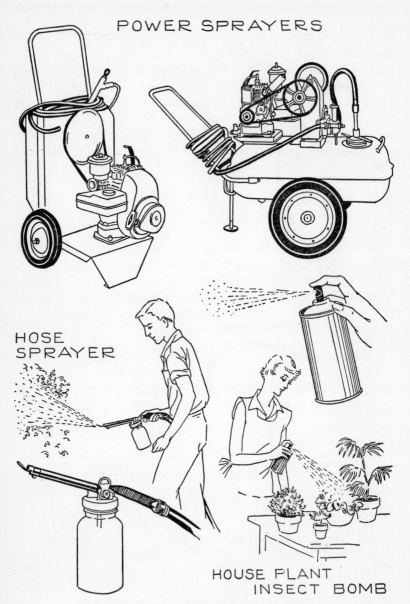

HOSE
SPRAYER

HOUSE PLANT
INSECT BOMB

3. More sprayers and ways to treat plants.

2 sections are best and you can cover a lot of ground in a short space of time. A wheelbarrow sprayer will finish up the job in a half or a third of the time required by a knapsack sprayer and in less than a quarter of the time it would take with a compressed-air sprayer.

The wheelbarrow sprayer that I have used in doctoring other people's gardens for nearly a quarter of a century is the Paragon type, a 12-gallon tank with a 2-wheel detachable truck. Tucked away in the back of my Ford coupé it has traveled all over the country. Despite heavy duty (and my helper and I spray more than 50 gardens every week from the end of March to November) one sprayer lasts several years because separate parts for replacement are readily available. A 10-foot hose comes with the sprayer, but I have this replaced with a 25-foot length of heavy-duty spray hose, to reach easily all sides of shrubbery, and to get into garden beds at some distance from paths. This type of sprayer is quite easily cleaned and costs little more than a good knapsack sprayer. It provides a fine mist with little visible residue to mar the beauty of ornamentals.

Power Sprayers are available now in all sizes, from the 5-gallon affair, which seems to me too small to be worth the cost (about 4 times as much as the hand-pumped wheelbarrow), to the large 300-gallon tank on a truck which delivers from 5 to 50 gallons a minute under 200 to 800 pounds pressure. For estates, sprayers of 15-, 25-, or 50-gallon capacity are practical if you can afford the initial investment and will keep them clean so they last long enough to give adequate return on that investment. They usually have a gasoline motor, but some are equipped with an electric motor. Power spraying usually takes more spray solution than hand spraying for the same amount of protection.

Mist Blowers or low-gallonage sprayers are used by commercial operators in addition to hydraulic equipment but seldom entirely replace the latter. The spray is very concentrated; air instead of water is used as the carrier so that a foglike mist comes out of the machine.

Hose Sprayers. Some people use water pressure via the garden hose to supply pressure for spraying and there are various attachments—jars and cartridge cylinders—sold for this purpose. You need constant pressure of 40 pounds or more and an ability to maneuver the hose around the garden without inadvertently pulling it over the corner of the bed and injuring the plants. I find the latter difficult.

Aerosol Bombs. For greenhouses there are fairly good-sized cylinders with a rod and nozzle like a sprayer. They contain parathion, TEPP, or other deadly poisons and have to be used with a special gas mask. For homes and gardens there are small push-button containers holding pressurized sprays of relatively non-toxic chemicals.

Airplanes and **Helicopters** are used for custom spraying of large acreages, either farms, for routine spraying of field crops, or forests, to control outbreaks of spruce budworm, gypsy moth, and other pests of great economic importance.

MAKING UP SPRAY MIXTURES

Measurements must be exact. Keep with your spray materials a set of plastic measuring spoons and a glass measuring cup marked in ounces. Remember your household measurements:

> 3 level teaspoons are 1 level tablespoon.
> 2 tablespoons are 1 fluid ounce.
> 16 tablespoons are 1 cup (8 fluid ounces).
> 2 cups are 1 pint.
> 4 cups are 1 quart.
> 16 cups (4 quarts) are 1 gallon.

By a little figuring you can save much time in measuring. If directions call for 1⅔ tablespoons you can be exact by measuring 1 tablespoon and 2 teaspoons. But if you need 8 tablespoons it is a lot quicker to measure out ½ cup. If you are making up a dormant oil spray at 1 to 15 dilution put in 1 cup of oil and add water to make 1 gallon. But if you want a summer spray of about 1 to 50 dilution you add 3 gallons (48 cups) of water to the 1 cup of oil. The actual dilution is then 1 to 49, but that is near enough at such a great dilution.

If directions in bulletins call for 1 pint in 100 gallons, just figure that that means 1 pint in 800 pints or a 1 to 800 dilution; 1 quart to 100 gallons is a 1 to 400 dilution. The following table will help in transposing figures for any amount of spray you wish.

DILUTION TABLE FOR SPRAYS

Desired Amount of Finished Spray	Amount of Concentrated Spray for Dilution			
	1–200	1–400	1–600	1–800
1 quart	1 tsp.	½ tsp.	⅓ tsp.	¼ tsp.
1 gallon	4 tsps.	2 tsps.	1½ tsps.	1 tsp.
5 gallons	6 tbsps.	3 tbsps.	2¼ tbsps.	1½ tbsps.
50 gallons	1 quart	1 pint	1½ cups	1 cup
100 gallons	2 quarts	1 quart	1½ pints	1 pint

When it comes to mixing sprays from dry materials, directions are usually given in pounds of chemical per 100 gallons of water; e.g., 3 pounds lead arsenate to 100, 1 pound actual DDT (which means 2 pounds of the 50 per cent wettable powder) to 100. Transplanting pounds to tablespoons for small amounts of spray is difficult because of the difference in weight of various compounds. One ounce of lead arsenate is 5½ tablespoons, but 1 ounce of calomel is only 1¾ tablespoons; wettable sulfur is about 3 tablespoons to an ounce; hydrated lime 4 to 5 tablespoons; and 50 per cent wettable DDT about 6. The measurement also varies according to whether the material is fluffed up or packed down hard.

In purchasing dry materials for garden use I read the label to see how many pounds are recommended to 100 gallons of water and then I figure how many grams or ounces that means for 1 gallon. I then weigh that amount out and see how many tablespoons it fills and mark it on the package for all subsequent use. My small scales weigh in grams, but it is easy to transpose from the metric system by knowing that 28.35 grams equal 1 ounce; 453.6 grams equal 1 pound.

In making up sprays the usual method is to make a slurry by adding water very slowly to the dry material, stirring constantly, but some chemicals work better sprinkled on top of the pail of water. The directions on the package sometimes tell you; sometimes you find it out by trial and error. Some compounds work better if a spreader, such as household Dreft, or DuPont Spreader-sticker, or Triton B-1956, is added to the diluted spray. Dry mixes usually have some inert materials which do not go into solution, so the diluted spray should always be *strained into the tank* through cheesecloth.

MANIPULATING THE SPRAY ROD

Handling the spray rod to get complete coverage, yet not to drench the plants so the spray runs off or builds up too much residue, is where the fine art of spraying comes in. Success depends on how the pump is operated. I have used the strong right arm of a good many assistants in spraying operations and only about 1 in 3 operators has the sense of timing that will provide a mist spray coming out with good even pressure. Some pump so hard that the cylinder head is blown off; others are uneven or never get up enough pressure to do a good job.

The type of spray droplets and the amount of unsightly residue depend somewhat on the hole in the nozzle. A very small hole is required for the fine spray we usually want for ornamentals. Since almost all chemicals have an abrasive action which constantly enlarges the hole, a new nozzle should replace the old whenever the droplets get larger or it takes more spray to cover the same number of plants.

In spraying, work from several different positions: first from one side, then the other, then around from the back, keeping the rod constantly in motion and sending the spray from the underside of the lowest leaves up through the foliage. You can end up with a swipe over the top of plants to get aphids on buds and new shoots, but ordinarily if you do a good job from underneath, with the nozzle turned up, enough spray falls back on top of the leaves to take care of that surface. Try to apply a fine even mist. Don't drench the plants so the water runs off or the spray collects at the tips of leaves to cause burning. With an even distribution of fine droplets, you don't have to worry about spraying in full sun, even in hot weather, unless the chemical you are using, as sulfur or oil, is one that is itself injurious at high temperatures. For beetles chewing flowers or thrips inside unfolding petals, you have to direct the full force of the spray into the flower. For such purposes it is better not to have much ferbam in the mixture for that leaves an ugly black residue.

TIMING THE SPRAY

Exact timing may be somewhat more important in applying fungicides than in dealing with insects, but it does play a large part in the successful use of all pesticides. The life histories given with specific pests often suggest the proper timing of control measures. Scale insects must be killed when plants are dormant or with a summer spray during the brief period when vulnerable young crawlers are moving. To be effective, the spray for boxwood leaf miner should be in place before the orange fly emerges. The most important time to spray apples for codling moth is when most of the petals have fallen but before the calyx closes. Japanese beetle sprays on roses have to be repeated weekly to keep new growth protected. Unless you plan an early spray for rose-slugs and pine sawflies, most of the damage will be done before you know the pests are out. On the other hand, it is foolish to waste money spraying for pests that have already finished their season. If there is only 1 brood, as with cankerworms, and they are only around for a month or so, a spray near the end of that month is scarcely justified whereas one at the beginning of the month is highly desirable.

HOW TO CLEAN A SPRAYER

The best way to clean a sprayer is to *keep it clean.* Strain all mixtures into the spray tank through close-mesh cheesecloth to avoid clogging nozzles and thoroughly rinse the sprayer at the end of *every operation.* This is necessary for the longevity of the plants as well as for the apparatus. Leftover solutions have unpredictable and often injurious results. Never, never put away a sprayer without discarding all liquid

4. Helpful garden tools.

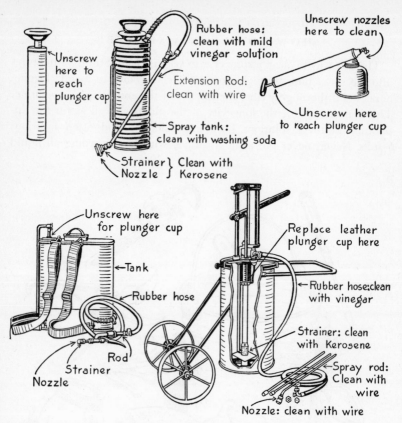

Unscrew here to reach plunger cap

Rubber hose: clean with mild vinegar solution

Unscrew nozzles here to clean

Extension Rod: clean with wire

Unscrew here to reach plunger cup

Spray tank: clean with washing soda

Strainer } Clean with
Nozzle } Kerosene

Unscrew here for plunger cup

Tank

Rubber hose

Replace leather plunger cup here

Rubber hose: clean with vinegar

Strainer: clean with Kerosene

Rod

Strainer

Nozzle

Spray rod: Clean with wire

Nozzle: clean with wire

5. *How to clean a sprayer.*

left in the tank and pumping at least 2 changes of water through the entire system. Don't just dump water in and pour out again; keep on pumping until the water comes out of the nozzle crystal clear.

Once or twice during the season more comprehensive treatment is needed. Assemble a couple of pails, a stiff scrubbing brush for the tank, a small bottle brush for strainer and nozzles, long heavy wire to poke through the rods, Stillson or pipe wrenches to unscrew the round rods, screwdriver, some trisodium phosphate (available at hardware stores; painters use it to clean brushes), a bottle of vinegar, and some kerosene.

Drop the small metal parts, nozzles, brass strainer, etc., into a jar of kerosene. Take off the hose connection, if it is the removable type. Pour warm water, with a handful of trisodium phosphate per pail, into the tank. Let that stand while you poke the wire through the extension rods and then let them soak. After scrubbing all parts, rinse the tank with pure water and start putting together. Now is the time to put in a new plunger cup, if you have not been getting enough pressure. Work it in firmly but gently, using a little oil if necessary. Tighten all bolts with a wrench; connect the rubber hose, extension rods, and nozzle; then pump through the hose water containing a cupful or two of vinegar per pail. Finally, give one last rinse with pure water. Your sprayer should now be as good as new.

At the end of the season, before putting the sprayer away for winter, follow exactly the same procedure but don't put it together again. Drain all water out of the hose and hang it up over a wooden peg, if possible where the temperature will not go below freezing. Coat the metal part lightly with oil, wrap in newspaper, and tie on to the pump. Wrap rubber parts separately, without oil. Sounds like a lot of work? It is. It may take 2 hours to really clean a sprayer, but it saves a lot of fussing and fuming and wasted time later. Make your original investment last 10 years instead of 1 or 2 and give you better results in the meantime.

If the sprayer has been used for killing weeds with 2,4-D it is next to impossible to clean it sufficiently for general spraying. If you want to try, rinse spray tank and hose with water; fill tank with water containing 2 teaspoons household ammonia per quart; stir and pump a little into hose and nozzle; let stand at least 18 hours; drain, rinse at least twice, pumping water through hose and nozzle; rinse again, pumping water through the whole system, immediately before putting in a spray mixture, for faint traces of 2,4-D will still be present.

DUSTING PREFERRED?

Dusting has a place in every garden. In my own, I have dusted vegetables and ornamentals I care little about and my guinea pig plants, which get all kinds of combinations tried out on them, but I much prefer spraying for roses and other flowers that are too glowingly beautiful to have their color dimmed by even the finest film of dust.

I don't subscribe to the theory that you do not have to wear old clothes for dusting and can do it any time you have a few spare moments. Dusts are harder on your shoes than sprays; you have to tie up your hair and cover up your arms and clothes. If you use sulfur you have to cry yourself to sleep at night to get the particles washed off your eyeballs (I tried goggles just once). If you are using rotenone you get it uncomfortably into your lungs (I don't enjoy respirators any more than goggles) and if you are using one of the toxic new chemicals you'll be a lot more than uncomfortable if you get it into your lungs. If you are using ferbam you cannot get into a bathtub quick enough to wash off that black fungicide and not even soap and water banish the lingering odor.

There is also a theory that you can dust plants between showers if necessary, and so get protection from a dust when there would be no chance to spray. But for ornamentals I believe just the opposite. If you dust a rose when the leaves are wet with either rain or dew, the dust goes on in lumps and stays in unsightly blotches that are an eyesore all summer. If you spray a rose when it is wet, you may not get the best control and you may have to make a second application a little sooner than usual, but you have not spoiled the beauty of that rosebush for the rest of the season. If, however, dust can be applied to a dry plant and can be blown up through the foliage from underneath, so that only a fine film settles down on upper surfaces, then dusts need not be too unsightly for the majority of plants.

Shaker-Type Dusters, cans or cartons with holes punched like those in salt shakers, are scarcely worthy of the name. They will sift dry material unevenly over the tops of plants but rarely place it where needed. A cheesecloth bag beaten with a stick will come a little nearer to getting dust on underside of foliage.

The **Telescope Duster,** often included in the purchase of dust, consists of one cardboard cylinder telescoped within another. It is hard to work, after the first day, for the dust cakes inside the tube in moist weather. It seldom gives adequate coverage.

Dust Guns, plunger-type dusters, are excellent for small gardens. They vary in capacity from 1 pint to 2 quarts, the larger sizes having an extension tube with a flared tip that allows easy coverage of underside of foliage. This type should not be oiled but can be treated with powdered graphite when the plunger rod gets rusty or squeaky.

Bellows Dusters are fine for large gardens. The Champion model holds several pounds of dust, has a good extension tube, and will cover rows of beans or a lot of roses very quickly; you don't have to stoop to protect even the lowest leaves. The cost is about $10.

DUST GUNS

TELESCOPE
DUSTER

BELLOWS
DUSTER

MIDGET
ROTARY DUSTER

PISTOL-GRIP
DUSTER

6. Various types of dusters.

Rotary Dusters. For about the same price as the bellows duster you can get a new midget rotary duster that is delightfully easy to operate, is light to carry around, and gives good coverage with a little bending down to get under leaves. The dust comes out in a fine even film, but the little machine uses quite a lot more dust, for the same number of plants, than a 1-quart dust gun.

For a farm garden there is a large rotary duster carried by means of a strap over one shoulder. A crank is turned with one hand while the other directs the tube delivering the dust. The amount of dust used per row can be regulated and the machine used with either 1 or 2 outlets. It is fine for truck crops and for the really large flower garden.

Spit-Gun Dusters are new, small, pistol-shaped affairs operated with one hand.

Airplanes are used for dusting cotton plantations, cranberry bogs, forests, even large fields of roses.

ADVANTAGES OF DUSTING

One big advantage in dusting is that the apparatus does not have to be emptied and cleaned after each use, though it should be cleaned out at the end of the season. If you wish to use two kinds of dusts it is better to have two inexpensive dust guns than to try to get all particles of one kind blown out of the duster before putting in the other mixture.

Dusting is quicker than spraying and probably somewhat more foolproof if you use prepared mixtures and don't try to roll your own. I mean that "roll" literally, for in making dust mixtures at home you put the ingredients in a tin with some round stones and roll back and forth, round and round. However, it is difficult to do a good job of mixing and few of us know enough about compatability and diluents and fluffers to make our own mixtures.

Chapter IV

INSECTS IN ORDER

THE entomologist says an insect is a very special creature with body divided into 3 sections, only 3 pairs of legs, and usually with wings. He also says that a bug is a very special kind of sucking insect. The layman says that any small crawling or flying animal is an insect and any insect is a bug. The dictionary says both are right, and in this *Bug Book* we are stretching several points to include rabbits, dogs, squirrels, and their relatives in one alphabetical treatment of garden pests.

Exact figures are unobtainable, but there are probably a million different species of animals in the world that have already been classified and many more unclassified. These are divided into a few main groups known as Phyla and then subdivided into Classes, Orders, Families, Genera, and Species. Man belongs in the Phylum Chordata, which includes all the vertebrates (creatures with a backbone), in the Class Mammalia, which includes animals with hair and mammary glands, in the Order Primates, which also includes monkeys, in the Family Hominidae, which does not include monkeys, the Genus *Homo* and the Species *sapiens*. Man is not always as wise as his species name would indicate and he is included among the garden pests. Other representatives of the Phylum Chordata treated briefly in this manual are the birds, Class Aves; snakes and lizards, Reptilia; toads and salamanders, Amphibia.

Slugs and snails are in the Phylum Mollusca, along with clams and oysters. Earthworms, which are not often pests, are in the Phylum Annelida, while roundworms, which include nematodes that are very often pests, belong in the Phylum Nemathelminthes.

At least three fourths of all animals are in the Phylum Arthropoda, which means they have segmented bodies, bilateral symmetry, paired jointed appendages usually terminating in claws, chitinous exoskeleton, ventral nervous system, and heart dorsal when present. The classes in this phylum listed below have members that are garden pests.

CLASSES OF THE PHYLUM ARTHROPODA

Insecta (Hexapoda). All true insects, about 90 per cent of all species in the Arthropoda. They have only 3 pairs of legs.

Arachnida. The spiders, ticks, and mites, with 4 pairs of legs.

Crustacea. Crayfish, lobsters, crabs, and sowbugs, with 5 to 7 pairs of legs, most species aquatic in habitat.

Chilopoda. Centipedes, "hundred-legged worms," but not quite literally. They have 1 pair of legs on each segment.

Diplopoda. Millipedes, "thousand-legged worms," with 2 pairs of legs on each segment.

INSECT MORPHOLOGY

Insects have an exoskeleton, a protective shell on the outside of soft body parts, rather than the internal skeleton of higher animals. The chief chemical in this outer covering is chitin. The surface of the body consists of a number of hardened plates, separated by membranous areas.

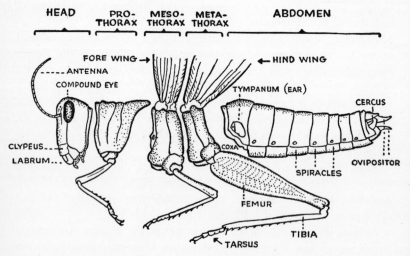

7. Diagram of an insect showing important parts.

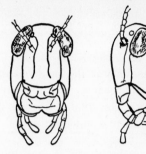

8. Front and side views of mouth parts of a chewing insect.

The segmented body is divided into 3 main sections—head, thorax, and abdomen. Six of the body segments are fused into the head, which is usually hard, heavily sclerotized. Most insects have a pair of large compound eyes made up of hexagonal facets. They also usually have 3 simple eyes, *ocelli*, located on the upper part of the head between the compound eyes. The head also bears a pair of *antennae*, feelers, which arise in front of the compound eyes. In chewing insects with biting mouth parts we have a *labrum*, upper lip, just below a plate called the *clypeus; mandibles*, the first pair of jaws; *maxillae*, second pair of jaws; and *labium*, lower lip. The mandibles act as teeth, cutting or tearing off leaf portions and then masticating the food. In sucking insects there is a long slender beak with the labium on the outside and inside 4 sharp *stylets* which pierce the plant and draw out the sap.

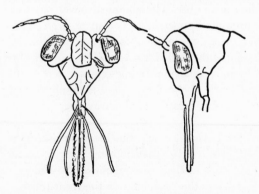

9. Mouth parts of a sucking insect.

These stylets are the mandibles and maxillae greatly modified. The labrum in this case is merely a short flap covering the groove in the labium.

The middle section of an insect is the *thorax*. This is further subdivided into *prothorax,* just back of the head; *mesothorax,* bearing the fore wings; and *metathorax,* bearing the hind wings. Each thoracic segment bears 1 pair of legs. This total of 6 legs is the chief diagnostic character separating insects from other arthropods.

The word "arthropod" means jointed leg or foot and insects are able to jump and hop about because of the way their legs are jointed. The first heavy leg section, corresponding to the thigh, is called the *femur,* the next, the *tibia.* The segmented foot is known as the *tarsus* and insects are differentiated from each other by the number of segments in the tarsus, usually 2 to 5, and the claws and pads on the *pretarsus,* the last segment. The tibia is joined to the thorax by 2 small segments called the *coxa* and the *trochanter.*

Insects are the only winged invertebrates and their wings are always attached to the thorax. When only 1 pair of wings is present, as in flies, it is the fore wings, attached to the mesothorax. The wings are thin sheets of parchmentlike cuticle with ribs known as *veins.* The number, branching, and arrangement of the veins are very important to entomologists classifying insects but are of little import to laymen.

The third section of the insect, the *abdomen,* typically has 11 segments, but the last is much reduced so there appear to be 10. The apex of the abdomen often bears a pair of structures called *cerci* (singular cercus) and the female usually has an *ovipositor,* the egg-laying apparatus. In wasps and bees this is modified into a stinger and drawn into the body when not in use. The abdomen never has true legs but may have fleshy unjointed appendages known as *prolegs.*

Insects breathe by means of *spiracles,* pores along the side of the body opening into tubes called *tracheae.* The number of tracheae varies, but usually there is a pair on the mesothorax, one on the metathorax, and a pair on each of the first 7 or 8 abdominal segments. Contact poisons work largely because of the way they affect this respiratory system.

Insects do not have a true ear but have various organs for the perception of sound waves. In grasshoppers there is an oval plate, *tympanum,* on each side of the first segment of the abdomen which serves as an ear. In crickets the "ears" are on the front tibiae.

INSECT METAMORPHOSIS

INSECT	EGG	INSTARS PERIOD OF GROWTH				PERIOD OF TRANSFORMATION	ADULT
SQUASH BUG	—HATCHING—	NYMPH —MOLT—	NYMPH —MOLT—	NYMPH —MOLT—	NYMPH —MOLT—	—MOLT—	BUG
JAPANESE BEETLE	—HATCHING—	GRUB —MOLT—	GRUB —MOLT—	GRUB —MOLT—	GRUB —MOLT—	PUPA —MOLT—	BEETLE MOLT
SPHINX MOTH	—HATCHING—	CATERPILLAR CATERPILLAR —MOLT—	CATERPILLAR —MOLT—	CATERPILLAR —MOLT—	CATERPILLAR —MOLT—	PUPA —MOLT—	MOTH MOLT

10. *Metamorphosis or growth stages of a sucking insect (squash bug) with gradual metamorphosis; and also of a beetle and a moth (chewing insects) with complete metamorphosis.*

HOW INSECTS GROW

Because insects live inside a chitinous exoskeleton which cannot be expanded as they grow, they progress by a series of molts, splitting and casting off the old shell or *cuticulum*. Such discarded shells are known as *exuviae,* which means clothes. Between the time the insect pulls free from its old covering and before the new form is heavily chitinized there is a chance for expansion in size. The stages between molts are called *instars*. The egg hatches into the first instar, terminated by the first molt; this molt produces the second instar where the young insect is larger and sometimes of different appearance. There may be 3, 4, 5, or even 20 molts depending on the species.

The adult insect never increases in size; growth is always in the life stage that follows directly from the egg. Some insects have a simple or *gradual metamorphosis,* with the young resembling adults except for size and possession of wings. Such young are called *nymphs* during their growing period. Figure 10 shows insect metamorphosis in diagrammatic form. The bug hatches from an egg into a nymph and grows in size through different instars (the number shown here does not represent the exact number for each species), acquires external wing pads, and then, without any prolonged resting stage, molts again into the adult form with wings, never growing after that.

Other insects have a *complete metamorphosis,* with the adult totally different from the young insect, often living in a different habitat. In the life stage following the egg the immature insect, usually wormlike, is called a *larva*. The wings, if any, are developed internally during the immature stages and there is a resting or pupal stage before the final molt.

The larva of a beetle is known as a *grub*. It increases in size in different instars but does not change much in appearance. In the resting stage the pupa is naked with the form of the legs showing on the outside of the pupa case.

The larva of a moth or butterfly is a *caterpillar* and may change considerably in size and appearance during different instars. The pupa may be a chrysalid attached to a twig by a strand of silk, or may be enclosed in a cocoon, or may be a naked pupa in the soil.

The larva of a fly is known as a *maggot* and it transforms to the adult stage in a *puparium*.

INSECT ORDERS

The orders of insects found in gardens are:

Collembola. Springtails: wingless; without metamorphosis; chewing mouth parts.

Orthoptera. Crickets, grasshoppers, katydids, mantids, walkingsticks: gradual metamorphosis; 4 wings; nymphs with compound eyes; chewing mouth parts.

Dermaptera. Earwigs: beetlelike but with simple metamorphosis; 4 wings; nymphs with compound eyes; chewing mouth parts.

Isoptera. Termites, "white ants": gradual metamorphosis; chewing mouth parts.

Thysanoptera. Thrips: rasping-sucking mouth parts; simple metamorphosis; 4 wings; nymphs with compound eyes.

Homoptera. Aphids, scale insects, cicadas, leafhoppers: with 4 uniform wings; piercing-sucking mouth parts; gradual metamorphosis.

Hemiptera. Chinch bugs, stink bugs, leaf bugs: with "half wings," part hard, part membranous; piercing-sucking mouth parts; gradual metamorphosis.

Coleoptera. Beetles and weevils: chewing mouth parts in larvae and adults; complete metamorphosis; 4 wings, the fore pair hardened into a sheath; larvae lack compound eyes.

Neuroptera. Aphid-lions, ant-lions: chewing mouth parts in larvae and adults; 4 wings; larvae carnivorous.

Lepidoptera. Butterflies, moths, skippers: chewing mouth parts in larvae, siphoning in adults; complete metamorphosis; 4 wings; larvae lack compound eyes.

Hymenoptera. Bees, wasps, ants, sawflies: chewing or reduced mouth parts in larvae and chewing-lapping in adults; complete metamorphosis; 4 wings; larvae lack compound eyes.

Diptera. Flies: chewing or reduced mouth parts in larvae, sponging in adults; complete metamorphosis; 2 wings; larvae lack compound eyes.

NAMES OF INSECTS

The only sure way to identify any particular insect is by its scientific name. Common names vary widely, not only in different parts of the country but with different gardeners in the same section. Insects are named by the universal system of binomial nomenclature, which means they have two names. The first is the genus name, corresponding to your own last name; the second is the species name, which really corresponds to a person's first name, for there can be several species in a genus just as there are several children in a family, all with the same last name but with different given names.

If you ask me what to do for your "aster beetles" I can't tell you for I don't know whether you have the Asiatic garden beetle, whose name, *Autoserica castanea,* identifies it beyond doubt, or the black blister beetle, *Epicauta pennsylvanica.* Perhaps you had the striped blister beetle, *Epicauta vittata,* or maybe the Oriental beetle, *Anomala orientalis.*

You will notice in these examples that the species name is usually descriptive. *Castanea* refers to the lovely chestnut color, *orientalis* and *pennsylvanica* refer to places of origin, while *vittata* means striped. In fact, the names often tell you a great deal about the insects and you often need the scientific names to get more information from books and other sources.

Unfortunately, with insects as with plants, names get shifted around a bit. A species is put into another genus, or the original name for a genus is revived, or one genus is split in two and so on. In the first edition of this *Bug Book* I used common and scientific names approved in 1942 by the American Association of Economic Entomologists. In preparing this new manual I have been working with the 1950 list of "Common Names of Insects Approved by the American Association of Economic Entomologists" and I have discovered there were many changes between 1942 and 1950.

There have also been changes since 1950, not the least of which is that the American Association of Economic Entomologists is no longer a separate entity but has been integrated into the Entomological Society of America. A new list of common names is in process and the chairman of the committee has been kind enough to go over the names being used here and to suggest changes already approved for the new list. With insects as with chemicals it is very hard to keep up with the latest developments and to get a text into print before it is already outmoded.

Chapter V

GARDEN PESTS
(AND A FEW FRIENDS)

AT LAST we come to them—the bugs and other insects, the slugs and snails and sowbugs, the mice and moles, birds and beetles, friends and foes—all grouped as we commonly think of them, and then discussed alphabetically in the different groups, which are themselves in alphabetical order.

A borer may be either a moth or a beetle, but if it is commonly called a borer it is discussed under Borers. But if the borer, for instance the shot-hole borer, should be more commonly known under its other name—the fruit tree bark beetle—then it would be treated under Beetles. With the aid of the Index, you can probably find the pest you want quite quickly if you know some common name for it, even if it is not the one presently approved by the Entomological Society of America. So far as possible insects are treated under their "official" common names, but other names are given in the text and in the Index. The scientific names, brought up-to-date so far as I am able, are given in parentheses, and in italics, after the common names printed in boldface.

If, however, all you know is that you have a caterpillar on a cherry, turn to the following Host Plants section (Chapter VI) and look up Cherry. There you will find a long list of pests with a brief comment sorting out some of the more important ones. If your caterpillar is officially known as a caterpillar you will find it in the list of insects following the word **"Caterpillar"** in boldface. Then you can turn back to the section on Caterpillars in this chapter and read up on the ones you think might be your specimen. If you live in New Jersey you obviously do not have the California Tent Caterpillar, but you may have the Eastern Tent Caterpillar.

But your caterpillar may be better known by its adult form, perhaps

codling moth, and so you look up Moths. Or maybe it is called a Cankerworm, or a Bud Moth, Casebearer, Leaf Crumpler, or Leaf Roller.
Perhaps it isn't a caterpillar at all but the larval stage of a sawfly, or
the maggot of a Fly or the grub of a Beetle. You may have to explore
several possibilities before you can, by a process of elimination, arrive
at the probable identification of your caterpillar.

I have given a rather involved example, but under many hosts you
will find very few possibilities listed and will not have to do much
checking back and forth. For our economic plants, common fruits and
vegetables, there is a great deal of information about pests available
in books and in bulletins and spray schedules from experiment stations.
For our ornamental plants the readily available information is much
more sketchy. Some, like camellias, are of enough economic importance
to have fairly good lists; some have been pretty much ignored. I have
been checking some of the new garden books from the South and they
list, of course, whiteflies, mealybugs, scale insects, and mites as general
problems but seldom give the specific species of each that occur on the
different hosts.

Consequently, you may find a good many more pests on some of
your plants than are specifically listed under each host, but probably
all the *types* of pests you are likely to encounter are described. In decid-
ing which insects to include, I have chosen those I commonly find as
I work in eastern gardens, those I have seen in many visits to southern
and western gardens, those that gardening friends in other sections
report, and those that seem important as I scan the literature—books
written for entomologists, books written for gardeners, books on special
plants, bulletins and circulars from many state experiment stations and
the United States Department of Agriculture, magazines of all descriptions from scientific periodicals to those for the beginning gardener.
The results are presented here.

ANT-LIONS

Ant-lion (*Myrmeleon* sp.)—The larvae are doodlebugs, queer creatures with sickle-shaped jaws, found mostly in the South. They dig
conical pits in sandy soil and lie in wait at the bottom for ants and
other victims to fall in. They pupate there in silken cocoons. The
adults, of the insect order Neuroptera, meaning "nerve-winged," family Myrmeleontidae, have 4 membranous wings marked with many
veins and a long, narrow, very soft abdomen.

11. Ant-lion larva waiting at the bottom of the pit dug for its ant victim, and winged adult ant-lion.

ANTS

Ants outnumber in individuals almost all other terrestrial animals and are to be found everywhere from the Arctic Circle to the tropics, on mountains or at the seashore, in wet regions or driest deserts. They belong to the order Hymenoptera, along with bees and wasps, and family Formicidae, living in colonies.

The body of an ant is sharply constricted into the 3 divisions of head, thorax, and abdomen. The antennae are hinged like an elbow, club-shaped at the tip. The abdomen, called a gaster, is attached to the thorax by 1 or 2 segments known as pedicels.

Ants have a complex social life that has fascinated naturalists for generations. I suggest Maurice Maeterlinck's classic, *The Life of the Ant,* as the most painless way of acquiring a general knowledge of ants and their strange ways. For the American classic, see *Ants: Their Structure, Development, and Behavior* by W. M. Wheeler.

Each ant colony has 3 castes, males, females, and workers, the latter being wingless, sterile, and usually females. After mating, the males die and the females shed their wings and found new colonies as queens. The queen raises her first brood of workers, feeding them with her saliva, but after that the workers not only feed the queen but tend the young, maggotlike larvae. They build new galleries for the nest and forage for food, which varies with the species. Some ants live on household foods, sweets or fats; some on aphid honeydew; some on seeds, grains, or vegetable roots; some on fungi which they cultivate in their nests; and some on other insects.

Ants nesting in lawns make disfiguring mounds of earth; those in gardens disturb plant roots and sometimes cause death. They help to distribute the bacteria causing fire blight and possibly help to disseminate Botrytis disease of peonies, although their presence on peony buds to get their sweet secretion is usually harmless. Ants eat beneficial insects that hold mealybugs, scales, etc., in check, but they are useful as pollinators and scavengers.

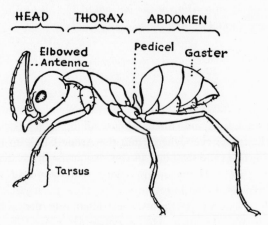

12. Diagram of an ant.

Until recently, control measures were limited to distribution of baits containing a slow poison, sodium arsenite or thallium sulfate, which workers could carry back to the nests. Chlordane, aldrin, or dieldrin, applied as dust or spray, is now the first line of defense.

Argentine Ant (*Iridomyrmex humilis*)—First noted here in 1891, probably brought to New Orleans in shipments of coffee from Brazil, and now a most serious house and garden pest in the Southeast and California. The workers are slender, $\frac{1}{12}$ to $\frac{1}{8}$ inch long, brown, with 1 segment in the pedicel, a musty greasy odor when crushed. They nest in large colonies in dark, moist places in orchard, lawn, or garden and travel in definite trails. They are injurious to citrus and other trees, attacking blossoms and distributing aphids, mealybugs, and scale insects.

Dieldrin is now approved for use in citrus groves, 6 to 8 pounds of 25 per cent wettable powder to 100 gallons of water, sprayed on tree trunks, and litter underneath, once a year in spring or summer. Community-wide distribution of Argentine Ant Bait has eradicated the pest in some towns. The government formula is: 1. Boil together for 30 minutes and then cool 1¼ pounds granulated sugar, 1¼ pints water, 1 gram tartaric acid (crystallized), 1 gram benzoate of soda. 2. Dissolve ⅛ ounce sodium arsenite in 1 fluid ounce hot water; cool. 3. Add second mixture to first, stir, and add ⅔ pound strained honey. 4. Place in ant cups, tin containers with indentations to admit the ants, and put 20 to 25 feet apart, out of reach of children. Commercial baits are available.

Black Carpenter Ant (*Camponotus herculeanus pennsylvanicus*)— Nesting in wood, responsible for damage often attributed to termites. It is the largest of our common ants, ¼ to ½ inch long, dark brown to black, pedicel 1-segmented, a circlet of hairs at tip of the abdomen, formic-acid odor when crushed. Trees are entered through wounds and stubs of broken branches, but galleries can extend into sound heartwood. Prune trees carefully; paint bark wounds; dust 5 per cent chlordane or 10 per cent DDT into holes. Or drench wood with 8 teaspoons 50 per cent wettable chlordane in 1 gallon of water.

California Harvester Ant (*Pogonomyrmex californicus*)—Common in Texas, New Mexico, Arizona, California, and Nevada. It is pale red, ¼ inch long, bites and stings severely, collects seeds and so interferes with planting operations. See Red Harvester Ant for control.

Cornfield Ant (*Lasius alienus americanus*)—A native species, distributed over most of the country, small (to ⅒ inch), robust, light to dark brown, 1-segmented pedicel, formic-acid odor. It makes nests in soil, sometimes lawns, or in rotten wood. The sweets-loving workers caress root aphids to stimulate the production of honeydew, put them in the best place for winter hibernation, and protect them from their enemies. See Corn Root Aphid.

Fire Ant (*Solenopsis geminata*)—Small, pale yellow or red, traveling in columns, stinging furiously, ranging from the tropics into the Southwest. In Arizona this ant eats tender shoots of nursery and orchard trees; it nests in strawberry patches in California and debarks young citrus trees. It sometimes girdles young vegetable stems.

Imported Fire Ant (*Solenopsis saevissima* v. *richteri*)—An imported species, first noticed near Mobile, Alabama, and now in 10 southern states. The ants are a menace to young vegetables and even young animals, often killing quail and other poultry. The workers are reddish to blackish red, ⅛ to ¼ inch, with 2-segmented pedicels. There may be 25,000 in an average mound, formed in pasture, garden, or lawn, 10 inches high and 15 across. Treat mounds or area with .25 per cent spray of chlordane, aldrin, or dieldrin. This means 4 tablespoons of 45 per cent chlordane emulsion or 2½ ounces of 40 per cent wettable powder to 3 gallons of water. With dieldrin use 12 tablespoons of 15½ per cent emulsifiable concentrate or 4 ounces of 25 per cent wettable powder to 3 gallons of water.

For lawns, use 7 tablespoons 40 per cent wettable chlordane or 5 tablespoons 25 per cent dieldrin in 3 to 6 gallons of water as a spray for each 1000 square feet. Water after treatment.

Little Black Ant (*Monomorium minimum*)—A native species, ¹⁄₁₀ to ¹⁄₁₂ inch long, shiny black, nesting outdoors in soil, sometimes in woodwork of buildings, feeding on sweets, honeydew, fruits, vegetables, or meat.

Odorous House Ant (*Tapinoma sessile*)—Deep brown to black, ¹⁄₁₀ to ⅛ inch, with a broad, soft body and a nauseating sweet odor. This species eats everything but is fond of sweets and attends honeydew-secreting aphids.

Pavement Ant (*Tetramorium caespitum*)—A common lawn pest along the Atlantic seaboard, nesting also under stones or edge of pavement. It is rather hairy, hard-bodied, ¹⁄₁₂ to ⅐ inch long, with 2-segmented pedicel, black with pale appendages. It is a garden as well as lawn pest, eating roots and tubers, and it forages into houses and greenhouses. Chlordane is widely used for control. For individual ant hills apply ⅛ teaspoon 50 per cent wettable powder into center of mound and water in well, or pour on chlordane emulsion, 1 ounce to a gallon of water. The whole lawn can be treated with 5 per cent chlordane dust, or with granular dieldrin, according to manufacturer's directions.

Red Harvester Ant (*Pogonomyrmex barbatus*)—Also known as the Agricultural Ant, particularly injurious in Arizona and other parts of the Southwest. It is ¼ inch or more long, with black head, thorax, and legs, red pedicel 2-segmented, red abdomen. It lives in large colonies, clearing the soil of all vegetation and often making bare circles in gardens or around trees 2 to 12 feet in diameter. The nest is deep, with the queen 2 to 6 feet underground. To control, apply ½ pound of 2 per cent dieldrin or 5 per cent chlordane dust in a 4 to 6 inch band circling the nest entrance but 2 or 3 feet away from it. For small colonies 4 ounces of carbon bisulfide can be squirted into the entrance hole, which is then covered with dirt. Methyl bromide will kill the ants but it must be released into moist soil with a mechanical dispenser **6 to 8** inches below ground level.

Texas Leaf-cutting Ant (*Atta texana*)—A native, confined to southern and eastern Texas and western Louisiana, interesting for its habit of cutting leaves from plants. These are macerated, fertilized in the nests, and in this compost the ants grow a fungus for food, a method comparable to man's culture of mushrooms. The workers vary from $\frac{1}{16}$ to $\frac{1}{2}$ inch long, are brown, with spines on head and thorax, 2-segmented pedicel. Their enormous nests can be 10 to 20 feet deep with numerous craters. They invade houses, steal seeds, ravage garden and field crops, destroy young pine seedlings.

Thief Ant (*Solenopsis molesta*)—Yellow to bronze, small, a common house pest in warm weather with a preference for protein foods. It may injure germinating corn seeds. The best control is cultivation to break up the nests before planting.

13. Aphid-lion: stalked eggs, larva, pupa case, and lacewing adult.

APHID-LIONS

Aphid-lion (*Chrysopa oculata*)—Larva of a lacewing fly, Golden-eye Lacewing, family Chrysopidae, order Neuroptera. This helpful insect is flat with an elongated body tapering at both ends, yellowish or gray mottled with red or brown, with projecting hairs or bristles, $\frac{1}{4}$ to $\frac{1}{3}$ inch long. The head bears double sickle-shaped jaws used to capture, puncture, and extract the juice from succulent plant lice or mealybugs, cottony-cushion scales, sometimes thrips and mites. The larva pupates in a globular white cocoon under bark or attached to underside of a fallen leaf and the adult cuts out a small lid which swings back as on a hinge. The female lacewing, a beautiful creature with gauzy green wings, long, hairlike antennae, iridescent red-gold eyes, places each of her small oval white eggs at the end of a hairlike stalk drawn out from her body. This is to keep her cannibalistic off-spring from eating each other when they hatch. There may be several generations a year with larvae eating from 200 to 400 aphids apiece.

Aphid-wolves, larvae of the related brown lacewing, are predators on thrips, mites, aphids, scale insects, and leafhopper nymphs.

APHIDS

Aphids, plant lice, are sucking insects in the order Homoptera. There are a great many species abundant on, and injurious to, all forms of vegetation. At least a few species are inevitable in every home garden and sometimes it seems much easier to control aphids than to under-stand their complicated life histories and taxonomy. Some scientists place aphids in 4 families, others in 2, and there are further divisions into subfamilies and tribes with a lot of changes in names of genera. We'll settle here for 2 families: Aphidae (Aphididae) and Chermidae (Phylloxeridae).

Typical aphids (family Aphidae) are small, soft-bodied, pear-shaped, with a pair of cornicles, wax-secreting tubes, projecting from the pos-terior end of the body. The antennae have 3 to 6 segments and the tarsi 2. The mouth parts form a hollow beak, which arises far back on the underside of the head. The beak encloses 4 needlelike stylets, which pierce plant tissue so the sap can be sucked out. All aphids excrete honeydew from the anus; this is really excess plant sap, rich in sugars. It attracts ants and is a medium for the growth of a black fungus known as sooty mold. Many aphids are wingless. When present, the wings have few veins and are held vertically over the body when at rest.

Aphids are of all colors: black, green, pink, red, yellow, lavender, brown, or grayish. Some live out their lives on a single plant; others infest several different plant species. Some aphids require an alternate host, wintering on one type of plant, usually woody, then migrating to one or more herbaceous species for the summer.

The life history of an aphid is complicated even for the single-host type. In a typical case, overwintering eggs hatch in spring into wingless females called stem mothers (fundatrix). These parthenogenetic (reproducing without fertilization) females are viviparous—that is, they hold their eggs in their bodies and give birth to living young. Their young are also parthenogenetic females, but some develop wings and migrate to other plants of the same species. Many more such generations are produced during the summer, but toward autumn male and female wingless forms are born. These mate, and the oviparous females lay fertilized eggs for overwintering. In warm climates living young may be produced continually with no overwintering egg stage.

Alternate-host aphids also winter as eggs and hatch into wingless females, but in the third or fourth generation they produce winged females which migrate to the summer food plant. There may be 6 or more generations of wingless females on the summer host before male and female winged forms appear for the trek back to the woody winter host. There the winged females give birth to wingless females which mate with the winged males and lay fertilized eggs, usually shiny black, on the bark of the winter host. The males thus appear in the life cycle but once a year, at the approach of cold weather.

In the subfamily Eriosomatinae, woolly and gall-making aphids, cornicles are lacking or reduced, but abundant wax glands cover the body with white cottony threads. Many species have alternate hosts, on one of which they produce galls. The sexual forms lack mouth parts and the ovipositing female lays only 1 egg.

14. An aphid getting ready to feed and in process of sucking sap.

The family Chermidae (Phylloxeridae) includes aphidlike insects that lack cornicles, have a reduced wing venation, and have only oviparous females, none giving birth to living young. The species in the subfamily Cherminae (Adelginae) are the spruce gall aphids, or chermids, all found on conifers, with spruce the primary host. See Eastern Spruce Gall Aphid, Cooley Spruce Gall Aphid. The antennae are 5-segmented in winged forms, 4-segmented in sexual forms, 3-segmented in wingless females. Wings at rest are held rooflike over the body, which is often covered with waxy threads.

In the subfamily Phylloxerinae the antennae are 3-segmented in all forms, wings at rest are held flat over the abdomen, waxy threads are not produced. The grape phylloxera is the most economically important member of this group.

Aphids cause loss of plant vigor and sometimes stunting, deformation of buds and flowers, curling or puckering of leaves. Their honeydew provides a substratum for ugly black sooty mold and is attractive to ants which herd destructive root aphids. They are perhaps most important as vectors (carriers) of mosaic and other virus diseases, fire blight and other bacterial diseases, and an occasional fungus disease.

Most aphids are readily controlled by applying contact insecticides at the proper time. That old reliable nicotine sulfate (Black Leaf 40) is still very good. Use 1 to 1½ teaspoons with 1 ounce of liquid soap or 1 cubic inch of soap flakes to a gallon of water. Rotenone and pyrethrum are still effective and particularly useful combined in the small aerosol bomb so easy to use on house plants. TEPP is used by commercial growers on vegetables because it leaves no poisonous residue, but it is very poisonous at time of use. Safer for amateurs is malathion, a good aphicide. Lindane is recommended especially for woolly and gall aphids. Isolan is promising. DDT is not recommended. It builds up large aphid populations by killing their predators, lady beetles, aphidlions, etc., and their parasites. Dinitro compounds are sometimes used as dormant sprays to kill aphid eggs.

Parasites—insects which live part of their lives *inside* other insects instead of merely preying on them—are important in aphid control.

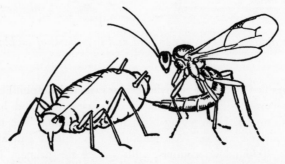

15. Parasitic wasp laying an egg in an aphid.

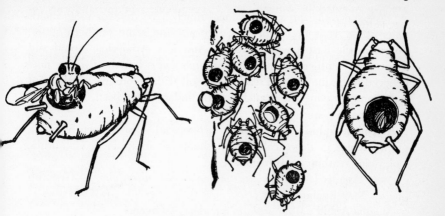

16. Young wasp emerging from parasitized aphid, and dead aphids showing emergence holes (greatly enlarged).

Figures 15, 16 show a hymenopterous wasp laying an egg in an aphid, then the young wasp produced from the egg emerging from the aphid, and finally the stiff dead bodies of parasitized aphids, all showing emergence holes in their backs. Whenever you find dry, brown aphid bodies with holes you may be sure you have friends in the garden.

In the following pages aphids are taken up alphabetically under their common names. Those of much importance are treated in some detail; others are dismissed in a line or two, giving host plants and salient characteristics. Though the list is long it includes but a fraction of the thousands of plant lice in the world—a fraction intended to be representative of aphids injuring trees, flowers, or vegetables on home properties in different sections of these United States.

Apple Aphid (*Aphis pomi*)—Often called Green Apple Aphid, a single-host species on apple, pear, wild crab, hawthorn, distributed generally in apple sections of North America. Shiny black eggs winter on twigs, producing green aphids which swarm on fruit buds, distort young apples. Add nicotine sulfate to the delayed dormant spray; or use a dinitro compound such as Elgetol.

Apple Grain Aphid (*Rhopalosiphum fitchii*)—Winters as eggs on apple, pear, or hawthorn twigs; produces greenish-yellow lice which migrate to small grains and grasses for almost the entire feeding period. No control on apple is necessary.

Arborvitae Aphid (*Cinara tujafilina*)—Reddish brown with a whitish bloom, on roots, stems, and branches of arborvitae, Italian cypress, and retinospora. It produces much honeydew for sooty molds to grow in. It is prevalent in California and some southern states. Found in the East it was called the American Arborvitae Aphid and ascribed to another species (*Cinara winonkae*), but the two are now believed to be the same. Treating the soil with chlordane for the root forms and spraying the branches with lindane have been effective on evergreens in a nursery.

Artemisia Aphid (*Macrosiphum artemisiae*)—Dark green or black, often present in dense colonies on shoots of artemisia in California, Colorado, Washington, Oregon.

Aster Aphids (*Macrosiphum anomalae; M. asterifoliae*)—Greenish lice on New England aster.

Aucuba Aphid (*Macrosiphum aucubae*)—Green.

Balsam Twig Aphid (*Mindarus abietinus*)—Greenish aphid covered with white wax, prevalent on young shoots of white and balsam firs; also attacks spruce; found from New England to the Pacific coast. Twigs are roughened and curled. Spray in late spring with lindane or nicotine.

Bamboo Aphid (*Myzocallis arundinariae*)—Yellow and black, on leaves of bamboo.

Barberry Aphid (*Liosomaphis berberidis*)--Small, yellowish green, on barberry and mahonia, usually found in groups on underside of leaves and on shoots.

Bean Aphid (*Aphis fabae*)—A common, important, dull black species (sometimes slaty blue or dark green with nymphs spotted with white wax). It is very gregarious, congregating in great numbers on succulent plant parts, causing general plant debility, and yellowing foliage. It is the bean aphid which is practically synonymous with nasturtium, thickly infesting underside of leaves and stems (Plate I).

This alternate-host species winters on euonymus and viburnum, migrating to globe artichoke, asparagus, bean, beet, broom, cowpea, dahlia, deutzia, English ivy, oleander, parsnip, pea, poppy, rhubarb, spinach, thistles, watercress, and zinnia for the summer.

Control. A 4 per cent nicotine dust or a nicotine spray has usually been successful in the past. Malathion is now effective and Isolan promising, especially for early spring treatment of snowball. If house ivies are treated to a weekly bath, aphids won't have much of a chance. Failing this, the pyrethrum-rotenone bombs are both handy and effective.

Beech Blight Aphid (*Prociphilus imbricator*)—Large, downy or woolly, infesting undersides of branches and sometimes trunks of beech, from New England west to Illinois and south to Georgia; also recorded on sycamore. It is sometimes abundant enough to kill twigs or young beech trees. Lindane should control it.

Black Cherry Aphid (*Myzus cerasi*)—Large, shiny black, commonly curling and distorting young leaves of sweet cherry; present on sour cherry to some extent but not curling the leaves. The eggs, wintering on the buds, hatch as the buds burst. There are several generations, winged forms migrating in summer to plants of the mustard family. Control with nicotine sulfate added to the dormant spray or applied separately at the green-tip stage.

Black Citrus Aphid (*Toxoptera aurantii*)—Small, $\frac{1}{15}$ inch, reddish brown or black, with long legs; important on citrus in coastal districts of California and in Florida. It also feeds on camellia, curling and deforming new leaves, secreting honeydew for sooty mold. The phosphate sprays are effective as well as nicotine sulfate.

Black Peach Aphid (*Anuraphis persicae-niger*)—A shiny black species with reddish-brown nymphs infesting roots, tender shoots, and fruits of peach, almond, apricot, or plum grafted on peach roots. Control the root forms with paradichlorobenzene as for peach tree borer. Spray foliage with malathion or nicotine sulfate.

Black Pecan Aphid (*Melanocallis caryaefoliae*)—Hickory Leaf Aphid, destructive to all pecan varieties in the South, causing premature defoliation and reducing the nut crop; also a pest of hickory in the North. The eggs winter in bark crevices, hatching late in March into dark green to nearly black lice. There may be 15 generations, with DDT or bordeaux mixture on the foliage helping to build up enormous populations. Control with nicotine sulfate added to a summer oil spray or to bordeaux used for scab control. Some growers use parathion.

Boxelder Aphid (*Periphyllus negundinis*)—Pale green, hairy.

Buckthorn Aphid (*Aphis abbreviata*)—Small, yellow to dark green, wintering on buckthorn, migrating to potato.

Cabbage Aphid (*Brevicoryne brassicae*)—Very small, whitish-green bugs in dense clusters on underside of leaves, causing them to cup and curl, or in flower heads. Found on broccoli, cabbage, cauliflower, Brussels sprouts, kohlrabi, collards, kale, turnip, and radish. Seedlings may be killed; plants are dwarfed. In the North black eggs are laid on petioles and leaves, but in the South living young are produced throughout the winter. Use a 3 per cent nicotine or 4 per cent malathion dust but not within 10 days of harvest.

Ceanothus Aphid (*Aphis ceanothi*)—Reddish brown and black, infesting limbs, twigs, leaves of ceanothus and soapbush in California.

Chrysanthemum Aphid (*Macrosiphoniella sanborni*)—Large, dark chocolate brown, with short cornicles, clustering on tender terminal shoots and on underside of leaves. The growth is stunted, leaves curl, and plants sometimes die. Spray with nicotine sulfate, malathion, pyrethrum, or rotenone.

Clover Aphid (*Anuraphis bakeri*)—Small, greenish, in Rocky Mountain states; on twigs, leaves, blossom buds of hawthorn, quince, apple, and pear, infesting clover in summer. It gums up seed heads with honeydew and clover crops grown for seed may be a total loss.

Columbine Aphid (*Pergandeidia trirhoda*)—Small, cream-colored, rather flat; appearing in late summer. Plants are sometimes stunted and sticky with honeydew.

Common Birch Aphid (*Calaphis betulaecolens*)—Large green species with short cornicles, densely infesting leaves of birch and producing copious honeydew followed by sooty mold. Eggs are laid in bark cracks and small crotches.

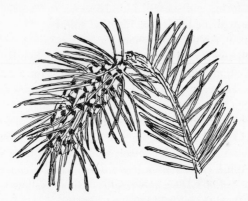

17. Aphid gall on blue spruce.

Cooley Spruce Gall Aphid (*Chermes cooleyi*)—Also known as Blue Spruce Gall Aphid or Chermid. It causes a gall or swelling, 1 to 3 inches long, at tips of new shoots of Engelmann, Sitka, oriental, and Colorado blue spruce. Immature stem mothers winter on spruce and lay eggs in early spring in masses of white cottony wax. The young nymphs feed at the base of needles of the new growth, producing galls which envelop them. They are green or purplish, becoming straw-colored after they open in July, and contain many cells. The aphids move from the cells to the needles, cast their nymphal skins, and migrate as winged adults to Douglas-fir, there to lay eggs on needles. The young winter on the needles, looking like bits of cotton in spring. Galls are not formed on this host. Eventually a winged stage takes the aphid back to spruce but the cycles can continue on either host.

Control. Avoid planting spruce and Douglas-fir together; cut off all the galls you can find and reach before they open in July. Spray in spring, just before new growth starts, with miscible oil, 1 part to 25 or 30 parts of water, making sure temperature is above 45°F. The oil may temporarily remove bloom from needles. There is some evidence that spraying with lindane after growth has started kills the aphids in their cells. A nicotine sulfate spray when the galls open in summer is partially effective.

Corn Leaf Aphid (*Rhopalosiphum maidis*)—A small green or blue-green species, densely congregated in the curl of the leaves and upper part of stalk, causing reddish-yellow patches and coating tassels and silk with honeydew, which interferes with pollination and attracts corn earworm moths. This aphid is more destructive in the South, where there may be 50 generations against 9 or so in the Midwest. Plant corn early; fertilize to hasten maturity.

Corn Root Aphid (*Anuraphis maidi-radicis*)—A serious pest east of the Rocky Mountains, dependent for its existence on ants, especially the cornfield ant. Roots of corn, cotton, grasses are often infested, the foliage taking on a yellowish tinge. Ants collect the eggs in fall and store them in their nests over winter. In spring the young are carried by ant nurses to smartweed roots where the stem mothers mature and produce 2 or 3 generations of bluish-green powdery lice, pinhead size, with short legs. They are then transferred to corn roots for 10 to 20 generations. If winged forms appear to fly to other cornfields, they are seized and carried back underground by the ants.

Many ornamentals, especially aster, browallia, calendula, primrose, and sweet pea, are stunted and chlorotic from the feeding of root aphids, but the species may be the western aster root aphid. Control lies chiefly in getting rid of the ants, cultivating before planting to break up the nests, and treating the soil with chlordane. When growing ornamentals are infested, scoop away the soil around the plant to make a saucer-shaped depression and pour in a nicotine sulfate solution (2 teaspoons to a gallon of water without soap) or lindane.

Cotton Aphid—See Melon Aphid.

Cowpea Aphid (*Aphis medicaginis*)—Also called, incorrectly, Laburnum Aphid. Black with white legs; immature forms dark green or reddish brown. Common on legumes including laburnum or golden-chain, rose-acacia, locust, and other ornamentals, as well as cowpea, beans, clovers, etc. It may also infest apple, eucalyptus, opuntia, orange, pear, primrose, rhubarb, and other plants.

Crapemyrtle Aphid (*Myzocallis kahawaluokalani*)—Confined to crapemyrtle and serious wherever this southern shrub is grown. Copious honeydew encourages the fungus, which covers foliage with black soot. Spray early and thoroughly with any good contact insecticide.

18. Sooty mold growing in aphid honeydew on crapemyrtle leaf.

Crescent-marked Lily Aphid (*Myzus circumflexus*)—Yellow and black, infesting terminal shoots, buds, and leaves of lilies in green-houses throughout the country; also infesting many other plants in-doors and out. A partial list includes asparagus fern, aster, California laurel, calla lily, crocus, cyclamen, freesia, fuchsia, gladiolus, gloxinia, hydrangea, iris, myrtle, rose, penstemon, snowberry, violet, and wall-flower. The lily aphid is a carrier of mosaic and other virus diseases.

Currant Aphid (*Capitophorus ribis*)—Pinkish, yellowish, or dark green. Leaves curl, crinkle, and hump up into half galls above the portions where stem mothers are producing their numerous progeny. Such humped areas turn red and leaves may drop. Currants and gooseberries are attacked throughout the United States and the species is recorded on deutzia and snowball. Glossy black eggs on twigs hatch into wingless females, which continue to reproduce parthenogenetically on currant while winged females migrate to various weeds for the summer. The aphids return to currant in autumn, produce males and females and overwintering eggs.

Control with a nicotine spray or dust early in the season, transferring to rotenone as the currants ripen. Be sure to reach the undersurface of cupped leaves (Figure 19).

19. Currant leaf showing deformation by aphids.

Cypress Aphid (*Siphonatrophia cupressi*)—A rather large, green aphid, with convex abdomen, infesting blue and Monterey cypress in southern California.

Dogwood Aphid (*Aphis cornifoliae*)—Greenish black, sometimes powdery, common throughout United States. It winters on dogwood and migrates to leaves of wild and cultivated sunflower for summer.

Eastern Spruce Gall Aphid (*Chermes abietis*)—On Norway and white spruce, rarely on black or red, in eastern half of the United States. Pineapple-shaped galls are formed at the base of new shoots (Plate II; Figure 20). Greenish nymphs hibernate at the base of buds, mature in spring, and lay eggs in masses of white cottony wax. The young

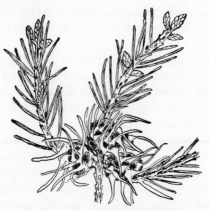

20. Aphid galls on Norway spruce.

nymphs feed at the base of the elongating shoot and the injection of their saliva into cells which have been preconditioned by the feeding of the stem mothers causes the needle bases to enlarge into bulblike hollows. Perhaps 50 of these cells will be joined together to form the gall, each cell holding up to a dozen aphids. New galls, ½ to 1 inch long, are green with the closed mouth of each cell marked with a red or purple line. They open in late July or early August (in New Jersey) releasing aphids which develop wings at maturity but do not migrate to another host. They lay eggs, 50 or so in a mass, on the needles. These hatch in a few days and the young seek winter quarters on the current year's growth. Only those at the bases of buds survive the winter. The galls turn brown after the aphids leave and infested branches often die back. Individual trees show a marked difference in susceptibility, some eventually dying, some with retarded growth, and some almost immune from attack.

Propagation from immune individuals would seem to be the best long-range control measure. The galls are so far back on the shoots cutting them out usually spoils the symmetry of the tree so that spraying is usually necessary. See Cooley Spruce Gall Aphid.

Elm Cockscomb Gall Aphid (*Colopha ulmicola*)—General on elm over the United States. The galls, a series of elevations growing out of the leaf, green with red tips resembling cocks' combs, ½ inch high by ¾ inch broad, are filled with small greenish or brownish aphids, which drip honeydew onto walks, people, and cars parked under trees. The winter is passed as shiny brown eggs in bark crevices. These hatch when leaves are half grown and the first 3 generations are passed on elm, then 2 in grass, before a migration back to elm where each female lays 1 egg. Spray with an aphicide as soon as leaves form in spring; cut off leaves showing galls.

Elm Leaf Aphid (*Myzocallis ulmifolii*)—A light green species with banded wings, on underside of leaves, producing much honeydew.

European Birch Aphid (*Euceraphis betulae*)—Large, green and black with a waxy covering, on all kinds of birch throughout the country; also on Japanese maple.

Fern Aphid (*Idiopterus nephrolepidis*)—Small, black, with whitish legs and black clouded areas in wings. It infests ferns in houses and greenhouses and outdoors in California. Boston fern is a favorite. Ferns are injured by many sprays; malathion may be the safest aphicide to try.

Foxglove Aphid (*Myzus solani*)—Primarily a potato pest, but common in the flower garden on campanula, columbine, chrysanthemum, evening primrose, foxglove, geranium, gladiolus, lily, pansy, penstemon, physostegia, scarlet sage, verbena, violet, and on African violet indoors. This is a green aphid overwintering in the egg stage on foxglove and other hosts, infesting lower leaves and stems of potatoes in summer. Feeding on flower hosts often results in a chlorotic condition and on lily produces curling of leaves resembling the virus rosette disease. Vegetable hosts besides potato include tomato, cucumber, and turnip. TEPP aerosols are fairly effective for florists' crops and DDT or nicotine spray or dust for potatoes.

Geranium Aphid (*Macrosiphum pelargonii*)—Green; found on geranium, pelargonium, calceolaria, calla lily, chrysanthemum, cineraria, verbena, and viola.

Goldenglow Aphid (*Macrosiphum rudbeckiae*)—Practically inevitable on goldenglow, rudbeckia, covering stems with large, bright red lice on long legs. They commonly infest larkspur buds and cause delphinium leaves to cup downward over dense clusters of red or dark brown aphids. Chrysanthemum, goldenrod, Fuller's teasel, sunflower, and lettuce are other hosts. In spraying with nicotine sulfate or other aphicide the spray must be directed with force toward the underside of delphinium leaves, terminal shoots of larkspur.

Grape Phylloxera (*Phylloxera vitifoliae*)—A common, injurious, gall-forming species (Figure 21). A native of America, this aphid made history when it was introduced into Europe, nearly wrecking the grape industry in France and pursuing its devastating career in Italy and Germany. It is still the most destructive grape pest in Europe and western United States but seldom causes serious damage in eastern vineyards. Here, in its original home, varieties have acquired resistance.

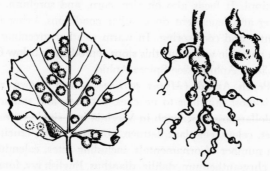

21. Grape phylloxera, showing galls on leaf and roots and root gall enlarged.

The life history varies according to location. In the East, young lice, hatching from overwintering eggs on canes, settle on grape leaves, producing, by their feeding, pea-shaped galls open on the underside. One female in each gall becomes a stem mother, laying 400 to 600 eggs. Young yellow-green nymphs, hatching from these eggs in 7 to 10 days, migrate to form new galls on other leaves. Several such generations occur during the season, but about every third generation some of the aphids move down to the roots to form nodules there. There may be 5 or more generations of the root-gall type, but finally some of the root forms acquire wings and migrate to vines where they lay 2 kinds of eggs. The small eggs produce males; the larger eggs hatch into females. Both are wingless. They mate and each female deposits a single overwintering egg under the bark of the cane.

In California vineyards, leaf galls are rare and there may be no true male and female forms. Nymphs winter on grape roots and summer generations succeed each other on the roots, although winged migrants sometimes appear. Feeding roots are destroyed; the vines often die. The only practical control seems to be grafting desirable vinifera varieties onto resistant rootstock.

Grapevine Aphid (*Aphis illinoisensis*)—East of the Mississippi River this small, dark brown aphid is often densely clustered on young grape shoots and leaves and sometimes infests young fruits, causing them to drop. In autumn the aphids migrate to black haw, returning to grapes in early summer. Spraying with nicotine sulfate and soap or one of the phosphate sprays is effective.

Greenbug (*Toxoptera graminum*)—A small green aphid of general distribution but mostly disastrous to wheat and other grains west of the Mississippi. It feeds also on rice, corn, and sorghum. Outbreaks of greenbug are dependent on weather conditions, being favored by a mild winter and cool spring. In warm weather greenbug is held in check by a parasitic wasp, but this stops reproducing below 65°F.

Green Citrus Aphid—See Spirea Aphid.

Green Peach Aphid (*Myzus persicae*)—Also known as Spinach Aphid. It is most injurious to peaches, potatoes, and spinach, causing a million dollars loss in spinach in Virginia in a single year, but it also attacks beet, celery, eggplant, lettuce, potato, tomato, crucifers, cucurbits, and a number of ornamentals, including aster, calendula, crocus, carnation, chrysanthemum, dahlia, dianthus, English ivy, forget-me-not, iris, lily, nasturtium, poppy, snapdragon, primrose, rose, tulip, verbena, and violet. Of fruits, it infests apricot, cherry, orange, peach, plum, and prune. It is a dangerous disease vector, transmitting tomato and tobacco mosaic, leaf roll of potatoes, and other virus diseases. A native of Europe, where it is called greenfly, the green peach aphid is now distributed all over the United States.

Shiny black eggs winter on bark of fruit trees—peach, plum, apricot, cherry—hatching into pale, yellowish-green aphids, with 3 dark lines on the back, about the time peaches come into bloom. They produce living young for 2 or 3 generations, sucking sap from twigs, then migrate to garden plants. In autumn winged females return to peach and give birth to true sexual females which mate with males flying over from spinach and other summer hosts.

Control. Nicotine sulfate as a spray for peaches, 1 teaspoon plus 1 ounce soap to a gallon, and 3 per cent nicotine dust for spinach is being somewhat replaced by the organic phosphates parathion, TEPP, and malathion. Home gardeners may still prefer rotenone dust for spinach, and if all the aphids are not killed a little salt or vinegar in the wash water will get them off the leaves after harvest.

Hawthorn Aphid (*Anuraphis crataegifoliae*)—Long-Beaked Clover Aphid. On hawthorn from New England to Illinois, also on Japanese quince, apple, pear, with clover and other legumes as summer hosts. The aphids are pinkish or yellowish green and their sucking causes young hawthorn leaves to curl tightly, older leaves to crinkle. Malathion and Isolan as well as the older nicotine and pyrethrum-rotenone combinations are helpful if applied when leaves are first unfolded.

The **Four-spotted Hawthorn Aphid** (*Amphorophora crataegi*) is another species frequenting hawthorn.

Hemlock Chermes (*Chermes tsugae*)—White tufts on bark and needles of western hemlock, sometimes killing ornamentals in Pacific Northwest.

Hickory Aphid (*Longistigma caryae*)—Also called Giant Aphid. This is the largest species we have; it occurs only in trees—beech, birch, chestnut, elm, hickory, linden, maple, oak, pecan, sycamore, walnut, and willow—in the eastern half of the country. Wingless forms are ash-gray with black spots on the thorax; winged forms have all-black thorax. They are about ½ inch long. They feed on twigs and small branches and when abundant may cause serious injury or death. There are several generations a year and it may pay to have the trees sprayed with nicotine or a phosphate when the first aphids appear.

Hickory Leaf Aphid—See Black Pecan Aphid.

Honeysuckle Aphid (*Rhopalosiphum conii*)—A green aphid infesting Tartarian honeysuckle, snowberry, California laurel, parsnip, celery, carrot, and dill.

Hop Aphid (*Phorodon humuli*)—This is one of the plum aphids, wintering in the egg stage on plum, prune, sometimes apple, cherry, peach, or alder. Pale, yellowish-green nymphs may nearly cover underside of foliage before green and black winged forms with long cornicles appear for the summer migration to hops, sometimes sunflower. A few stay on the winter host. Spray fruit trees in very early spring with nicotine-soap solution or use a dormant dinitro spray for the eggs.

Impatiens Aphid (*Macrosiphum carnosa* var. *impatientis*)—Sometimes troublesome on garden balsam.

Iris Root Aphid—See Tulip Bulb Aphid.

Ivy Aphid (*Aphis hederae*)—A dark, purplish-green, brown, or black species common on growing tips of English ivy; also reported on *Euonymus europae, Viburnum opulus* and *Aralia*. See Bean Aphid for control.

Laburnum Aphid—See Cowpea Aphid.

Lantana Aphid (*Cerataphis lataniae*)—Also called Palm Aphid and often mistaken for a whitefly in its wingless form, which is dark, disk-like, with a white fringe. Winged forms are dull brown or black. Besides lantana it infests orchids, ferns, and palms in greenhouses.

Leaf-curling Plum Aphid (*Anuraphis helichrysi*)—Pest of plum and prune, the winter hosts, in western states. Summer hosts include aster, carrot, chrysanthemum, cynoglossum, cineraria, dahlia, erigeron, eupatorium, gerbera, heliotrope, lobelia, mertensia, marguerite, sunflower. The summer forms are pale green, the others dark green to reddish brown. A dormant oil spray is fairly effective on plum, or nicotine sulfate added to a lime-sulfur spray. If there has been no dormant spray and infestation becomes serious, growers may use parathion.

Lily Aphid—See Crescent-marked Lily Aphid and Purple-spotted Lily Aphid.

Linden Aphid (*Myzocallis tiliae*)—A yellow and black species with clouded wings, often very abundant on linden leaves.

Lupine Aphid (*Macrosiphum albifrons*)—A large green species entirely covered with white powdery wax, with long legs and cornicles. It infests tips of annual and perennial lupines in spring and early summer.

Manzanita Leaf-gall Aphid (*Tamalia coweni*)—Dark green and black, producing numerous green or reddish roll galls on edges of manzanita leaves in Colorado, Nevada, and California.

Mealy Plum Aphid (*Hyalopterus arundinis*)—An alternate-host species wintering in the egg stage at base of buds on plum and prune twigs, migrating to reed grass or cattails. This is a pale green aphid with a mealy or powdery coating, a native of Europe, and especially important in the West. It may infest apple, apricot, peach, as well as plum. It curls foliage, causes general stunting, fruit splitting, and spoilage by excrement and sooty mold. Use a dormant dinitro or oil spray or nicotine or parathion or malathion when aphids appear.

Melon Aphid (*Aphis gossypii*)—Also known as the Cotton Aphid and considered our most destructive species. It is a common pest of cucumbers, melons, and squashes everywhere, is serious on cotton in the South, on citrus in Florida and California, and is a frequent greenhouse pest. Most cosmopolitan in its tastes, the melon aphid has been recorded on at least 46 plant species in Maine, 64 in Florida. A partial list includes asparagus, aster, avocado, begonia, buckthorn, California poppy, catalpa, chrysanthemum, cineraria, citron, cyclamen, dogwood, gourd, hydrangea, ironwood, lily, nemesia, pomegranate, rose, sunflower, strawberry, syringa, thistle, verbena; also bean, beet, eggplant, okra, spinach, and many weeds.

The aphid is small, usually very dark green but varying to yellow green, brown, or black. It winters in the North in the egg stage on live-forever and other weeds. In the South living young are produced through the year, as many as 51 generations having been recorded, with the average young per female more than 80. When the aphids get too crowded winged forms migrate to start a new colony.

The first sign of aphid infestation in the melon or cucumber patch is the wilting and curling of leaves (Plate I) accompanied by visits of ants, bees, wasps, and flies to get the honeydew. This aphid is a vector of cucumber and melon mosaic, a strain of which is responsible for the serious mosaic disease of lilies. On cucurbits, the mosaic shows as mottled dark and light green foliage and stunting of vines. The melon aphid is the worst watermelon pest in Florida, large acreages often being destroyed before the melons can be shipped. On orange, grapefruit, and other citrus trees the aphids distort and curl young twigs.

Control is difficult after the leaves and tender tips start curling. A nicotine dust has been generally recommended with lindane and phosphate sprays or dusts also possible. In normal seasons natural parasites and predators are quite efficient in keeping this aphid in check, but if a cool, wet spring unfavorable for the beneficial insects is followed by a hot, dry summer favorable for aphid reproduction there may be trouble.

Monterey Pine Aphid (*Essigella californica*)—A small, light green species with very long hind legs. It feeds on needles of Monterey and ponderosa pines and Douglas-fir in California and Oregon.

Norway-maple Aphid (*Periphyllus lyropictus*)—A nuisance to large numbers of people, most of whom have never seen or heard of it. This is a large, hairy, green to brown aphid infesting underside of Norway maple (sometimes sugar maple) foliage through the summer and dropping copious quantities of honeydew down to smear windshields and bodies of cars parked under street trees. Heavy aphid infestations may be followed by heavy summer leaf drop. Spray street trees with nicotine sulfate or other aphicide early in summer, wetting underside of leaves thoroughly.

Oleander Aphid (*Aphis nerii*)—A pretty yellow and black species common in Florida and California and occurring in other states. It appears in spring on young oleander shoots and later migrates to milkweed, though it can stay on oleander the whole year.

Oleaster-thistle Aphid (*Capitophorus braggii*)—Artichoke Aphid, pale yellow and green with darker green markings, often abundant on globe artichoke in California and Louisiana. It winters on Elaeagnus, Russian olive, and Shepherdia. Various thistles are summer hosts.

Ornate Aphid (*Myzus ornatus*)—A pest of fuchsia in California, controlled with nicotine sulfate and soap or toxaphene and a summer oil.

Painted-maple Aphid (*Drepanaphis acerifoliae*)—Gray and black in winged form, yellow in wingless state, infesting leaves of sugar and silver maple.

Pea Aphid (*Macrosiphum pisi*)—A smooth green species, generally distributed but of special importance to large growers and the pea-canning industry. In large pea fields aphids may be so abundant that plants and ground look white from cast skins; vines wilt and die. Even when less abundant the quality of the peas is affected. Limited to legumes, it winters on clovers and alfalfa, migrating to peas about May 1, there to produce 7 to 20 generations. It transmits the virus causing pea enation.

Control measures include rotenone, nicotine, DDT, lindane, TEPP, and parathion dusts. Some pea varieties are resistant to attack, but the aphid is a complex species made up of several different biological races, so that maintaining plant resistance is difficult.

Pecan Phylloxera (*Phylloxera devastatrix*)—Galls on stems caused by aphidlike insects.

Pine Bark Aphid or Chermid (*Pineus strobi*)—On white, Scotch, and Austrian pines over most of the country. It is a small dark insect covered with wax, congregating in conspicuous white, flocculent colonies on underside of the larger limbs or on main trunk, giving a whitewashed appearance. The immature forms winter under the felty white masses or under the bark, maturing and laying eggs in April or May, from which come both winged and wingless forms. Most of the former migrate to other pines; the latter lay eggs for a brood of adults appearing in August and September whose young are the hibernating nymphs. This aphid is more unsightly than injurious on older trees, but may damage unthrifty young trees in ornamental plantings.

Control. A dormant spray, miscible oil at 1 to 25 dilution, has been standard, often followed with nicotine sulfate when the young are present, but lindane (at rate of 1 pound of 25 per cent wettable powder to 100 gallons of water) seems quite effective now. A strong stream of water from the hose is also helpful.

Pine Leaf Aphid or Chermid (*Pineus pinifoliae*)—On white and lodgepole pines and red, Engelmann, black, and Sitka spruces. The nymphs winter on pine, migrate to spruce in spring where they produce compact terminal galls, 1 aphid in each chamber. The galls open in June and the aphids migrate back to old needles of white pine where they give birth to nymphs, which move to the new growth and are covered with white wax for the winter. The needles may turn yellow and the new growth sickly. Try lindane for control; break terminal galls off spruce and destroy before cells open.

Poplar Leaf Aphids—A number of species may be present on leaves of poplar and cottonwood but are not important enough to discuss in detail.

Poplar Petiole Gall Aphid (*Pemphigus populitransversus*)—Galls are produced on the leaf petioles of various poplars. Two other species produce semi-globular galls at the base of leaves, where blade and petiole unite.

Poplar Vagabond Aphid (*Mordwilkoja vagabunda*)—Causes peculiar convoluted galls at tops of twigs of various poplar species. It migrates in summer to unknown hosts, then returns to the same gall in autumn.

Potato Aphid (*Macrosiphum solanifolii*)—Often called pink and green potato aphid, common throughout the United States (Plate II).

This aphid is a menace as a vector of mosaic and other virus diseases of potato and tomato. Years of great abundance, when the aphid is present in epidemic proportions, are followed by lean years. Rose is the winter host, occasionally apple. Black eggs on rose canes hatch into glistening pink and green lice, about ⅙ inch long, with long cornicles, which feed on rosebuds and succulent young leaves. In early summer migrants fly or crawl to potatoes and other summer hosts— asparagus, aster, bean, cineraria, citrus, corn, eggplant, fuchsia, gladiolus, groundcherry, iris, Jerusalem-cherry, oxalis, pea, pepper, sunflower, sweetpotato, tomato, turnip, and many weeds.

Potato foliage is curled and distorted by aphid feeding; the vines often turn brown and die. On tomatoes the blossom clusters are so devitalized that no fruit is set. Generations develop every 2 or 3 weeks, with vines rapidly covered with lice. On a single tomato plant 24,688 aphids were once counted. In September and October they return to roses, there to produce egg-laying females which mate with males flying over from summer hosts.

Control. Spraying with nicotine sulfate, 1½ teaspoons per gallon of soapy water, at intervals of 2 or 3 days for 2 or 3 applications will control outbreaks. Nicotine or malathion dust may be used. On roses a pyrethrum-rotenone spray at 5-day intervals is usually satisfactory.

Privet Aphid (*Myzus ligustri*)—Privet, ligustrum, sometimes has new leaves tightly curled lengthwise. The aphids leave in midsummer but return in fall to lay eggs.

Purple-spotted Lily Aphid (*Macrosiphum lilii*)—A spotted yellow species confined to lily.

Raspberry Aphid (*Amphorophora rubi*)—Found in small numbers on underside of raspberry leaves; more important as vector of mosaic than for direct injury.

Red-cedar Aphid (*Cinara sabinae*)—A small, reddish-brown aphid with a thin waxy coating closely resembling bark of red-cedar, which it may infest in large numbers. The aphids feed on new growth in spring, checking it, and secrete much honeydew, so that the leaves are coated and the pores choked with sooty mold. Weakened trees may succumb to bark beetle attacks. Spray promptly with nicotine sulfate and soap or lindane.

Red Violet Aphid (*Micromyzus violae*)—Wine red with clouded wing veins, infesting young shoots, buds, and leaves of outdoor violets in California; present in greenhouses in other sections of the country.

Rhododendron Aphid (*Masonaphis rhododendri*)—Pink and green species infesting this host in Oregon.

Rose Aphid (*Macrosiphum rosae*)—A large species feeding on tender buds, with pink and green forms resembling those of the potato aphid. It is, however, a single-host species, continuing to breed on roses through the season. It injures tender leaves, stems, and buds and lays eggs for the winter on canes. There are several predators and parasites and when lady beetle larvae or aphid-lions are at work it is sometimes better to stop spraying temporarily and give the beneficial insects a chance. Malathion, lindane, nicotine sulfate, or pyrethrum and rotenone can usually be included in a spray or dust aimed at other insects as well.

A small green aphid (*Myzaphis rosarum*) is also a serious rose pest on occasion. It is much smaller than the rose aphid, has no pink forms, and is not restricted to succulent new growth.

Rosy Apple Aphid (*Anuraphis roseus*)—An important apple pest (Plate II). It curls the leaves and deforms young fruit, producing "aphis apples." It is present throughout the United States in apple-growing sections and may also feed on pear, hawthorn, and mountain-ash. It winters as dark green shiny eggs attached to twigs or in bark crevices, hatching over a period of 2 weeks when buds are opening. The stem mothers, purplish or rose with a waxy coating, feed on outside of buds until leaves start to unfold, then work their way down into the cluster. When their sucking makes the leaves curl around them they are well protected from sprays. Stem mothers continue to produce living young through spring and early summer, but about July winged forms, rosy but with black head and thorax, migrate to stems of narrow-leaved plantain. The aphids return to apple and lay eggs from October to November.

Control efforts are best directed at the overwintering eggs by means of dormant dinitro sprays but parathion, TEPP, and other phosphate sprays seem able to kill aphids even after they have curled the leaves. Isolan and malathion have prevented leaf curling on hawthorn when applied in April. Syrphid flies, lady beetles, lacewing flies, and parasitic wasps are very helpful in warm seasons, but when the weather is cold and wet, aphids get the upper hand unless man steps in.

Rusty Plum Aphid (*Hysteroneura setariae*)—A rusty-brown aphid common on plums in the East and west to Colorado. It also feeds on corn, grasses, sugar cane, and Virginia creeper. Use a dormant dinitro spray or nicotine sulfate and soap when aphids appear.

22. Snowball leaves curled by aphids.

Snowball Aphid (*Anuraphis viburnicola*)—Cause of the familiar curling and deforming of new leaves of the common snowball (*Viburnum opulus*) in early spring (Plate II). The aphids vary in color from ash gray to dark green and start curling the leaves long before they are out. Control is difficult because the lice are protected almost from the beginning inside the curled portions. Spray or dust with malathion, lindane, or nicotine, starting very early. Isolan has prevented curling when applied in early April. It may be easier to replace the common snowball with resistant *Viburnum tomentosum*. Another aphid (*Aphis viburnicola*) lives on snowball and other viburnums through the entire season.

Spinach Aphid—See Green Peach Aphid.

Spirea Aphid (*Aphis spiraecola*)—Also known as Green Citrus Aphid. This is a common green species on spirea, covering new growth in early summer with myriads of green lice. On citrus it curls and stunts leaves and twigs, deforms fruit, and covers everything with honeydew, medium for sooty mold. The eggs and sexual forms appear on spirea, the parthenogenetic viviparous forms on citrus and other hosts. The life cycle is only 6 to 10 days, with possibility of large populations built up in a short time. Newly planted trees suffer most. In addition to spirea and citrus the aphid may infest Japanese quince, haw, apple, pear, cherry-laurel, and various herbs. Citrus growers often use the dangerous phosphate sprays, parathion or TEPP, but malathion, nicotine sulfate, or lindane will suffice for ornamentals.

Spruce Aphid (*Aphis abietina*)—Very destructive to Sitka spruce in Oregon and Washington, having killed millions of board feet in forests. The aphids are dull green, $\frac{3}{16}$ inch; the alternate host is unknown. Needles turn yellow and fall. On ornamentals the aphids can be controlled with nicotine sulfate, miscible oil, or lime-sulfur.

Strawberry Aphid (*Pentatrichopus fragaefolii*)—A small, pale yellow species occurring in dense populations on strawberry leaves or on stems in the crown. It transmits strawberry yellows or crinkle and other virus diseases. The eggs winter either on strawberry or potentilla. To control the disease use certified plants. Dust with nicotine or rotenone; some of the newer insecticides give an off-flavor to the crop.

Strawberry Root Aphid (*Aphis forbesi*)—A single-host aphid on strawberries east of the Rockies and particularly injurious in New Jersey, Delaware, and Maryland. Black, shiny eggs, overwintered on leaves and stems, hatch in early spring into dark, bluish-green aphids, which feed on new leaves. They are found there by the little brown cornfield ant and carried to strawberry roots where they feed on root sap. There several generations keep the ants in honeydew, but in the fall winged forms fly to the leaves and give birth to sexual males and females which mate and provide overwintering eggs. In mild winters the root forms also persist. The best control is to select uninfested plants for new beds where the ground has been cultivated deeply and thoroughly. Chlordane will help control the ants.

Sugar-beet Root Aphid (*Pemphigus betae*)—Found in the western half of the United States. The small, wingless, oval, white or yellow aphid with a cottony tuft over the end of the abdomen feeds on roots of beet, sugar beet, mangel, and many weeds and wild grasses. A winged form, black with a white waxy covering, migrates to poplar for winter, feeding on poplar leaves in spring before returning to beet.

Sycamore Aphid (*Drepanosiphum platanoides*)—A common, large green or reddish aphid infesting maples and sycamores.

Thistle Aphid (*Anuraphis cardui*)—A large, shiny green species summering on thistles, chrysanthemum, and weeds, wintering on apricot, plum, prune.

Tulip Bulb Aphid (*Anuraphis tulipae*)—Often called Iris Root Aphid. A whitish powdery species with black head and thorax in the winged forms. It infests bases of plants at or below surface of ground and seeks hiding places in flower stems, under leaf sheaths, or in seed pods. It attacks all varieties of bearded and beardless iris and continues to feed on stored rhizomes. It may be present in quantity on tulip, lily, freesia, or crocus bulbs or stored gladiolus corms. The bulbs are shriveled from the sucking of masses of grayish plant lice and subsequent growth is stunted with poor flowers. Hot-water treatment or fumigation with Cyanogas has been used in the past. A new simple recommendation is to dust bulbs before storing with 1 to 1½ per cent lindane and to dust or spray growing plants with lindane or malathion.

Tulip Leaf Aphid (*Rhopalosiphoninus tulipaella*)—Clusters on leaves and shoots of tulips and iris; leaves may fail to open; plants are sometimes killed. The aphids winter on dormant bulbs in the ground. Spray plants with malathion or lindane.

Tuliptree Aphid (*Macrosiphum liriodendri*)—A small, green species abundant on underside of leaves and secreting copious quantities of honeydew. Leaves of tuliptrees and foliage of broad-leaved evergreens growing underneath are often densely coated with black sooty mold. Spray with lindane or nicotine-soap solution.

Turnip Aphid (*Rhopalosiphum pseudobrassicae*)—Also called False Cabbage Aphid. A greenish species covered with white bloom like the common cabbage aphid. Host plants are cabbage, cauliflower, collards, kale, kohlrabi, mustard, radish, rutabaga, turnip, bean, lettuce. It occurs anywhere in the United States, being particularly abundant in the Gulf states, where it continues to reproduce during the winter. Commercial growers use TEPP or parathion dusts fairly widely. Home gardeners may be content with nicotine or rotenone, possibly malathion if discontinued some time before harvest.

Violet Aphid (*Micromyzus violae*)—A black aphid common on violets, especially in greenhouses.

Walnut Aphid (*Chromaphis juglandicola*)—A small pale yellow aphid common on English walnut throughout California and Oregon. Feeding on underside of leaves it injures both by extracting sap and by the sooty mold growing in its honeydew. The DDT used in control of codling moth on walnut has resulted in a marked increase in aphid populations, through killing predators, unless an aphicide is included in the spray. Parathion and TEPP are good but hazardous for the operator. Nicotine dry concentrate 14 per cent, used at the rate of 60 pounds to 100 gallons of water, offers less hazard and has the least adverse effect on natural enemies of this aphid.

Waterlily Aphid (*Rhopalosiphum nymphaeae*)—Small, varying from dull to shiny green or black on its summer host—waterlily, water plantain, cattail, pondweed, knotweed. On its winter fruit-tree hosts—almond, apricot, plum—it is larger, reddish brown, covered with white powder. Waterlily leaves are disfigured and decayed, flowers discolored, and stems distorted. Japanese cherry grown near waterlily ponds may be seriously injured.

Control. In pools with fish, remove fish, lower water level to expose foliage and spray with pyrethrum or nicotine. Let the water run enough to change it before replacing fish. If they cannot be removed, fill pool to overflowing and wash aphids off foliage onto lawn with the hose; then spray them. Control aphids on plums before they migrate.

Western Aster Root Aphid (*Anuraphis middletonii*)—Light gray or dark green; common on roots of aster, buttercup, cosmos, dahlia, erigeron, and other composite flowers and weeds. For control see Corn Root Aphid.

White-pine Aphid (*Cinara strobi*)—Found on eastern white pine from New England to Illinois and south to the Carolinas. The aphid feeds on twigs and branches; small trees may be heavily damaged or killed. Sooty mold develops in the honeydew. Eggs are laid in lines on the needles. Spray with nicotine or lindane or wash the aphids off with a strong stream of water from the hose.

Woolly Alder Aphid (*Prociphilus tessellatus*)—Also called Alder Blight Aphid and Maple Leaf Aphid. Widely distributed. Maple is considered the primary host, alder the secondary. Branches of alder or leaves of maple are covered with masses of white cottony material covering blue-black aphids. In early fall males and females, the latter small and orange, migrate from alder to maple to mate and lay eggs on bark. At the same time a wingless hibernating form is produced on alder and this crawls down the trunk to spend the winter under leaves on the ground. Lady beetles and the caterpillar of an orange butterfly feed on these aphids and ants protect them in exchange for honeydew.

Woolly Apple Aphid (*Eriosoma lanigerum*)—Of world-wide distribution wherever apples are grown. It also attacks pear, hawthorn, mountain-ash, and elm. It covers trunks and branches with white cottony masses enclosing purplish lice and forms knots on the roots, causing many fibrous roots, stunting, and sometimes death of young apple trees (Plate II).

The life history is complicated. This woolly aphid winters in several forms—eggs on the bark of elm trees, immature nymphs on apple roots, or, in warm climates, as egg-laying females on apple bark. The eggs on elm hatch in spring into wingless forms which feed on elm buds for 2 generations, turning young leaves into curled rosettes, which protect the purplish aphids with their powdery coatings. The next generation has wings and migrates to apple, hawthorn, and mountain-ash where some of the lice feed in wounds on trunk and branches and others work their way down to the roots where the most important injury is produced. In autumn winged migrants return to elm while other wingless aphids remain to produce living young on apple roots.

Control. An effective parasite, *Aphelinus mali*, has been distributed to many countries, but it works best at fairly high temperatures and is killed when DDT, DDD, or methoxychlor is used in the spray schedule. It is not decreased by parathion and TEPP, which are effective for the aphids. Plant clean nursery stock; dip infested seedlings in strong nicotine sulfate solution before planting.

Woolly Beech Aphid (*Phyllaphis fagi*)—Common on underside of leaves of purple beech and other species. The greenish aphid is covered with prominent white waxy threads which look like trailing cotton robes. Nicotine sulfate, directed with pressure from underneath the trees, gives excellent control; lindane is also good. On mature trees in home gardens the pest can often be ignored.

Woolly Elm Aphid (*Eriosoma americanum*)—Attacks only American elm with roots of shadbush or serviceberry the alternate host. It produces curled or rolled leaves like the woolly apple aphid but no rosettes. Another species (*E. ulmi*) produces a similar leaf roll on English elm.

Woolly Hawthorn Aphid (*Eriosoma crataegi*)—Much like the woolly apple aphid with which it has been confused. It does not make galls on roots but is parasitized by the same wasp.

Woolly Larch Aphid or Chermid (*Chermes strobilobius*)—On larch and spruce, mostly red and black. It appears as white woolly masses on large needles and as dark aphids on underside of twigs and clustered at base of leaves. On spruce it forms small galls at the base of current growth.

Woolly Pear Aphid (*Eriosoma pyricola*)—Also similar to the woolly apple aphid and for a long time considered the same. It is established on the Pacific coast and in limited locations further east. The life cycle is completed on elm, where leaf galls are formed.

ARMYWORMS

Armyworms are related to cutworms. They are larvae of moths, caterpillars which work in armies devouring everything in their paths.

Control by baits is being superseded by spraying or dusting with organic chemicals.

Armyworm (*Pseudaletia unipuncta*)—Common east of the Rocky Mountains, also known in New Mexico, Arizona, and California, traveling in dense armies, devouring all crops along the line of march. This native pest has been serious on cereal and forage crops since early Colonial times. It fluctuates in importance, reaching epidemic numbers at varying intervals of years, usually worse after a cold spring. The caterpillars are 1½ inches long, smooth, greenish with dark stripes and a fine, broken, light-colored stripe down the center of the back. They winter mainly as larvae, then form dark brown pupae in the soil, whence emerge brownish-gray moths, "millers," with a small white dot in the center of each front wing, 1½ inches across the wings. The moths fly only at night and are attracted to lights and decaying fruits. The females lay greenish-white eggs in long rows on lower leaves of grasses. There may be 2 or 3 generations a year with the first most injurious. Wheat, corn, oats, and rye are favorite food plants and may be devoured down to the ground.

Control. Spray or dust fields with 20 per cent toxaphene or 10 per cent DDT, or scatter a poison bait as for cutworms, of wheat bran mixed with Paris green or white arsenic, over the field or across the line of march. Many insects, especially tachinid flies, are parasitic on armyworms. They are eaten by birds, skunks, and toads.

Beet Armyworm (*Laphygma exigua*)—Also known as Asparagus Fern Caterpillar. The larvae are green above, yellow underneath, with a dark stripe on the back and yellowish stripes on each side. They eat corn, cotton, peas, and peppers as well as beets and asparagus fern. Adults are a mottled gray.

Fall Armyworm (*Laphygma frugiperda*)—So named because it does not appear before fall in the northern states. It is a tropical insect wintering in southern Florida and along the Gulf coast, migrating north in summer as far as New England and Michigan. Called the southern grassworm in Florida it eats all grass in easy range (lawns as well as meadows) before moving to corn, second choice. On corn it is sometimes called budworm and works like the corn earworm. It is particularly injurious following a cold, wet spring on vegetables—bean, cabbage, cowpea, cucumber, peanut, potato, sweetpotato, spinach, tomato, turnip—as well as on grass, corn, clover, and grains.

The moths, 1½ inches across, with grayish-white hind wings, dark mottled fore wings with a white spot near the tip, fly northward in swarms, mostly at night. They lay up to 1000 eggs, in clusters of about 150 each, on green plants. The young larvae start feeding near the ground and do a lot of damage before they are noticed, though they do not hide in the soil during the day as does the true armyworm. The caterpillars are light tan to green or black, with 3 yellowish hairlines down the back, then a darker stripe next to a waxy yellow stripe splotched with red. They have a conspicuous V-shaped white mark on the head. When they have eaten all the food in one garden they start a forced march on the next. Only one generation is abundant in the North; there may be 5 or 6 in the South.

Control. Several organic insecticides can be used as sprays or dusts. In experiments, parathion, dieldrin, aldrin, lindane, toxaphene, chlordane, and DDT were effective in that order, with toxaphene being quite a lot better than chlordane and DDT in the field. Cultivate soil in gardens to expose pupae to natural enemies, of which there are many.

Southern Armyworm (*Prodenia eridania*)—Also called Semi-tropical Armyworm. This species is prevalent in Florida and has been noted as far north as South Carolina. It is a major pest of celery and sweetpotato, attacks cotton and some other plants. The larvae are black, or yellow with black markings.

Yellow-striped Armyworm (*Prodenia ornithogalli*)—Also known as Sweetpotato Caterpillar or Cotton Cutworm. This is a sweetpotato pest in Florida, often defoliating whole fields in July and August. In California and southwestern states it infests truck and field crops, flowers, fruits, forest and shade trees. The caterpillars are day-feeding, olive green to brown, with a double row of green or black spots on the back and usually a bright orange stripe outside the spots. The moths have mottled gray or brown fore wings, pale hind wings.

BAGWORMS

Bagworms are caterpillars which carry their baglike houses around with them. They are larvae of moths, family Psychidae, with wingless, almost legless females that practically never leave their bags. Of the 20 species in this country only 1 is commonly mentioned.

Bagworm (*Thyridopteryx ephemeraeformis*)—Distributed from Massachusetts south to Florida and west into Texas. Although called the Evergreen Bagworm and a frequent pest of conifers, it is a general feeder, sometimes defoliating sycamores, Norway and soft maples, locust, boxelder, linden, citrus, as well as arborvitae, juniper, hemlock, larch, and pine. It seems to be somewhat more devastating in the South. I have seen miles of red-cedars in Virginia and many arborvitae in Texas killed with bagworms but never such total destruction in New Jersey.

The spindle-shaped bag, 1 to 2 inches long, of unbelievably tough silk, is covered with bits of leaves and twigs from the host plant, a bag hanging on a juniper looking different from one on a pine (Plate III). The eggs winter in the bag and the larvae hatch in late spring, perhaps April in Florida, late May and early June in New Jersey. The larvae, dark brown to black with white to yellowish, black-spotted head and thorax, ¾ to 1 inch long when grown, crawl from the bag to nearest foliage and construct their cases as they feed, weaving a band of silk around themselves and attaching to it leaves and leaf petioles. The bagworm moves around freely with its bag but fastens it to a twig with a silken thread whenever it stops to eat, or to molt, which it does four times. It pupates in late summer, and the black male moth, with furry body and feathered antennae, wingspread about 1 inch, flies to mate with the maggotlike yellowish female through an opening at the base of her bag. She lays her eggs, 500 to 1000, in the pupal case in the bag and then dies.

Control. When there is a light infestation picking off the bags in winter or spring is the easiest control. Some recommend burning; others suggest placing the bags in deep open containers near the infested trees. The larvae, helpless to crawl for food, will die, but their beneficial parasites will be liberated. For heavy infestations, spray with lead arsenate, 3 to 4 level tablespoons per gallon, as soon as the caterpillars start feeding. Parathion also gives good control but is too dangerous in many circumstances. Toxaphene is also effective; DDT is ineffective. Sometimes woodpeckers and sapsuckers feed on the succulent morsels within the bags.

BEES

Bees are tremendously important in the garden, especially in the orchard, for pollination. Apples rarely set fruit unless they are fertilized by pollen from some other variety. Honeybees accomplish about 90 per cent of the pollen transfer in the apple orchard but bumblebees, solitary bees, and other insects are also helpful. Pears, cherries, plums, peaches, strawberries, and some vegetables need insect help for a good crop or to set seed. Commercial orchardists frequently rent hives of bees for the flowering period.

DDT has focused attention on the effect of poison sprays on bees. Even older insecticides like lead arsenate kill bees and that is one reason why a fruit spray schedule is so carefully timed. The pre-pink spray is put on before the blossoms open and the calyx spray is applied when most of the petals have fallen. *No poison should be used while the bees are coming to the flowers for nectar.*

Bees are in the insect order Hymenoptera, superfamily Apoidea.

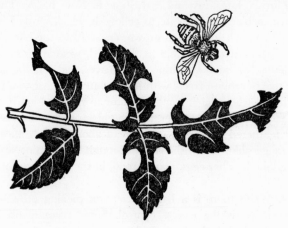

23. Leaf-cutter bee and its work on rose.

Leaf-cutter Bee (*Megachile* spp.)—Moderate-sized, stout-bodied, solitary bee, nesting in wood or hollow stems of woody plants. The bees are hairy, black or metallic blue, green, or purple, with short, elbowed antennae. The long legs are not equipped with pollen baskets, the pollen being carried on brushes under the abdomen. All members of this group are important pollinators; some are particularly useful with cultivated alfalfa and clovers. The female cuts dime-size, very precise ovals and circles from margins of leaves, usually rose leaves. The ovals line the bottom and sides of her nest, the circles cap each cell after an egg has been laid inside. The nests are made either in broken ends of branches or in the pithy stem of plants such as dahlia. There is no control except to cut out wilted or dying shoots containing the nests. And because the bees are essentially useful, one should not begrudge them a few rose leaves. I'd rather admire them for the perfection of their tailoring.

Small Carpenter Bee (*Ceratinia* spp.)—Dark bluish green, less than ½ inch long, nesting in tunnels in the pith of various woody shrubs, especially rose. When the cut stem shows a hole in the pith, slitting it lengthwise usually reveals a half dozen or so yellowish, curved maggots lined up in cavities. Cut canes below infested portions. Paint cut surface with tree paint or other wound dressing to prevent egg-laying.

BEETLES

Beetles belong to the order Coleoptera, which means "sheath wings." This order comprises 40 per cent of all insects, with perhaps 275,000 beetles already described and over 26,000 of these known in the United States. Some beetles are predaceous, preying on other insects; some are scavengers, cleaning up rotting animal and plant refuse; and many feed on healthy plant tissues. They are doubly injurious because both larvae and adults have chewing mouth parts.

The chief characteristic of members of the order Coleoptera is the modification of the first pair of wings into hard, horny sheaths (elytra) commonly called wing covers. They meet, in most species, in a straight line down the middle of the back and in flight are held stiffly out at the sides. All movement is by the membranous hind wings, which are folded transversely under the elytra when at rest. Some running ground beetles and some weevils lack hind wings and have the horny elytra grown together down the back.

Beetles have complete metamorphosis. The egg hatches into a soft grub, usually with 6 legs, occasionally legless, then turns into a pupa with the sacs enclosing appendages freely movable, and finally transforms into the adult beetle (see Figure 24). The mouth parts often indicate beetle habits. Short, chunky mandibles usually belong to a plant-eating species while a predator has long pointed jaws right for grasping other insects. If the mandibles lack distinct teeth and are covered with stiff hairs, the beetle is likely a harmless pollen feeder. Snout beetles and weevils have the head prolonged forward and downward into a cylindrical snout that may be shorter than the head or much longer than the body. Beetles called curculios have a long curved snout with the mouth parts at the tip of this projection.

Adult beetles have compound eyes but no ocelli (simple eyes), while the larvae have a small group of ocelli on each side of the head but no compound eyes. The antennae have 10 to 11 segments and the tarsi 3 to 5. There are no cerci (projections of the posterior end of the abdomen) in the adult and often none in the larva; there is no firm ovipositor.

There are about 200 beetle families. The few listed here include those individuals markedly injurious to garden plants and predators that are especially helpful to gardeners.

The families are divided by many technical taxonomic characters such as structure of the antennae, form of legs, number of tarsal segments, etc., and they are grouped under 2 suborders.

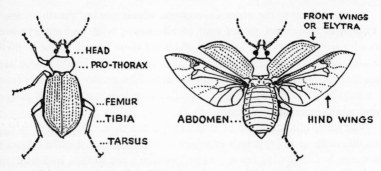

...HEAD
...PRO-THORAX
...FEMUR
...TIBIA
...TARSUS

FRONT WINGS OR ELYTRA
ABDOMEN...
HIND WINGS

24. Diagram of beetle with wings in normal position and spread for flight.

Suborder ADEPHAGA. Predaceous beetles mostly beneficial to us; tarsi with 5 segments; antennae filiform; hind wings with veins; ventral part of first segment of abdomen divided into 3 areas; larvae active, carnivorous, each leg with 6 segments and 2 claws at the end.

Cicindelidae. Tiger beetles; beautifully colored adults with ugly larvae, waiting in burrows for prey; many forms semi-aquatic.

Carabidae. Ground beetles; common on surface of ground, lurking under stones and rubbish.

Suborder POLYPHAGA. Beetles varying in form, habit; legs of larvae with not more than 5 segments, ending in a single claw; hind wings with reduced venation; first ventral segment of abdomen in a single piece.

Staphylinidae. Rove beetles, a large group of predators; rather flat, elongate; head wide as thorax; fore wings much shortened, elevated when disturbed; tarsi 5-segmented.

Coccinellidae. Lady beetles, "lady bugs," among most useful of all predators; hemispherical shape; antennae club-shaped; tarsi 3-segmented.

Cleridae. Checkered beetles, important enemies of many wood-boring beetles; long, almost cylindrical; brightly marked; covered with dense hairs; antennae serrate (saw-horned); tarsi 5-segmented.

Lampyridae. Fireflies or lightning beetles, feeding on snails and slugs; soft-bodied, elongate, flattish, with luminous segments near end of abdomen; antennae slender; eyes large; tarsi 5-segmented.

Cantharidae. Soldier beetles; similar to lightning beetles but without light-producing organs; adults often found on flowers; larvae predaceous on other insects.

Buprestidae. Metallic wood-borers; hard-bodied, flat, small to medium in size; striking iridescent blue or bronze coloring. Head very short; eyes large; antennae short, saw-toothed, 11-segmented; tarsi 5-segmented. Larvae long, legless, with small head and very broad flat thorax; e.g., flatheaded apple tree borer.

Elateridae. Click beetles, having a special joint at union of prothorax and mesothorax, enabling them to snap back into position when placed on their backs. Body elongate, rounded at each end; large eyes; antennae serrate; tarsi 5-segmented; larvae are wireworms.

Nitulidae. Dried fruit and sap beetles; very small, active; elytra shorter than abdomen; head large; eyes conspicuous; antennae club-shaped, 11-segmented; tarsi 5-segmented.

Meloidae. Blister beetles; elongate, soft-bodied, usually cylindrical; large head, set off from thorax; short, filiform antennae; 5 segments in tarsi of front and middle legs, 4 in hind tarsi.

Lucanidae. Stag beetles, with lamellate antennae, having a cylindrical basal part and several flat, leaflike segments at the tip. Beetles are large, brownish, with very large mandibles, those of some males being branched like the antlers of a stag; antennae elbowed; tarsi 5-segmented. Stag beetles work mainly in rotting wood. They are not particularly injurious but are noticeable when attracted to lights at night. The pugnacious males indulge in duels.

Scarabaeidae. Scarab beetles; a very large family with some dung beetles beneficial as scavengers, but with many plant feeders—chafers, June beetles, Japanese beetles, etc. Adults are oval, robust, with short, usually elbowed antennae, having clubs made of several thin plates pressed together; tarsi 5-segmented; larvae are plump, whitish, usually C-shaped.

Cerambycidae. Long-horned beetles; wood-borers as larvae, feeding on flowers, foliage, or bark as adults. Small to large, elongate, with very long filiform antennae; tarsi apparently 4-segmented, the fifth segment being small and concealed.

Chrysomelidae. Leaf beetles, feeding mostly on flowers and foliage; closely related to Cerambycidae but with shorter antennae, smaller, more oval in shape; tarsi apparently 4-segmented. This family includes the small flea beetles, destructive Colorado potato beetles, asparagus and cucumber beetles.

Bruchidae (Mylabridae). Seed weevils; very small, oval insects; head relatively large; prominent eyes; straight, sometimes clubbed antennae; tarsi apparently 4-segmented. Feeding mostly on seeds of legumes.

Curculionidae. Snout beetles, curculios, or typical weevils, with head prolonged into a long or short snout; antennae elbowed, with a club; tarsi apparently 4-segmented.

Scolytidae (Ipidae). Engraver or bark beetles, mining on surface of hardwood and making patterns under the bark. Very small beetles, brownish or black, with a small head and large first thoracic segment; antennae short, with a club; tarsi apparently 4-segmented. This family also includes ambrosia or timber beetles, which penetrate sapwood and heartwood of dead trees and feed on fungi growing on the walls of their tunnels.

In considering the different beetles I am following the entirely artificial system set up for this book as a whole; *i.e.,* treating them alphabetically under approved common names. If a beetle is commonly known as a borer, from its larval state, then it is discussed under Borers; if its approved name is curculio it is considered under Curculios; and if it is called a weevil, it is treated under Weevils. If your pest is called a borer, then look up Borers and not Beetles first.

Alder Bark Beetle (*Alniphagus aspericollis*)—Commonly destructive to western alders, attacking weakened or dying trees. Small, black, robust beetles, ⅛ inch long, bore through bark in pairs, usually at base of branches, and construct longitudinal egg galleries 2 to 5 inches long. Larvae pupate in soft inner bark. There are 2 generations a year.

Alder Flea Beetle (*Altica ambiens*)—Feeding on foliage of alders from Maine to New Mexico, normally scarce but periodically epidemic and defoliating the host. Color cobalt to greenish blue, shiny, ⅕ inch long, elytra wider at base, finely punctate. Adults hibernate in protected places, lay orange eggs on leaves in spring. Larvae, dark brown with black heads, eat everything but veins during July and August. Pupation is in the ground. There is 1 generation in Maine, sometimes 2 farther south. Spray with lead arsenate or DDT. Parathion is highly effective but dangerous.

Alfalfa Snout Beetle (*Brachyrhinus ligustici*)—A European pest first noted in this country near Oswego, New York, in 1933, feeding on raspberries. Since then it has been found on rhubarb and strawberry as well as alfalfa, its chief host. A bait made of soybean meal, sugar, and sodium fluosilicate in pellet form is effective, applied when the wingless adults migrate in April.

Ambrosia Beetles (*Xyleborus* spp.)—Small, cylindrical brown to black beetles that make small pinholes in trunk and limbs of many weakened or dying fruit and shade trees, including avocado. They live on ambrosial fungi cultured in their tunnels.

Argus Tortoise Beetle (*Chelymorpha cassidea*)—A tortoise-shaped, yellow to bright red beetle with black spots, very convex, $\frac{1}{3}$ inch long; larva yellow with brown spots, $\frac{1}{2}$ inch long, with long marginal spines holding a mass of excrement. This species is present throughout the East and west to New Mexico, feeding on morning glory, moonflower, sweetpotato, and related plants.

Ash-gray Blister Beetle (*Epicauta fabricii*)—A common eastern species, destructive to forage and truck crops. It is about $\frac{1}{2}$ inch long, ash gray in color. It ranges west into Arizona and Idaho, where it may be abundant, with larvae feeding on grasshopper eggs. See Black Blister Beetle for life history and control.

Asiatic Beetle—See Oriental Beetle.

Asiatic Garden Beetle (*Autoserica castanea*)—An oriental pest, first reported in New Jersey in 1922 and since found at scattered points along the Atlantic seaboard from Massachusetts to South Carolina. The area of continuous infestation covers about 4000 square miles around New York City. Apparently this beetle dies out in regions of low summer rainfall. It resembles the Japanese beetle in shape and size but is a uniform cinnamon brown and comes out to feed *only at night*. It is attracted to lights, bangs into screens, flies into automobiles. Asters are first choice as food plants, but more than 100 different plants are acceptable, including beet, carrot, corn, eggplant, kohlrabi, parsnip, pepper, turnip among vegetables; aster, azalea, chrysanthemum, dahlia, delphinium, rose, zinnia, viburnum in the ornamentals; and such fruits as cherry, peach, and strawberry. They strip the foliage, especially that near the ground, sometimes severely damaging nursery seedlings of pine, hemlock, yew, barberry, and others, and they feed on flowers. The larvae cause brown patches in the lawn and feed on roots of many garden plants.

There is a one-year cycle, adults emerging in late June with peak of abundance July to mid-August. Eggs are laid in grassy areas, sometimes in cultivated soil. The grubs, grayish with light brown heads, ¾ inch long when grown, found in a curved position, differ from Japanese beetles chiefly in having the spines at tip of abdomen arranged in a semi-circle rather than a V.

Control. Grubproof lawns as for Japanese beetles with DDT, chlordane, dieldrin, endrin, or lead arsenate. Spray or dust plants with DDT, methoxychlor, lead arsenate, or rotenone. The bacterial milky disease used for Japanese beetles has some effect on this species also.

Asparagus Beetle (*Crioceris asparagi*)—Introduced from Europe about 1856 and now present in most asparagus regions. The beetles are slender, ¼ inch long, metallic blue black with 3 yellow squares along each wing cover, reddish margins, prothorax, and head (Plate IV). Beetles winter in protected places about the garden, feed on asparagus shoots when they come up in spring, and lay dark brown eggs attached by one end. These hatch into olive green or dark gray, soft, wrinkled larvae with black heads, ⅓ inch long, which gnaw stems and leaves for 10 to 12 days. Asparagus can be almost defoliated and is often stained by a dark fluid. The larvae pupate in cells in the soil. The life cycle takes 3 to 8 weeks and there are at least 2 generations in the North, 3 or more in the South.

Control. Cut frequently; keep tips dusted with rotenone or pyrethrum. After the cutting season dust with 10 per cent DDT or cryolite or calcium arsenate (1 part to 2 parts lime). Lady beetle larvae and predaceous plant bugs help keep this beetle in bounds; a chalcid wasp is a parasite.

Banded Cucumber Beetle (*Diabrotica balteata*)—Primarily a pest of beans, sometimes sweetpotatoes, in southern states and not so important on cucumbers. The adult is light green with 3 bands of darker green.

Bean Leaf Beetle (*Cerotoma trifurcata*)—Abundant in southeastern states, occasional elsewhere. The beetle is yellow buff to dull red, ¼ inch long, with 3 or 4 black spots on inner edge of wing covers and a black band near outer margins. The adults chew holes in leaves, feeding from the underside, but slender white larvae feed on roots and nodules, chewing stems under the soil line, sometimes girdling them. There are

1 or 2 broods a year on beans, peas, cowpeas, soybeans, and various weeds. See Mexican Bean Beetle for control measures.

Beet Leaf Beetle (*Erynephala puncticollis*)—A western pest now extending east to the Atlantic states, injuring table and sugar beets and spinach. The adult is ⅓ inch long, dull yellow with black margins and black spots on the thorax. The grayish olive-brown larvae are marked with raised tubercles and yellow spots resembling those of lady beetles. Both larvae and adults feed on foliage, with the former most injurious. Destroying weed hosts and cleaning up winter shelters may be sufficient control measures.

25. Bean leaf beetle.

Black Blister Beetle (*Epicauta pennsylvanica*)—An all-black species common in the East. A special pest of asters and Japanese anemone in late summer but feeding also on flowers and foliage of many other plants, including ivy. This species is typical of all blister beetles. They are rather long, ¾ inch, slender, with the prothorax narrower than the soft and flexible wing covers. The name comes from the cantharidin in their bodies, which will blister the skin if beetles are crushed on it. This powerful agent, obtained from the "Spanish Fly," a European blister beetle, was formerly used in much the same fashion as a mustard plaster and also as an aphrodisiac. Cantharidin still has a few uses in modern medicine and animal breeding and certain drug companies purchase beetles collected in quantities.

Old-fashioned potato bug and Yankee bug, favored in the South, are other names for blister beetles. Their life history is peculiar, to say the least (Plate V). They differ from most beetles in being predaceous, and therefore helpful, in the larval state but plant eating as adults. The beetle winters as a partly transformed larva, pseudopupa, in an earthen cell in the soil. More than one winter may be spent in this suspended state but in some spring the pseudopupa molts, acquires functional legs, moves about for a while, then goes into the true pupal stage which lasts about 2 weeks. The beetles appear in swarms in June or July or later and feed gregariously. The females lay yellow eggs in clusters of about 100 in holes in the soil and in 10 to 21 days active, strong-jawed larvae start burrowing through the soil until they find the egg mass of a grasshopper. They gnaw into the egg pod and eat the eggs. The larvae molt 4 times, going through a series of changes in form. The first larval state is called a triungulin, and the active triungulins specialize in eating eggs of the two-striped and differential grasshoppers. Some ascend to flowers and may be carried thence by bees to their nests. When the triungulin sheds its skin after the first molt it looks more like a grub. After the last molt the larva burrows into the soil to form the cells in which it turns into the hard-shelled, immobile pseudopupa.

There are about 250 species of blister beetles in this country. They are black or gray, brown or yellow, sometimes striped or margined. They feed on many vegetables—bean, beet, cabbage, cowpea, corn, carrot, eggplant, melon, onion, pea, pepper, potato, pumpkin, radish, soybean, spinach, sweetpotato, Swiss chard, tomato. They injure some vines, clematis especially, sometimes ivy. They feed on young trees in nurseries and ornamental plantings. They like many flowers—aster, Japanese anemone, chrysanthemum and zinnia preferred.

Control. Blister beetles have been hard to control because they are resistant to, or repelled by, arsenicals but cryolite and 5 per cent DDT dust are quite effective. In a small infestation the beetles can be picked off into a jar of kerosene; wear a glove to keep from getting blistered.

Black Hills Beetle (*Dendroctonus ponderosae*)—The worst enemy of ponderosa pine in the Rocky Mountain region, attacking other pines when epidemic, then killing trees of all sizes and types, though normally attacking only weakened trees. The beetles are reddish brown, up to ⅜ inch. Egg galleries are longitudinal and straight; the larval mines are short, broad, packed with reddish boring dust. As with all bark beetles, infested wood should be burned, normal trees kept growing vigorously.

Black-legged Tortoise Beetle (*Jonthonota nigripes*)—Golden yellow with 3 black dots arranged in a triangle on each wing cover. Larvae are straw yellow with 2 dark spots behind the head (Plate XI). See also Tortoise Beetles.

Black Turpentine Beetle (*Dendroctonus terebrans*)—An eastern bark beetle working near the base of pine and spruce, especially pitch pine.

Blueberry Flea Beetle (*Altica torquata*)—Copper bronze, feeding on blueberry foliage in Maine, also recorded in Connecticut.

Bumble Flower Beetle (*Euphoria inda*)—An eastern species ranging west into New Mexico. The adult resembles a bumblebee, is ½ inch long, broadly oval, yellowish brown mottled with black. It feeds on ears of ripening corn, sometimes on apples, grapes, and peaches. Larvae develop in dung and rotting fruit which should be cleaned up.

Carrot Beetle (*Ligyrus gibbosus*)—Occurring over most of the country except far northern states. The beetles, ½ inch long, broad, reddish brown with stout legs, gouge out roots and base of stems of carrot, beet, celery, corn, cotton, dahlia, elm, oak, parsnip, potato, sunflower, and weeds, especially amaranthus. The adults are nocturnal and winter in the soil laying eggs there in spring. The larvae, bluish white, curved, with brown heads, feed on roots of grasses and sometimes corn and other crops. There is one generation. No control is suggested except cleaning up piles of rotting vegetables. Parasites play an important part in reducing the population.

Cherry Leaf Beetle (*Galerucella cavicollis*)—Present in the East in large numbers at intervals of several years. Adults are small red beetles, less than ¼ inch long, feeding on foliage of cherry and peach, sometimes plum, occasionally apple. Brown larvae with yellow and black spots feed only on wild cherry. There is 1 generation a year and attacks are so sudden protective sprays are usually too late.

Clematis Blister Beetle (*Epicauta cinerea*)—Formerly known as Gray Blister Beetle. It is gray with a yellowish tinge, found on clematis, sometimes on aster, verbena, and other ornamentals. See Black Blister Beetle for life history and control measures.

Colorado Potato Beetle (*Leptinotarsa decemlineata*)—A large leaf beetle, an example of a native insect which suddenly became dangerous to cultivated plants (Plate IV). For many years this beetle lived on the sandbur weed on high plateaus at the base of the Rocky Mountains. It was described in 1824 and had probably been around as an obscure beetle for a long time. But the pioneer settlers of the West brought with them the potato, which the beetle found much to its taste. In a short time this almost unknown insect became, under the title of "potato bug" the best-known beetle in all America. It migrated eastward at the rate of about 85 miles a year, following potato plantings, appearing in Nebraska in 1859, Illinois in 1864, Ohio in 1869, reaching the

Atlantic coast by 1874. Eventually it made its way to Europe, where it is well established in France, Holland, Belgium, Spain, parts of Italy, and many other countries. It appeared in England but was eradicated there. It is now a problem throughout the United States except parts of Florida, Nevada, and California.

The Colorado potato beetle is hard-shelled, very broad, 3/8 by 1/4 inch, very convex, yellow with 10 longitudinal black lines and with black spots on the thorax. It winters as an adult in the ground, emerging as soon as potatoes are up to lay bright, orange-yellow eggs in small clusters on undersurface of leaves. These hatch in 4 to 7 days into very humpbacked, fat red grubs, which feed for 2 or 3 weeks, then pupate in the ground. Beetles emerge in another week or two to lay eggs for the second generation, adults appearing early in autumn to feed for a while, then enter the soil for hibernation. In the South there may be 3 generations.

Both beetles and larvae completely ravage potato foliage, often destroying whole fields. Although potato is preferred, the beetles may go to other members of the nightshade family such as eggplant, tomato, pepper, petunia, nicotiana, groundcherry.

Control. Hand-picking was the first control measure tried. What farm boy of great-grandfather's day did not have to pick his quota of potato bugs. Paris green was the first poison, followed by London purple, then calcium or lead arsenate, sometimes cryolite, and now DDT. Potato fields can be sprayed with 50 per cent wettable DDT, at 2 to 3 pounds per 100 gallons of water or dusted with 3 per cent DDT in the East, 5 per cent in the West. They can also be dusted with calcium arsenate, 1 part to 3 parts of hydrated lime or talc; or with cryolite (equal parts with talc; do not combine cryolite with lime); or with rotenone. Make first application when potatoes are only a few inches high and repeat in a week or two. *Keep foliage covered during periods of most rapid growth.*

Corn Billbugs (*Calendra* spp.)—Snout beetles present in grasslands and cultivated areas throughout the country but more destructive east of the Great Plains. The maize billbug (*Calendra maidis*) and the curlew-bug (*C. callosa*) are important in the South. Billbugs cause serious losses to corn by tunneling and feeding inside the stalk and making holes in developing leaves. The grubs feed on fibrous roots of small grains and cultivated grasses, on rice and peanuts.

Billbugs vary from 1/5 to 3/4 inch in length, have a cylindrical curved snout like a curculio, hard body wall and wing covers. They "play possum" when disturbed. They are reddish brown to black, often so covered with mud that the color cannot be told. They gouge out a small hole in the stalk for each white, kidney-shaped egg. The grubs are chunky, white, humpbacked, legless, with a hard brown or yellow head. They eat out the pith of the stem and then go down to the roots.

Control by crop rotation and fall spading or plowing followed by clean cultivation.

Corn Flea Beetle (*Chaetocnema pulicaria*)—A small, brassy beetle more dangerous for its ability to disseminate bacterial wilt of corn, known as Stewart's disease, than for its feeding on corn foliage, resulting in small perforations. The beetles inoculate the corn with bacteria which have wintered in their alimentary tracts. Control with DDT.

Corn Sap Beetle (*Carpophilus dimidiatus*)—A very small brown scavenger beetle that also eats corn kernels, getting into the ear when the husk is loosened by birds, or following after earworms. It is serious at times, but aldrin, lindane, or toxaphene may control it. Other species are also injurious.

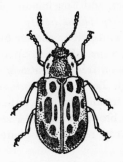

26. Cottonwood leaf beetle.

Cottonwood Leaf Beetle (*Chrysomela scripta*)—Occurring from coast to coast, often more injurious to willows than to cottonwood and other poplars. The beetle, 1/4 inch long, has black head and thorax, the latter bordered with orange red, and gold wing covers with a purplish line at the inner edge and each bearing 7 purple-black spots. The larvae are black when young, later dirty yellow, with black legs, brown heads. They emit drops of pungent milky fluid when disturbed. They skeletonize leaves and may partially defoliate trees, especially in the West. Basket willows are particularly subject to attack. The pupae hang downward from the leaves. Spray with lead arsenate or DDT early in the season when larvae are young.

Darkling Ground Beetle (*Coniontis subpubescens*)—Native California beetle, shining black and brown, 1/3 inch long; flying into sugar-beet fields, sometimes attacking young avocados.

Desert Corn Flea Beetle (*Chaetocnema ectypa*)—Injures corn, sorghum, small grains in arid Southwest. The beetles feed on foliage, larvae on roots.

Diabrotica Beetles—This name is popularly given to the spotted species of cucumber beetles when they infest flowers in the garden. See Spotted Cucumber Beetle and Western Spotted Cucumber Beetle.

Douglas-fir Beetle (*Dendroctonus pseudotsugae*)—The most important bark beetle enemy of Douglas-fir, also attacking western larch. The small reddish to dark brown beetle, 1/5 inch long, covered with hairs, usually works on injured or dying trees but may feed on healthy trees. Keep them growing vigorously; cut down seriously weakened trees.

Douglas-fir Engraver (*Scolytus unispinosus*)—A very small, shiny black beetle making galleries in the bark of normal, injured, or dying Douglas-fir, western larch, and Engelmann spruce.

Dried-fruit Beetle (*Carpophilus hemipterus*)—A small, broad, flat beetle, brown with pale spots, elytra shorter than the body. This is one of the scavenger beetles, a special pest of dried fruit. Clean fruit stored at 40° to 45°F. will remain free from attack.

Eastern Juniper Bark Beetle (*Phloeosinus dentatus*)—Red-cedar Bark Beetle, infesting, usually, eastern red-cedars, killing weakened trees. The beetle is light brown to black, 1/6 inch long, and its galleries resemble engravings. Keep newly transplanted shrubs well watered to prevent attack.

Eastern Larch Beetle (*Dendroctonus simplex*)—A small red to brown bark beetle infesting injured, dying, or living larches. The galleries in the bark are longitudinal, wavy, or branched.

Eastern Spruce Beetle (*Dendroctonus piceaperda*)—A most injurious eastern bark beetle, killing native red, white, and black spruces. The adult is 1/4 inch long, black with reddish-brown wing covers. The female, after making a 6-inch longitudinal egg gallery in one tree, may repeat in another. Red boring dust, pitch tubes on the bark, and fading and dropping of needles indicate beetles at work.

Eggplant Flea Beetle (*Epitrix fuscula*)—Very small, 1/16 inch, black, riddling foliage of eggplant and related plants with minute holes. See Flea Beetles.

Elm Calligrapha (*Calligrapha scalaris*)—Also known as Linden

Leaf Beetle. This beautifully colored beetle feeds on elm, linden, alder, and willow. It is oval, convex, ⅜ inch long, head and thorax dark coppery green, wing covers yellowish with a pattern of 2 branched stripes down the inside and 11 green dots. The larvae are dirty white with yellow heads, humped like the potato beetle. Larvae and beetles feed on foliage and may be controlled by spraying with lead arsenate or DDT in midsummer.

Elm Leaf Beetle (*Galerucella xanthomelaena*)—A very serious elm pest which should be the concern of every citizen, whether or not he be homeowner or gardener. Our fine old elms are a national heritage; they should be protected for future generations. Where shade-tree commissions are lax, or property owners heedless, all residents of a community should band together to remedy the situation, to provide funds and education.

This European beetle was found near Baltimore, Maryland, in 1838 and apparently arrived in this country a few years before that. It attacks American, English, Scotch, and Camperdown elms but does not much bother slippery, rock, and winged elms. It is distributed across the country but is not a pest in parts of the Middle West (where the larger elm leaf beetle is on the job). It is definitely injurious in Idaho, Washington, Oregon, and California and in the latter state has been found feeding on almond and beans.

The beetles are about ¼ inch long, rather slender, yellow to olive green, with a dark line near the outer edge of each wing cover (Plate VI). As they grow older and get ready to hibernate they darken so that the lines are scarcely visible. Hordes of sluggish beetles crawl into houses in late summer, often through cracks around cellar windows or doors. The elm leaf beetle is chiefly a pest of towns or cities where buildings offer dry winter hiding places.

The beetles come out from attics and cellars in early spring, mate, and start eating small holes in elm leaves as they unfold. During late May and early June (in New Jersey) they lay clusters of lemon-shaped yellow eggs, 5 to 25 in a cluster, on underside of leaves. The egg-laying period may last several weeks, until 500 or more eggs have been laid. These hatch in 5 or 6 days. The yellow, ½-inch-long larvae are so spotted and striped with black they appear dark. They skeletonize the leaves, eating everything but veins and upper cuticle. Maturing in 15 to 20 days, each larva drops or crawls to the ground and transforms to a yellow pupa at the base of the tree. Beetles emerge in 6 to 10 days to lay eggs for the second generation. The number of generations depends on the season and locality. There are usually 2, sometimes 1 and a partial second, or 2 and a partial third. In California, where this beetle is a most important pest, there may be 4 generations.

Unsprayed trees are covered with brown leaves which look like lace or are completely defoliated by midsummer—a terrible eyesore in towns priding themselves on their shade trees. Often the elms put out new leaves in late summer, a weakening process. It is said that 3 years' defoliation in succession will kill a tree. Weakened trees are hosts to elm bark beetles, which carry the fungus causing Dutch elm disease, so neglect means a vicious circle.

Control. DDT in a hydraulic spray, 2 pounds of 50 per cent wettable powder per 100 gallons of water, gives excellent control of the elm leaf beetle but may be followed by a tremendous build-up of mites, which turn foliage dusty, aphids, and some scales. DDT in a mist blower, 6 per cent emulsion, does not have quite such bad aftereffects. Many arborists continue to use lead arsenate, 4 pounds per 100 gallons of water, plus 1 pint of fish oil or other suitable sticker. This has no harmful effects and is highly satisfactory if applied early enough. Two sprays are preferable: one, which will take care of cankerworms also, is applied when leaves are nearly expanded and overwintering beetles are starting to feed; the second, about 3 weeks later, when eggs are hatching. If only one spray is possible it should be in late May or early June.

Engelmann Spruce Beetle (*Dendroctonus engelmanni*)—A small, ¼ inch, dark reddish-brown bark beetle, with sparse long hairs, at intervals vastly destructive to Engelmann and other spruces in the Rocky Mountain region. Breeding in forests on windfalls, it reaches epidemic proportions and kills living trees. In 1949 in Colorado the air was full of beetles. A fraction that fell in a small lake formed a drift of dead beetles a foot deep, 6 feet wide and 2 miles long. The survivors killed 400,000 previously uninfested trees in a mass attack. Most attacks are made on the lowest 6 feet of trunk. Spraying bark of dead or dying trees with benzene hexachloride or with orthodichlorobenzene in fuel oil kills beetles before they can migrate. It takes 2 years to complete a generation.

European Chafer (*Amphimallon majalis*)—A European beetle first noted in western New York in 1940, also reported from Connecticut and West Virginia. It causes a turf injury similar to that of Japanese beetles and has a similar life history. The adult, a typical scarab, with dark bands at inner edge of wing covers, feeds on leaves of some trees at dusk but the damage is negligible. Chief injury is from grubs which prefer grass roots but also feed on roots of chrysanthemum, strawberry, gladiolus, and evergreen seedlings. DDT at 25 pounds per acre, chlordane at 10 to 20 pounds, and aldrin, dieldrin, lindane, or heptachlor at 5 to 10 pounds provide effective control.

European Ground Beetle (*Calosoma sycophanta*)—Imported from Europe to aid in the control of gypsy and brown-tail moths. It is brilliant golden green with a dark blue thorax, about 1 inch long. Adults hibernate in cells in the ground, emerging in late spring. Eggs are laid in the soil in June and July. The active larvae, hatching in about a week, run over the ground or climb trees in search of caterpillars or pupae. Do not destroy this beautiful friend.

Eyed Click Beetle (*Alaus oculatus*)—A very large, shiny black beetle with 2 conspicuous eyelike spots on the thorax, sometimes called the owl beetle. Like all click beetles, this can snap itself upright with a click when placed on its back. The larval stage is a wireworm. The adult is carnivorous and is often found in trunks of old apple trees.

Fiery Hunter (*Calosoma calidum*)—A black ground beetle with 3 rows of large copper-colored pits in each wing cover. It is often seen searching for cutworms, potato beetle grubs, and other succulent larvae.

Fig Beetle (*Cotinis texana*)—A large, flat, broad beetle, over 1 inch long, usually green, sometimes copper to violet; a fruit pest in Arizona, New Mexico, and Texas. It prefers ripe peaches but also feeds on apricot, apple, grape, muskmelon, nectarine, pear, tomato, and fruit of cacti. The larvae breed in dung of old corrals and the best control seems to be thorough cleaning of corrals and stack bottoms in late winter and early spring.

FIREFLIES—Lightning Bugs or Glowworms, family Lampyridae, known for their luminescence at night. They are a delight to see and are equally delightful to gardeners for their predilection for slugs and snails, sometimes cutworms. Adults, larvae, and eggs are all luminous in some species. True nocturnal fireflies are found chiefly east of the Rockies. In the West the forms are of the glowworm type, where the female is like a larva and emits light, while the male has wings but is not phosphorescent.

Fireflies are soft-bodied beetles of medium size, with light-producing organs on the underside of the abdomen. According to Fabre the contortions of the female resulting in flashes of light are signals for the male. But because the light is often present in larvae as well as adults its exact function is in doubt. It is produced by oxidation of a substance called luciferin in a heatless reaction.

FLEA BEETLES—A very large group of very small leaf beetles, family Chrysomelidae, named for their habit of jumping like fleas when disturbed. They usually feed on plants early in the season, often on seedlings set out from greenhouses, sometimes on ornamentals like forget-me-not, perforating foliage with tiny shot-holes. The various species go under such names as corn, eggplant, grape, horseradish, mint, pale-striped, potato, sinuate-striped, spinach, strawberry, and sweet-potato flea beetles—some of which are treated separately in this section. Flea beetles can be controlled with DDT or rotenone dusts or sprays.

Fruit Tree Bark Beetle—See Shot-hole Borer, under Borers.

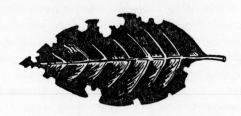

27. Leaf chewed by Fuller rose beetle.

Fuller Rose Beetle (*Pantomorus godmani*)—A grayish-brown weevil, probably from South America; 1/3 inch long with a short, broad snout, a white diagonal stripe across each wing cover, eating ragged areas from margins of leaves at night. A greenhouse pest in the North, it is numerous outdoors in the South Atlantic states and California, feeding on abutilon, acacia, apple, apricot, avocado, azalea, bean, begonia, blackberry, camellia, canna, cape jasmine, carnation, chrysanthemum, cissus, citron, currant, deutzia, dracaena, fuchsia, gardenia, geranium, goldenglow, grapefruit, hibiscus, lemon, lilies, oak, orange, palm, peach, pear, penstemon, persimmon, plum, plumbago, potato, prune, primrose, raspberry, rose, scabiosa, strawberry, tangerine, and vinca.

The larvae are white, legless grubs feeding on roots of young citrus trees, and on roots of blackberry, loganberry, raspberry, rose, strawberry, and other plants. When larvae are abundant the foliage turns yellow. They pupate in the soil. The beetles—wingless, parthenogenetic females only—lay eggs in late summer in crevices of tree bark or under buttons of citrus fruit or at the base of plants. There is 1 generation a year.

Control. Formerly, dusting with cryolite and applying a sticky band around young trees were the chief control measures. Now dusting with DDT, lindane, or chlordane is easier and quite effective. DDT should be used with caution; it leads to mites and other troubles.

Golden Tortoise Beetle (*Metriona bicolor*)—A small, tortoise-shaped beetle, looking like a drop of burnished gold, sometimes called a gold-bug. The larvae are dull brown, spiny, and carry their excrement and cast skins in a mass on their backs. They feed on morning glory, sweet-potato, and bindweed. Spraying with lead arsenate or cryolite or dusting with DDT or rotenone should give control.

Goldsmith Beetle (*Cotalpa lanigera*)—Related to June beetles, feeding on leaves of aspen or cottonwood, willow, oak, and other hardwoods. The beetle is lemon yellow above, with gold head and thorax, and bronze underneath. Covered with white hairs, about 1 inch long. The larvae, resembling white grubs, feed at roots of roses, chrysanthemums, cannas, sometimes young conifers. The life cycle takes 2 or 3 years.

Grape Bud Beetle (*Glytoscelis squamulata*)—Light gray, ¼ inch long, found on grape buds in California vineyards, usually at dusk in early spring. The larvae feed on grape roots. Canes may be smeared with tanglefoot for control.

Grape Colaspis (*Colaspis flavida*)—The Clover Rootworm, distributed from eastern states into Arizona. The adults are very small, pale brown, elliptical beetles covered with rows of punctures. They are general feeders, making long, curved feeding marks, sometimes in a zigzag pattern, on apple, bean, cowpea, clover, dahlia, grape, melons, okra, potato, rose, or strawberry. In summer eggs are laid at roots of timothy, grape, or clover, sometimes other plants; the larvae—small, fat, short-legged grubs—winter there. There is 1 generation a year. Most severe injury occurs on corn planted in clover sod, larvae at the roots often causing wilting when plants are 6 to 10 inches high. Plow or spade in fall rather than spring; do not plant corn after clover.

Grape Flea Beetle (*Altica chalybea*)—A small, metallic dark blue beetle feeding on unfolding leaves of grape in spring. Light brown, black-spotted grubs also feed on buds and chew foliage ragged. Distributed through the eastern two-thirds of the country, the beetles feed also on apple, beech, elm, plum, quince, and Virginia creeper. The adults hibernate near vineyards; the larvae pupate in soil. To control adults, spray or dust with DDT as the buds are swelling; repeat when shoots are 6 to 8 inches long for larvae.

Green June Beetle (*Cotinis nitida*)—An eastern species related to the fig beetle of the Southwest, occurring east of the Mississippi and from Long Island south. The adult is rather flat, green with bronze or yellow margins, nearly an inch long and half as broad. The beetles feed on foliage of various trees and shrubs and on many fruits—fig, peach, various berries, apple, apricot, nectarine, pear, plum, prune—and sometimes on corn and other vegetables. The thick, dirty white grubs feed on roots of grasses in lawns and golf courses and various ornamentals. The adults are around in July and August and lay eggs in soil rich in decaying vegetable matter. Avoid piles of grass clippings or manure near lawn or orchard.

GROUND BEETLES—Members of the family Carabidae feed chiefly on insects, sometimes on earthworms and snails. One or two species may feed on plants but not disastrously and most members of this family are worth-while additions to the garden. They are found most often lurking under stones and it ill behooves the gardener to step on them. Ground beetles do not fly, but they can run very fast and may climb trees in search of prey.

The shield-shaped elytra are hard, with fine longitudinal ridges and rows of punctures. They are grown together down the back. A common species, *Calosoma frigidum*, is black, but some are brown and some are beautifully iridescent. (See European Ground Beetle and Fiery Hunter.) All are large, with ferocious-looking jaws and a very definite indentation between thorax and elytra. Many secrete an offensive liquid for defense.

They hibernate as adults in the soil, some passing through 2 winters, although the cycle is usually 1 year. Eggs are laid in soil. Larvae are flat, heavily chitinized, black and white, with sharp projecting jaws

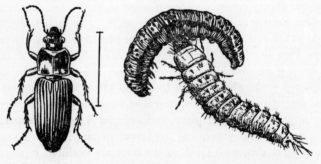

28. Ground beetle: adult and larva working on a caterpillar.

and a pair of bristly appendages at the posterior end of the body. They are shy, less frequently seen than the adults but equally predaceous. According to the books, most ground beetles feed at night and only the brilliantly colored climb trees, but I frequently find black ground beetles climbing trees and lunching on cankerworms during the day. They will even scurry into buildings, especially those with stone floors, in search of their prey. DON'T STEP ON GROUND BEETLES; THEY ARE YOUR FRIENDS.

Helenium Snout Beetle (*Baris confinis*)—A very small black snout beetle commonly found on young growing tips of helenium (sneeze-weed) in May and June, sometimes later in the season. Weekly spraying or dusting with DDT or lead arsenate keeps it subdued enough to allow fall bloom.

Hickory Bark Beetle (*Scolytus quadrispinosus*)—The most injurious pest of hickories, found from Quebec to Georgia, Mississippi, and Texas. Breeding normally in broken or weakened trees, they will attack and kill healthy trees in epidemics. The beetle is very small, dark brown; the legless white grub, with brown head, is only ¼ inch long. The grubs mine in the sapwood and inner bark, sometimes girdling trunk and branches. Adults bore into bases of leaf stems, terminal buds, or green nuts. Infested trees lose leaves early in summer; tops and branches sometimes die back. The bark is covered with small perforations, exit holes of the beetles.

Larvae hibernate in the bark, pupate in the wood in spring. The beetles emerge in early summer and fly to living hickories, feeding on young twigs. The female bores through the bark to sapwood and makes her longitudinal egg gallery, with eggs deposited in niches along the sides of the straight tunnel. Grubs burrow out at right angles. There is 1 generation a year in the North, often 2 in the South.

Control. Injury is most severe in dry summers. Trees kept well watered are more resistant to injury. Spraying with DDT or lead arsenate while beetles are feeding may give some control. Cut and burn badly infested trees between October and May, while the larvae are in their burrows, to prevent beetles from invading other hickories. There are several hymenopterous parasites.

Hickory Saperda (*Saperda discoidea*)—Found from New York to Kansas and south to Louisiana. The female is ¾ inch long with brownish wing covers and curved yellow marking; the male is smaller and dark. Large grubs bore in the sapwood, especially that previously attacked by bark beetles.

Horseradish Flea Beetle (*Phyllotreta armoraciae*)—Small, ⅛ inch long, black, with a yellow stripe on wing covers. It deposits eggs in clusters on leaf petioles and larvae burrow into petioles on hatching. It attacks mustard as well as horseradish.

Imbricated Snout Beetle (*Epicaerus imbricatus*)—A brownish-gray weevil about ½ inch long, with 2 pale zigzag lines across the wing covers, occurring over most of the United States. It is a general feeder on apple, blackberry, cabbage, cherry, clover, corn, cucumber, gooseberry, muskmelon, onion, pea, potato, raspberry, squash, sugar beet, and watermelon. It injures apples by eating out the buds or cutting off young fruit and leaves. Strawberries may be defoliated. Eggs are laid on foliage and larvae live in roots or stems of legumes and other field crops. Adults appear on apples in late May or June, feeding for about a month; there is 1 generation a year. A general fruit spray schedule should take care of this pest on apples.

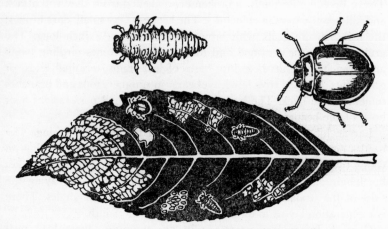

29. *Work of imported willow leaf beetle, with detail or larva and adult.*

Imported Willow Leaf Beetle (*Plagiodera versicolora*)—First recorded in this country in 1915 and now abundant in the Northeast from Washington, D.C., to Maine. All willows are attacked, the smooth-leaf types most severely, and Lombardy poplar occasionally. The adult looks like a flea beetle, 3⁄16 inch long, metallic blue. The larvae are bluish black, sluglike, with abdomen tapering toward the end. The beetles eat holes through the leaves, but the larvae rapidly skeletonize them, feeding from the underside. Adults hibernate under bark, emerge in late April or May to lay clusters of lemon-yellow eggs on underside of leaves. They hatch in 4 to 8 days, then the larvae feed for 2 weeks or so before pupating on the leaf. There may be 2 to 4 broods a season.

Control. Spray about the end of May with lead arsenate, 5 pounds to 100 gallons of water with 20 ounces of fish oil or linseed oil, or with DDT, 2 pounds of 50 per cent wettable powder to 100 gallons or 2 tablespoons to 1 gallon. Repeat if necessary the first of July.

Japanese Beetle (*Popillia japonica*)—A horrible example of an introduced pest which has cost untold millions for lack of a little money and prompt eradication measures when it was first discovered. It probably came from Japan as a grub in soil around plant roots, prior to 1912, the year when earth balls around imported plant roots were prohibited. It was first noticed in 1916, in a nursery near Riverton, New Jersey. The next year it had covered 3 square miles, with ½ mile heavily infested. In 1918 the infested area was 48 square miles. Now 5 per cent of the total area of the United States is under quarantine. The area of continuous infestation covers 12 coastal states—North Carolina, Virginia, Maryland, Delaware, New Jersey, New York, Connecticut, Rhode Island, Massachusetts, New Hampshire, Maine, and Vermont—and parts of Ohio, Pennsylvania, and West Virginia. Occasional beetles have been taken in California, Florida, Kentucky, Illinois, Indiana, Michigan, Missouri, and South Carolina. In many instances the beetles have been trapped near airports and immediate eradication measures instituted.

Adult Japanese beetles feed on about 275 kinds of deciduous fruits, shade trees, shrubs, and garden flowers, but only a few vegetables— chiefly asparagus, corn, rhubarb, and soybeans. They are exceedingly fond of Boston ivy and Virginia creeper, birch, canna, chestnut, elm, hollyhock, horsechestnut, linden, mallow, kerria, marigold (African but not French), grape, peach, plum, quince, Japanese quince, rose, rose-of-Sharon, sassafras, turquoise vine, zinnia—to name a mere handful of plants on which the beetles can be expected. They feed on apple and cherry but not as severely as on grape, raspberry, and peach. Evergreens are seldom ravaged and phlox, chrysanthemums, gladiolus, iris, and some other flowers are not favored.

A Japanese beetle is a most beautiful insect, until you see it hanging in a cluster of 100 or so over a peach or a rose (Plate VIII). It is oval, just under ½ inch long, a gorgeous metallic green with coppery wing covers which are striated with fine longitudinal lines. There are 2 patches of white hairs at the tip of the abdomen and 5 tufts of hairs projecting from under the wing covers on each side. The adult beetle feeds from about the middle of June to late October, with peak of abundance usually in July and a rather sharp falling off in numbers after Labor Day. It likes succulent young foliage, chewing new rose leaves almost to lace, feeds in hot sunshine on plant parts in the sun, and is attracted to light-colored, showy flowers. It is gregarious, a whole group of beetles demolishing one rose, sometimes in a very short time, before trying the next.

Each female lives from 30 to 45 days, lays 40 to 60 eggs, mostly under grass roots in lawns and golf courses. The grubs hatch in 10 to 12 days, feed on grass roots until cold weather, then move down 8 to 10 inches in the soil to avoid freezing. They move upward in spring, feed on grass roots again until pupation in the soil in late May. The grubs are grayish white with brown heads, ¾ to 1 inch long when full grown and distinguished from similar white grubs by a V-shaped row of spines on the underside of the last segment of the body. They eat off grass roots so that the turf can be rolled back like a carpet.

Control of Adults. In regions of serious beetle infestation summer spraying or dusting is almost obligatory. DDT, at 2 pounds of 50 per cent wettable per 100 gallons, or 2 level tablespoons to 1 gallon, or as a 5 per cent dust is very effective. But this increases the mite problem and in many instances lead arsenate may be preferred for ornamental trees and shrubs, using 6 pounds with 4 pounds of wheat flour to 100 gallons of water or 3 tablespoons lead arsenate and 2½ tablespoons flour to 1 gallon of water. For vegetables and fruits near harvest use a rotenone spray or dust. Methoxychlor is less toxic to man than DDT but should not be used within 2 weeks of harvest.

Many of the newer insecticides give a satisfactory kill of beetles, but DDT may have a longer residual effect than malathion, lindane, chlordane, or dieldrin. For roses and other plants growing rapidly through the summer, *weekly* treatment is necessary to keep the foliage whole. It is practically impossible to keep the blooms, opening between sprays, from being eaten. The easiest solution with roses is to cut the best buds in the morning and let them open in the house, at the peak of beetle infestation. The best roses come before and after the beetle season anyway, so the beetles are not too much of a menace.

Traps are wisely used to check beetle distribution in new areas, but they are not very useful in the garden unless there is a community effort, for they attract more beetles than are caught. The best traps are painted yellow, baited with a mixture of 10 parts geraniol to 1 part eugenol. Hand-picking into a jar of kerosene or soapy water is helpful, but not many people have time for this daily chore.

Control of Larvae. Lawns may be grubproofed with DDT, using 6 pounds 10 per cent dust per 1000 square feet, or 1¼ pounds 50 per cent wettable powder applied in a spray; or with chlordane, 2¼ pounds 10 per cent dust per 1000 square feet, or ½ pound 50 per cent wettable chlordane as a spray; or with dieldrin, using 2½ pounds 5 per cent dust or 5 pounds of 2½ per cent granulated dieldrin. DDT has a long residual effect, up to 5 years, but the other chemicals work more quickly and are effective in smaller dosages. Some proprietary grub-proofing materials combine DDT and chlordane. In applying the dry dust the chemical should be mixed with several times the amount of sand or soil, broadcast very evenly, then well watered in. Applications may be made in spring or fall.

Insect parasites have been brought from Asia for natural control. Two Tiphia wasps have become established; nematodes have made a start. The most promising natural control is a bacterial disease, called milky disease, disseminated by applying a spore-dust mixture made from inoculated grubs. This is available under trade names, such as Jap-a-demic, and is applied at 3- to 5-foot intervals, about a teaspoon per dose. It takes about 3 years to effect control.

All plants leaving nurseries in beetle areas during their season must be certified. Airplanes departing in daylight hours in summer months have to be sprayed lest they carry these unwelcome hitchhikers. Undoubtedly many live beetles travel in private automobiles which are not so easily regulated.

June Beetles (*Phyllophaga* spp.)—Familiar large, reddish-brown or black beetles, known also as May Beetles, June Bugs, or Daw Bugs. They are equally well known as White Grubs, the larval state. There are about 200 species, not to be distinguished by the layman, with similar life histories. They are distributed over the country, probably more serious in the Middle West and South than in the East. The life cycle takes from 2 to 4 years, depending on species and location, but averages 3 years in the middle states. There is also an annual white grub with a 1-year cycle, but this is a different beetle (*Ochrosidia villosa*).

Adults appear in May, June, or July (earlier in the South) and fly at night, feeding on foliage of ash, birch, butternut, elm, hickory, poplar, oaks, tuliptree, willow, and other trees. Most species prefer hardwoods, but a few southern forms feed on pine and cypress. They are attracted to lights and try to enter houses. During the day they remain hidden under grass or debris. The females enter the soil for egg-laying, depositing each egg in a separate ball of earth 1 to several inches below the surface of sod land. The eggs hatch in 2 or 3 weeks and the young grubs feed on roots and underground plant parts until fall, when they burrow downward. The next spring they move up and feed on roots of grass, corn, cereals, potatoes, strawberries, and other crops, but not much on legumes. That autumn they again move down in the soil, coming up to feed for a short time in spring prior to forming a pupal cell in the soil. The adults are formed but stay in their cells until the next spring before emerging and feeding as beetles. Most damage from grubs comes the year after heavy beetle flight. The grubs are similar to Japanese beetle grubs but larger, ½ to 1½ inches, and the spines on the underside of the end of the abdomen are in the pattern of an elongated diamond. The adults are an inch or more long.

Control. Valuable shade trees can be sprayed with lead arsenate during beetle years, previous records in a locality showing when to expect injury. Lawns and golf courses can be grubproofed with lead arsenate, 10 pounds to 1000 square feet, with 5 per cent chlordane dust, 5 pounds per 1000 square feet, or with dieldrin. DDT is not so satisfactory. Avoid larval injury to roots by not planting susceptible crops like corn or strawberries in land recently taken over from sod. Summer or fall spading or plowing kills some larvae and pupae, exposes others to birds.

LADY BEETLES—also called Ladybird Beetles and Ladybugs. They are members of the large family Coccinellidae, which means scarlet red. With the exception of one genus, containing the Mexican bean beetle and the somewhat less infamous squash beetle, all members of this family are beneficial, preying on aphids or scale insects or mealybugs in both their larval and beetle stages. In recent years they have been having a hard time staying alive because DDT and some other new insecticides are as harmful to them as to injurious insects.

Lady beetles are small, ⅙ to ¼ inch long, red or sometimes tan with black spots or black with red spots. They are broadly oval and can be distinguished from destructive leaf beetles by having only 3 segments in the tarsus (foot). The larvae have flat, carrot-shaped bodies, broad at the head end, tapering at the other, with rather warty backs spotted with blue or orange on a grayish-black background. The eggs are usually orange and stand on end in a cluster of a dozen or so. The pupae, exposed on the leaf, are cemented to it by one end.

The progeny and potential usefulness of a single female lady beetle are enormous. Depending on her species, she may lay up to 1500 eggs over a period of 2 months, though the normal period is 1 month. The life cycle takes 12 days in warm weather, 20 to 35 days in cool weather. As full-grown larvae lady beetles consume about 25 aphids a day and when they change to beetles the daily quota goes up to 50. In an average season the aphid population may be reduced enough so that spraying is unnecessary, but in a cool wet season the beetles reproduce less rapidly, the aphids flourish, and the gardener has to get busy.

The aphid-eating species of lady beetles require a lot of plant lice around to maintain themselves; when aphids are reduced too much most of the beetles starve to death and so the species practically disappears until a large aphid colony is built up again. Some lady beetles feeding on scales and mealybugs can, however, survive even when they have reduced harmful insects to a minimum.

30. Vedalia, Australian lady beetle.

Vedalia, the Australian lady beetle (*Rodolia cardinalis*) is one of these. This small beetle, ⅛ inch long, red with black markings, represents the first successful use of an imported predator to control an injurious insect, the classic example of biological control. The cottony-cushion scale arrived in California from Australia about 1868 on acacia. By the early eighties it had overrun citrus orchards, killing hundreds of thousands of orange trees, threatening the entire citrus industry. So the United States Government and the State of California sent Albert Koebele to Australia to look up some native parasites. He sent some back to California in 1888 but also included Vedalia, a predator, in the shipment. There were only 28 specimens of Vedalia in the first lot and only 514 all together. But Vedalia thrived and within 2 years had the scale under complete control. A trip which cost less than $5000 saved millions for the citrus industry. Vedalia, as larva and adult, feeds only on cottony-cushion scale, but she manages to survive even when this is reduced to low numbers and comes out of her hiding places to check incipient outbreaks.

Another Australian importation, the **Mealybug Destroyer** (*Cryptolaemus montrouzieri*) eats itself out of business. A way was found to keep it alive by maintaining mealybug colonies on potato sprouts, but the destroyer is now being replaced by internal parasites.

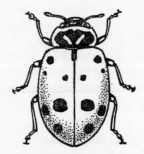

31. Convergent lady beetle.

The **Convergent Lady Beetle** (*Hippodamia convergens*) works hard to control aphids. The adult has 12 small black spots on reddish wing covers and 2 convergent white lines on the thorax. This species hibernates in huge masses in the mountains. Formerly the beetles were collected there and brought to the crops, but it was found that the beetles felt the urge to migrate anyway and so would fly away from the crops.

There are many other species of these beneficial beetles. The **Two-spotted Lady Beetle** (*Adalia bipunctata*), with red elytra and 2 round black spots, is the form I see most often in gardens and the one that comes to spend the winter with me, flying over to the typewriter from the window sill.

Larger Elm Leaf Beetle (*Monocesta coryli*)—A large, yellowish beetle with 9 blue-black patches. Occasionally it appears in large numbers on slippery or red elm, sometimes on American elm, and it is known to feed on hazel and hawthorn. It was first described in 1824, from Illinois, and has since been a pest in Arkansas, Florida, Kansas, Mississippi, Missouri, Maryland, Pennsylvania, Virginia, and West Virginia. It appears suddenly in a locality, does a great deal of damage in a small area, completely defoliating trees for a year or so, and then disappears for an indefinite period. The yellow to orange larvae feed in groups. They hibernate in soil, pupate in spring, with adults appearing in late May. Owing to the sporadic nature of outbreaks, control measures are not often attempted. Presumably spraying with lead arsenate or DDT would be satisfactory.

Margined Blister Beetle (*Epicauta pestifera*)—Black, with a narrow gray or yellow margin around wing covers. See Black Blister Beetle.

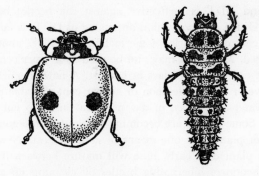

32. Two-spotted lady beetle and larva.

Mexican Bean Beetle (*Epilachna varivestis*)—Doubtless the worst enemy of eastern home vegetable gardens (Plate IX). Like the Colorado potato beetle this is an example of an insect long present suddenly assuming great importance. Probably originally from Mexico, the beetle has been known in the Southwest since 1850 but did not become really dangerous until it reached Alabama about 1920. Since then it has spread to all of the states east of the Mississippi. The adult has the convex shape of other lady beetles but is somewhat larger, up to 1/3 inch, and is coppery yellow with 16 black dots, 8 on each wing cover. It infests all kinds of garden beans and cowpeas, is especially fond of lima beans but does not care much about soybeans, though it will attack them. It feeds on pods and stems as well as leaves.

Mexican bean beetles winter as adults in rubbish or weeds, appearing in bean fields late in March in the South, June in New York. After feeding for a week or two the females lay groups of orange-yellow eggs on the underside of leaves. These hatch in 5 to 14 days. Soft yellow larvae, ⅓ inch long and half as wide, protected by black-tipped spines on the back, skeletonize the leaves, always working from underneath and eating out very regular areas in a lacy pattern. When full grown the larvae cement their hind ends to an uninjured leaf and the pupae push out of crushed larval skins, adults emerging in 10 days or less. A complete cycle takes about a month. Near New York City there are usually 2 generations; farther north 1 and a partial second, farther south 3 or 4.

Control. The easiest way to control Mexican bean beetles is to dust the plants with ¾ per cent rotenone, blowing it up from underneath. This is safe for the plants and the operator. Lead arsenate is injurious to beans and DDT is ineffective against the beetle; both leave a poisonous residue. Methoxychlor, an analog of DDT, is fairly effective as a 5 per cent dust and less toxic to humans; TDE, another analog, has been used. Malathion may also be used as a 5 per cent dust or as a spray but not within 10 days of harvest. A new chemical, Dilan, is also effective; 1 level tablespoon of 50 per cent wettable powder to a gallon of water as a spray, or a 2 per cent dust. Do not apply after pod forms. Some beetles are becoming resistant to rotenone.

Timing of planting is one means of control. Near New York City snap beans planted in early June will mature between beetle broods in July. Discourage hibernating beetles by cleaning up and burning all plant debris after harvest.

Mottled Tortoise Beetle (*Deloyala guttata*)—Golden around the margins of elytra, the rest mottled black and yellow. The larvae are dull green, bluish along the back, covered with broad branching masses of excrement.

Mountain Pine Beetle (*Dendroctonus monticolae*)—Very destructive to pines in mountains of the Northwest. It has practically wiped out thousands of acres of lodgepole and western white pine, is damaging to sugar, ponderosa, and other pines, and may attack fir, spruce, and hemlock near pines. The stout, black, bark beetles, 1½ inches long, excavate very long perpendicular egg galleries.

Native Elm Bark Beetle (*Hylurgopinus rufipes*)—Widely distributed throughout the eastern states on elms and basswood. It is chiefly important because, along with the smaller European elm bark beetle, it may spread the Dutch elm disease. It is a small brownish-black beetle, ⅒ inch long, not so shiny as its European cousin. It works under the bark making its egg gallery transversely across the wood with

larval tunnels coming out at right angles. There are 1 or more generations a year and the winter is passed as both larvae and adults. Often
adults of this species emerge in the fall and burrow into the bark of
living elm trees. A dormant DDT spray, 12 per cent by mist blower,
or 2 per cent in a hydraulic sprayer, is the best way to protect elms.
(See Smaller European Elm Bark Beetle.) Dying limbs and logs should
be immediately removed and burned.

Northeastern Sawyer (*Monochamus notatus*)—Also called Pine
Sawyer, common in northeastern states, attacking white spruce and
various pines. The larvae usually burrow extensively in dead or dying
trees but may injure apparently healthy trees. The large beetles, ½ to
1½ inches, blackish with a white or gray pubescence, have very long
legs and antennae, and a spiny projection from each side of the thorax.

Northern Cedar Bark Beetle (*Phloeosinus canadensis*)—Breeds in
northern white cedar or arborvitae and may cause twigs in ornamental
hedges to break and wilt. The injury is unsightly but not too injurious.

Northern Masked Chafer (*Cyclocephala borealis*)—Another lawn
pest, controlled the same as other grubs.

Nuttall Blister Beetle (*Lytta nuttallii*)—A large, inch or more long,
metallic green or purplish beetle, prevalent in the Rocky Mountains.
It feeds on legumes and grasshopper eggs.

Oriental Beetle (*Anomala orientalis*)—Formerly known as the
Asiatic Beetle and a near relative of Asiatic garden and Japanese
beetles. It was first discovered at New Haven, Connecticut, in 1920
and is now present in various parts of that state and in New York and
New Jersey. It was previously known in Japan and Hawaii. The adult,
straw-colored with varying dark markings, feeds a little in the daytime, being sometimes found on rose blooms, but it is not conspicuous
nor very injurious. The grubs, however, account for much damage in
lawns attributed to Japanese beetles and may also injure roots of
azaleas, rhododendron, and other ornamentals grown in nurseries. They
cannot be distinguished from Japanese beetle grubs except by the
arrangement of spines in 2 parallel lines on the underside of the abdomen. The same chemicals, DDT, chlordane, dieldrin, applied to the
lawn will control them.

Pale-striped Flea Beetle (*Systena blanda*)—Probably a native species,
generally distributed. The adult is ⅙ inch long, with a broad white
stripe down the center of each pale to dark brown wing cover. It
perforates leaves of many different plants—alfalfa, bean, beet, carrot,
clovers, corn, cotton, eggplant, grasses, lettuce, melon, parsnip, pea,

peanut, pear, pumpkin, radish, sunflower, strawberry, turnip—and many weeds. The larvae are slender, white, with light brown heads, just over ¼ inch long. They feed on roots of many plants and on corn seed, causing failure to sprout or a sickly plant. Injury is most serious when cool weather retards seed germination. Control by keeping down weeds, early and late spading or plowing of land to starve out larvae. Spray for adults with DDT or rotenone.

Peach Bark Beetle (*Phloeotribus liminaris*)—A native pest found in eastern states, attacking mainly peach, sometimes cherry. The small brownish beetle, similar to the shot-hole borer, only ⅟₁₀ inch long, winters as an adult in dead or dying wood or in special cells cut in the bark of a healthy tree. The egg gallery runs across the wood rather than lengthwise as with most bark beetles. Keep trees vigorous by proper cultural methods. Destroy peach prunings and dying trees.

Pine Chafer (*Anomala oblivia*)—In the same genus as the oriental beetle; sometimes harmful to pine.

Pine Colaspis (*Colaspis pini*)—Feeds on conifers, pines, and sometimes *Cedrus deodara;* may be numerous in the South. It is a small beetle, ⅟₁₆ to ⅛ inch long, gregarious, feeding on green needles, often leaving them hanging by one edge with the tips turning brown. Young trees may die. This forest pest may be important on ornamentals. Spray or dust small trees with DDT or lead arsenate.

Pine Engraver (*Ips pini*)—Common through northern United States, attacking all kinds of pines, though favoring white pine and sometimes spruce (Plate X). It frequently infests small white pines that have been transplanted, its presence told by small circular holes on branches or trunk. It has also been a frequent visitor to pitch pine after New England hurricanes. The beetle varies from brown to black, is ⅛ inch long, burrows in sapwood. Five or 6 long galleries radiate from a circular brood chamber.

A closely related beetle (*Ips calligraphus*), called the coarse-writing bark beetle, is larger and more of a pest in the South, where it is the first to attack pines suffering from drought.

Pitted Ambrosia Beetle (*Corthylus punctatissimus*)—From Massachusetts to Colorado and southward, on rhododendron, dogwood, blueberry, mountain mahogany, sometimes hazel, ironwood, sassafras, water birch. The beetle, dark brown to black, stout, ⅛ inch long, makes horizontal galleries in the wood at the base of the stem, causing it to wilt and break over. Shrubs that are heavily mulched are more likely to be attacked. Cut out and burn wilted stems below point of entrance of beetles. Remove excess mulch.

Plum Gouger (*Anthonomus scutellaris*)—A reddish-brown snout beetle, living on wild plum and occasionally going over to domestic plums, prunes, apricots, sometimes peaches and cherries. It resembles the plum curculio but lacks the characteristic humps. The gouger emerges from hibernation earlier than the curculio and the larvae bore into the seed of the fruit to pupate. Spray before blossoms open and then follow the curculio schedule. See Plum Curculio.

Potato Flea Beetle (*Epitrix cucumeris*)—A common and very destructive small, black, jumping flea beetle (Plate VII). It feeds on potato and related solanaceous plants such as eggplant, groundcherry, pepper, petunia, tomato, and also on apple, arbutus, ash, bean, beet, cabbage, carrot, celery, clover, corn, cucumber, dogbane, elder, holly, honeysuckle, horsechestnut, lettuce, maple, muskmelon, phlox, primrose, pumpkin, radish, raspberry, rhubarb, spinach, sumac, sunflower, sweetpotato, viburnum, violet, and watermelon. It is present throughout the country.

The tiny beetle, $\frac{1}{16}$ inch long, winters as an adult and in spring goes first to weeds, sometimes to tree leaves, but as soon as potatoes or tomatoes appear in the garden the beetles descend on young plants in hordes, completely riddling the foliage. Eggs are laid in the soil; the larvae feed on roots and tubers and may be quite destructive, causing scurfy or pimply potatoes. There are usually 2 broods. This species is a vector of potato virus diseases.

Control. A 3 or 5 per cent DDT dust is probably most satisfactory, though DDT spray can be applied to potatoes along with bordeaux mixture. The latter has some repellent effect on flea beetles as well as acting as a fungicide. Rotenone dust can be used for some vegetables. For DDT-resistant flea beetles use dieldrin, Dilan, or endrin.

Red Turnip Beetle (*Entomoscelis americana*)—More of a pest in the Northwest. The beetles are bright red with black patches on the head and 3 black lines on elytra, $\frac{1}{4}$ inch long. Bright red eggs, orange to black larvae, and bright orange pupae complete the colorful cycle. Feeding is at night, on cabbage, radish, turnip, wallflower, sometimes beans.

Red Turpentine Beetle (*Dendroctonus valens*)—Found in pine forests through the country, it also injures ornamental pines in the Atlantic states and Monterey pine in California. It is a large bark beetle, $\frac{1}{4}$ to $\frac{3}{8}$ inch long, reddish, sometimes nearly black. Trees are attacked near the base and have reddish pitch tubes. When these are noticed it may be possible to cut out the beetles with a knife or to fumigate them by injecting carbon bisulfide into the galleries.

Red Spider Destroyer (*Somatium oviformis*)—One of the rove beetles, very small, slender, black. It lays orange eggs on surface of leaves. The yellow larvae, ⅛ inch long, consume about 20 mites apiece a day. The adults may be numerous on foliage of deciduous fruit and citrus trees infested with various species of mites.

Rhabdopterus Beetles—Several species feed on young foliage of camellias and other shrubs. *Rhabdopterus deceptor* is found in Texas on camellia, Chinese holly, redbud, pyracantha, photinia, rose, yaupon, and other plants. *R. bowditchi* appears in southern Florida; *R. picipes,* also known as the Cranberry Rootworm, appears in coastal lowland areas from New England to the Mississippi River; *R. praetextus* is found inland from Canada to the Rio Grande River and is probably the common species in northern Florida. It injures all camellias, redbud, rhododendron, ampelopsis, rose, loblolly bay, aronia, myrica, and others. The beetles are small, compact, elongate-oval in outline, shining blackish bronze, ¼ inch long by ⅛ inch wide. They feed, only at night, on buds and tender new leaves, leaving long, rather narrow, usually curved, holes or slits in the foliage.

Do not use DDT to control the beetle on camellias. Either magnesium or lead arsenate should be effective without injuring the plants.

33. Rhinoceros beetles, the male having a horn.

Rhinoceros Beetle (*Xyloryctes satyrus*)—Member of a group of very large beetles with a projection like a rhinoceros, mostly southern but this species found as far north as Connecticut. The male is very dark brown, practically black, very broad, over an inch long, with a horn curving back from its head (Plate XI). The female is similar but has a small tubercle instead of a horn. The larvae, looking like large white grubs, attack lilacs and sometimes other shrubs just under the surface of the ground, girdling and often killing them. They are also found near ash trees. The beetles come out at dusk but life histories and control measures are not clear.

Another species, *Dynastes tityus,* is also called the rhinoceros beetle, as well as unicorn beetle. It is greenish gray mottled with black, 2 to 2½ inches long, with a horn extending forward over the head, and inhabits decaying wood.

Rose Chafer (*Macrodactylus subspinosus*)—Familiar to almost everyone as the "Rose Bug" even though it is a beetle, perhaps because its wing covers are not so hard and horny as most. The adult is tan, rather slender, ⅓ inch long, with prominent, long spiny legs (Plate XI). It is distributed through the eastern states and goes as far west as Colorado and Texas, feeding on a long list of plants—apple, bean, beet, blackberry, cabbage, corn, cherry, elder, elm, hollyhock, hydrangea, grape, New Jersey tea, peach, pear, peony, pepper, poppy, raspberry, rose, strawberry, Virginia creeper—small grains and grasses. It is more troublesome in sandy areas and seems to increase in importance as one goes north from New York City.

The beetles appear in swarms in late May or early June and feed first on flowers, especially roses and peonies, sometimes iris, then go to newly set fruit, being most injurious to grape blossoms, foliage, and young berries. In some areas they damage elm leaves rather severely. There is only 1 generation, the feeding period lasting 3 to 4 weeks. The eggs, laid in sandy soil, hatch in 1 to 2 weeks and the larvae, resembling white grubs but thinner and smaller, up to ¾ inch long, feed on roots of grasses and sometimes nursery seedlings, then move down in the soil for winter.

Control. DDT (3 level tablespoons of 50 per cent wettable powder to 1 gallon of water) is much more effective than earlier insecticides but should be applied very promptly. Hand-picking helps to keep the chafers off roses, and some gardeners protect their choicest plants with a temporary cheesecloth fence, stretching somewhat higher than the bushes. Even if it is open on top, the beetles seem not to fly over the barrier. Chickens are poisoned by eating rose chafers.

Rose Leaf Beetle (*Nodonota puncticollis*)—A small, shiny green to blue beetle resembling a flea beetle, though not so active, ⅛ inch long. It is distributed from New England south and west to Arizona and Montana. Besides feeding on buds and blossoms as well as foliage of rose, peony, and iris, it favors blackberry, raspberry, strawberry, pear, peach, plum, apple (scarring the fruit), and willow. It feeds in spring on clover and other meadow plants before migrating to roses and fruits.

Seed-corn Beetle (*Agonoderus lecontei*)—Sometimes the cause of corn failing to sprout. This species is dark brown, striped, ¼ to ⅓ inch long. Two other species, *A. comma* and *A. lineola,* also attack corn seed as adults. The larvae are carnivorous, feeding on other insects. Damage is worse in cold, wet springs with slow germination or when seed of low vitality has been used. Use good seed; plant late to ensure quick germination. Treating seed with 5 per cent chlordane dust before planting seems to be helpful.

Sinuate-striped Flea Beetle (*Phyllotreta zimmermanni*)—Much like the cabbage flea beetle, but with a wavy yellowish stripe on each wing cover, $\frac{1}{12}$ inch long. The eggs are laid singly on leaves of cabbage, turnip, and radish, and the larvae mine inside.

Smaller European Elm Bark Beetle (*Scolytus multistriatus*)—Most famous as the vector of Dutch elm disease (Plate X). First reported in Massachusetts in 1909, and probably arrived from Europe several years before, it is now known in most of New England, New York, New Jersey, Delaware, Pennsylvania, Maryland, Virginia, West Virginia, Indiana, Kentucky, Ohio, and Kansas.

The beetle is shiny, brown to black, ⅒ to ⅛ inch long, the female slightly larger than the male. Both sexes have a toothlike projection from the undersurface of the abdomen, serving to distinguish this species from other bark beetles. The grub is white, legless, ¼ inch long, much larger at the head end, somewhat curved in its natural position. The beetles attack sickly, dying, and recently dead elms and logs by boring small holes through the bark to the sapwood, throwing out sawdust. Each female tunnels out a brood gallery 1 to 2 inches longitudinally in the wood, and lays from 80 to 100 eggs along this. The grubs make tunnels going out at right angles from the egg gallery, so that characteristic engravings are made in the wood and inner surface of the bark. If many beetles enter, the bark may be separated from the wood all around the trunk or limb.

The grubs transform to beetles in the larval galleries, then exit through small holes, looking like shot-holes, in the bark. After emergence the beetles fly to healthy trees and feed by gnawing at the crotches of small twigs before making brood chambers in the older wood. The spores of the Dutch elm disease fungus, formed along the galleries, cling to the beetle when it emerges. When the beetles feed, they inoculate healthy elms with the fungus. There are normally 2 broods, beetles of the first appearing in May or June, adults of the second about 2 months later.

The elm disease fungus came to this country originally via these bark beetles. They arrived alive in elm burls used for furniture veneer and even in dish crates made of elm wood.

Control. Dead and dying elms should be cut and burned before beetles emerge in spring. If removal is impossible, the bark surfaces of such trees should be thoroughly sprayed with a DDT-oil solution. Healthy trees can be kept free of bark beetle attack and consequent Dutch elm disease by two heavy doses of DDT, the first applied before the leaves come out, the second about 2½ months later. For hydraulic sprayers, the dormant spray is 2 per cent DDT, prepared by dissolving 14 pounds technical DDT in 4 gallons of industrial grade xylene, adding 1 pint Triton X-100, and diluting with water to 100 gallons. For the second spray, water is added to the same chemicals to make 200 gallons.

For mist blowers the first application is 12 per cent DDT, made by dissolving 20 pounds technical DDT in 5 gallons xylene, 2½ gallons Acme white oil, plus 1½ pints Triton X-100, and water added to make 20 gallons. For the second, 6 per cent spray, add water to make 40 gallons.

These high concentrations of DDT are drastic measures to save elms in communities threatened with disease; they will probably cause other troubles, such as a great increase in mites, various scales, and aphids. It may be necessary to add malathion or other miticide or aphicide to the spray.

Southern Pine Beetle (*Dendroctonus frontalis*)—A small, native bark beetle, the most serious pest of pine in its range, Pennsylvania to Florida and west to Texas and Oklahoma. It kills healthy trees, as well as attacking weakened and felled specimens. The adult, brown or black, ⅛ inch long, makes winding or S-shaped egg galleries in the inner bark. There can be 5 generations a season, with epidemics when rainfall is below normal. There are a number of natural parasites.

Southwestern Pine Beetle (*Dendroctonus barberi*)—Very dark brown or black, making winding transverse egg galleries. It commonly attacks ponderosa pine in New Mexico, Arizona, Colorado, Utah, Nevada, and California.

Spinach Carrion Beetle (*Silpha bituberosa*)—Black with 3 longitudinal ridges on each elytron; occurring in Montana, Wyoming,

Washington, Kansas, and Nebraska. Eggs are laid in soil. Black and white larvae feed at night on edges of leaves of beets, spinach, squash, pumpkin, and some other vegetables.

Spinach Flea Beetle (*Disonycha xanthomelas*)—The largest of the common flea beetles, ⅕ inch long, with greenish-black wing covers, yellow thorax, and black head. It feeds exposed on leaves of spinach, beet, and various weeds, and lays eggs in clusters on leaves. The larva is a gray to purple, warty, wrinkled grub about ¼ inch long. Pupation is in the soil and there are usually 2 generations a year. Rotenone is the safest control.

Spotted Asparagus Beetle (*Crioceris duodecimpunctata*)—Introduced from Europe a few years after the common asparagus beetle, first seen near Baltimore in 1881, now distributed over much of the same territory east of the Mississippi. Confined to this host, the beetles can be quite destructive, but the larvae feed only on berries. The adult is reddish orange or tan, with 6 prominent black spots on each wing cover (Plate IV). Greenish eggs are glued singly by their sides to leaves just before the berries form. Orange larvae appear in a week or two, bore into the developing berry and eat pulp and seeds. Each larva destroys 3 or 4 berries before pupating in soil. Beetles of the new brood emerge in July and lay eggs for the overwintering generation appearing in September. Control measures are the same as for the asparagus beetle, but collecting and burning berries may be sufficient.

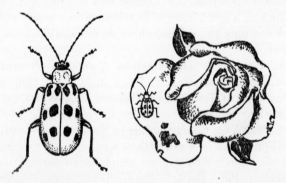

34. Spotted cucumber beetle, Diabrotica beetle, with injury to rose.

Spotted Cucumber Beetle (*Diabrotica undecimpunctata howardi*)— Also known as Southern Corn Rootworm. This species occurs anywhere east of the Rockies, but it is more destructive in southern states.

West of the Rocky Mountains its place is taken by the western spotted cucumber beetle. The adult is greenish yellow, rather slender, with 12 black spots, a black head, ¼ inch long, and feeds on a vast number of flowers and vegetable besides cucumber. It eats foliage but prefers petals of many late summer flowers, particularly those with light colors —aster, calendula, canna, chrysanthemum, cosmos, dahlia, rose, Shasta daisy, sweet pea, zinnia, and others. Vegetable food plants include snap and lima beans early in the season, all of the cucurbits—cucumber, melon, squash, gourds—and asparagus, beet, cabbage, eggplant, peas, potato, and tomato.

The spotted cucumber beetle hibernates as an adult at the base of weeds or other overwintering plants and starts flying when the temperature nears 70°F. in spring. Females lay eggs just below soil level, on or near young corn plants, beans, or weeds. The larvae, which feed on roots and bore into underground parts of stems, are more wormlike than most beetle grubs, ½ to ¾ inch long, slender with yellowish-white wrinkled bodies and brown heads (Plate XII). They are sometimes called overflow worms or budworms or drillworms because they bore out the crown of the corn plant and kill the bud. Corn so injured either breaks off or is dwarfed and yellowish. There are at least 3 generations in the South, 1 and a partial second in the North.

This spotted beetle harbors the bacteria causing cucurbit wilt disease in its intestines and inoculates plants as it feeds. It also acts as a vector of other diseases.

Control. Avert damage to corn by planting late in the season, thoroughly cultivating the soil first, and by not planting corn where a legume crop was last grown. Reduce overwintering beetles by cleaning up weeds, burning over waste places. DDT spray is effective and can be used on ornamentals but may be injurious to cucurbits as well as presenting a residue problem. Cryolite and lindane may also be used on flowers, but rotenone is still safest for vegetables. See also Striped Cucumber Beetle.

Spotted Grapevine Beetle (*Pelidnota punctata*)—A large beetle looking more dangerous than it actually is. It is conspicuous on grape foliage in summer but causes relatively little injury. The adult is over an inch long, broad, tan, glossy, with black spots around the outer edge of the elytra. The grubs live in decaying wood.

Squash Beetle (*Epilachna borealis*)—Sharing with the Mexican bean beetle the dubious distinction of being a gangster member of the usually beneficial lady beetle family. It is not as destructive as the bean

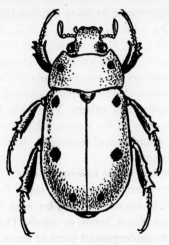

35. Spotted grapevine beetle.

beetle but fairly common east of the Rocky Mountains on squash, melon, pumpkin, and relatives. It is slightly larger than the Mexican bean beetle, yellow with 7 black spots on each wing cover. Beetles emerge in June to lay eggs on host plants and these hatch in a week. The spiny larva feeds on foliage for 2 to 4 weeks, then pushes its larval skin down over the back while it pupates. The adults hibernate under trash.

Steel-blue Flea Beetle (*Altica torquata*)—A small, metallic blue or purple beetle, abundant on grapes in New Mexico, Arizona, and southern California. Native hosts are desert and evening primroses.

Strawberry Flea Beetle (*Altica ignita*)—Metallic green, golden bronze, or purple, very small, feeding on leaves of strawberry, evening primrose, fuchsia, and other plants. Foliage riddled with great numbers of round holes often turns brown around the holes. The beetles winter as adults and do most of their damage before strawberries bloom. Spraying plants with 8–8–100 bordeaux mixture a week or so before bloom is said to be effective.

Striped Blister Beetle (*Epicauta vittata*)—Black with a yellow border and median stripe on each wing cover, just over ½ inch long. It is a very common species ranging west as far as Montana and is reported as occurring in large swarms in Arkansas, both in alfalfa fields and in vegetable gardens. There can be several hundred blister beetles in a square foot of area. Together with the three-striped blister beetle (*E. lemniscata*) it feeds on bean, beet, corn, melon, peas, potato, radish, tomato, turnip, and other vegetables. DDT or cryolite can be used where residue is not a problem, a 2 per cent rotenone dust near harvest.

Striped Cucumber Beetle (*Acalymma vittata*)—A native insect, the most serious cucumber pest east of the Rocky Mountains. A related species takes over cucurbit destruction in the West. The larvae feed only on roots of cucumber, muskmelon, winter squash, pumpkin, gourds, summer squash, and watermelon about in the order named, but the beetles feed also on beans, corn, peas, and blossoms of other plants.

The beetles are yellowish with 3 black stripes, $\frac{1}{5}$ by $\frac{1}{10}$ inch (Plate XII). As unmated adults they winter in woodlands near the vegetable garden under leaves or rotting logs, in lowland hedgerows, or near wild food plants such as goldenrod and aster, but nearly always keeping in direct contact with the ground. They become active in spring when the temperature gets above 55°F. Before cucurbits are up they feed on pollen, petals, or leaves of buckeye, willow, wild plum, hawthorn, apple, elm, syringa, and other plants, settling on young cucumber and related vines as soon as these appear above ground. Mating takes place as they feed on the vine crops, with the female laying orange eggs in or on the soil at the base of such plants.

The very slender, white wormlike larvae, $\frac{1}{3}$ inch long, feed on roots and underground parts of stems for 2 to 6 weeks, often destroying the whole root system with consequent death of vines. From white pupae in the soil, the adults appear in midsummer to feed on cucurbits and legumes for another 6 weeks, often eating into the rind of fruits as well as chewing leaves and flowers. There is 1 generation in the North, 2 or 3, possibly 4, in the South.

The beetles are especially dangerous because they transmit bacterial wilt of cucurbits and cucumber mosaic. In my own garden they are frequently found in spring on Chinese lantern, the leaves of which are often mottled with the mosaic pattern.

Control. Early feeding by beetles can be avoided by starting seeds under Hotkaps or boxes pushed down into the ground, open at the bottom, covered with mosquito netting or fine wire screening over the top. Unprotected vines should be dusted as soon as they appear and weekly thereafter with rotenone, cryolite, or a mixture of 1 part calcium arsenate with 15 parts gypsum. DDT, methoxychlor, and lindane are highly effective against cucumber beetles and can be used on ornamentals but may be injurious to some young cucurbits. Insecticide mixtures containing sulfur should be avoided for fear of injuring many squash and melon varieties.

Striped Flea Beetle (*Phyllotreta striolata*)—Widely distributed pest of cabbage, $\frac{1}{12}$ inch long with a crooked yellow stripe on each wing cover. Eggs are laid in small cavities gnawed in the stem. See Flea Beetles.

Striped Tortoise Beetle (*Cassida bivittata*)—Dull yellow, with 5 longitudinal black stripes; larvae are yellowish white with a median gray line, short marginal spines, and a tail-like projection bearing shed skins but no excrement. White eggs are laid singly on leaf stems or veins, each covered with a daub of black pitch.

Sweetpotato Flea Beetle (*Chaetocnema confinis*)—Very small, $\frac{1}{16}$ inch long, black with a bronzy reflection. It eats narrow grooves in leaves along the veins. Leaves wilt, plants turn brown. Besides sweetpotato, the beetle infests morning glory, sugar beet, raspberry, boxelder, corn, cereals, grasses. The larvae feed on roots of bindweed.

Sweetpotato Leaf Beetle (*Typophorus viridicyaneus*)—A metallic blue-green, oblong beetle, a little over $\frac{1}{4}$ inch long, which eats tender leaves at the crown of the plant, devouring them from the margin inward. Pale yellow, plump larvae burrow through the vine underground.

Syneta Leaf Beetle (*Syneta albida*)—Common on cherry in the Pacific Northwest, occasional on pear, prune, apple. The beetles, light gray or yellowish, $\frac{1}{4}$ inch long, emerge from the ground as the trees bloom and stay in the tree near buds for about 2 months. They scar and deform young fruit, feed also on stems, blossoms, leaves. Eggs are dropped to the ground and grubs feed in fine, fibrous tree roots. Spraying the trees twice with lead arsenate, using an equal amount of lime, just before blossoms open and just after petals have fallen, greatly reduces injury.

Ten-lined June Beetle (*Polyphylla 10-lineata*)—Robust, brown, large, covered with yellowish and white scales, the latter arranged to make 2 stripes on the head, 3 on the thorax, and 4 long stripes and 1 short on each wing cover. Larvae are very large white grubs, up to 2 inches long. This June beetle occurs primarily in the Rocky Mountain states and on the Pacific coast. Larvae may girdle and destroy roots of ornamental shrubs and nursery trees, including Califonia privet, black locust, and wisteria.

Three-lined Potato Beetle (*Lema trilineata*)—In some areas damaging to foliage of potatoes and related plants. The adult is reddish yellow with 3 broad black stripes; the larva plasters granular masses of its own excrement over its body.

Tobacco Flea Beetle (*Epitrix hirtipennis*)—Very small, reddish to dark brown, often with a dark transverse band across the elytra. It is most injurious to solanaceous plants—tobacco, tomato, potato, ground-cherry, eggplant, and related weeds—but it also feeds on almond, orange, and squash. It occurs throughout the country, hibernates as an adult, and may have 2 or more generations a year. DDT dust, 3 to 5 per cent, is effective though possibly injurious to tomato. Dieldrin, endrin, dilan, and isodrin are other possibilities.

TORTOISE BEETLES—Sometimes called sweetpotato beetles or goldbugs. They comprise several species distributed over the United States, feeding on sweetpotato, morning glory, and other members of that family. They are leaf-eaters, relatively small, none over ¼ inch, nearly as wide as long. The margins of the body are extended to hide the head and most of the legs making them look like tortoises. They eat holes through the leaves or devour entire leaves, sometimes seriously injuring newly set plants. They winter as beetles in dry protected places, under bark or trash. The larvae, about ⅜ inch long, have conspicuous horny spines with 2 longer ones at the posterior. On these, the larva packs its own excrement and cast skins from molting, then curls them over its back like a squirrel's tail (Plate XI). Larvae look like moving bits of dirt. When full grown they fasten themselves to leaves to pupate. Spraying with DDT, lead arsenate, or cryolite should control. See also Argus, Black-legged, Golden, Mottled, and Striped Tortoise Beetles.

Watercress Leaf Beetle (*Phaedon aeruginosus*)—Small, bronze black, about ⅛ inch long; larvae brownish black with many tubercles of hairs. There seems to be no satisfactory control.

Waterlily Leaf Beetle (*Galerucella nymphaeae*)—Dark brown beetles, with dull yellow thorax, just over ¼ inch long, feeding on leaves and flowers of pond lilies and other water plants. The larvae are dark brown above, yellow underneath; they feed first on upper leaf surface, then on under, making leaves ragged and brown. There are 2 generations. Adults winter in dead stems of plants and under bark of nearby trees, laying yellow egg clusters in spring on waterlily leaves. Other leaf beetles (*Donacia* spp.), metallic blue or brown, also feed on water plants.

Control is difficult. If fish are removed, leaves can be dusted lightly or have a fine mist spray of lead arsenate. Submerging the plants for a few days with weighted hoops on the leaves will help to get rid of the beetles.

Western Black Flea Beetle (*Phyllotreta pusilla*)—Important in the West. The very small, shiny olive-green to black beetles often appear in swarms on cabbage, cauliflower, horseradish, mustard, cress, radish, watercress, peppergrass, turnip, sugar beet, and corn; also stock, wallflower, rock cress. The larvae mine in leaves and feed on roots. Where residue is not a problem dust with DDT, lindane, or cryolite. Use rotenone on edible plant parts.

Western Pine Beetle (*Dendroctonus brevicomis*)—The most important pest of ponderosa and Coulter pine from Lower California to Canada, responsible for tremendous annual damage to timber. The adults are small, ⅛ to ⅕ inch, brown to black bark beetles. They construct a network of winding egg galleries between bark and sapwood. When healthy trees are attacked (seldom those under 6 inches in diameter) resin tubes are formed about the entrance holes. Primarily a forest insect, it may appear in parks and home gardens where infested trees should be felled and bark burned in fall or winter. Woodpeckers and some beetles are natural enemies.

Western Potato Flea Beetle (*Epitrix subcrinita*)—Shiny bronze, 1/16 inch long, injuring most seriously potatoes and tomatoes but also attacking about the same plants as the potato flea beetle. The western species is serious in Arizona, California, Colorado, Idaho, Montana, Nevada, Oregon, Utah, and Washington.

Western Spotted Cucumber Beetle (*Diabrotica undecimpunctata*)—Replacing the spotted cucumber beetle west of the Rocky Mountains. It has the same greenish-yellow wing covers but is slightly smaller, with slightly larger black spots. Soon after native grasses dry up in pastures the adults swarm into the garden, devastating flowers, lawns, ornamental trees and shrubs, truck crops, fruit trees—in fact, nearly every green plant except conifers. The pest is called Diabolical Diabrotica by irate gardeners. The larvae feed on roots of corn and sweet pea as well as native grasses. Beetles eat holes in ripening fruit, especially in orchards in uncultivated areas, and spread the fungus causing brown rot of apricots, peaches, and other stone fruits.

Control. DDT is most effective but may increase melon aphids and be injurious to some young cucurbits. Some growers start with cryolite, then change to DDT later in the season. Both DDT and lindane are satisfactory for ornamentals, though a miticide may need to be included.

Western Striped Cucumber Beetle (*Acalymma trivittata*)—Like the eastern species with yellowish body and 3 black stripes but the basal portion of the antenna is yellow instead of black. It is most abundant and injurious in southern California but ranges into Arizona and Oregon. The larvae attack roots of cucumber, melon, pumpkin, squash, and other cucurbits, while the adults feed on tops of these plants and also on bean, beet, corn, pea, sunflower, almond, apple, prune, etc.

Western Striped Flea Beetle (*Phyllotreta ramosa*)—Shiny black with a brassy reflection and a conspicuous irregular yellow-white band down each wing cover; $\frac{1}{16}$ inch long. It may be destructive to cabbage, cauliflower, brussels sprouts, radish, mustard, stocks, turnip, wallflowers, watercress, and other crucifers in California.

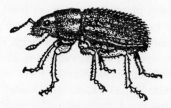

36. White-fringed beetle.

White-fringed Beetle (*Graphognathus leucoloma* and perhaps other species)—A native of South America first seen in Florida in 1936, now known in parts of Alabama, Florida, Georgia, Louisiana, Mississippi, North Carolina, South Carolina, and Tennessee. It was discovered in New Jersey in 1954. By 1952, 340,000 southern acres had been invaded and the beetle recorded as feeding on at least 385 species of plants. Most damage is done by the larvae.

The beetles are brownish gray, just under ½ inch long, with a broad, short snout, the elytra faintly margined with white and covered with pale, short hairs. They are gregarious, as many as 200 or 300 beetles being found on one plant, eating in from the margins of the leaves or crawling along the ground. They cannot fly because the wing covers are fused together. All the adults are parthenogenetic females; no males are known. They feed on herbaceous weeds, vines, trees, and various crops.

The larvae are yellow white, legless, about ½ inch long when grown. They winter in the soil, usually in the top 9 inches, sometimes lower down, and pupate in a soil cell in spring. The beetles start emerging in

May and reach a peak in June and July. They live for 2 or 3 months, each female averaging 600 to 700 eggs, laid in masses of 11 to 14 at the base of some object, plant, stick, or stone, in contact with the soil. During this time they may crawl ¼ to ¾ mile. The larvae, hatching in 2 weeks to 2 months, eat the soft outer root tissues or may sever the main root. The plants, velvetbeans, cabbage, chufa, collards, corn, cotton, cowpea, sugar cane, sweetpotatoes, blackberries, and many others, including herbaceous ornamentals, turn yellow, wilt, and die. There is normally 1 generation a year.

Control. For home gardeners, 10 per cent DDT dust, thoroughly worked into the top 3 inches of soil at the rate of 1 pound to 432 square feet, should give satisfactory control for about 5 years. For nurseries, DDT is applied at the rate of 50 pounds technical grade per acre to allow certification of plants for movement from regulated areas. This treatment is a little hard for certain camellia varieties that resent DDT. All vegetation near nurseries is sprayed with DDT every 2 or 3 weeks in spring and summer. In some cases plants are fumigated with methyl bromide in special chambers to make them safe for shipment.

White-pine Cone Beetle (*Conopthorus coniperda*)—A very small, shining black beetle destructive to cones of white pine from Canada to North Carolina. The adults bore into the stem of young cones to lay their eggs and the larvae feed on scales, seeds, and other tissues of wilting cones that fall to the ground. Gather and burn infested cones in ornamental plants.

BIRDS

Birds are our friends in the garden not so much for utilitarian purposes as for the joy they bring us. Birds do eat a great many insects, sometimes their total weight in a single day. They have done spectacular things. Flocks of gulls terminated a terrific outbreak of Mormon crickets in Utah in 1848 so successfully a monument was erected to them. A hundred years later warblers were given much of the credit for stopping an outbreak of spruce budworms in the Adirondacks.

In my own garden even unlovely starlings do their good deeds by swarming over the lawn in search of grubs while sparrows flock on it for crabgrass seed. Many birds hover over rose shoots all summer to collect aphids; brown thrashers wham hard-shelled Japanese beetles down on the cement walk to make them edible; downy woodpeckers have cleaned most of the insects out of the pear tree and I have to offer other inducements to keep them around. I cheerfully turn over the entire cherry crop to keep a pair of cardinals calling my yard home. I love birds, and I spend more money than I can afford for food so they'll keep me company on winter days. But I don't expect birds to do all, or even very much, of my garden work for me!

I know that despite birds I shall always have to spray and dust to protect my plants from noxious insects and that the beneficial insects in my garden are probably of more dollars-and-cents value to me than the birds who eat them along with the bad insects. As Dr. Lutz wrote in his *A Lot of Insects:* "Let us protect birds because they are pretty and sing sweetly and because they are a part of nature; but let us admit that, on the one hand, their value as destroyers of insects injurious to man has been grossly overestimated and, on the other hand, the value of insects as destroyers of our insect pests has been shamefully overlooked."

Amateur gardeners are frequently worried about the effect of stomach poisons, lead arsenate, and more particularly DDT, on birds. Here, too, the harmful effect has been somewhat overestimated. If sprays are used at the right time in *recommended* dosages there should be little trouble, but heavy dosages and high-pressure sprays in the midst of the nesting season may cause some bird mortality. However, one should not jump to conclusions. Several dead birds found under a tree that had been sprayed with DDT were autopsied—and found full of BB shot. A couple of small boys lived near that tree.

If after the continued use of artificial control measures you have fewer birds in the garden, it does not mean you have killed them; you have merely starved them out by reducing the insect population so the birds have gone on to more fruitful hunting grounds. An entomologist has listed as one of the beneficial effects of insects the fact that they attract the birds we love to our gardens, which is quite different from the usual slant that we have to have birds to get rid of the insects.

A few birds can be classed as garden pests despite some good habits and some birds are occasionally annoying even though they are mostly beneficial.

Crows have voracious appetites; 28 per cent of their food is made up of insects and other animals, 72 per cent is vegetable matter, half of it corn. Treating seed with one of the crow repellents on the market may save it. Scarecrows, if they can be made to move, or dangling strips of white cloth or aluminum foil may save some of the ripened corn ears for you. Blackbirds and grackles have some of the bad habits of crows but eat more insects.

Woodpeckers are almost all beneficial but not the yellow-bellied sapsucker (*Sphyrapicus varius varius*) and its relatives. It makes a horizontal series of holes around trees—apple, pine, birch, and others—and keeps returning to lap up sap from these holes. Scotch pine, particularly susceptible to injury, can be protected by wrapping the trunk with burlap.

Some of our nicest bird friends are very fond of fruit, especially cherries, strawberries, grapes, and blueberries. Small trees and strawberry beds can be covered with netting; a bag can be tied around grape clusters.

BOLLWORMS

Bollworm is the name given to the larva of a moth devouring the unripe pods or bolls of cotton. The true bollworm (*Heliothis zea*) is better known to gardeners as the corn earworm or the tomato fruitworm. It is discussed under Earworms.

Pink Bollworm (*Pectinophora gossypiella*)—Considered one of six most destructive insects in the world. Probably a native of India, it came to Mexico from Egypt in 1911 and by 1917 had reached Texas. It is now present in Arizona, Florida, Louisiana, New Mexico, and Oklahoma, as well as Texas. A Georgia infestation has been wiped out. Where established, it causes a loss of ⅕ to ½ of the cotton crop. It is spread on okra pods as well as plants, seeds, lint, or waste products of cotton. Mallow, rose-of-Sharon, abutilon, and hibiscus are occasional hosts.

The caterpillars are cylindrical, pinkish, sometimes remaining for more than a year curled up in seed, bolls, or in the soil. The moths are small, dark brown, with narrow fringed wings, pointed at the tip. Worms can be killed in cottonseed by heat. Various sanitary measures plus weekly dusting with DDT help in control.

BORERS

Borers are grubs or caterpillars, larvae of beetles or moths, working in woody tissues or herbaceous stems. There are a great many borers affecting shade and fruit trees, ornamental shrubs, herbaceous annuals and perennials. The proportion selected for inclusion in this manual is small compared to the total number. Borers are particularly destructive to newly set trees and to those weakened from various causes. Some of the factors predisposing trees to borer attack are listed here.

1. *Drought* seems to be the primary factor in making trees susceptible to borer attack; the rootlets dry out, the roots are injured, and the whole tree systemically weakened. Two or three seasons with deficient rainfall are usually followed by large numbers of borers. Newly transplanted trees are subject to attack before they get their root systems established.

2. *Sunscald* is important with newly transplanted trees and also on established trees suddenly exposed to the sun by removal of another tree, hedge, or building which had previously kept the trunks shaded.

3. *Injuries* from hurricanes, ice storms, frost cracks, bonfires, etc., provide easy entrance for borers.

4. *Defoliation by leaf-eating insects* produces a weakened condition highly inviting to borers.

5. *Construction activities,* with change of grade, lowering or raising of water tables, mechanical injuries from excavations in ditch digging, pipe laying, road building, may gravely weaken established trees. Moreover, bulldozers in housing developments seldom leave even weakened trees. One of my friends selected a lot with many dogwoods. She arrived one day to find the bulldozer had laid them all low. When she sat down and wept the foreman looked at her in astonishment. "But they were just trees, lady, just trees!"

6. *Chemical injuries* from leaking illuminating gas in the soil, chlorides applied to roads to lay dust or to melt ice in winter, or fumes from factories are conducive to poor health and borer attack.

The best control measure is the promotion of good health and vigor by proper watering, especially of newly transplanted trees, fertilizing where necessary, spraying to control leaf-eating insects. Wrapping tree trunks the first year or two after transplanting prevents drying out and sunscald and provides a mechanical barrier to borer attack. The wrapping can be done with strips of burlap or with a special double-thickness paper with a layer of asphaltum in between that comes in rolls 4 inches wide. Start at the first branch and wind spirally downward, overlapping half the width at each spiral, and tie firmly with twine wound spirally in the opposite direction. The wrapping should be removed in a year, to make sure no borers have gotten under and gone to work, but then it can be replaced for a second year.

Spraying transplanted trees and shrubs with an antidesiccant also helps to prevent borer attack. Wax and rubber emulsions are on the market under various trade names. Spraying trunks and branches of trees and shrubs with a 2 to 5 per cent DDT emulsion or wettable powder is effective in preventing egg-laying by many borers.

If, despite all precautions, holes and sawdust or pitchtubes on the bark indicate borers already at work, there are still several remedies. Hand-worming is first, but a sharp knife should be used with caution lest it injure the wood still more. Usually you can probe with a flexible wire and kill the borer in place. Fumigants are helpful. You can squirt in a few drops of carbon bisulfide from a machine oil can and plug up the hole with putty or gum. Or you can inject a special paste made for borers, sold as Bor-tox or Borerkil. These used to contain nicotine, then lindane was substituted.

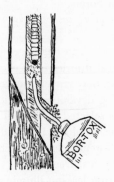

37. One way to kill borers—injecting a fumigant in paste form.

Spraying the whole trunk with a fumigant, such as an emulsion made of 12 parts orthodichlorobenzene, 1 part soap to 3 parts soft water, and diluted 1 to 6 with water at the time of spraying is a tricky procedure best left to the commercial arborist. It may be injurious. Another possibility is to paint the infested places on the bark with an emulsion made of 2 pounds paradichlorobenzene dissolved in 1 gallon crude cottonseed oil, emulsified with fish-oil soap, and diluted with 2 to 4 parts of water.

It is always important to trim injured trees promptly, making smooth cuts flush with the bark, and to trim all infested wood before the borers can emerge to attack other trees.

Apple Bark Borer (*Thamnosphecia pyri*)—Formerly known as Pear Borer, but renamed because it more often infests apple. It also bores in hawthorn, mountain-ash, and shadbush from Maine to Texas. The borers are found in crotches and in rough bark of neglected trees. They can be controlled with 2 sprays of parathion, using 2 pounds 15 per cent wettable powder to 100 gallons of water.

Ash Borer (*Podosesia syringae fraxini*)—Generally distributed but apparently limited to ash and mountain-ash, more serious in the prairie states. The adult is a moth, front wings opaque blackish brown with a violet reflection and a red crossbar, hind wings transparent with a narrow black border, abdomen black with yellow bands. The larvae commonly bore in the tree just below ground level or near the base, making so many burrows the trees are readily broken over. Cut and burn infested parts or trees.

Australian-pine Borer (*Chrysobothris tranquebarica*)—Also called Mangrove Borer. This attacks living red mangrove and casuarina trees planted as ornamentals and windbreaks in Florida. The adults, greenish bronze, ½ to ¾ inch long, with 3 lighter impressions on each wing cover, appear in April, laying eggs under the bark. The flatheaded larvae bore through the bark and into the wood to construct pupal cells. DDT sprays may help but best control is to cut out beetle-infested branches or trees in fall or winter.

Azalea Stem Borer (*Oberea myops*)—A beetle girdling tips of stems of azalea, rhododendron, blueberry, mountain-laurel, and perhaps other plants in spring. It is slender, ½ inch long, with yellow head and thorax, the latter with 2 black spots, and grayish-yellow punctate wing covers. Twigs are girdled in 2 places, ½ inch apart, and a yellow egg is thrust through the bark halfway between. The tip dies and the yellow grub, legless, an inch long, bores down the twig and into the trunk, pushing out sawdust from holes near the ground. After 2 or 3 weeks it pupates, producing beetles in summer. Cut off and burn wilted twigs an inch or more below the girdled portion as soon as noticed. Kill grubs in burrows with fumigants.

Branch and Twig Borer (*Polycaon confertus*)—A cylindrical beetle, ½ inch long, black with brown elytra, burrowing into twig crotches or buds of apricot, olive, avocado, citrus, and fig trees, sometimes grapevines. The large whitish larvae, with fine hairs, work in dead heartwood of many ornamental trees in California and Oregon. Often there is rather extensive killing of twigs and branches. Prune off infested twigs on small fruit trees; burn dead brush and orchard prunings.

Broad-necked Root Borer (*Prionus laticollis*)—A brownish-black beetle with long serrated antennae, 1 to 1¾ inches long. The large, yellowish, legless grub, 2½ to 3 inches, excavates a burrow in roots of oaks, sometimes poplar, chestnut, apple, pine, and grape. Rhododendrons growing among old roots may also be attacked, infested stems being broken off at ground level. The life cycle may take 3 years.

Bronze Birch Borer (*Agrilus anxius*)—A native beetle distributed through northern United States as far west as Colorado and Idaho. It attacks white, gray, black, and canoe birches, poplar, quaking aspen, cottonwood, and willow. It is more injurious to ornamental trees grown in the open than to forest trees and flourishes on decadent rather than vigorous trees. The beetle is slender, olive bronze, with a blunt head, tapering body, nearly 1 inch long; the grub is white, slender, with the region just back of the head enlarged, and with a horny, forceps-like appendage at the tip of the abdomen. It mines in irregular winding galleries just under the bark, which is loosened. The first sign of injury is the dying back of the trees at the top, by which time it is rather late for control measures. Spraying with DDT may prevent such injury. Infested trees should be cut and burned before beetles emerge in late April or May to lay eggs in slits in the bark of other trees. Ornamental birches should be watered in times of drought.

Brown Wood Borer (*Parandra brunnea*)—Also called Pole Borer, a native beetle occurring east of the Rocky Mountains in dead wood and sometimes in cavities in living trees, practically all hardwood shade trees and some conifers. The glossy, chestnut-brown beetle, ¾ inch long, appears in July and August on apple, pear, and cherry. This borer enters living trees through wounds, so prune carefully, leaving no broken, projecting branch stubs.

Burdock Borer (*Papaipema cataphracta*)—A smooth, pale brown caterpillar, with a white stripe down the back and along each side, sometimes infesting stalks of delphinium, dahlia, hollyhock, goldenglow, and iris.

California Prionus (*Prionus californicus*)—Also called Giant Apple Root Borer. This very large, 1½ to 2½ inches, shiny reddish-brown beetle is common along the Pacific coast from Alaska through California and eastward into the Rocky Mountain region and the Southwest. The larvae, white grubs 2 to 3 inches long, bore in dead or living roots of oak, alder, poplar, and other hardwoods, and in pine, redwood, Douglas-fir, and fir. Fruit trees are sometimes killed. The adults fly at night, midsummer to fall. They are attracted to lights and may hit windows with great force. Control by probing for and destroying larvae.

Carpenterworm (*Prionoxystus robiniae*)—Widely distributed through the country, attacking many shade trees—ash, elm, locust, maple, oak, poplar, willow, and others—sometimes apricot and pear. It is particularly injurious to live oaks and elm on the Pacific coast. The name comes from the large tunnels, as much as 1 to 1½ inches in diameter, which the caterpillar excavates in solid wood of trees. The borer is white tinted with rose, with small brown tubercles over the body and dark brown head; 1 to 2½ inches long. The larvae feed in the sapwood when young, later through the heartwood of the trunk, which may be riddled with burrows. The life cycle may take 3 years or more. The moth comes out in June and July, leaving the pupal skin protruding from the burrow. The female is 2½ to 3 inches across the wings, with a stout body, mottled gray fore wings, smaller, smoky hind wings. The male is similar but smaller, with an orange margin on hind wings. The greenish-white sticky eggs are laid in bark crevices, wounds, and old burrows.

Control. Keep all wounds painted. Inject carbon bisulfide into openings, about 1 tablespoon to each, and close with putty.

Cedar Tree Borer (*Semanotus ligneus*)—A western beetle, working in bark and wood of cedars, arborvitae, redwood, Douglas-fir, and Monterey pine. The adult is black, ½ inch long, with orange or red markings on elytra. The larvae make winding burrows in inner bark and sapwood, girdling and killing trees.

Chestnut Timberworm (*Melittomma sericeum*)—A pest of chestnut (when we had any) and also of oak. The beetle is chestnut brown, slender, ½ inch long. The larva is a slender white borer shading to dark brown toward the rear. It bores galleries in sapwood and heartwood of dead and living trees; it probably enters through wounds.

Clematis Borer (*Alcathoe caudata*)—The dull white larva, ⅔ inch long, of a clear-winged moth. It attacks fleshy roots and crown of clematis, especially virgins-bower, and may hollow out base of stems. Vines are stunted, lack vigor. Dig out the larvae, or cut out and burn infested portions.

Columbine Borer (*Papaipema purpurifascia*)—Larva of a moth, restricted to stems and fleshy roots of wild and cultivated columbine. The reddish-brown moth scatters its eggs over the ground near the plant, larvae hatching in late April or early May. They enter petioles of new leaves, then bore down until they reach the roots by midsummer. The caterpillar is salmon-colored with a pale stripe down the back, 1½ inches long when grown. Sawdust-like castings on the ground and dying back of the plant indicate borers at work. Rake or scrape the soil thoroughly in spring to kill eggs; cut out and burn infested parts. Try dusting with DDT.

Cottonwood Borer (*Plectrodera scalator*)—A large beetle distributed from Maryland to Louisiana, particularly injurious in the central and southern states to cottonwood, poplar, and willow. The adult is black, mottled with a white pubescence, 1½ inches long, with antennae longer than the body. The larva is a large grub, 1¾ to 2 inches, deeply constricted into segments. It tunnels beneath bark and into wood at base of trunks, infested trees blowing over easily. Sawdust and shredded wood cuttings mark its presence. It feeds as a larva for 2 years before coming out as a beetle to lay eggs at the base of trees. A protective wash on the trunk, 1 part lime-sulfur to 10 parts whitewash, or DDT, or a wire screen guard can be used.

Currant Borer (*Ramosia tipuliformis*)—A yellowish caterpillar, ½ inch long, larva of a small black and yellow clear-winged moth that looks like a wasp. It is distributed throughout North America, attacks gooseberry, black elder, sumac, and red and black currants, being more destructive on the latter. The borer lives in a tunnel in the wood every winter, pupates in spring, with adults emerging in June and July to lay eggs on bark of canes. These look yellowish in spring and die within a few weeks. Cut such canes close to the ground and burn before moths emerge.

Dendrobium Borer (*Xyleborus morigerus*)—Minute brown beetles boring into pseudobulbs and depositing eggs in broad galleries; larvae make long galleries. Badly infested bulbs wither and die. Cut out and burn infested orchid bulbs as soon as noticed. Spray with DDT.

Dogwood Borer (*Thamnosphecia scitula*)—Sometimes called the Pecan Borer. Whitish caterpillar with brown head, ½ inch long, works in cambium of flowering dogwood and sometimes pecan. The infested area may be 2 or more feet long and contain as many as 50 borers. Small trees or the base of branches may be girdled and die. Small moths, with blue-black margins to their clear wings, emerge from late spring to midsummer to lay eggs in roughened places on the bark. Keep bark smooth at base of branches; apply a drenching spray to bark of DDT or dieldrin (4 to 6 teaspoons to 1 gallon of water) about June 1 and in late July.

Dogwood Cambium Borer (*Agrilus cephalicus*)—The flatheaded larva of a beetle, working in soft wood; widely distributed but only rarely injurious. Wrap newly transplanted trees; water them properly.

Dogwood Twig Borer (*Oberea tripunctata*)—Also known as Elm Twig Girdler, a lemon-yellow grub, larva of a long-horned beetle, boring in the center of twigs. It makes a long series of closely placed round holes for the exudation of frass. The adult, yellow with blackish wing covers, emerges in early summer and, after girdling the tip, deposits eggs in twigs of elm, viburnum, and many fruit trees, as well as dogwood. Cut out and burn infested twigs.

Elder Borer (*Desmocerus pallidus*)—Cloaked Knotty Horn, a dark blue beetle with a yellow "cloak" thrown over the upper portions of elytra. The borer is creamy white, an inch long, riddling base of stems of wild and cultivated elders with burrows, causing dying back of branches, sometimes death of whole shrub. The beetles sometimes eat notches out of the leaves.

Elder Shoot Borer (*Achatodes zeae*)—The spindleworm of corn, working in the tassel or spindle, found near golden elder. The larva is yellowish white with a double row of black dots across each segment and a black head. The moth has rusty fore wings mottled with gray and yellowish-gray hind wings. Cut out dead elder wood in fall to destroy eggs.

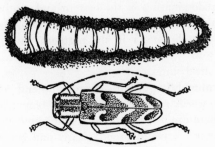

38. Elm borer—beetle and larva.

Elm Borer (*Saperda tridentata*)—Roundheaded larva of a long-horned beetle, gray with orange-red bands across the elytra, occurring in eastern states. Park and shade trees are often severely injured, particularly those weakened from defoliation by elm leaf beetles. Eggs are laid in cracks in bark, and grubs work in the inner bark and sapwood, cutting off much of the sap flow. Escaping sap and frass appear as moist spots on bark. The borers are reddish at first, later creamy white, an inch long when grown. Keep trees growing vigorously with plenty of water; watch for signs of injury and dig out borers; protect bark with DDT spray.

European Corn Borer (*Pyrausta nubilalis*)—One of the most destructive corn pests (Plate XIII). It probably arrived in shipments of broomcorn from Italy or Hungary about 1909 but was not recorded until 1917, in Massachusetts. It has since spread through New England, south to North Carolina, and west to Wisconsin and Iowa. It is chiefly a stalk pest, not only in corn but in dahlia, aster, chrysanthemum, gladiolus, and other ornamentals, as well as beans, beets, celery, potatoes. In fact, it is recognized on about 200 species of plants with stems large enough for the worms to enter.

The larvae, flesh-colored caterpillars with rows of small, round dark brown spots, up to 1 inch long, winter in old stalks left around the garden and pupate in spring. The female moth is yellow brown with wavy dark bands; the male somewhat darker. They have a wingspread of 1 inch, fly mostly at night. Eggs are laid in flat masses on underside of corn leaves over a period of 3 to 4 weeks, each female averaging about 400 eggs. These hatch in early June, young larvae working down into the stalks and into the base of ears. Broken tassels, bent stalks, sawdust castings outside small holes signify borers at work. They are occasionally found in fruit or flowers of other plants.

The borers predominating in the eastern and southern portions of the infested area are of a multiple-generation strain where the generations vary with the climate, 1 in the northern part, 2 around New Jersey, perhaps 3 in Virginia. A single-generation strain predominates in the North Central states.

Control. Sanitation is important—cleaning up and burning all stalks, corn, dahlia, or weed, capable of harboring borers over winter. In regions where there are 2 generations, corn planted the latter half of May usually matures between broods. Early and late corn should be dusted with 5 per cent DDT or 1 per cent rotenone or 40 per cent Ryania every 5 to 7 days, starting when the tassels are barely discernible, for 4 or 5 applications. The dust should be directed down into the whorl of leaves. Granular DDT is promising.

Flatheaded Apple Tree Borer (*Chrysobothris femorata*)—A common pest throughout North America (Plate XIV). The larvae mine inner bark, cambium, sapwood, and heartwood of healthy, injured, or dying deciduous fruit and shade trees, including apple, apricot, ash, mountain-ash, beech, boxelder, cherry, chestnut, cottonwood, currant, dogwood, elm, hickory, horsechestnut, linden, maple, oak, peach, pear, pecan, plum, poplar, prune, sycamore, willow; also raspberry, rose. In the West, oak is often the preferred food plant; in the East, maples and fruits are frequently attacked. This borer kills many trees and shrubs in the nursery and many trees the first 2 or 3 years after transplanting. Injury is worse in dry seasons and to tree trunks exposed to too much sun through excessive pruning.

The winter is passed as a grub, up to 1¼ inches long, yellowish white, rather slender, with a broad flat enlargement just behind the head, usually lying with the body curved to one side, looking rather U-shaped. The grub burrows just under the bark until full size, then bores deeper in the wood. The tunnels, filled with dry frass, run 6 inches or more down the trunk of a small tree or may go around the trunk to girdle it. Overlying bark is discolored, often slightly sunken, and may die, but the injury is not marked by castings as with other borers.

The beetles, dark olive gray to brown with a metallic luster, blunt at the head end, tapering at the posterior, ½ inch long, emerge in May or June and hang around the sunny side of trees or logs. They lay eggs in bark cracks or some portion of the trunk injured by sunscald or bruising. There is a 1-year cycle.

Control. Preventive measures are best. Wrap newly transplanted trees with paper or burlap. Shade exposed trunks of young fruit trees by placing an upright board about 6 inches wide close to the trunk on the south side. Prune young fruit trees to keep them headed low; fertilize and water properly. Remove borers already in tree with knife or wire and paint the wounds. Woodpeckers, crows, kingbirds, vireos, and ants destroy borers, and there are several wasp parasites.

Flatheaded Fir Borer (*Melanophila drummondi*)—Present but not important in the East, infesting normal or injured trees in the West— firs, Douglas-fir, hemlock, larch, yellow pine, spruce. Adults are metallic black or bronze beetles, ⅜ to ½ inch long, some with golden spots on wing covers. The curved, flatheaded larvae excavate shallow, winding burrows.

Gall-making Maple Borer (*Xylotrechus aceris*)—A small brown beetle attacking red, silver, Norway, and sugar maples. The cream-colored larvae mine in trunks of small trees and branches of larger trees so extensively the branch beyond the wound is broken off by wind. The new wood produced to heal the wound makes a conspicuous gall.

Grape Root Borer (*Vitacea polistiformis*)—Larva of a brown and orange clear-wing moth, found in the East and Pacific Northwest but not too important. Eggs are laid on foliage, and the round, whitish caterpillars, up to 1¾ inches long, drop to the ground and bore into roots, remaining there for 2 years before pupation in soil outside roots. Cultivate soil to destroy pupae.

Hemlock Borer (*Melanophila fulvoguttata*)—Also called Spotted Hemlock Borer and Eastern Flatheaded Hemlock Borer. It ranges from Maine to North Carolina, attacks hemlock and, more rarely, spruce. The beetle is flat, ½ inch long, dark bronze with wing covers marked with yellow spots. The larva is white, small, with the same type of enlargement behind the head as the flatheaded apple tree borer. The larvae separate the bark from the wood with wide, shallow galleries, often killing trees in parks and on estates as well as those in forests. The beetles emerge in May, June, and July; there is 1 generation a year. Drought is most conducive to injury by this borer, so be sure trees have enough water. Prune off and burn infested branches; cut down fatally injured trees and remove and destroy the bark before storing the wood. There are several parasites.

Iris Borer (*Macronoctua onusta*)—The most destructive pest of iris and apparently limited to this host (Plate XV). The borer winters in the egg stage on old iris leaves and other nearby debris. The larvae, hatching in late April or early May, crawl up the iris leaves and make pinpoint holes as they enter. They gnaw out soft leaf tissue between leaf surfaces and work their way slowly down toward the rhizomes, leaving a water-soaked (due to exuding drops of sap) and ragged appearance to the leaf fans. While in the leaves the larvae are slender and about 1 inch long, but after reaching the rhizomes, usually in early July, they become fat and repulsive, 1½ to 2 inches long, smooth-skinned, pinkish, with a brown head. After eating out the interior of the rhizome, leaving only a papery skin, the borer pupates in a brown pupa case loose in the soil in August. The moths are brown with black markings, a 2-inch wingspread. They appear in late August and September to lay eggs, at night, on old iris leaves and sometimes other leaves near iris. There is only 1 brood a year.

The chief damage from borers is not so much from their own chewing, voracious as that is, but because they carry around the bacteria causing that vile-smelling squashy soft rot.

Control. Fall sanitation destroys a good many borer eggs. After first frost, pull off old iris leaves which loosen easily, leaving only short new fans for winter. Clean up and burn other debris near iris. In spring, starting when leaves are about 6 inches high, spray with DDT, 3 level tablespoons 50 per cent wettable to a gallon of water, or apply 5 per cent DDT dust, repeating at 7- to 10-day intervals until the flower spike shows. This can be combined with zineb, ferbam, or copper as a fungicide. By inspecting plantings frequently, looking for wet and ragged leaves, it is possible to kill borers in place by pressing the leaf between thumb and finger.

If iris is to be divided, do it as soon as possible after flowering, long before the borers get into the rhizome. Cut out all infested portions. If soft rot is present, soak rhizomes for 20 minutes in 1–1000 bichloride of mercury (2 tablets to a quart of water) or in Semesan (1 rounded tablespoon to a gallon of water) or dust the rhizomes with gypsum. Let them lie around in the sun a few days before replanting.

Larger Shot-hole Borer (*Scolytus mali*)—Sometimes a pest of fruit trees growing near woodpiles. Leaf and fruit spurs may wilt and brown if the beetle feeds in the crotch between spur and twig. This bark beetle is known to occur in Connecticut, New Jersey, and New York and has been taken from elms dying of Dutch elm disease, but its status as a vector is not proved.

Lesser Cornstalk Borer (*Elasmopalpus lignosellus*)—Found almost anywhere but only injurious in the South. Slender, greenish, brown-striped worms bore into lower part of stalk, not more than 2 inches from soil surface, causing distortion and curling of stalks of young corn, often failure to produce ears. The borer feeds also on pea, bean, cowpea, peanut, turnip, and is worse in sandy soils. The larvae spin their cocoons on the ground under trash; the moths, brownish yellow with gray margins and black spots, appear in 2 or 3 weeks to lay eggs on leaves or stalks. There are 2 generations. Early planting, fall and winter cleanup of land, and rotating corn with a resistant crop, are recommended control measures. Dusting late snapbeans with a combination of 5 per cent DDT and 3 per cent benzene hexachloride has given control in North Carolina.

Lesser Peach Tree Borer (*Synanthedon pictipes*)—Nearly as important as the peach tree borer, attacking stone fruits—peach, plum, cherry—in all peach-growing sections except the West, most abundant in the South. Masses of gum mixed with brown sawdust exude from upper trunk and branches, especially at forks. White caterpillars with brown heads, 3/4 inch long, work in bark under such gum masses. They pupate inside the burrows but close to the openings which are covered with silk webs. Metallic, blue-black, yellow-marked moths emerge in May in the South, June in Connecticut, to lay eggs in bark crevices, around crotches or wounds. They are very active on sunny days.

Control. DDT is apparently not effective, though good for the peach tree borer. Parathion, 15 per cent, at rate of 1½ to 2 pounds per 100 gallons of water or the same amount of 25 per cent EPN wettable powder has given good results if applied at time of emergence (mid-June in Connecticut) and repeated once or twice at 2-week intervals. But these phosphate sprays are too dangerous for back-yard farmers. Digging borers out by hand, keeping trees properly fed and watered, prevention of cultivator damage, prompt treatment of wounds with asphalt paint, and choosing trees with wide-angle crotches are good general control measures.

Lilac Borer (*Podosesia syringae syringae*)—Also known as the Ash Borer and much more important than the true ash borer, attacking lilacs, ash, mountain-ash, occasionally privet, through eastern states to Colorado and Texas. Surely every gardener is familiar with old lilac trunks full of holes and protruding sawdust. On ash there are large, scarlike outgrowths where the caterpillars have burrowed in the trunk (Plate XV).

The white borer, ¾ to 1½ inches long, with a brown head, winters in the wood, usually near the ground, feeds again in spring, pushing its burrow out nearly through the bark, and then pupates. There seems to be some confusion as to time of emergence and different species may be involved. Late summer, August and September, is reported from Virginia, late April and May in New England, May to July in Illinois. The adult is a wasplike clear-wing moth with brown fore wings, transparent hind wings with a dark border, wing expanse 1½ inches, an active flier. The females lay their eggs in masses at the base of lilac stems, or roughened and wounded places on bark. There is 1 generation a year.

Control. Lilac trunks can be sprayed or painted with DDT or dieldrin (4 teaspoons to 1 gallon of water) to prevent egg-laying. Borers in their burrows can be killed by injecting carbon bisulfide or by inserting a flexible wire. Wounds should be trimmed smooth and painted with shellac or tree-wound dressing.

Linden Borer (*Saperda vestita*)—Principally a linden pest, although it may attack poplars. The beetles, up to ¾ inch long, dark reddish brown with olive-yellow pubescence, 3 dark spots on each wing cover, feed on bark of growing shoots, leaf petioles, and large veins of leaves, often killing tips of branches. Eggs are laid in incisions in trunk and branches. Larvae, white, slender, 1 inch long, mine in bark and wood.

Old, unthrifty trees, rather frequently attacked, die slowly, larger branches first. Worming by hand seems the most feasible control.

Little Carpenterworm (*Prionoxystus macmurtrei*)—Present throughout eastern United States and west to Minnesota; often more injurious to oaks than the carpenterworm, but similar to it in habit and character of damage. Red oaks are favored, especially young trees in street plantings. The female is pepper-and-salt gray, with black, veinlike markings on fore wings, which spread to 2 or 2½ inches; hind wings are clear. Larvae are greenish white, with light brown heads, 2½ inches long. See Carpenterworm for control.

Live-oak Root Borer (*Archodontes melanopus*)—A very large beetle working on eastern live oak, pecan, and hackberry, from Virginia to Florida and along the Gulf coast. The adult is dark brown, flat, broad, 1¾ to 2¼ inches long with slender antennae; the larva is white, as thick as a finger, nearly 3½ inches long, with prominent body segments. The female lays eggs in a collar on young trees just below ground surface and the larvae bore into roots of young oaks, enlarging the root into a huge gall and preventing formation of new roots. New suckers around old stumps make for scrub-oak barrens rather than stately live-oak forests. Digging out the worms by hand is the best control.

Locust Borer (*Megacyllene robiniae*)—Common wherever black or yellow locust is grown and especially injurious to locusts used as street trees. It is a black beetle, ½ to ¾ inch long, with bright yellow crossbands on thorax and wing covers and a conspicuous W-shaped mark at the base of the latter. It feeds on pollen of goldenrod and other composites in autumn. The larvae, white, cylindrical, widest just behind the head, mine in inner bark and sapwood, later burrow into solid wood. Infested trees may be full of longitudinal burrows a half inch in diameter, up to 3 inches long. The trunk may have swollen areas, with bark cracked open. Pupation is in the burrows, beetles emerging in August and September to lay white eggs in bark scars and crevices. These hatch within 2 weeks and the larvae bore through the corky layer of the bark to fashion a small cell for winter. Trees under 6 inches in diameter are more likely to be attacked. Control by spraying trunks with a 2 per cent DDT-xylene emulsion before growth starts in spring.

Locust Twig Borer (*Ecdytolopha insiticiana*)—Causes elongate galls, up to 3 inches long, in twigs of black locust. The caterpillar is reddish to yellow, ½ to ¾ inch long; the adult is a small moth with brown fore wings, gray hind wings. Cut out and burn infested twigs.

Maple Callus Borer (*Sylvora acerni*)—Also known as Maple Sesian. A clear-winged moth seriously injuring hard and soft maples in New England and west to Illinois and Nebraska. It is responsible for rough, enlarged scars and deformities on trunks and branches. The trees have difficulty healing wounds because the larvae, white, ½ inch long with light brown heads, work in new callus tissue, enlarging small wounds so that young trees are girdled and killed. The moths are amber, with yellow heads and bands on abdomen, 1-inch wingspread. They appear in late May or June to deposit eggs around old scars and other rough places. Smooth off roughened bark areas; dig out borers under the bark in spring; keep wounds painted.

Maple Petiole Borer (*Caulocampus acericaulis*)—A sawfly fairly common in Connecticut, Massachusetts, New York, and New Jersey on maple. The larvae, ⅓ inch long, yellow with a brown head when grown, tunnel in leaf petioles in May and June, causing leaf drop. Defoliation seldom exceeds a third of the total foliage so the effect is not too serious. There is only 1 generation a year.

Oak Sapling Borer (*Goes tesselatus*)—Kills many oaks by cutting them off at the base, weakens others with mines so they break in wind or icestorm. The larva is yellow white, fleshy; the beetle is long-horned with yellow-brown wing covers mottled with yellow. The life cycle may last 2 or 3 years.

Oak Timberworm (*Arrhenodes minutus*)—Also known as Northern Brenthian, a slender beetle with a very long snout. The shiny brown female, marked with yellow spots, bores a hole in the bark with her snout and pushes an egg to the bottom of the tunnel. The long, slender larvae bore in solid wood of elm, beech, chestnut, and oak, usually in felled timber, sometimes entering living trees through wounds.

Orchid Bulb Borer (*Eucactophagus weissi*)—Blackish beetles, slightly over ½ inch long, with pale yellow blotches on wing covers, feed on leaves and other plant parts. The larvae feed inside bulbs and open the way for fungus rots. Remove and destroy infested bulbs, detected by pressing between the fingers. Spray plants with DDT.

Pacific Flatheaded Borer (*Chrysobothris mali*)—Distributed throughout the western states. The adult is a dark brown to reddish-copper beetle, ¼ to ½ inch long. The larva is similar to the flatheaded apple tree borer and mines normal and injured trees, preferring sunny limbs. Ceanothus is preferred host, but alder, apple, apricot, ash, mountain-ash, beech, blackberry, boxelder, California coffeeberry, Catalina cherry, currant, elm, eucalyptus, gooseberry, loquat, manzanita, maple, mesquite, mountain mahogany, oak, peach, pear, plum, poplar, prune, rose, sycamore, and willow may be attacked. Control measures are the same as for the flatheaded apple tree borer.

Painted Hickory Borer (*Megacyllene caryae*)—Distributed from New England to Texas, or wherever hickory is grown, chiefly a pest of cut timber. It is partial to shagbark hickory, may also infest black walnut, butternut, honey locust, osage orange, and hackberry. The adult is similar to the locust borer, with long antennae, yellow transverse bands, and a yellow W on dark brown elytra.

Peach Tree Borer (*Sanninoidea exitiosa*)—A native moth, the most important enemy of peach trees and also attacking plum, wild and cultivated cherry, prune, nectarine, apricot, and some ornamental shrubs in the genus Prunus (Plate XVI). First sign of injury is usually a mass of gum and brown frass at the base of the trunk, indicating that the white, brown-headed worms are at work in the bark anywhere from 2 to 3 inches below ground to 10 inches above. They winter as larvae of all sizes in the burrows, finish feeding in spring, when they are about 1 inch in length, then pupate in brown silk cocoons in soil near the base of the tree. Just before the moth emerges the pupa is forced out of the cocoon.

In the North, most of the moths emerge during July and August, in the South during August and September. The female is blue black with clear hind wings and an orange crossband on the abdomen; the male has mostly clear wings and narrow yellow bands on the abdomen. Each female lays several hundred eggs near the base of the tree trunk, the young worms hatching in 10 days to bore inside the bark. Peaches seldom survive repeated borer attacks.

Control. The standard remedy has been a ring of paradichlorobenzene crystals placed around the tree trunk in fall after all eggs are hatched but while the temperature is above 55°F. This means late September in the vicinity of New York City or about the middle of October in Georgia. The soil is loosened around the tree, the crystals applied in a ring 1 inch away from the trunk and then mounded with 2 or 3 shovelfuls of earth to hold in the fumes. The dosage, which must be exact, varies with the age of the tree: ½ ounce for 3-year trees, ¾ ounce up to 6 years, 1 to 1½ ounces for older trees. Ethylene dichloride emulsion and propylene dichloride emulsion are also used in the soil, following manufacturer's directions for application and dosage.

Treating the trunk with DDT has now somewhat replaced soil fumigation. Back-yard fruit trees can be dusted with 5 per cent or 10 per
cent DDT near the base of the trunk, and the ground around, or
sprayed with 50 per cent wettable DDT, up to 4 level tablespoons per
gallon of water, on July 1, August 1, and September 1 in Middle Atlantic states. Commercial orchardists may use parathion instead of DDT.

Peach Twig Borer (*Anarsia lineatella*)—A small, reddish-brown
larva, under ½ inch long, boring in and killing tips of twigs, infesting
fruit later in the season. This borer, a minor pest in the East but quite
injurious on the West coast, infests plums, prunes, nectarines, almonds,
apricots, as well as peaches. The grayish moth is so small it is seldom
noticed. A dormant lime-sulfur spray, 1 to 15 dilution, is helpful, as
is spraying with lead arsenate before the blossoms reach the pink stage
and after petal fall.

Pecan Borer. See Dogwood Borer. This attacks pecan in North
Carolina, Georgia, Florida, Mississippi, being worse on recently top-
worked trees. Protect scions from borer injury by covering all graft
wounds with grafting wax which will not crack.

Pecan Carpenterworm (*Cossula magnifica*)—Also known as the Oak
or Hickory Cossid. It bores into trunk and larger branches of pecan,
oak, and hickory in southern states. Reddish pellets of wood at the base
of the tree indicate that the pinkish larva, 1½ inches long with fine
short hairs, is boring within. The moth is gray, mottled with brown
and black.

Pigeon Tremex (*Tremex columba*)—A native wasplike insect, also
known as Pigeon Horntail, occurring through most of North America.
The cylindrical white larvae, up to 2 inches long, with a short horn
at the tip of the abdomen, bore tunnels in diseased and dying trees,
most commonly elm and sugar maple, sometimes beech, apple, pear,
sycamore, and oak. The female moth, with a 2-inch body and wingspread, has a reddish head and thorax, black abdomen with yellow
bands, bluish wings, and an ovipositor extending an inch beyond the
body. For control, squirt carbon bisulfide into burrows. The ichneumon
wasp is a helpful parasite; the female lays her eggs right through wood
into the horntail larva in its burrow.

Poplar Borer (*Saperda calcarata*)—A large native beetle, distributed
throughout the country, attacking Lombardy and other poplars, cottonwood, except for a resistant form in the Mississippi Valley, aspen,
and willows. It severely injures ornamental shade trees, marring them
with blackened swollen scars on the outside of wood honeycombed with

irregular galleries. The beetle is reddish brown with gray and yellow pubescence, yellow stripes on thorax and elytra, 1⅛ inches long. Adults, appearing from July to September, feed on bark of young twigs and lay eggs in slits in the bark. The larvae work in the bark the first year, tunneling into the wood the second year, sending out frass to the openings. This accumulates at the base of trees. Cut and burn badly infested trees in spring before beetles emerge. Probe borers with a wire or fumigate with carbon bisulfide. Creosote painted on egg scars in autumn will kill young grubs.

Poplar and Willow Borer (*Sternochetus lapathi*)—Also called Mottled Willow Borer. This is a small European weevil which has spread from Maine to Wisconsin and North Dakota since it was first noticed in New York in 1882, and is now reported in the Northwest. It attacks willow, poplar, alder, and birch with serious injury frequent on poplars and willows over a year old. The grubs, thick, legless, ½ inch long, make burrows around the trunk in the cambium, girdling the tree; as they mature they enter hardwood and honeycomb it with galleries. Smaller limbs and branches have swollen knotty areas; foliage may wilt. The dark brown beetles, ⅓ inch long, are covered with light brown and gray scales in a mottled effect. Eggs are usually laid in June and July. Cut and burn seriously infested trees; prevent egg-laying with DDT. Painting the trunk with a mixture made by emulsifying 1 quart of carbolineum with 1 pound sodium carbonate dissolved in 1 quart of water, the whole diluted with 2 quarts of water, has been recommended for painting on the trunk but is rather risky. It must not reach roots.

Potato Stalk Borer (*Trichobaris trinotata*)—Injures potatoes, early varieties in particular, and may attack eggplant, groundcherry, and related weeds. It is present in most sections of the country, except states farthest north, and when abundant may destroy entire fields of potatoes. It hibernates as an adult, a bluish-gray snout beetle, ⅕ inch long, with 3 black spots at the base of wing covers. It eats deep holes in stems of new plants in spring and deposits eggs singly in such cavities in stem or leaf petioles. The very small, yellow-white, wrinkled grubs hollow out the stems for several inches, causing wilting and death of plants. Before pupating the larva packs its burrow with "excelsior" scrapings from the stem and chews an exit passage for the adult to use in spring. There is only 1 generation a year. Clean up and burn all potato vines after harvest; destroy nearby weeds with stalks large enough to harbor borers.

Potato Tuberworm (*Gnorimoschema operculella*)—Sometimes called

Tuber Moth. Destructive to potatoes from Florida north to Virginia and west to California. Eggplant, tomato, tobacco, and related weeds are also attacked. The small moths, narrow-winged, gray brown mottled with darker brown, ½ inch across the wings, escape from storehouses in spring and lay eggs, singly, on underside of leaves or eyes of exposed tubers. The larvae, pinkish or white, with dark brown heads, ¾ inch long, burrow in stems or petioles or mine in leaves. Maturing in 2 or 3 weeks, they pupate inside dirt-covered silk cocoons in trash on the ground, emerging as adults in 7 to 10 days. The entire life cycle takes only a month and there may be 5 or 6 generations a season, with most severe injury in hot, dry summers. The adults of late broods work down through cracks in soil to lay eggs in tubers, the larvae making dirty silk-lined burrows through the flesh. They come out of the tubers to pupate in odd corners around the storage room.

Control. Keep potatoes well cultivated and deeply hilled during growth. Spray foliage with DDT. Cut and burn infested vines a few days before digging; do not leave newly dug potatoes exposed to egg-laying by moths during late afternoon or night; destroy culls. Screen storage places in warm weather. Burlap potato bags should be sprayed with 2 per cent DDT in xylene to prevent reinfestation or to kill larvae in already infested tubers.

Raspberry Cane Borer (*Oberea bimaculata*)—A long-horned beetle generally distributed from Kansas eastward, a pest of raspberry and blackberry, sometimes rose, also reported on azalea. The slender black and yellow striped female, with 2 black dots on a yellow thorax, makes a double row of punctures around the stem near the tip and lays an egg between the girdles. The tip wilts and the grub, when it hatches in summer, bores down the cane 1 or 2 inches before hibernating. The next season it continues to bore down inside the canes and pupates inside the burrow. The cane dies. Cut out and burn wilted tips as soon as noticed, pruning 6 inches below the punctured area. Cut and burn wilted or dead fruiting canes.

Raspberry Root Borer (*Bembecia marginata*)—Also called Raspberry Crown Borer, causing wilting and dying of fruiting canes of blackberry and raspberry in early summer, often when berries are ripening. The adult is a clear-wing moth, with black body crossed by 4 yellow bands. Eggs, oval, reddish brown, the size of mustard seed, are deposited on underside of leaves near the edge in late summer. Small white caterpillars hibernate the first winter in blister-like elevations of bark just beneath soil level or at base of stems. They make extensive galleries in spring and by the second summer the whole crown may be hollowed out. Apply a DDT-oil emulsion or a spray (2 tablespoons 50 per cent wettable DDT to 1 gallon of water) 2 weeks after the first egg is deposited (about September 10 in New Jersey) to crown of plant and new canes; repeat in 2 weeks.

Red-necked Cane Borer (*Agrilus ruficollis*)—Causes cigar-shaped swellings in raspberry, blackberry, or dewberry canes in eastern United States. Canes may die or break off at the swollen joint. Bluish-black beetles, with a coppery thorax, 1/3 inch long, lay eggs in bark of canes, usually near a leaf, which may be eaten and look ragged. The young larvae burrow upward in sapwood and several times around the canes, girdling them. The easiest remedy is to cut out and burn swollen canes. Some varieties are rather resistant to attack.

Rhododendron Borer (*Ramosia rhododendri*)—A small, native clear-wing moth injuring rhododendrons and sometimes adjacent mountain-laurel and azalea in eastern United States. The moths, black with 3 yellow transverse bands on the abdomen, only 3/8- to 1/2-inch wing-spread, lay eggs in May and June on twigs. The yellow-white larvae, 1/2 inch long, bore in the sapwood under the bark, causing branches to wilt or break off. Injury in the same shrub increases from year to year, with leaves turning brown, main trunks filled with holes protruding fine sawdust. Cut out and burn infested portions whenever noticed. Spray or paint trunks and branches with DDT before moths deposit eggs.

Rose Stem Girdler (*Agrilus rubicola*)—Primarily a rose pest, sometimes found in raspberry. Small greenish beetles lay eggs under bark, preferably *Rosa rugosa* or *R. hugonis*. The grubs make 1 or 2 spiral mines around the canes, which swell at such points and sometimes split. Cut out swollen canes early in spring.

Roundheaded Apple Tree Borer (*Saperda candida*)—A native beetle distributed generally east of the Rocky Mountains (Plate XIV). It is best known as an apple pest but may be injurious to quince, pear, plum, peach, mountain-ash, hawthorn, wild crab, shadbush, and choke-cherry. It usually works in tree trunks at ground level or just above or below, killing young trees, seriously injuring older specimens. The life cycle is normally completed in 3 years in the North, 2 in the South. The young grub, first brownish red, later creamy white, with a rounded thickening just behind the head, starts work in the bark, producing brown sap stains, then tunnels in the sapwood for a year or two, ejecting conspicuous coils of rusty brown frass. The next season it bores into the heartwood, tunneling outward in fall to prepare a winter chamber near the bark. The upper end of the chamber, curved out so it almost touches the bark, is filled with sawdust-like frass; the lower end is packed with coarse wood cuttings. The larvae pupates here in spring; the beetle emerges from late May to July.

The adults, just under an inch long, yellow or reddish brown above, white underneath, have 2 conspicuous white stripes the length of the body and prominent gray antennae. They crawl over the tree, feeding somewhat on foliage and fruit, and lay eggs in slits made in the bark near ground level.

Control. Examine trees carefully, scooping away an inch or two of earth at the base, for brown castings or stained areas in bark. Cut out borers in shallow tunnels with tip of a knife; probe for deep-seated borers with a flexible wire; or inject a fumigant. Farmers use an injection gun for applying a mixture of 10 grams of paradichlorobenzene in 10 c.c. of carbon bisulfide or rotenone or pyrethrum extract in alcohol. The regular spray schedule (or 2 special sprays of lead arsenate, the first 2 or 3 weeks after petal fall, the second 2 or 3 weeks later) takes care of beetles feeding and egg-laying.

Roundheaded Fir Borer (*Tetropium abietis*)—A pest of western conifers, a velvety brown, long-horned beetle, ¾ inch long. The grubs work under bark of felled and standing firs.

Rustic Borer (*Xylotrechus colonus*)—A dark brown beetle with white or yellow irregular markings, found under bark of almost all dead hardwoods.

Shot-hole Borer (*Scolytus rugulosus*)—Equally well known as the Fruit Tree Bark Beetle, a European insect generally distributed over the country. It makes small holes, like shot holes, in the bark of healthy twigs of fruit trees and in branches and trunks of weakened trees, attacking almond, apple, apricot, loquat, mountain-ash, cherry, elm, hawthorn, Juneberry, nectarine, peach, pear, plum, prune. On stone fruits the shot-holes are usually covered with gum. If beetles are abundant, the foliage yellows, wilts, the tree may die. The pinkish-white grub, ⅛ inch long, winters in the inner bark. The galleries are winding, sawdust-filled, leading out from a shorter central gallery. The black, blunt beetles, ¹⁄₁₀ inch long, emerge in early summer and the females fly to unhealthy trees to excavate an egg gallery in branch or twig, depositing eggs on each side of this. There may be 1 to 3 generations, depending on climate.

Control. Keep trees in vigorous condition with nitrogenous fertilizers and sufficient water; remove and burn prunings and dying trees. Spray trunks and branches of infested trees with DDT, 2 pounds per 100 gallons or 2 tablespoons per gallon, in late spring. This treatment is repeated in September in the Pacific Northwest. Parathion is also effective but more dangerous to apply.

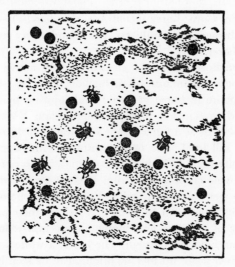

39. Shot-hole borer: section of bark showing emergence holes, small beetles.

Sinuate Pear Tree Borer (*Agrilus sinuatus*)—A European beetle first noticed in New Jersey in 1894, now known also in New England, New York, and Ohio. It is primarily a pear pest but may injure hawthorn, mountain-ash, and cotoneaster. The beetles are slender, very flat, 1/3 inch long, purplish bronze. They feed on foliage and lay eggs in bark cracks. The grubs are long, slender, flat, and make sinuate galleries in trunk and branches, with swelling or cracking of bark. Clean up dead or dying trees or branches during the winter; spray pear foliage with lead arsenate or DDT when beetles emerge (May or June) and repeat 2 weeks later.

Southern Cornstalk Borer (*Diatraea crambidoides*)—A southern insect, found from Kansas south, principally on corn. Infested stalks are twisted and stunted, with an enlargement near the ground. Leaves are ragged, showing holes eaten out while still in the whorl. Borers are dirty gray white, with many dark brown spots, 1 inch long. They pupate in stalks near the ground. Straw-colored moths emerge in late spring to lay many overlapping eggs on underside of leaves. The borers may move from one plant to another; there are 1 to 3 generations. Control by sanitation, cleaning up corn stubble and refuse right after harvest, late fall or winter plowing or spading, and rotation with some other crop.

Southwestern Corn Borer (*Diatraea grandiosella*)—A corn pest from Kansas through the Southwest. Insect and injury resemble southern cornstalk borer.

Squash Vine Borer (*Melittia cucurbitae*)—A native pest, present east of the Rocky Mountains, often spoiling up to 25 per cent of the squash crop (more in home gardens) and injuring pumpkin, gourd, cucumber, and muskmelon in that order (Plate XVI). The borer winters as a larva or as a pupa inside a silk-lined dark cocoon an inch or two below soil level. The moth, wasplike with copper-green fore wings and orange and black abdomen, 1 to 1½ inches across the wings, appears when vine crops start to run. It glues small, oval, flat brown eggs singly on stems and leaf stalks. Young borers hatch in about a week, tunnel into the stem to feed, first sign of their presence being sudden wilting of the vine and masses of greenish-yellow excrement protruding from holes in the stem. The borer, a white wrinkled caterpillar with brown head, up to 1 inch long, can be seen by slitting the stem with a knife. Later in the season it is found in fruits as well as stems. After feeding for 4 to 6 weeks it goes to the soil to make its cocoon. There are 2 generations in the Gulf states, usually 1 in the North, sometimes a partial second.

Control is difficult. Dusting at weekly intervals, starting when vines begin to run, kills some young larvae before they enter the stem. Rotenone, 1 per cent dust, is safest, with 5 per cent chlordane sometimes recommended, though it is possibly injurious to some varieties under some circumstances. If the vine starts to wilt, kill the borer with a knife and heap earth over the stem joints to start new roots. Make a second planting of summer squash to mature after the borers are through feeding. Pull up and burn vines immediately after harvest. Harrow soil in fall and turn under deeply in spring.

Stalk Borer (*Papaipema nebris*)—A universal feeder, occurring everywhere east of the Rocky Mountains. The brown, white-striped caterpillar, ¾ to 2 inches long, works in the stem of any plant large enough and soft enough for its operations, although preferring giant ragweed and corn in later stages. It is a frequent pest of dahlia and iris, is often found on hollyhock, aster, lily, rhubarb, pepper, potato, and tomato, to name but a few. It winters as grayish ridged eggs on grasses and weeds. These hatch very early in spring with the borers working first in grasses before going over to herbaceous stalks, entering at the side and burrowing up. The young larva has a dark brown or purple band around the body and several brown or purple lengthwise stripes, but these almost disappear and the full-grown larva is grayish or light purple. The borers are very restless, often changing one host for another. They pupate in late summer just under the soil surface or, rarely, inside stalks. The grayish-brown moths, with white spots on fore wings, an inch across, appear in August and September to lay upward of 2000 eggs per female. There is only 1 generation a year.

Control. By the time injury is noted it is usually too late to save the plant, but it is sometimes possible to slit a stem, kill the borer with a knife, and then bind the stem together. A few drops of carbon bisulfide injected into holes may help, or borer paste. Dusting with DDT may prevent entrance. Clean up the garden in autumn, getting rid of weeds and crop refuse.

Strawberry Crown Borer (*Tyloderma fragariae*)—Found rather generally east of the Rocky Mountains and especially important in Kentucky, Tennessee, and Arkansas. The adult is a small brown snout beetle, less than ⅕ inch long, shaped like a grape seed, each wing cover marked with 3 black bars. The grub is small and yellow, taking on a pinkish tinge when it starts to feed on strawberry tissues. The adults, which cannot fly, winter under trash in beds and appear about blossom time to lay eggs, glistening white, elliptical, in shallow holes in crowns and at base of leaf stalks. The grubs hatch in about a week and burrow downward into the center of the crown, killing or stunting the plants. They pupate in the burrow in late summer and the beetles feed on strawberry foliage in early fall, making characteristic small feeding holes. There is 1 generation.

Control. Apply 20 per cent toxaphene dust or 5 per cent chlordane dust to plants and soil just before blooming. Set new strawberry beds with certified plants and, if possible, not less than 350 yards from old fields. Grow only 2 crops before plowing up and destroying the old planting. The borer also lives in wild strawberries and cinquefoil.

Sugar-maple Borer (*Glycobius speciosus*)—A native, dangerous to sugar maples in the Northeast and apparently confined to them. The adult is a striking long-horned beetle, black with yellow markings and tips of wing covers, and a yellow W near the base, 1 inch long. The roundheaded larva is 2 inches long, somewhat flattened, rose white. It bores a wide channel several feet long in inner bark and sapwood, often going halfway around the tree. The bark over this section cracks, producing an ugly scar to which other injurious insects are attracted. There is a 2-year cycle, beetles laying eggs in summer. Remove dead branches before June 1. Cut out grubs with a sharp chisel where possible or kill borers with a bent wire; cover wounds with tree paint. Carbon bisulfide or borer paste can be squirted into burrows.

Tiger Hickory Borer (*Goes tigrinus*)—A long-horned beetle widely distributed in eastern and central United States. It attacks hickory, mines in wood of oak, preferring white oak and walnut. The adult is a brown beetle with a dark band, covered with fine gray hairs, and pinkish antennae. The larva is lemon yellow, with prominent segments, 1 inch long. It excavates large burrows in sapwood and inner bark. The life cycle may last 3 years.

Tile-horned Prionus (*Prionus imbricornis*)—Common on oak and chestnut in the Southeast. Adult is a large, brownish-black beetle; larva elongate, tapering posteriorly, with a wide head. It bores in roots of living trees.

Twig Girdler (*Oncideres cingulata*)—Twigs and small branches up to several feet long are found neatly cut off and lying on the ground under hickory, pecan, persimmon, oak, poplar, sour gum, honey locust, and other trees in eastern states. Grayish, hard-shelled beetles, with antennae longer than the body, girdle the twigs by cutting round and round from the bark inward. In young trees injury may be considerable, especially in pecans where the tree may be deformed and the nut crop reduced. In persimmons the beetle wounds afford entrance for the deadly persimmon wilt fungus. Gather and burn all severed branches in late fall when eggs and grubs are inside. Three sprays of DDT, at 2-week intervals, starting in late August, are sometimes recommended for pecans.

Twig Pruner (*Elaphidion villosum*)—Also called Oak Twig Pruner, found west to Michigan and south to the Gulf states attacking oak, hickory, pecan, maple, locust, hackberry, elm, walnut, sweet gum, and some fruit trees. Shade trees are often so severely pruned by larvae burrowing in the twigs that their shape is ruined. The ground may be thickly strewn with twigs. The adults, brownish, elongate beetles, about ½ inch, appear when oak leaves unfold and lay eggs in leaf axils near tips of twigs. Clean up and burn all severed twigs.

Two-lined Chestnut Borer (*Agrilus bilineatus*)—A native beetle distributed from Maine to Texas. It attacks apparently normal but actually weakened oaks, chestnut, beech, ironwood. The beetle is slender, 1/3 inch long, greenish black, covered with golden hairs and with a golden stripe down each wing cover. It emerges in May or June, feeds on foliage for some time, then lays eggs under bark scales. The larvae are slender, white, flat, with an enlargement behind the head. They mine in cambium, girdling trunk and branches and working from 40 to 50 feet in the air down to the ground. Weakened trees die rapidly. Foliage sprays of DDT or lead arsenate may help protect valuable shade trees. Water and fertilizer will aid in recovery.

Western Cedar Borer (*Trachykele blondeli*)—Bright emerald green sculptured beetles, 5/8 inch long, destructive to western red-cedar, cypress, California incense cedar, and related species. Flatheaded larvae mine in sapwood and heartwood of living or dying trees.

Western Peach Tree Borer (*Sanninoidea exitiosa graefi*)—A western variety of the peach tree borer, also injuring plum, prune, apricot, sometimes apple and almond. See Peach Tree Borer for control.

BUDWORMS (BUD MOTHS)

Budworms are small caterpillars that feed in or on opening buds. Sometimes the approved common name is that of the adult stage, bud moth.

Eye-spotted Bud Moth (*Spilonota ocellana*)—A fruit pest through northern apple-growing sections, on apple, pear, cherry, wild plum, and haw. The larvae, small brown worms with black heads, winter in small silken cases attached to twigs or bud axils. They eat out the buds as they open in spring or tie leaves together with silken threads. They pupate in early summer in their silken nests, and small brown moths, with a light band on each wing, lay eggs on underside of leaves for the summer brood which hatches in 7 to 10 days.

Control. DN dormant sprays are effective, 3 to 4 quarts of Elgetol or Krenite to 100 gallons of water. Parathion, 3/4 to 1 pound of 15 per cent wettable powder per 100 gallons, is used by some orchardists for the summer generation.

Holly Bud Moth (*Rhopobota naevana* var. *ilicifolia*)—A serious pest of holly in the Pacific Northwest. The larvae, 5/8 inch long, feed on buds and terminal growth inside a web. There is only 1 brood. Spray with arsenate of lead or DDT at the beginning of infestation.

Lesser Bud Moth (*Recurvaria nanella*)—Similar in appearance and habit to the eye-spotted bud moth but mining in leaves to some extent.

Pecan Bud Moth (*Gretchena bolliana*)—Primarily a bud feeder, sometimes causing excessive branching or stunting of pecans. Young larvae are black, older caterpillars yellow green with brown heads, just over ½ inch long. Eggs are laid on foliage or, early in the season, on twigs. Spray with calcium or lead arsenate or DDT in spring and summer.

Rose Budworm (*Pyrrhia umbra*)—On buds of rose, snapdragon, columbine, and other garden flowers. There are 2 kinds of caterpillars. One is green, spotted with black tubercles and prominent dark, longitudinal stripes, the other has whitish-orange markings on the back. The adult is the bordered sallow moth. Remove infested buds as soon as noticed. Spray or dust with lead arsenate or DDT.

Spruce Budworm (*Choristoneura fumiferana*)—A serious enemy of forest trees and ornamentals, distributed all over northern United States. It has ranked third in importance of all our insects, next to the cotton boll weevil and corn earworm. It has cycles of enormous abundance in spruce and balsam forests and injures ornamental spruce, balsam fir, Douglas-fir, pine, larch, and hemlock. An infested forest looks as if it had been struck by fire. The trees that do recover have their terminals killed.

Dark reddish-brown caterpillars with a yellow stripe along the side, 1 inch long, feed on opening buds and needles, tying them together with silk. Partly grown larvae winter in silken cases on branches, starting activity when buds break in spring. They pass through 5 instars, growing larger with each molt, migrating from older buds to younger and more succulent food, including tender foliage. Sometimes they spin downward on silk, like cankerworms, and drift with the wind to other trees. They pupate in a cocoon of silk and leaf remnants for 3 or 4 weeks; the moths emerge in late June and early July. They are dull gray, marked with brown bands and spots, ¾ inch across the wings. They lay green, flat, overlapping eggs on the needles and the young larvae feed for a while before hibernating. There are several biological races of this budworm.

Control. Spray ornamentals with lead arsenate or DDT just as new growth is starting. DDT applied to forests from an airplane has been fairly effective. Adverse weather conditions, birds, insect parasites and predators combine to reduce large outbreaks.

Tobacco Budworm (*Heliothis virescens*)—Found from Connecticut south, most injurious in Gulf states. Tiny rust to green striped caterpillars eat holes in buds or unfolded leaves of tobacco, cotton, geranium, ageratum, groundcherry, and other solanaceous plants. Moths have light green wings with 4 oblique light bands, a wingspread of 1½ inches. Eggs are laid singly on underside of leaves. Pupation is in the soil and there are 2 generations a year. A bait of 1 part lead arsenate or cryolite mixed with 75 parts cornmeal is recommended for placing directly on the buds by hand or with a sifter can.

Verbena Bud Moth (*Endothenia herbesana*)—A pest of verbena and physostegia. The larva is greenish yellow with a black head, less than ½ inch long; the adult is a small purplish-brown moth. Clip off and burn wilted new shoots.

BUGS

To a layman almost any insect is a bug. To an entomologist the word "bug" means a member of the insect order Hemiptera, which means "half-winged." In this order most species have the basal part of the front wing thickened and leathery, the lower half thin and membranous. The hind wings are entirely membranous and slightly shorter than the front wings. Wings of true bugs are folded flat over the abdomen, instead of being held in a rooflike position like those of leafhoppers and aphids in the order Homoptera. Bugs have piercing-sucking mouth parts, but the beak arises from the front part of the head instead of the posterior. Bugs have a gradual metamorphosis, nymphs resembling adults except for size and possession of wings. Some adult bugs have short wings and a few are wingless. The antennae have no more than 5 segments.

The water bugs—water boatmen, backswimmers, water scorpions, water striders, and giant water bugs—are of little importance to gardeners. Bedbugs are household pests. The families of bugs afflicting plants, and those with useful predators, are listed here, followed by descriptions of the more important bugs. Mealybugs and spittlebugs, not true bugs, are listed under those headings.

Anthocoridae. Flower bugs or minute pirate bugs, found on flowers or under loose bark, or in leaf litter. Most species are black with white markings, very small, less than ⅛ inch long, and feed on small insects, mites, or insect eggs. This is a beneficial family.

Miridae. Leaf bugs or plant bugs, a very large group, with almost all members injurious, a few predaceous on other insects. This family includes tarnished plant, four-lined plant, and apple red bugs, also garden fleahoppers. Members of this family possess a cuneus, the apex of the thickened portion of the front wing set apart by a groove; antennae and beak are 4-segmented; eyes fairly large but no ocelli (simple eyes).

Phymatidae. Ambush bugs, predaceous insects waiting for their prey on flowers, particularly goldenrod. They are small, less than ½ inch long, stout-bodied but with odd shapes, spiny armor and camouflaging color patterns. The front legs are modified for grasping.

Reduviidae. Assassin bugs, predators with large eyes midway or far back on long, narrow heads. Ocelli, when present, only 2. Antennae have 4 segments, beaks 3. The abdomen is often widened beyond the margins of the wings. They are beneficial, preying on caterpillars, Japanese beetles, and other harmful insects, but injurious when they feed on honeybees or bite people. Some are called "kissing bugs."

Nabidae. Damsel bugs, wholly predaceous, small, brown or black, soft-bodied with front legs modified for grasping small insects. The beak is long, usually 4-segmented; head and first segment of thorax narrow; eyes large; ocelli present; antennae 4- or 5-segmented.

Tingidae (Tingididae). Lace bugs, exclusively plant feeders, sucking sap from underside of leaves which they cover with brown specks. The family name means "ornamented" and the beautiful small, flat bugs, oval or rectangular in shape, have transparent wings reticulated or netted in a lacelike effect and the head covered with a sort of hood. The nymphs are dark, spiny.

Lygaeidae. Chinch bugs and relatives, mostly feeding on plants, with some predators. Very small bugs; beak and antennae 4-segmented; ocelli present, cuneus lacking; only a few simple veins in wing membrane.

Coreidae. Squash bugs, leaf-footed bugs, and allies, some plant-eating, some predaceous. These are small to large, with rather large compound eyes and 4-segmented antennae; membranous portion of fore wings is transversed by numerous parallel, longitudinal veins. Some species have conspicuously enlarged legs, some have an offensive odor. The boxelder bug is included in this family by some entomologists, placed in the Corizidae by others. Members of the latter family, called grass bugs, are usually small and lack scent glands.

Pentatomidae. Stink bugs. Small to medium in size, body shield-shaped; antennae 5-segmented; eyes small, 2 ocelli; glands at side of thorax emit strong odor. Some are plant-eating, some are predaceous on Colorado potato beetles, caterpillars, etc.; some are both.

Alder Lace Bug (*Corythucha pergandei*)—Infesting alder, occasionally birch, crabapple, elm, and hazel.

Andromeda Lace Bug (*Stephanitis globulifera*)—A new pest, probably from Japan, seriously damaging *Pieris japonica*. It was first reported from Connecticut in 1946, near the Sound, and was soon prevalent on Long Island. It has also invaded Rhode Island, and in New Jersey by 1953 it was devastating to nearly every garden. The upper leaf surface is mottled gray or entirely blanched, the undersurface stained with dark, molasseslike spots of excrement; inflorescence is poor; plants may die in a few years from repeated loss of vitality. The adults are about ⅛ x 1⁄16 inch, with intensely black hood and wing veins. Overwintering eggs are imbedded at random over underside of leaves and hatch much earlier than most lace bugs, sometimes late April in New Jersey, mid-May in Connecticut. There may be nearly 60 dark, spiny nymphs on a single leaf and they go through 5 molts to adult form in 2 or 3 weeks. There may be 4 or 5 generations a season with some adults still alive in December.

Control. I have had excellent results with lindane, using 1 tablespoon of 25 per cent wettable powder to a gallon of water, spraying soon after first nymphs hatch in May and repeating if necessary for a later brood. Reinfestation may come from untreated gardens within several hundred feet. Experiments at the Connecticut Experiment Station showed that DDT, chlordane, lindane, heptachlor, aldrin, dieldrin, and endrin were all effective for this lace bug. Malathion is also recommended, 1 teaspoon of an emulsion per gallon.

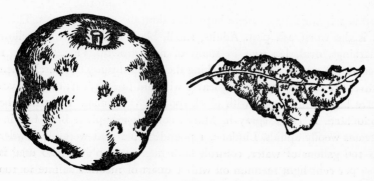

40. Red bug injury to apple fruit and foliage.

Apple Red Bug (*Lygidea mendax*)—Distributed east of the Mississippi River, more destructive in New York and New England to nearly all varieties of apples; may also attack pear, hawthorn, and wild crab. The active, bright red bugs, ¼ inch long, fly readily from tree to tree. Leaves are curled with numerous small sunken spots, each marking where the insect beak has punctured the surface. The fruit is deformed, pitted in a dimpled effect, sometimes russeted; the texture is woody. The bugs winter in the egg stage in lenticels on the bark on smaller branches, and the nymphs appear in the early pink stage of apple bloom, puncturing leaves as they unfold, feeding on fruit as soon as it reaches ¼ inch in diameter. Adults appear in June and there is only 1 generation.

Control has been by a dormant or delayed dormant oil and nicotine spray against nymphs and adults. DDT at the rate of 2 pounds 50 per cent wettable powder per 100 gallons of water is applied as a calyx spray at petal fall by many orchardists. Home gardeners with dwarf apples can use a 5 per cent dust.

Ash Lace Bug (*Leptophya minor*)—Also called ash tingid, common in California, reported from Arizona. This differs from other lace bugs in having a brown compact body, with darker dorsal markings without lacy lateral lobes. Adults hibernate in or near trees, lay eggs in April, and generations follow at monthly intervals until October. The leaves are whitened and covered with black spots on the undersurface, the injury increasing during the summer. Lindane used as for the ash plant bug will control lace bugs if repeated 2 weeks after the first application.

Ash Plant Bug (*Neoborus amoenus,* eastern species; *N. illitus* common in California; *N. pacificus,* Oregon and California)—The California ash mirid seems more important than the eastern species. There it is the worst ash pest. Adults, small, black or brown with yellow markings, oval, lay eggs in stems of new growth. There is only 1 generation a year, the eggs hatching the next February or March when leaves are developing. Young leaves wilt and turn brown; older leaves have large white areas with black spots of excrement. Trees may be defoliated. A DDT spray in March controls ash plant bugs but increases woolly aphids. Lindane, 1 pound 25 per cent wettable powder to 100 gallons of water, controls both bugs and aphids. Also used is 1½ per cent light medium oil with 1 quart of nicotine sulfate to 100 gallons, applied in March or April.

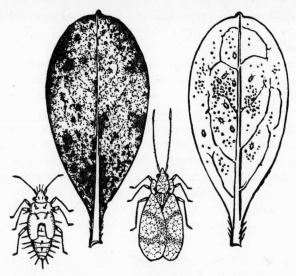

41. Azalea lace bug, showing loss of color from upper leaf surface, excrement and nymphs on lower surface; nymph and adult enlarged.

Azalea Lace Bug (*Stephanitis pyrioides*)—A major pest of azaleas wherever they are grown. Nymphs and adults suck sap from underside of leaves, resulting in grayish splotched, stippled, or blanched appearance of the upper surface. The injury is most unsightly and the plant vitality greatly reduced. The small adult, ⅛ inch long, has lacy wings with brown and black markings, light brown legs and antennae. The nymphs are nearly colorless at first, later black and spiny. Elongate eggs laid in leaf tissues along the veins hatch in 20 to 25 days, the life cycle being completed in 35 to 45 days. There are 2 or more generations. The rusty color of the underside of leaves from excrement is a diagnostic sign of lace bugs.

In Alabama overwintered eggs start hatching in February, building up a dense population during March, April, and May; another brood comes along in July, August, and September. In New Jersey eggs start hatching in late May or early June, slightly later than rhododendron lace bugs. The second brood builds up a heavy population in August and September and even later, with evergreen azaleas of the *amoena* or *hinodegiri* type appearing entirely coffee-colored and foliage of deciduous azaleas stippled grayish.

Control. Former recommendations called for nicotine sulfate and soap sprays in the North, applied when nymphs were present, and for a white oil emulsion with derris in the South. DDT has also been recommended but increases southern red mite. At present lindane seems highly satisfactory, 1 tablespoon of a 25 per cent wettable powder to 1 gallon of water. A second treatment may be desirable 10 days after the first, and a late summer spray for the second brood.

Big-legged Bug (*Ancanthocephala femorata*)—The largest plant bug in Florida, common on early potatoes. It is brown, more than an inch long, with hind legs much enlarged. Its sucking causes tops to wilt. Hand-picking is often sufficient control; sunflowers have been used as a trap crop. Eliminate thistles, the weed host.

Birch Lace Bug (*Corythucha pallipes*)—Principally on yellow birch, also on white birch, eastern hornbeam, willow, mountain-ash, and maple.

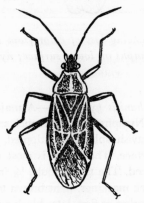

42. Boxelder bug.

Boxelder Bug (*Leptocoris trivittatus*)—A pest where boxelder is grown as a shade tree, more of a nuisance in the Mississippi Valley, but also present in Delaware and some other eastern states. The nymphs are bright red; the adults are brownish black with 3 red stripes on the thorax and red veins on the wings, flat, narrowly oval, ½ inch long. They feed on the flowers, fruits, foliage, and tender twigs of boxelder, sometimes on ash, maple, fruit trees. They are actually more of a nuisance in houses than on trees, swarming in to hibernate in fall or else congregating in great numbers on porches, walls, and walks. They cannot bite food or clothing, but they may feed on house plants.

Control. Spraying tree trunks, sunny walls of houses, etc., where bugs congregate with 2 per cent lindane, chlordane, or toxaphene kills a high percentage of insects with some residual effect. Spraying with pyrethrum, derris, or nicotine sulfate at twice the strength used for aphids kills those bugs wet with the spray but has no residual effect. For houses, try one of the new bombs for house plants containing pyrethrum and rotenone. If the bugs continue to be too much of a nuisance remove all pistillate boxelder trees near the house.

Ceanothus Lace Bug (*Corythucha obliqua*)—Common on ceanothus in California, Oregon, and Idaho. The body is black, wings pale, marked with brown.

Chinch Bug (*Blissus leucopterus*)—Distributed throughout the United States, but especially injurious in the Mississippi, Ohio, and Missouri River valleys, and in Texas and Oklahoma. See Hairy Chinch Bug for the species common on eastern lawns. The species discussed here is a grain pest, causes barley, wheat, rye, oats, corn, and sorghum plants to wilt and die, but another form (*Blissus leucopterus insularis*) is harmful to St. Augustine grass in Florida and elsewhere in the Gulf states, causing yellow spots in turf which turn brown when the grass dies. The chinch bug has caused enormous damage to corn and grain crops for more than a century and a half, the losses in 1 year in 1 state running up to $40,000,000.

This very small bug, ⅙ inch long, black with white wings, which have a triangular black patch in the middle of the outer margins, and red legs, gives off a distinctive vile odor when crushed. It hibernates as an adult in hedgerows, stubble, and clumps of prairie grasses. When the days warm up to 70°F. the bugs fly to the grain fields, feed by sucking sap, mate and lay eggs behind lower leaf sheaths of the plants, on the roots, or on the ground. One female lays several hundred eggs, at the rate of 15 to 20 a day. They hatch in 2 weeks into minute brick-red nymphs with a white band across the middle. They darken as they grow older, acquiring wings and the black and white color at the last molt. As the grain ripens and plants dry up, they migrate, usually while still wingless, by crawling to a field of young corn or sorghum. There they mature, mate and lay eggs for a second generation, on corn or grasses, adults of which fly to winter quarters for hibernation. In the Southwest, however, there are usually 3 generations instead of 2. In Florida, the chinch bugs feed throughout life, for 3 or more generations, on St. Augustine grass.

Control. Farmers can reduce food supply of chinch bugs by not growing small grains in an area where corn is the main crop or by substituting legumes for corn in an area where small grains are of chief importance. Ample fertilizer and early planting reduce chinch bug injury; some corn strains are resistant. Barriers to prevent crawling bugs from reaching the new crop are used effectively: dieldrin at the rate of ½ pound per acre in strips 4 rods wide between grain and cornfields; or a ridge of earth turned up with a plow and a line of coal-tar creosote applied along the brow of the ridge; or a band of dust, DDT or a dinitro such as DNOC. Florida lawns can be dusted with 5 per cent chlordane or 10 per cent DDT at the rate of 5 pounds per 1000 square feet.

Chrysanthemum Lace Bug (*Corythucha marmorata*)—Common in many areas (though I seldom see it in New Jersey), bleaching foliage, injuring stems of chrysanthemum, aster, scabiosa. The nymphs are spiny and leave dark, resinous spots of excreta on underside of leaves; adults have lacy wings and hood. They breed on weeds, frequently goldenrod. Spray or dust with lindane, nicotine, or pyrethrum.

Cotton Stainer (*Dysdercus suturellus*)—A southern cotton insect also injurious to hibiscus, sometimes staining eggplant and orange fruit. It stains the lint red or yellow when it punctures the seeds in cotton bolls. The bugs are narrow, long-legged, up to ⅗ inch long, with a bright red thorax and brown wings crossed with yellow. Control nymphs with strong contact insecticides; hand-pick adults.

Eggplant Lace Bug (*Gargaphia solani*)—On eggplant and other solanaceous hosts.

Elm Lace Bug (*Corythucha ulmi*)—Found only on American elm but wherever this grows. Foliage may lose color as early as mid-June; new leaves sometimes die. Adults winter in leaves on ground. Control with a contact insecticide.

False Chinch Bug (*Nysius ericae*)—Similar to but even smaller than the chinch bug. A pest of avocado, sometimes killing young trees, of beets, especially sugar beets, cabbage and other crucifers, sometimes corn. It is more important in semi-arid areas. The nymphs feed on weeds and grasses, only the adults on cultivated plants, where they can be controlled with nicotine sulfate or other contact insecticide. For avocado, 5 per cent chlordane dust is helpful.

Four-lined Plant Bug (*Poecilocapsus lineatus*)—A general plant pest east of the Rocky Mountains, attacking fruits, chiefly currant and gooseberry, mint and many ornamentals, with chrysanthemums most injured if the bug is in the neighborhood. The sucking causes round depressed spots, usually tan, sometimes nearly white or almost black, on foliage of acanthopanax, aconite, aster, chrysanthemum, coreopsis, dahlia, delphinium, forsythia, gaillardia, globe thistle, goldenglow, heliopsis, heliotrope, honeysuckle, lavender, lupine, morning glory, peony, poppy, rose, snapdragon, Shasta daisy, sunflower, sweetpea, weigela, zinnia, and other flowers and shrubs. The injury varies some-what with the plant, aconite showing dark spots and chrysanthemums many round light tan areas on new leaves and sometimes the whole tip wilting. This is one of the few enemies of mint, and young leaves are often covered with black rather angular spots.

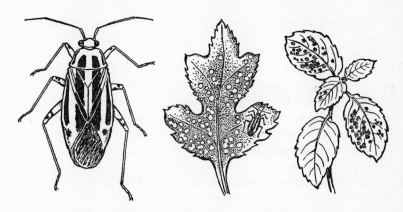

43. Four-lined plant bug, and injury to chrysanthemum and mint.

Slender white eggs winter in slits in canes of currant and other plants. They hatch in May or June into bright red nymphs with black dots on the thorax, but when they change to adults they are greenish yellow with four wide black stripes down the wings. There is only 1 genera-tion a year, with feeding injury to plants lasting about 6 weeks. Usually these bugs stop about the time Japanese beetles begin.

Control. Ornamentals can be dusted with 5 per cent DDT or sprayed with DDT (using 3 level tablespoons 50 per cent wettable to a gallon of water) or with nicotine sulfate, rotenone, or pyrethrum. Use 1 per cent rotenone dust for edible plant parts. Start treatment early, as soon as the first nymphs appear.

Garden Fleahopper (*Halticus bracteatus*)—General except in the far western states. The small bugs look something like aphids and suck sap from stems and foliage in the same manner, but they jump like flea beetles. The nymphs are greenish, adults black, $\frac{1}{10}$ inch long or less, with long legs, and antennae longer than the body. They appear sporadically on many vegetables—bean, beet, celery, corn, cowpea, cucumber, eggplant, lettuce, pea, pepper, potato, pumpkin, squash, sweetpotato, tomato—and on various ornamentals—chrysanthemum, gladiolus, marigold, morning glory, verbena, zinnia, and others. The foliage has small pale or whitish spots and heavily infested leaves are killed. Plants in shade are preferred. Fleahoppers winter as adults in trash and there can be up to 5 generations a season.

Control weeds. Spray twice with DDT, 1 level tablespoon of 50 per cent wettable powder per gallon, or with nicotine sulfate, $1\frac{1}{4}$ teaspoons per gallon with soap, or dust with 1 per cent DDT, or 3 per cent nicotine.

Green Stink Bug (*Acrosternum hilare*)—A large oval, bright green bug, $\frac{5}{8}$ inch long, bad-smelling. It is a special pest of beans, causing pods to fall, distorting seeds, and of peaches and nectarines, which are "catfaced" by the feeding punctures. It is also found occasionally on apple, boxelder, cabbage, catalpa, corn, dogwood, eggplant, elderberry, linden, maple, mustard, okra, orange, pea, tomato, and turnip. Spraying with a strong soap solution containing rotenone or pyrethrum is somewhat effective.

Hairy Chinch Bug (*Blissus leucopterus hirtus*)—A lawn pest in the Northeast, killing the grass in brown patches similar to fungus brown patch or Japanese beetle injury. The hairy chinch bug differs from the chinch bug in that the adults are predominantly short-winged. They winter in tall grass and weeds, migrating to the lawn in April or May to lay eggs at the grass roots. When the soil temperature is high enough, usually in June, the bright red nymphs, with a white crossband, start sucking at the base of grass blades. They darken and grow a little larger as they go through various molts, with a brownish stage before they change to black adults with short white wings. The females lay eggs for a second and more disastrous brood which appears in August with nymphs and adults continuing to feed into October. In November the adults either settle down in the lawn or, more often, migrate to tall grasses for winter.

Injury is most serious in hot, dry weather and where grass is in full sun. Chinch bugs show a preference for bent grasses but are not limited to them. Grass blades are punctured close to the roots and are often stained reddish. The brown, more or less circular areas are usually surrounded by a sickly yellow margin where the bugs have just started feeding. When you cannot roll the grass back like a carpet you can suspect chinch bugs rather than beetle grubs as the cause, but you must see them to be sure. This is difficult unless you get nearly flat on the ground, part the grass blades, and gaze intently at one area for a few minutes. Flooding part of the lawn with warm water and covering it with a piece of white cloth is said to bring up the bugs onto the underside of the cloth, but I have not tried it.

Control. Chlordane is quick-acting and effective. Use 5 pounds of 5 per cent dust, mixed with fine sand, to 100 square feet. Apply with a fertilizer spreader or broadcast evenly by hand. Or use 10 per cent DDT dust at 6 pounds per 1000 square feet (this is slower-acting but has a long residual effect) or use 2½ pounds 5 per cent dieldrin dust or 10 per cent sabadilla dust. There are many commercial preparations for chinch bug control. Some combine chlordane and DDT. The first treatment is made in June, when the bugs start action, the second in August, unless you kill enough bugs in June so there is no second brood. Keep grass growing vigorously by proper liming, fertilizing, and cutting; keep down weeds and tall grass in areas adjacent to the lawn.

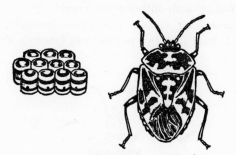

44. Harlequin bug and eggs.

Harlequin Bug (*Murgantia histrionica*)—The most important pest of cabbage and related crops in the southern half of the United States. Crucifers, cabbage, cauliflower, collards, cress, mustard, Brussels sprouts, turnip, kohlrabi, radish, horseradish, are favored food plants, but the bugs may wander over to asparagus, bean, beet, citrus, cherry, chrysanthemum, corn, eggplant, grape, lettuce, locust, loquat, okra, plum, potato, rose, squash, and sunflower. The bugs are black with bright red markings, flat, ⅜ inch long. They winter around old cabbage stalks and other garden rubbish and lay distinctive eggs on underside of leaves of early garden crops. They look like tiny white barrels with black hoops, and they stand on end in a double row. They hatch in 4 to 7 days, and the nymphs suck so much sap that cabbages wilt, turn brown, and die. Whole crops may be lost. There are usually 3 generations a season.

Control. Dust with 10 per cent DDT or toxaphene until edible plant parts are formed, then use rotenone or 20 per cent sabadilla dust. Keep weeds down; hand-pick bugs in spring.

Hawthorn Lace Bug (*Corythucha cydoniae*)—Found on English hawthorn and other thorns, cotoneaster, pyracantha, Japanese quince. I find this small, dark lace bug, with spiny nymphs, very common on English hawthorn in New Jersey, prevalent in midsummer, but in the mid-South it is more serious on pyracantha, with the first brood at work by April and a late brood still going strong in October. The upper surface of leaves loses color in a speckled fashion while the undersurface is colored with dark bits of excrement. This species winters as an adult and the eggs are laid on new leaves in clusters, each standing on end and covered with a black conical mass. Spray with lindane, or malathion, or nicotine sulfate and soap for the nymph stage, treating underside of foliage with sufficient pressure.

Horned Squash Bug (*Anasa armigera*)—Southern Squash Bug, similar to the Squash Bug, but feeding and breeding also on cabbage and collards.

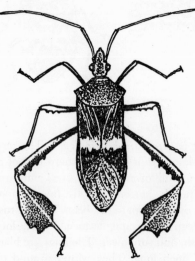

45. *Leaf-footed bug.*

Leaf-footed Bug (*Leptoglossus phyllopus*)—Present in the Southeast and as far west as Arizona. The bug is dark brown with a yellow band across the body, ¾ inch long, and with hind legs expanded like a leaf. It attacks pecans and many garden crops, with potatoes, beans, cowpeas, and tomatoes great favorites. It likes sunflower, may swarm on Satsuma oranges and tangerines, and breeds on thistle. Hand-picking and a strong soap spray on a cloudy day or late afternoon have been recommended in the past. DDT is now used for potatoes. Sabadilla dust is useful for bugs in this hard-to-kill group.

Lygus Bugs (*Lygus hesperus, L. elisus,* other species)—Small, flat bugs, greenish to yellowish brown, somewhat mottled, ¼ inch long, relatives of tarnished plant bugs. They are pests of peaches, pears, and apple in the Pacific Northwest, infesting leaf buds, puncturing young fruit. They also injure many legumes, ornamentals, and trees throughout the Rocky Mountain and Pacific states. Dusting with DDT is helpful, but a miticide should be added.

Negro Bug (*Corimelaena pulicaria*)—Distributed generally east of the Rocky Mountains. The bugs are short, black, oval, ⅒ inch long, with an enlarged hard thoracic shield which makes them look like small beetles. They winter as adults and lay eggs singly on leaves. They hatch in 2 weeks and congregate in great numbers, sporadically, on corn, wheat, celery, and other crops, causing wilting and death. They also feed on lobelia, cardinal flower, and other ornamentals, and some fruits, imparting a bad taste to raspberries and blackberries. Spraying with nicotine sulfate, 2 teaspoons to a gallon, plus soap, will kill all bugs wet with the spray.

Oak Lace Bug (*Corythucha arcuata*)—On various species of oak through eastern states north of the Carolinas. Feeding by great numbers of lace bugs on underside of leaves turns them white. They may curl, turn brown, and drop prematurely. The lace bugs winter as adults or eggs and there are 2 generations with damage usually conspicuous in midsummer. Spray with lindane, DDT, or nicotine sulfate when nymphs hatch, and repeat in 2 weeks.

One-spot Stink Bug (*Euschistus variolarius*)—Also called Spined Stink Bug, Brown Stink Bug. It is brown, shield-shaped, about ¾ inch long. It feeds on fruits of eggplant, tomato, and other plants, causing depressed blemishes known as catfacing.

Orchid Plant Bug (*Tenthecoris bicolor*)—Causes irregular white spots on underside of orchid leaves. The bug has an orange to red body with black and steel-blue wings. Use a contact spray safe for orchids.

Pameras (*Pachybrachius bilobata*)—Very small bugs, related to chinch bugs, often destructive to strawberries in Florida. Nymphs look like yellow ants; adults are black with yellow markings, about ⅕ inch long. They appear in strawberry beds toward the end of the season, turning young berries into hard buttons; plants wither. Destroy wild spurge, the weed host; apply nicotine or other contact spray with force down into crowns of plants.

Pear Plant Bug (*Neolygus communis*)—Also called Green Apple Bug or False Tarnished Plant Bug. The pear bug resembles the tarnished plant bug but is smaller and darker except at tips of wings. It winters on bark; nymphs hatching in early spring injure young fruits by feeding punctures, causing drop or deformities. A DDT dust or nicotine spray directed at the nymphs should give control.

Phlox Plant Bug (*Lopidea davisi*)—A pest of perennial phlox. The active bugs, dull orange or reddish with a black stripe on the back, feed on the upper surface of the more tender leaves and on buds, causing white or pale green spots. The plant may be stunted, occasionally killed; the blossom head loses its symmetry. There are 2 or more generations. Eggs are laid in fall in phlox stems behind leaf petioles and begin to hatch early in May. Cut and burn old stalks after first frost; rake up all debris in bed. Spray when bugs appear with strong pyrethrum or nicotine (3 teaspoons nicotine sulfate with soap to a gallon of water) or dust with a mixture of 3 parts sulfur to 1 part pyrethrum dust or with DDT.

Red-and-Black Stink Bug (*Cosmopepla bimaculata*)—A small, shining black and red bug, ⅓ inch long, with a disagreeable odor. It sucks on snapdragon, beard-tongue, columbine, verbascum, and other flowering plants, and winters as an adult in protected places.

Rhododendron Lace Bug (*Stephanitis rhododendri*)—A European pest important from New England to Ohio and south to the Carolinas, also present, though not so injurious, in the Pacific Northwest. The injury is prominent when plants are growing in full sun, the whole shrub having a yellow cast, while individual leaves are mottled with a fine stippling of creamy-white or grayish dots, each indicating where the bug has inserted its beak on the underside. The small, spined nymphs with light and dark areas on their flat bodies hatch in late spring, mid-May near Philadelphia, late May or early June near New York City. They start as a group of dark specks and the undersurface of leaves is covered with bits of excrement looking like dots of dark molasses when fresh, later giving the leaf a mottled rusty appearance on the undersurface. This is an excellent diagnostic sign of lace bug injury even when the bugs themselves cannot be seen.

The nymphs move about very little, and then with a peculiar side-wise motion. They turn into adults during June, acquiring beautiful wings, twice as long as the body, rounded at the apex, with veins in a lacy pattern (Plate XVII). They insert eggs, covered with brownish scabs, in irregular rows along the midrib. There are 2 generations a year, the second brood appearing in July, maturing in August, and depositing overwintering eggs in the leaves. Rhododendrons are rarely killed by lace bugs, but infestations unchecked from year to year result in yellowed, sickly bushes and a gradual decline in vigor.

Control. Almost any good contact insecticide applied with pressure to the undersurface of leaves soon after nymphs hatch should be effective. Nicotine sulfate, 1½ teaspoons plus 1 ounce of soap to a gallon of water, has been standard in the past but lindane and malathion are now preferred for their residual effect. I use lindane at the rate of 1 tablespoon of 25 per cent wettable powder to a gallon of water and malathion emulsion at 1 teaspoon per gallon. DDT is also effective, but it also encourages a new scale on rhododendrons in my area. A second spray 2 weeks after the first may be necessary for late-hatching nymphs and possibly a third for the second brood in July.

Say Stink Bug (*Chlorochroa sayi*)—A western plant bug distributed east to Kansas, flat, bright green with 3 orange spots and minute white specks, ½ inch long. It destroys wheat, wilts potato shoots, feeds on asparagus, bean, pea, sunflower, grains, grasses, and weeds.

Southern Green Stink Bug (*Nezara viridula*)—Prevalent in Florida and other Gulf states, commonly known as the pumpkin bug, similar to the green stink bug of the North but somewhat larger. It breeds on cowpeas and other legumes grown as a summer crop in Florida, dwarfing pods, causing drop; then attacks citrus fruits and pecans, causing black pit and kernel spot of the nuts. Although the feeding adult is bright green, the hibernating form may be dark olive green or pinkish. The nymphs are bluish with red markings, and almost circular in form. There are 4 or 5 generations a season. The bugs may also feed on eggplant, potato, okra, and sunflower. Control is difficult. Hand-picking has been advocated for adults, knocking them off into a pan with a little kerosene early in the morning or on cloudy days when the bugs are sluggish. To protect orchards, avoid a legume cover crop in summer. The older insecticides are not effective; DDT and other chlorinated hydrocarbons are effective but leave a toxic residue on food plants. Sabadilla dust, 10 to 20 per cent, is safe and probably effective.

Squash Bug (*Anasa tristis*)—Distributed throughout the country, attacking all vine crops with preference for squash and pumpkin, gourds and melons next (Plate XII). During the feeding process the squash bug apparently injects a toxic substance into the vines, causing a wilting known as Anasa wilt of cucurbits, closely resembling bacterial wilt, a true disease of cucurbits. After wilting, the vines turn black and crisp; small plants are killed entirely; larger vines have several runners affected. The bugs may be so numerous no squashes are formed, or they may congregate in dense clusters on unripe fruits.

The adult is dark brown, sometimes mottled with gray or light brown, hard-shelled, ⅝ inch long. It gives off such a disagreeable odor when crushed it is commonly called a stink bug, but true stink bugs belong to a related family. Unmated adults hibernate in shelter of dead leaves, vines, boards, or buildings and fly to cucurbits when vines start to run. Mating takes place at that time. Clusters of brownish eggs are laid in angles between veins on underside of leaves and hatch in 7 to 14 days into nymphs with green abdomen, crimson head, thorax, and legs. Older nymphs are a somber grayish white with dark legs. There are 5 molts before the winged adult. There is usually 1 generation a year.

Control. Sanitation is the primary control measure. Remove all rubbish offering winter protection; stimulate plant growth with fertilizer; hand-pick adults and leaves bearing eggs. Dusting the vines with 10 to 20 per cent sabadilla dust will kill the nymphs. Do not use DDT or any dust containing sulfur; both are injurious to squashes. Nicotine or pyrethrum dust will kill young nymphs but not mature bugs. Some squash varieties are rather resistant; winter squashes, hubbards and marrows, are very susceptible. A tachinid fly is a hard-working parasite.

Sycamore Lace Bug (*Corythucha ciliata*)—Widely distributed and common on sycamore, recorded occasionally from ash, hickory, and mulberry. The adults are small, ⅛ inch long, but with wide, flat, white lacelike wings and prominent lacy projections from the thorax. They winter under bark and in spring glue black eggs along ribs on underside of leaves. The nymphs are light-colored, spiny, and their feeding turns foliage white. There are 2 generations and injury resulting in defoliation may be severe on street and shade trees. Two sprays, with a 2-week interval, of lindane, malathion, or nicotine sulfate and soap should give adequate control.

Sycamore Plant Bug (*Plagiognathus albatus*)—Recorded from Connecticut, New Jersey, New York, Pennsylvania, and District of Columbia. Nymphs are tan or brown with dark eyes and brown spots on wings, ⅛ inch long. Their feeding produces small, irregular yellowish or reddish spots over leaves and sometimes holes where dead tissue drops out. Nicotine sulfate, 1 to 600 dilution with soap, has given control. The first spray is applied in early May, the second 10 days later.

Tarnished Plant Bug (*Lygus lineolaris*)—Found throughout the country (Plate V). It is injurious to more than 50 economic plants. Vegetables include bean, beet, cauliflower, cabbage, chard, celery, cucumber, potato, turnip; fruits include apple, peach, pear, strawberry, occasionally citrus. Among flowers, dahlias and asters are frequent victims and the bug occasionally injures calendula, chrysanthemum, cosmos, gladiolus, impatiens, marigold, poppy, salvia, sunflower, verbena, zinnia, and others. The toxin liberated in the plant by the feeding process of the bug causes deformed beet and chard leaves, black joints of celery, blackened terminal shoots and dwarfed pitted fruit of peach, buds dying or opening to imperfect flowers on dahlia.

The adult is small, ¼ inch long, flattened, oval, irregularly mottled with white, yellow and black splotches giving a generally "tarnished" appearance, but with a clear yellow triangle, marked with a black dot, on the lower third of each side. Adults hibernate among weeds, under leaves, stones, or bark, flying early in spring to feed on fruit-tree buds, then migrating to other plants to lay eggs in leaves or flowers. Nymphs are very small, greenish yellow, marked with 4 black dots on the thorax and 1 on the abdomen. The cycle takes 3 to 4 weeks and there are 3 to 5 generations a season. In the South feeding and breeding continue through the winter. Young terminal shoots of dahlia turn black; buds are blasted; small spots appear on the leaves.

Control. The tarnished plant bug has been very hard to control, most efforts being put on removing weeds and trash in the fall to prevent overwintering. Now DDT is quite effective. Apply a 3 to 5 per cent dust, or a spray of 2 level tablespoons 50 per cent wettable powder to a gallon of water, to flower buds as they start to form; repeat just before they open. Peaches can be sprayed with DDT at full bloom or at petal fall. Sabadilla dust is useful for edible plant parts near harvest.

Toyon Lace Bug (*Corythucha incurvata*)—A most disfiguring pest of the lovely red-berried photinia or toyon, California Christmasberry, limited to California and Arizona. The nymphs are dirty brown with spines; adults are yellowish brown. Eggs are inserted in underside of leaves and covered with a brown, sticky, cone-shaped mass. Nymphs and adults secrete quantities of honeydew, a medium for black sooty mold. There are several broods a year, with adults hibernating under bark and leaves. Spray with lindane, malathion, or nicotine sulfate.

Walnut Lace Bug (*Corythucha juglandis*)—Occasionally abundant on walnut, butternut, basswood, and linden. This pale yellow or brown lace bug, with a brown band on the wings, can be controlled with an early application of a contact insecticide.

Western Leaf-footed Bug (*Leptoglossus zonatus*)—Ranging from New Mexico into Arizona and southern California. The bug is large, ¾ inch, brown with 2 yellow spots on thorax, and with leaflike enlargement of hind legs. It breeds on pomegranate, where it is thought to spread heart-rot disease. It may damage orange trees, limes, cotton, dates, or watermelon. It also occurs in Florida.

Willow Lace Bug (*Corythucha mollicula*)—Limited to willow, which it may seriously injure when present in large numbers.

Yucca Plant Bug (*Halticotoma valida*)—Long known in the Southwest, now also found in the Southeast. The leaves are stippled, covered with black specks of excrement, and turn yellowish. The adult is small but stout, ⅛ inch long, blue black, with reddish-brown head and thorax. It does not fly readily but runs fast. The nymphs are bright scarlet and may be numerous on leaves. Spray with nicotine, pyrethrum, DDT, or other contact insecticide.

BUTTERFLIES

Butterflies, along with moths, belong to the order Lepidoptera. Their wings, usually large and beautiful, are covered with tiny overlapping scales that rub off like dust on the fingers. Their brilliant iridescent coloring comes from light refracted by many fine ridges on these scales and not actual pigmentation. Antennae of butterflies usually end in knobs, while those of moths are feathery. Butterflies are day fliers, moths nocturnal. Their mouth parts, adapted for getting nectar out of the throats of flowers, are formed into a long tube, proboscis or tongue, which is coiled beneath the head like a watch spring when not in use. Eggs are laid in exposed places singly or in small groups. Larvae are caterpillars, sometimes called "worms." The pupae, chrysalids, of butterflies are not enclosed in cocoons but are attached to the surface of a leaf or stem by a silken disk, sometimes also by a silken band around the middle. Only the larval stage is destructive to living plant tissue. The adults do no harm as they sip nectar and many are valuable pollinators. Some of the caterpillars, too, are beneficial, acting as scavengers or eating other insects, serving as food for birds.

Only those families of interest to gardeners are given here, followed by descriptions of a few species named for their adult state. Those named for the larval stage are discussed under Caterpillars.

Hesperiidae. Skippers, a connecting link between moths and butterflies. They are mostly small, wingspread seldom more than 1½ inches, and they are named for their erratic, close-to-the-ground flight habit, a kind of skipping. The antennae are not knobbed but have a short hook, pointed backward. At rest, the fore wings are held vertically, the hind wings partially spread. The bodies are more robust than most butterflies. The larva has a large, bulbous head, separated from the rest of the body by a narrowly constricted neck. They tie leaves together with silk for their nests.

Papilionidae. Swallowtails. Our largest butterflies, brightly colored, most with tail-like extensions of their hind wings. The caterpillars are large, smooth-skinned, with a forked, malodorous retractile organ that can be thrust out from an opening in the first thoracic segment just back of the head.

Pieridae. The pierids, or whites, sulfurs, and orange-tips, including the common cabbage butterfly. They are average size, frequent open fields and roadsides. Fore and hind wings are nearly the same size but the latter are rounded. Color differences between the sexes and seasonal color variations may be striking. The larvae are slender, greenish or whitish with longitudinal stripes.

Danaidae. Milkweed butterflies, bright colored, feeding on Asclepias. There are only 2 common species, the familiar monarch and the queen, known in the Southwest.

Nymphalidae. Four-footed butterflies. The fore legs are much reduced and not fitted for walking; antennae are very distinctly knobbed; coloring, patterns, and wing outlines vary greatly; larvae are usually spiny. Mourning-cloak, painted lady, red admiral, and viceroy are in this group.

Black Swallowtail—See Celeryworm under Caterpillars.

Cabbage Butterfly—See Imported Cabbageworm under Caterpillars.

Checker Spot or Chalcedon Butterfly (*Euphydryas chalcedona*)— Adults have black wings covered with many yellow spots. Caterpillars are large, bluish black with small orange markings and numerous large black compound spines. They feed on aster, buddleia, chrysanthemum, Shasta daisy, monkeyflower, penstemon, veronica, and other plants. They often web the plants as they feed and are quite a garden pest in the Rocky Mountain and Pacific states.

Columbine Skipper (*Erynnis lucilius*)—The caterpillar, ¾ inch long, velvety green, rather stout with small black head, chews holes in columbine leaves and hides in a rolled-up leaf. The adult is a typical skipper with purplish wings. Spray or dust with lead arsenate or DDT.

Monarch Butterfly (*Danaus plexippus*)—Milkweed Butterfly, common, orange brown, with wings bordered and tipped with black. Eggs are laid on various species of milkweed and larvae feed on them. Caterpillars are yellow green marked with numerous crossbands of black. The jade-green chrysalid is held by a belt with spots of gold. This species migrates south, roosting in trees at night like flocks of birds.

Mourning-cloak Butterfly (*Nymphalis antiopa*)—Spiny Elm Caterpillar. This common species occurs all over America. The adults have purplish-brown wings bordered with a wide yellow stripe, inside of which is a row of blue or purple spots; wingspread 2½ to 3½ inches. They hide in autumn in nooks and crannies, including tree cavities, fly on sunny March days, but wait until May to deposit sculptured eggs in masses of 300 to 450 around a small branch. The larvae feed in groups on elm, poplar, willow, often defoliating branches. They are black, covered with small white dots and a row of orange or red spots along the back, and lengthwise rows of black, branched spines. They transform to chrysalids in late June or early July, with butterflies emerging in a few days to lay eggs for a second brood in August.

Spray with lead arsenate or DDT when larvae are young; cut and burn infested twigs and small branches. Several wasps are parasites. Yellow-billed cuckoos and some bugs are predators.

Painted Beauty (*Vanessa virginiensis*)—American Painted Lady, Hunter's Butterfly, ranging throughout North America. The caterpillars are banded dark purple, yellow, and green, with a short row of silver-white spots on each side of the back. They feed on thistles, hollyhock, mallow, malva, forget-me-not, senecio, sunflower. The butterflies are tortoise-marked, with 2 large eyespots on the hind wings.

Painted Lady (*Vanessa cardui*)—Thistle Butterfly, said to be the most widely distributed butterfly in the world; often abundant in the

West, sometimes in great migratory flights. The adult is large, 2½ inches across the wings, orange red with black and white markings. The caterpillar varies from green to brown mottled with black, has a light dorsal stripe and a yellow stripe along each side, grayish spines; it is 1¼ to 1½ inches long. It feeds on calendula and hollyhock, lupine, sunflower, as well as thistles, mallows, and weeds, often tying together terminal portions. The iridescent chrysalids seem to have been dipped in gold. There are at least 2 broods a year, with butterflies in evidence from early spring to late fall. Spray ornamentals with lead arsenate or other stomach poison. Remove infested tips.

Pine Butterfly (*Neophasia menapia*)—Chiefly a pest of coniferous forests in the West, where great areas of yellow pine and Douglas-fir are defoliated, followed by death of trees. The adults are white, marked with black, the larvae green with white stripes. A wasplike parasite is effective in bringing outbreaks under control in about 3 years. Meanwhile forests can be sprayed by airplane.

Pipevine Swallowtail (*Battus philenor*)—Feeding on and defoliating Dutchmans pipe. Caterpillars are dark brown with 4 rows of orange to coral spots and soft hornlike projections; they are 2 inches long. Adults are blue-green butterflies with white spots on undermargin of fore wings and yellow and orange spots on hind wings. Spray with lead arsenate or DDT.

Silver-spotted Skipper (*Epargyreus clarus*)—One of the largest of the skipper butterflies, feeding on locust and wisteria, sometimes causing serious defoliation. The caterpillar is leaf green with a dull red head and it fastens together several leaflets for a case in which it lives and feeds. The butterfly is brown and yellow with white triangular spots on the fore wings.

Spicebush Swallowtail (*Papilio troilus*)—Feeding on spicebush and sassafras, not too serious. Larva is 1½ inches long, largest on the third thoracic segment, pea green on top, sides yellow, head and underside pink, with 4 large and 10 small orange spots.

Tiger Swallowtail (*Papilio glaucus*)—Not very important but feeding on apple, ash, birch, cherry, lilac, poplar, and other trees. Larva is dark green, 1½ inches long, third thoracic segment enlarged and marked with a large yellow spot enclosing a purple spot on each side.

Viceroy (*Limenitis archippus*)—Like the monarch, feeding on poplar and willow. The head of the larva is green, bilobed, grooved vertically. The body segments are pink, brown, and green with tubercles.

CANKERWORMS

Cankerworms, often called inchworms or measuring worms, are larvae of small moths, family Geometridae. Two species in this group are obnoxious pests of fruit and shade trees and known as cankerworms; the others are called loopers or spanworms. They all move by a series of looping movements, drawing up the abdomen to the thorax in a loop, grasping the support by their prolegs (false legs at the end of the body), loosening the thoracic legs, stretching the body forward, and so on in rapid succession. They also have a habit of letting themselves down on a thread of silk.

Fall Cankerworm (*Alsophila pometaria*)—Distributed generally across the United States from North Carolina northward, a threat to fruit trees, apple preferred, but also feeding on apricot, cherry, plum, prune, and other fruits, and to shade trees, especially oak and elm, sometimes basswood or linden, birch, and maple. They even feed on rosebushes near apple trees.

The moths emerge from pupae in the ground in late fall, after there have been freezing temperatures. The males are brownish gray with a 1¼-inch wingspread; the females have wingless gray bodies, ½ inch long (Plate XVIII). They crawl up tree trunks to deposit eggs, grayish, shaped like a flowerpot, in a compact single-layered mass on main trunk or branches or around smaller twigs. They hatch in spring about the time leaves unfold and the larvae feed on foliage until June. The caterpillars are brownish above, green below, with 3 narrow white stripes along the body above the spiracles and a yellow stripe below, about an inch long. They often drop down from trees on a silken thread, climbing up again to resume feeding. There is only 1 generation a year and toward the end of their season they may eat conspicuous holes in leaves of rhododendron and other shrubs growing under or near favored food plants. When full grown they drop to the ground and pupate in a silken cocoon, 1 to 4 inches deep in the soil.

Control. Banding trees with a sticky material such as Tanglefoot, to prevent the wingless female from crawling up the tree to lay eggs, is a practice less popular now than some years ago, for it has been determined that young cankerworms balloon over via their silken threads from unbanded trees nearby and that actual foliage injury is reduced by only a small per cent. Also, unless properly applied to a band of paper or Balsam Wool around the trunk so that the Tanglefoot does not come in direct contact with the bark, there may be serious injury to the bark. The band should be in place by late September and the sticky surface scraped or renewed through the fall to prevent late arrivals from crawling up on the backs of their fallen comrades.

Spraying is far more effective as a control measure, and in seasons when a heavy infestation has been forecast property owners should arrange to have elms, oaks, and other trees preferred by cankerworms sprayed in late April or early May as soon as the leaves are out far enough to hold a poison. DDT, at the rate of 2 pounds 50 per cent wettable powder to 100 gallons of water, or in a 6 per cent emulsion for a mist blower, gives excellent control but brings other problems. Many arborists have gone back to lead arsenate, 3 pounds to 100 gallons of water. For woodland areas, spraying or dusting by airplane is practical. Of the many natural enemies of cankerworms, ground beetles should be recognized as special friends of man.

Spring Cankerworm (*Paleacrita vernata*)—Found from Maine to North Carolina, west to Texas and Colorado, and in California. Apple and elm are preferred hosts, then oak, hickory, cherry, maple, sometimes other fruit and shade trees. One of our oldest pests, a native known in New England for more than 200 years. Along with the fall cankerworm, it appears in cycles, being very abundant for 2 or 3 years, nearly defoliating trees in an area, feeding in such numbers you can actually hear the leaves being crunched, and dropping down on unwary pedestrians. Then they almost disappear for a few years and gradually recruit their armies for another peak of abundance. Trees defoliated every 2 or 3 years in succession may die.

The moths appear in early spring, sometimes on a warm day in February, more often in March. The females are wingless, about the same nondescript gray as the fall cankerworm, but they have a dark stripe down the back and transverse rows of stiff reddish spines on the first 7 joints of the abdomen. The male moths are silky gray with 3 transverse dark lines on the fore wings. They often appear around trees (and even in attics) about the time females are crawling up trunks to lay loose clusters of oval, brownish-purple eggs under bark scales on main trunk or branches. These hatch in about a month. The caterpillars vary from green to brown to nearly black, usually with a yellowish stripe under the spiracles, up to an inch long. They differ from fall cankerworms in having only 2 pairs of prolegs instead of 3.

Control measures are the same as for the fall cankerworm, except that if banding is practiced, Tanglefoot is applied or renewed in February. In apple orchards the codling moth spray schedule will also control cankerworms.

CASEBEARERS

Casebearers (family Coleophoridae) are moths whose larvae live in portable cases and feed or mine in leaves, fruits, flowers, or seeds. This is a small family and most of the American species belong to 1 genus, Coleophora. Casebearers of the genus Acrobasis (family Phycitidae) secrete their cases between leaves webbed together.

Birch Casebearer (*Coleophora salmani*)—First found in Maine in 1927 and spreading in that state, attacking all varieties of birch and speckled alder. The moth is very small, grayish brown with fringes on narrow hind wings. The caterpillar is light yellow to green, with a black head, ⅕ inch long. It lives in a small brown cylindrical case, mining and cutting holes in leaves. Badly mined foliage dries and trees appear scorched; buds may be eaten; twigs and limbs die back. There is 1 generation. Larvae hibernate in cases on twigs. Control with a dormant lime-sulfur spray, 1 to 8 dilution, in early spring.

California Casebearer (*Coleophora sacramenta*)—Willow is the normal host, but the larvae commonly feed on almond, apricot, apple, cherry, peach, plum, prune in the San Francisco Bay region of California. The moth is bluish white with gray scales, ⅝-inch wingspread; the larva is orange, making a black case widened at bottom with a winglike projection. There is 1 generation. Spraying with lead arsenate gives control.

Cherry Casebearer (*Coleophora pruniella*)—Normally feeding on wild cherry, but reported injuring cultivated cherries and sometimes apple in the Middle West and Oregon. It winters in its case attached to twigs, moving to young foliage in spring, producing skeletonized and dead areas as it grows and enlarges the case with leaf tissue. Pupation is in late spring. Moths lay eggs on underside of leaves and new caterpillars are making overwintering cases by late summer. There are several natural parasites. A dormant dinitro spray is effective.

Cigar Casebearer (*Coleophora occidentis*)—General in apple-growing regions, attacking apple, except Jonathan variety, pear, plum, cherry, hawthorn, quince. The light brown partly grown larva hibernates inside a cigar-shaped, brownish-gray silken case, about ¼ inch long, attached to twigs or branches, and starts feeding as buds unfold in spring. It feeds until July, making blotch mines between the leaf surfaces, then pupates and produces mottled gray moths with narrow fringed wings, ½-inch wingspread. Eggs are laid on underside of leaves with larvae appearing in late summer to make new cases. The ordinary apple spray schedule should take care of casebearers. Spraying at the cluster bud stage with lead arsenate, DDT, or nicotine sulfate 1 to 800 is effective.

Elm Casebearer (*Coleophora limosipennella*)—A European insect established in the Northeast favoring English, Scotch, and American elms in local outbreaks. The moth, buff-colored with gray markings, appears in July. The larvae and their cases are dark brown and the mines are between the principal veins of the leaves. Elms sprayed for cankerworms and leaf beetles will not suffer from this pest.

Larch Casebearer (*Coleophora laricella*)—Another European pest, first noted in Massachusetts in 1886 and now found throughout the range of American and European larch in the eastern half of the country. The moth is silver gray, appears from late May to July. The dark, reddish-brown larva feeds as a miner until September when it constructs its case for winter hibernation. When larvae are abundant the needles turn white and die, growth is checked, and the tree weakened. Spray with lime-sulfur, dormant strength, in spring before growth starts. There are many natural parasites, but they do not give sufficient control.

Pecan Casebearer (*Coleophora caryaefoliella*)—Found from New Hampshire to Florida and Texas on pecan, hickory, and black walnut. The moth is brownish, the larva reddish with a black head and the case is brown, cigar-shaped, ¼ inch long. Mined areas turn brown and sometimes drop out, leaving holes in foliage. There may also be some defoliation. Spray hickories with lead arsenate at 3 pounds per 100 gallons of water and pecans with lead arsenate at 2 pounds per 100 with the addition of 6 pounds hydrated lime, or with DDT.

Pecan Leaf Casebearer (*Acrobasis juglandis*)—Present in the southern part of the pecan belt, from southern Georgia and northern Florida to Texas. The moths are variable, white, gray, brown, or black. The very small larvae feed on young buds and leaves and are damaging chiefly to weakened plants which cannot grow faster than the larvae can eat. Control for the pecan nut casebearer takes care of this species.

Pecan Nut Casebearer (*Acrobasis caryae*)—A most serious pecan pest, especially in Texas, often damaging in the other Gulf states, destroying a large percentage of the crop. The larva is olive green, ½ inch long; the moth is dark gray with ¾-inch wingspread. The larva winters in a hibernaculum, small cocoon, at the base of a bud. In spring larvae feed on buds and bore into tender shoots, pupating in tunnels. The moths, emerging in May, deposit eggs on the nuts. The young larvae spin a web around several nuts, then enter to feed. This brood pupates inside the nut; moths come out in late June and July. There are 3, possibly 4, generations, but the first does the most damage.

Control. If not over 3 per cent of shoots of the previous year are infested with overwintering larvae, control is considered unnecessary. Otherwise spray with DDT, 2 to 3 pounds 50 per cent wettable powder to 100 gallons of water. This is the most effective spray but leads to trouble with mites and aphids. Parathion controls all but must be used with great caution. Lead arsenate, 6 pounds to 100 gallons, is safe in semi-arid Texas, may injure in more humid sections. Nicotine sulfate, ¾ pint plus 2 quarts summer oil emulsion to 100 gallons water, is a safe and fairly effective spray. One application before first-generation larvae enter nuts—between April 20 and May 25—may be sufficient, but a second application a week later is advised for heavy infestations.

46. Pistol casebearer.

Pistol Casebearer (*Coleophora malivorella*)—Found from the Mississippi Valley eastward, a minor pest of apple and other fruits. This is similar to the cigar casebearer, but the case is bent over like a pistol. The larva winters in the case; buds are injured in spring and leaves mined. Eggs are laid on leaves in June. Control with the regular orchard spray schedule or with a special cluster bud spray of DDT or lead arsenate or with a summer oil to kill eggs.

CATERPILLARS

Caterpillars are the wormlike larvae of moths and butterflies. Some are commonly known by the adult form and so are discussed under Butterflies or under Moths. Some have special names, budworm, cankerworm, casebearer, cutworm, earworm, fruitworm, hornworm, leaf miner, leaf tier, spanworm, webworm, and are treated under such headings. A few of the other thousands of caterpillars are here in this section.

Caterpillars are of various shapes but the majority have cylindrical soft bodies which are naked, hairy, or adorned with spines. They are composed of 13 segments behind the head with its chewing mouth parts. The first 3 segments each bear a pair of jointed legs terminating in a single claw. In addition to these true legs, abdominal segments 3, 4, 5, and 6 typically have a pair of prolegs or false legs which are unjointed sucker feet provided with tiny hooks, crotchets, for holding on to a leaf or twig. There is another pair of prolegs on the last abdominal segment. There is also, in many caterpillars, a spinneret near the mouth for making silk.

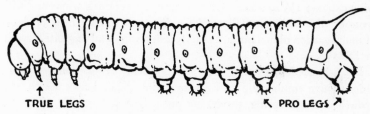

TRUE LEGS   PRO LEGS

47. Diagram of a caterpillar.

Control is usually by means of protective spraying, which means a stomach poison on the foliage before the larvae start eating. Sometimes contact sprays are used and sometimes eradication measures are taken against the egg stage.

Alfalfa Caterpillar (*Colias philodice eurytheme*)—A southwestern alfalfa pest occasionally present on garden peas, beans, and other legumes. The caterpillar is dark green with a pale yellow or white line down the side. The butterflies are sulfur yellow, less frequently white, with wings tipped with wide black bands. Parasites and a wilt disease are often sufficient control; sulfur dust can be used when necessary.

Alfalfa Looper (*Autographa californica*)—Causes sporadic damage on the Pacific coast. This caterpillar is a general feeder, injuring, in addition to alfalfa, many cereal and truck crops, fruits, flowers, ornamental trees and shrubs. The looper is about an inch long, dark olive green with a paler head and 3 dark lines along the back, and only 3 pairs of prolegs. The gray moth, with a silver mark on each fore wing, appears at dusk to visit flowers. Control with rotenone or pyrethrum dust on vegetables, lead arsenate or DDT on ornamentals.

Avocado Caterpillar (*Amorbia essigana*)—Limited to California and mostly to avocado. This is a tortricid or leaf roller moth, with reddish-brown fore wings an inch across, first noticed in 1922. The yellowish-green larvae skeletonize the leaves or web them together and scar young fruits. See Omnivorous Looper for control.

Azalea Caterpillar (*Datana major*)—Serious in Georgia and Florida.

Banded Woollybear (*Isia isabella*)—Generally distributed, our familiar densely hairy "hedgehog" caterpillar, which rolls into a ball when disturbed or for hibernating. It is about 1¼ inches long, black at both ends with a reddish-brown band around the middle. The width of this band is said to forecast the winter; the narrower the band, the colder and longer will be the winter. The adult is the tiger moth, yellow, wing expanse 1½ to 2 inches, a few dusky spots on the wings and black spots on the abdomen (Plate XX). The caterpillars feed on leaves of many garden plants but are readily killed with lead arsenate, cryolite, or DDT.

Black-headed Fireworm (*Rhopobota naevana*)—Cranberry Worm, a destructive cranberry pest. Eggs, overwintered on leaves, hatch when growth starts in spring, producing green larvae, first pale, then dark with black heads, which web leaves together and feed inside. They pupate on the ground. The first brood of moths, ash gray with irregular brownish bands across the fore wings, spreading to ⅜ inch, emerge in June and those of the second brood in July or August. Dust when new growth is ¼ to ½ inch long with 2 per cent parathion, or a mixture of 1 per cent parathion with 5 per cent DDT, or with 10 per cent DDT.

Cabbage Looper (*Trichoplusia ni*)—A native caterpillar common throughout the country. It attacks all members of the cabbage family—broccoli, Brussels sprouts, cabbage, cauliflower, collards, horseradish, kale, kohlrabi, mustard, radish, turnip, and also feeds on beet, celery, lettuce, parsley, pea, potato, spinach, tomato, and on flowers—carnation, chrysanthemum, mignonette, geranium, and others. The looper winters as a green to brown pupa wrapped in a cocoon attached by one side to a plant leaf, and transforms in spring into a moth with mottled brownish fore wings, with a small silvery spot in the middle, and paler brown hind wings; wing expanse is just under 1½ inches.

The females lay many small, round, greenish-white eggs, singly, on upper surface of leaves. The larva has a body tapering to the head, greenish, with a thin white line above the spiracles and 2 others down the back; there are 3 pairs of prolegs. After feeding 2 to 4 weeks, the looper spins a cocoon. There may be 3 or more generations a season.

Control. DDT, toxaphene, or cryolite can be used on young plants. Change to rotenone spray or dust as heads form. A wilt disease often destroys loopers late in the season. Endrin controls DDT-resistant loopers.

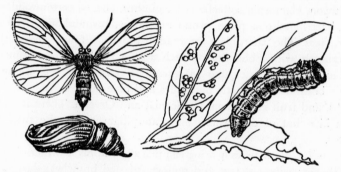

48. California oakworm—moth, pupa, eggs, and larva eating.

California Oakworm (*Phryganidia californica*)—On live and other oaks, sometimes on chestnut and eucalyptus in California. It is particularly destructive to live oaks in the San Francisco Bay region, defoliating them periodically in much the same fashion as cankerworms injure eastern oaks. Immature caterpillars feed on live oak foliage during the winter, but on deciduous trees the oakworm winters in the egg stage. Mature caterpillars are olive brown with black and yellow longitudinal stripes on back and sides. After feeding in spring first by skeletonizing leaves, then by eating holes in foliage, they pupate in May and June in smooth white or yellow chrysalids attached by the rear end to leaves, limbs, or tree trunks. The moths emerge in June and July, lay flattened white eggs for the summer brood on any kind of oak, adults appearing in October and November. They are uniformly pale brown, with slightly darker antennae and wing veins,

1- to 1¼-inch wing expanse. Although they are abundant enough to cause complete defoliation only at long and irregular intervals, protective measures should be taken each season.

Control. Spray in March and April when worms are small with lead arsenate, 3 to 4 pounds per 100 gallons plus ½ pint fish oil, or with DDT emulsion, prepared to give 1 pound actual DDT per 100 gallons. DDT is more effective than lead arsenate, but it kills parasites and predators that normally hold the oakworm in check. Lindane, dieldrin, toxaphene have performed well in tests. A virus wilt disease markedly reduces oakworm populations.

California Tent Caterpillar (*Malacosoma californica*)—Common in California. This species constructs large tents like the eastern tent caterpillar. It infests oak in particular but also almond, apple, apricot, ash, toyon, California coffeeberry, ceanothus, cherry, cottonwood, currant, hazel, madrona, plum, prune, redbud, willow, and other fruit and forest trees. The caterpillars are reddish brown or tawny above, paler underneath, with a blue line on each side. A similar species, known as the blue-sided tent caterpillar (*Malacosoma constricta*), has an orange-brown body with distinctly blue sides and blue dots. It feeds on oaks, shrubs, and fruit in Arizona, California, and Oregon. There is an egg band like that of the eastern tent caterpillar around the twig over winter.

Control. Cut off twigs bearing egg masses or apply a winter oil spray to kill eggs; wipe out nest and remove infested branches; dust young caterpillars with sulfur; spray or dust trees with lead arsenate or DDT. There are many natural enemies, including an efficient wilt disease.

Celery Looper (*Anagrapha falcifera*)—General throughout the country and much like the cabbage looper. The moth is large with purple-brown fore wings; the larvae are pale green, with light and dark stripes, up to 1 inch long. They feed on celery, beets, lettuce, and other succulent plants and weeds. Young celery plants can be dusted with DDT. Change to rotenone or pyrethrum near harvest.

Celeryworm, Black Swallowtail, Parsleyworm (*Papilio polyxenes asterius*)—The most important of the swallowtail butterflies, occurring all over the United States east of the Rocky Mountains, feeding on celery, carrot, caraway, dill, parsnip, parsley, but not considered a major pest. The caterpillar is a striking creature, 2 inches long, with a black crossband in each segment and just back of the head an opening for 2 soft forked orange horns (Plate XIX). When disturbed, the larva protrudes these horns and gives out a sickeningly sweet odor. The butterfly has a spread of 3 to 4 inches, black wings with 2 rows of yellow spots, hind wings with blue shadings between the rows, a black spot bordered with orange on the inner margin, and a projecting lobe, the "swallowtail."

In the North the winter is passed as a tan chrysalid suspended from host plants; in the South the butterflies live over winter. Eggs are laid singly on leaves of food plants, hatching in 10 days. The larvae feed for 10 days to several weeks, occasionally stripping plants of foliage. There are 2 generations in the North, more in the South. Another, but similar, species occurs in the West.

Control. Hand-picking may be sufficient. Young plants can be dusted with lead or calcium arsenate, changing to rotenone as they approach edible stage.

Convict Caterpillar (*Xanthopastis timais*)—Also called Spanish Moth, usually found in southeastern states, although the recorded range goes to Maine. Spider lily is the natural host, but the larvae devour leaves of amaryllis, narcissus, lilies, and tuberose, often eating foliage down to the ground. The caterpillars are brownish or grayish or black, smooth, about 2 inches long, and they have cream-colored bands around the body like convict stripes. The dark brown pupa is found in the soil near plants. The moth is pinkish cream to white with wings spreading almost 2 inches. Control by dusting with lead or calcium arsenate or DDT.

Cross-striped Cabbageworm (*Evergestis rimosalis*)—The larva has numerous transverse black bands across its green body. The moth is small, yellow brown. See Imported Cabbageworm for control.

Eastern Tent Caterpillar (*Malacosoma americana*)—Also called Apple-tree Tent Caterpillar, present throughout eastern United States and west to the Rocky Mountains. Black cherry, chokecherry, and apple are favored food plants, but when these are scarce it makes ugly nests on hawthorn, pear, plum, birch, bean, elm, maple, oak, poplar, willow, and other fruit and ornamental trees. The winter is spent in the egg stage—a dark brown varnished collar or belt encircling twigs (Plate XVIII). The young larvae, hatching very early in March, gather in a fork of the limbs to spin their large webby nest. They leave it during the day to feed on foliage but return at night or in rainy weather. They are hairy caterpillars, black with a white stripe down the back, brown and yellow lines along the sides, and a row of oval blue spots. They are full grown, 2 to 2½ inches long, in 4 to 6 weeks, and are often seen in groups crawling down the sides of houses or feeding on roses and other shrubs before spinning their dirty white cocoons on tree trunks or buildings.

The moths, light reddish brown with 2 diagonal stripes across each fore wing, emerge in about 3 weeks. Each female lays a single egg collar around a twig, containing 150 to 350 eggs, and covers this with a sticky substance which hardens and glistens like varnish. There is only 1 generation a year. The periods of greatest abundance appear at about 10-year intervals.

Control. Apples are protected by the regular spray schedule used for codling moths. Wild cherries growing near apple orchards should be removed. Young caterpillars can be killed by dusting with sulfur or any contact spray. Spraying or dusting ornamentals with lead arsenate or DDT will protect foliage from older caterpillars, but if egg masses are systematically pruned out during the winter and nests wiped out with a crumpled newspaper when first started, spraying should not be necessary. Burning out nests with a flaming torch is almost always harmful to the tree and very often starts brush fires. There are many natural enemies, ground beetles and other predators, egg parasites, a wilt disease, all of which account for the periodic rise and fall in abundance. It sometimes helps to work along with natural enemies. If egg masses are cut off, encased in fine wire mesh, and left in the open instead of being burned, it gives beneficial parasites a chance to emerge.

Filbertworm (*Melissopus latiferreanus*)—Catalina Cherry Moth, a serious pest of filberts and walnuts in the Pacific Northwest but distributed through much of the United States. The larvae are borers in oak acorns, beechnuts, hazelnuts (filberts), chestnut burs. The moth is pale to dusky with 2 coppery bands near the tip of fore wings. Eggs are laid on leaves near the nuts or on the husks, and worms enter the nuts at the base. They feed for 3 or 4 weeks, then winter in cocoons on the ground. Spray with lead arsenate in summer just before worms enter nuts.

Florida Fern Caterpillar (*Callopistria floridensis*)—Native to tropical America and introduced into northern greenhouses on infested plants from Florida. It seems to feed only on ferns, chiefly nephrolepis and adiantum. It works at night or on cloudy days, stripping leaflets from old growth, devouring new growth entirely. The caterpillars are at first pale green, later velvety black, 1½ inches long. During the day they are concealed in the crown of the fern, along the midrib of a frond or in soil. They pupate underground in an oval cocoon. The moth, with brown patterned wings, emerges in about 2 weeks. There may be a new generation every 7 or 8 weeks. Control by hand-picking caterpillars at night or with a pyrethrum dust or spray.

Forest Tent Caterpillar (*Malacosoma disstria*)—A native pest of forest, ornamental, and fruit trees, widely distributed from the Atlantic to the Pacific, similar to the eastern tent caterpillar but without a tent. Favorite food plants include maple, oak, poplar, ash, birch, and it is also found on apple, boxelder, cherry, hawthorn, peach, pear, plum, prune, quince, rose, willow, and other trees. The caterpillars are gregarious, armyworm style, living in large colonies on a silken mat on larger limbs and tree trunks but not making a nest. The winter egg collars around twigs are cut squarely off at the ends and not rounded down to the twig as those of the eastern tent caterpillar. The larvae, 1½ to 2 inches long, are bluish spattered with black dots and points, with a row of diamond-shaped spots alternating with small white spots down the back, and also pale longitudinal yellow stripes; they are sparsely clothed with soft hair. They eat ravenously in early spring for about 6 weeks. In June or July white cocoons are spun within a leaf or attached to fences or ground objects. The moths emerge in 10 to 14 days to lay about 200 eggs in the band around a twig. They are brownish buff with 2 dark oblique lines across the fore wings, which expand to 1 or 1½ inches. There is only 1 brood a year.

Control. There are many natural enemies to keep this pest in check, including birds. Inspect ornamental trees for egg bands and cut them off. Shade trees can have a 6 per cent DDT emulsion applied with a mist blower as soon as foliage opens or can be sprayed with lead arsenate.

Genista Caterpillar (*Tholeria reversalis*)—Genista Moth. The caterpillars are orange green with black and white markings and are covered with tubercles. They web foliage of broom (Genista) and may completely defoliate plants. Adults are snout moths, brown with orange hind wings. Spray or dust with lead or calcium arsenate or DDT or cryolite.

Great Basin Tent Caterpillar (*Malacosoma fragilis*)—Common in the West, especially at high altitudes. The caterpillars have tawny hairs on a black body with blue and orange markings. They are omnivorous feeders, webbing orchard trees and ash, aspen, ceanothus, cottonwood, and others. They defoliate bitterbrush, an important browse plant for sheep.

Green Cloverworm (*Plathypena scabra*)—Found in eastern United States to the Plains, on clover, alfalfa, garden beans, soybeans, cowpeas, strawberry, raspberry, and some other plants. The moths are dark brown, black-spotted, wingspread 1¼ inches. They lay eggs on underside of leaves and the green larvae feed on them for about a month. There may be 2 to 4 generations but normally they are not abundant enough to justify control measures.

Green-striped Mapleworm (*Anisota rubicunda*)—A native eastern caterpillar found west to Kansas and Nebraska, attacking various maples, boxelder, and oak. The larvae are pale yellowish green, striped above with 8 light and 7 dark green lines, with red head, 1½ inches long. They have 2 horns on the thorax, 2 rows of spines on each side of the body, and 4 large spines near the end of the abdomen. They are said to feed somewhat more ravenously in the western part of their range, often defoliating maples twice in a season and every tree on an avenue.

The moths are pale yellow banded with rose, wing expanse 1½ to 2 inches. They lay pale green eggs in large masses on leaves. The larvae appear in 10 days, feed for a month, pupate in the soil. Moths appear in 2 weeks and the caterpillars of the second brood pupate in the soil for winter. There may be 3 generations in the South.

Control. Spray with lead arsenate, 3 to 4 pounds per 100 gallons, or with DDT, in time for young larvae of the first brood. Several insect parasites and birds aid in control.

Hemlock Looper (*Lambdina fiscellaria*)—Also called a spanworm, an enemy of forest and home plantings from New England to Wisconsin and south to Georgia. Hemlock and balsam fir are preferred, but the looper may also feed on arborvitae, beech, birch, blueberry, wild cherry, elm, soft maple, oak, pine, spruce, and willow. The larvae are greenish yellow to gray with a double row of small black dots on the back. Trees may be defoliated and killed or have their symmetry spoiled. Eggs winter on twigs, needles, or in bark crevices and hatch in early June. The larvae feed on needles from the top of the tree downward, dropping on a thread of silk when disturbed. Pupation is under bark or in protected places. Tan to grayish-brown moths with purple markings appear at the end of August and fly for several weeks. Another species of Lambdina is also a looper infesting hemlock.

Control. For ornamental plantings 6 per cent DDT emulsion applied by mist blower has been recommended. For woodland areas an oil solution with 12 per cent DDT is applied by airplane.

Hickory Horned Devil (*Citheronia regalis*)—Our largest native caterpillar, larva of the regal moth. It is found from Massachusetts to Louisiana and Texas, feeding on hickory, black walnut, butternut, sycamore, sweet gum, ash, persimmon, lilac, sassafras, sumac, and cotton. It is seldom abundant enough to do much damage. The caterpillar, 4 to 5 inches long, has a green body with black spines. Just back of the head are the devil's horns, very long reddish spines bending backward and tipped with black. The moth has a wing expanse of 4½ to 6 inches. Fore wings are dusky olive spotted with yellow, the veins bordered with red scales; hind wings are orange red spotted with yellow. Control measures are usually unnecessary.

Hickory Shuckworm (*Laspeyresia caryana*)—Pecan Shuckworm, usually the most destructive pest of pecans, present also on native hickories, with 50 per cent of the crop sometimes destroyed. Inconspicuous, dark, small moths deposit eggs on young nuts or leaves; on hatching, the larvae gnaw into the green nuts, causing them to drop. There are several generations and the last finds the shells too hard to penetrate and so stays in the shucks. Full-grown larvae winter in shucks on the ground or in the trees. Moths of the first generation emerge in Florida from February to April. No very satisfactory control is known. Keep dropped nuts cleaned up or covered with soil, using a disk tiller.

Imported Cabbageworm (*Pieris rapae*)—A pest in North America since 1860. Within 20 years of its arrival at Quebec it had spread over the country east of the Mississippi River and now is present practically everywhere. It attacks all of the cabbage family—cabbage, cauliflower, kale, collards, kohlrabi, Brussels sprouts, mustard, radish, turnip, horse-radish, and related weeds; also nasturtium, sweet alyssum, mignonette, and lettuce.

The adult is the familiar white cabbage butterfly which has 3 or 4 black spots on wings spreading 1¼ to nearly 2 inches (Plate XXVI). The butterflies are around on sunny days very early in spring, the females alighting frequently to glue an egg on the underside of a leaf until each has deposited several hundred. The eggs are yellow, bullet-shaped, ridged. Velvety smooth green caterpillars, with alternating light and dark longitudinal stripes, start feeding in about a week, depositing repulsive pellets of excrement as they eat huge holes in leaves. When full grown, about an inch long, they pupate in a naked gray, green, or tan chrysalid, with angular projections, suspended by a belt of silk from some part of the plant or from some nearby object, even a building. Adults emerge in a week or so and there may be 5 or 6 generations. Hibernation is in the pupal stage.

Control. DDT, DDD, toxaphene, or cryolite are recommended for young larvae before edible heads form, but recent reports indicate that the cabbageworm is not as susceptible to DDT now as it was a few years ago. Use rotenone spray or dust as plants near the edible stage. Clean up old plant parts after harvest; destroy weeds.

Imported Currantworm. See under Sawflies.

Lesser Appleworm (*Grapholitha prunivora*)—An eastern pest, relative of the codling moth with the same type of life cycle. The larvae are smaller and brighter pink; they make shallow blotch mines on surface of apples. There are 2 generations. Apples properly sprayed for codling moth will not require special treatment for this appleworm.

Linden Looper (*Erannis tiliaria*)—Also known as Lime-tree or Basswood Looper, fairly common through eastern states and west to the Rocky Mountains. The larvae feed on forest and shade trees—oaks, apple, birch, elm, hickory, basswood, maple—and may cause rather serious defoliation. The loopers are bright yellow with 10 longitudinal wavy black lines down the back, 1½ inches long. The moth is buff, marked with brown, with 1¾-inch wingspread. Eggs are laid from October to November.

Melonworm (*Diaphania hyalinata*)—Rarely injurious north of the Gulf states, although it may be seen elsewhere. The day-flying moth has pearly white wings margined with a narrow dark band, spreading to 1¾ inches (Plate XXXVI). The body is brown in front of the wings; the abdomen is silver white tipped with a bushy tuft of slender, hairlike scales. The caterpillar is slender, greenish, with 2 white stripes along the body in most stages. It feeds chiefly on foliage of muskmelon, cucumber, squash, pumpkin, rarely on watermelon. Dusts containing 1 per cent rotenone are effective. Do not use mixtures with sulfur, which may prevent fruit formation of some melon varieties.

Omnivorous Looper (*Sabulodes caberata*)—A native of, and apparently confined to, California. Most serious as an avocado pest, often numerous enough to strip trees of all foliage, it also feeds on acacia, alder, aralia, boxelder, buckeye, California laurel, California Christmasberry (toyon), cherry, chestnut, clematis, daisy, elm, English ivy, eucalyptus, geranium, ginkgo, grevillea, groundsel, honeysuckle, lemon verbena, magnolia, maple, olive, orange, passion-flower, pecan, peppertree, privet, rose, sumac, sycamore, tecoma, violet, black walnut, willow. Truly it is well named omnivorous.

The moth is dull brown or yellow, with 2 darker transverse bands, wingspread up to 2 inches. It is nocturnal but may be found during the day on underside of leaves where it lays clusters of eggs. The larvae vary from yellow to pale pink or green, with yellow, brown, or green stripes on sides and back, and black markings as well. It is 1½ to 2 inches long in the last instar and can eat an entire avocado leaf in a day. The pupa is usually webbed between 2 leaves or inside a leaf folded over. There may be 5 or 6 generations a year. Spraying with DDT, at rate of 1 pound 50 per cent wettable powder to 100 gallons, seems to be effective.

Orange Dog (*Papilio cresphontes*)—A common and destructive butterfly attacking citrus in Florida. It is called "dog" because one end of the caterpillar looks like the nose of a dog, 2 black spots on the thorax serving as eyes. It is 2½ inches long, dark brown with blotches of light yellow. When disturbed, orange-red hornlike processes are protruded and a strong odor given off. The dogs feed voraciously on foliage, often defoliating a young tree in 2 or 3 days. The adult is a large yellow and black butterfly very common in Florida. Eggs, white with a reddish tinge, are laid singly on new shoots about February, hatching in 10 days. The best control is to remove caterpillars by hand from young nursery stock.

Orange-striped Oakworm (*Anisota senatoria*)—A native eastern moth, sometimes found in other states, preferring white and scrub oaks, occasionally feeding on other trees. The adult, appearing in early June, is bright tan, with black dots and a white center spot on the fore wings, which expand to 2½ inches. Females lay white to coral-red eggs in clusters on underside of leaves. The male is smaller and darker. The caterpillar is coal black with orange-yellow longitudinal stripes and black, hornlike appendages at the end of the body, which is covered with short spines. Local infestations may strip foliage from trees in midsummer. Pupation is in soil. There is usually 1 generation; sometimes 2 in the South. Spraying with lead arsenate, 3 pounds to 100 gallons, or with DDT, is effective.

Orange Tortrix (*Argyrotaenia citrana*)—An important orange pest in California and other warm climates, also feeding on oak, pine, black walnut, willow, acacia, apricot, asparagus, begonia, cineraria, Jobstears, eucalyptus, ferns, geranium, Jerusalem-cherry, lantana, lavender, penstemon, rose, and wandering Jew. It has become a raspberry pest in western Washington. The dirty-white, brown-headed caterpillar webs and rolls the leaves on which it feeds, and bores into orange rind, causing premature drop and leaving avenues of infection for decay organisms. Young oranges are scarred around the button. Grapefruit may also be infested, but it is not grown so much where the tortrix is injurious. Moths are fawn or gray with darker mottlings. Eggs are cream-colored sculptured disks, laid in overlapping masses on both leaf surfaces. There are 2 to 4 generations. Spraying or dusting with cryolite or pyrethrum is helpful. There are many natural enemies.

Palmerworm (*Dichomeris ligulella*)—A pest so ancient it is mentioned in the Bible. It occurs from Maine to Texas and is occasionally serious on apple in northeastern states, the peak coming only once in 60 years. It may also feed on cherry, hazel, oak, pear, and plum. The caterpillars are olive green with 2 white stripes along the side and 2 narrow white lines on the back, ½ inch long. They skeletonize the leaves, partially protected by a light web, and sometimes eat into young fruit. The small moths, only ½ inch across the wings, appear in July and later hibernate, laying eggs the next spring. The regular spray schedule for codling moth will control palmerworms.

Pickleworm (*Diaphania nitidalis*)—Especially destructive in the Gulf states, but found as far north as New York and Michigan. Muskmelon, cucumber, and squash may be seriously injured, watermelon rarely, pumpkin not at all. Ripening fruits are bored into by white to green caterpillars up to ¾ inch long, with brown heads. They have black spots across each segment in younger stages, are a uniform green or copper when grown (Plate XXXVI). Masses of green sawdust-like excrement are pushed out from holes in the fruit, which rots and turns sour. Early in the season the caterpillars work on stems, terminal buds, and in squash blossoms. Late crops may be almost totally destroyed. Hibernation is as a pupa inside a rolled leaf, the moth not coming out until late spring, sometimes early June. The adult has a long slender body with a prominent brush of long hairlike scales at the end of the abdomen. The wings, yellowish white with a wide yellow-brown margin, spread to just over an inch. The moths fly at night, lay clusters of 2 to 7 eggs on underside of fruits, or on stems, tender buds, or new leaves. The first generation is not large, but moths emerging from pupation in July lay many eggs and the third and fourth broods in August really get down to their devastating business. Each worm may enter several fruits before its growth is completed.

Control. As soon as a crop is harvested, burn vines, unused fruits, adjoining weeds, and trash. Bury pupae by spading or plowing in early fall. Plan for an early crop; use squash for a trap crop to keep worms away from melons, but destroy vines before larvae are full grown in squash blossoms. Dusting with 3 per cent DDT is effective but may be injurious to some varieties. TDE (DDD) is also recommended. Zineb used for control of mildew apparently aids in control of pickleworm.

Poplar Tent Maker (*Ichthyura inclusa*)—Distributed from New England to Colorado, feeding mostly on poplar, sometimes on willow. The caterpillars are black, mottled with gray, striped with yellow and brown. They have a pair of black tubercles on abdominal segments 1 and 8, are about 1¼ inches long. They are gregarious and make silken nests by webbing several leaves together or folding over a leaf. As they feed on the surface they gradually add other leaves. Pupae winter under leaves; moths appear in early spring. They are brownish gray with 3 irregular white lines bordered with red on the outer edge; wingspread just over an inch. It is usually possible to cut out and burn whole colonies. Spraying with lead arsenate or DDT when larvae are small will check infestations, as will natural enemies in many cases.

Puss Caterpillar (*Megalopyge opercularis*)—One of the stinging caterpillars, found from Virginia to Texas and southward, on oak, citrus, hackberry, elm, plum, maple, rose, sycamore, and other deciduous trees and shrubs, and even on English ivy. Gardeners should beware of this inch-long larva, covered with long, soft, reddish-yellow hairs interspersed with stinging spines. If a caterpillar falls on the neck, there may be severe irritation; if on the wrist, the whole arm may swell. Children are more seriously injured than adults. Lead-arsenate sprays will control it. Hand-picking is possible if you wear thick gloves. A formula to soothe the nettling caused by stinging is: 10 grains menthol, 2 drams zinc oxide, 8 ounces aq. calcis, 15 drops acid carbolici.

Range Caterpillar (*Hemileuca oliviae*)—A range pest on wild grasses in New Mexico and Colorado, but sometimes infesting corn and other cultivated crops. Larvae are yellow, gray, or black, densely covered with coarse poisonous spines; they have white spiracles encircled with a black line.

Red-humped Caterpillar (*Schizura concinna*)—Also called Red-humped Appleworm, distributed over most of the country. The larvae are yellow brown with a bright red head, a red hump on the fourth segment, dark tubercles on each segment, striped longitudinally with white, brown, red, and black, 1 inch long (Plate XX). They rest with the rear end of the abdomen elevated. They feed on both fruit and ornamental trees, stripping foliage of apple, apricot, aspen, bayberry, birch, blackberry, cottonwood, cherry, dogwood, hawthorn, hickory, huckleberry, locust, pear, persimmon, plum, poplar, prune, rose, sweet gum, willow, and walnut.

The larva winters in a cocoon in the soil, pupates in late spring or early summer. The moths are grayish brown, wingspread about 1¼ inches; they lay eggs in masses on underside of leaves. The larvae are gregarious, first skeletonizing foliage, then eating everything but midribs. When disturbed they raise both ends of their bodies. They defoliate one branch before moving to another.

The simplest control is to collect and burn young colonies. A regular orchard spray schedule should keep them in bounds. Other plants can be sprayed with lead arsenate, DDT, or cryolite.

Saddleback Caterpillar (*Sibine stimulea*)—A stinging caterpillar widely distributed through the Atlantic states. It feeds on oak, cherry, sometimes other trees, may attack canna, dahlia, holly, lily, palm, rose, and other plants. Its appearance is most distinctive, flat underneath, rounded above, reddish but with a pea-green patch (the saddle blanket) in the middle of the back and on that a broad purple-brown patch edged with white (the saddle). There are fascicles of spines along the sides and 2 large tufts of spines at both ends. The irritation is severe; see Puss Caterpillar for soothing formula.

Saddled Prominent (*Heterocampa guttivitta*)—Also called Antlered Maple Caterpillar, common in Atlantic states, ranging also to Texas. It prefers beech, with sugar maple and apple next, but it also feeds on other maples, oak, occasionally blackberry, cherry, poplar, spirea, and witch-hazel. The young larva bears 9 pairs of horns, starting at the head with a large branched pair like antlers; the mature caterpillar has no horns. It is green to brown or yellow, with a reddish-brown saddle spot in the middle of the back. The moth is olive gray with darker wavy areas and dark dots. Occasionally New England woodlands may be defoliated by this pest and at such times it also feeds on shade trees, but it is not considered a serious pest of ornamentals. Parasites usually take care of the saddled prominent; shade trees can be sprayed with lead arsenate or DDT if the abundance warrants the expense.

Salt-marsh Caterpillar (*Estigmene acrea*)—Generally distributed, one of the woollybears. The caterpillars are very hairy, gray when young, then black with yellow broken lines and cinnamon-red hairs, up to 2 inches long. At times, usually late summer, they may be as bad as armyworms, eating everything in sight—sugar beets, beans, other vegetables and flowers. Moths have white wings with black spots and an orange, black-spotted abdomen. Dusting with toxaphene or DDT is effective in control.

Southern Cabbageworm (*Pieris protodice*)—A southern species resembling the imported cabbageworm, with similar control measures. The butterfly has more black markings on the wings and the caterpillar has 4 longitudinal yellow bands.

Spiny Oakworm (*Anisota stigma*)—A southern species much like the orange-striped oakworm. The caterpillar is bright tawny or orange with a dusky stripe along the back and prominent spines on thoracic segments.

Stinging Rose Caterpillar (*Parasa indetermina*)—A sluglike creature feeding on rose leaves from the underside, also on dogwood, chestnut, oak, wild cherry, hickory, pawpaw, bayberry, plum, apple, and pear. The caterpillar is marked with red, white and violet stripes, and 7 pairs of large, spine-bearing processes, ¾ inch long. It winters in a dark cocoon among refuse. The pale cinnamon-brown moth, wings marked with green and brown, lays eggs in July.

Striped Garden Caterpillar (*Polia legitima*)—Generally distributed, more abundant in late summer, a dark, yellow-striped cutworm, similar to the zebra caterpillar, with some preference for crucifers. The moth is grayish with an irregular pattern.

Tomato Pinworm (*Keiferia lycopersicella*)—Found outdoors in the far South and in southern California, where it is one of the worst tomato pests, and in greenhouses. The larvae, yellow, gray, or green with purple spots, only ¼ inch long, make serpentine or blotch mines in leaves which are folded and held together with light webs. Developing buds and ripening fruits have pinholes bored in them with entrance usually at the stem end. Injury to vines is not serious, but the fruit can be a total loss. The pinworm may also injure eggplant and potato. Dusting with cryolite and sulfur, starting when fruits are about the size of marbles, is said to be effective.

Ugly-nest Caterpillar (*Archips cerasivorana*)—Cherry-tree Tortrix. This leaf roller is a northern pest, abundant only at long intervals, mostly on wild cherry, sometimes on cultivated cherry, rarely on apple. The larvae, yellow with black heads, ¾ inch long, tie twigs and leaves together, making a large nest. The moths are yellow with brown spots and blue band, 1-inch wingspread.

Variable Oak Leaf Caterpillar (*Heterocampa manteo*)—Distributed from Maine to Alabama, more destructive in the South. The greenish-yellow caterpillar, with variable markings, 1½ inches long, devours leaves of oak, especially white oak, basswood, walnut, birch, elm, hawthorn, and persimmon. The moth is pale ash gray with 3 wavy dark lines crossing the fore wings.

Velvetbean Caterpillar (*Anticarsia gemmatilis*)—Found only in the Gulf states on soybeans, velvetbeans, cowpeas, peanuts, kudzu-vine, and young tips of black locust. Soybeans are usually defoliated first. The caterpillars vary from dull green to olive brown or black with white lines running the length of the body. Nocturnal moths are buff to dark brown or black, with a white diagonal line across the wings. Larvae can be controlled with a 3 or 5 per cent DDT dust, 5 per cent methoxychlor, or 10 per cent toxaphene. There is a rather efficient egg parasite and a fungus which attacks the worms.

Walnut Caterpillar (*Datana integerrima*)—A native moth found from Maine to Florida and west to Kansas, feeding on butternut, black walnut, hickory, and pecan. The caterpillars are 2 inches long, dull black, reddish when young, covered with long white hairs. The moths are dark buff with 4 brown transverse lines on the fore wings. Eggs are laid in masses on underside of leaves. The larvae feed in colonies, crawling to the tree trunk to molt, then going back to feed again. Pupation is in the soil. There are 2 generations in the South, 1 in the North. Caterpillar masses can be destroyed or trees sprayed.

Western Oak Looper (*Lambdina somniaria*)—Very closely related to the hemlock looper, periodically destructive to oak in Oregon and Washington. The caterpillars are pale brown mottled with black spots up to 1¼ inches long. Every few years they get so numerous it is impossible to walk under trees without being covered with them; the trees look as if they had been burned. The moths are yellow to dark brown, dotted with darker scales. In October they cover limbs and branches of trees.

Western Tent Caterpillar (*Malacosoma pluviale*)—A common species in the Pacific Northwest. The larvae, tawny with blue and orange spots, live in small, compact nests. They feed on alder, apple, hawthorn, cherry, currant, and rose.

Yellow-headed Fireworm (*Acleris minuta*)—Cranberry Worm, sometimes injurious on the drier cranberry bogs. The moth, slate gray, ¾-inch wingspread, lays eggs on leaves in May. Yellow-headed caterpillars web leaves together and feed inside, pupating in their nest in June, producing a second brood to feed in July, and a third in September. Keeping bogs flooded until about May 20 helps in control. Spray drier bogs with lead arsenate as eggs hatch, 1 pound to 10 gallons of water, or dust with 10 per cent DDT.

Yellow-necked Caterpillar (*Datana ministra*)—General, primarily on fruit trees—apple, apricot, blackberry, blueberry, cherry, peach, pear, plum, quince—also on beech, birch, hazel, hickory, linden, oak, walnut, and other ornamental trees and shrubs. The caterpillar is black with a yellow thorax (the neck), 4 yellow stripes along each side, covered with long white hairs. The larvae work in groups and when disturbed elevate both ends. Young larvae skeletonize leaves, older caterpillars eat all but stem and midrib. The moths have brown fore wings, 1½-inch wingspread. Pupation is in the soil. There is 1 generation a year with chief injury in July and August. Shake caterpillars off small trees and crush them. Spray larger trees with lead arsenate when larvae are young.

Yellow Woollybear (*Diacrisia virginica*)—Virginia Tiger Moth. The caterpillars are very hairy, yellow or straw-colored with black lines. They are general feeders, injuring many vegetables and flowers— asparagus, bean, beet, blackberry, cabbage, canna, carrot, cauliflower, celery, cherry, corn, currant, dahlia, eggplant, gooseberry, grape, hollyhock, lily, melon, morning glory, parsnip, peanut, pea, potato, pumpkin, radish, raspberry, rhubarb, Spanish needles, squash, sunflower, sweetpotato, turnip. The moths have white wings with black spots and a yellow-brown, black-spotted abdomen. There are 2 broods. Pupae winter inside hairy cocoons. Spray or dust with lead arsenate, cryolite, DDT, or toxaphene.

Zebra Caterpillar (*Ceramica picta*)—General, feeding on truck, cereal, and fruit crops, trees, and flowers, including sweet peas, lilies, gladiolus. It is most injurious in late summer. The larvae are velvety black with 2 bright yellow stripes on each side and many fine yellow transverse lines. The moth is rusty brown. Arsenical or DDT sprays and dusts will give control when larvae are young.

CENTIPEDES AND SYMPHYLIDS

Centipedes, "hundred-legged worms," are members of the class Chilopoda, closest relatives of true insects. They differ from insects in having only 2 main body parts (they lack a thorax) and no wings. Instead of 3 pairs of legs they have 1 pair on each of their many body segments but these do not really add up to 100 as the name implies. They are like insects in having a single pair of antennae, breathing by tracheae, and with reproductive organs at the posterior end of the body. They look something like worms but are flatter. They have a distinct head, and jointed legs. They have a pair of poison claws on the first segment behind the head that they use to paralyze their prey. They usually rest under logs or stones and are swift runners, predaceous on earthworms, snails, and some insects. Their bite is painful to man but not often serious. There are many species and some of the tropical forms go up to 18 inches in length, but as a class they can be considered more beneficial than harmful. True centipedes are not garden pests.

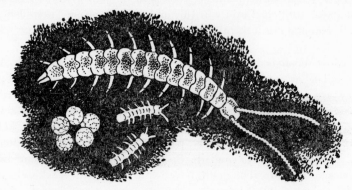

49. Garden centipede or symphylid, showing adult, young, and eggs.

Garden Centipede (*Scutigerella immaculata*)—Called a centipede only because it looks something like one. Actually it is a symphylid, belonging to the class Symphyla, the members of which are distinguished from true centipedes by having only 12 pairs of legs in the adult form, fewer when young, no poison claws, and no eyes. They live in damp places rich in organic matter, in leafmold, manure piles, or peaty soils.

The garden centipede is small, ¼ inch long, pure white, very active. It keeps its long antennae constantly moving as it travels through the soil in cracks and tunnels left by decaying plant roots. It is an outdoor soil pest in warm climates, particularly injurious to asparagus in California, and is a greenhouse pest nearly everywhere. The symphylids eat off fine roots and root hairs and scar underground parts of stems so plants die or are stunted. Besides asparagus, which has its roots riddled with tunnels while they are below ground, the garden centipede seriously injures lettuce, radishes, tomatoes, cucumbers, and many ornamentals, including sweet pea, snapdragon, aster, and other flowers.

Small white eggs are laid in clusters of 5 to 20 about a foot deep in soil, any time between April and September; the minute young hatch 7 to 10 days later. At first they have only 6 pairs of legs, 10 body segments, and very short antennae, but they add another pair of legs and lengthen antennae at each molt. When greenhouse soil is wet down and crops are started in fall symphylids start feeding on roots; in outdoor gardens they are active in spring. They are rarely seen on the surface of soil, being strongly repelled by light.

Control. Asparagus fields in California are flooded with water to a depth of 1 to 3 feet for 3 weeks during late December and early January. Fumigating greenhouse soil with ethylene dibromide or D-D mixture, or sterilizing soil with steam has been practiced. Now lindane is suggested, 3 pounds of 25 per cent wettable powder in 100 gallons of water applied to 2200 square feet of bench space. In rose houses this can be forcefully sprayed on the beds through the mulch. DDT can also be used, but it is slower-acting; apply 2 pounds 50 per cent wettable powder per 1000 square feet.

CICADAS

The cicadas, order Homoptera, family Cicadidae, are sometimes erroneously called locusts. They are members of a large family—1500 species in the world although only 75 in North America—but we commonly distinguish only 2 kinds, the periodical cicada or 17-year locust and the annual or dogday cicada. They are large sucking insects, have front wings of the same texture throughout, and hold their wings in a rooflike position. They are noted chiefly for their shrill noises, "singing," produced by special vibratory organs under the base of the abdomen of the male.

Dogday Cicada (*Tibicen linnei* and other species)—Also called Harvestman and Annual Cicada, but it is not literally annual. It has a 2- to 5-year cycle, but the broods overlap so that some appear every summer. This is larger than the periodical cicada, has a black body with whitish bloom, green margins on the wings, and numerous light markings on thorax and abdomen. The cicadas are around on summer dogdays, July and August, but do not cause injury enough to worry about. The cicada-killer or digger wasp gets rid of some.

Periodical Cicada (*Magicicada septendecim*)—A native of North America, named for its regular occurrence at long intervals. There are 2 races. The southern race, with its northern boundary Virginia to

Oklahoma, has a 13-year cycle; the northern race appears every 17 years and is the one called the 17-year locust. Both are more abundant east of the Mississippi River and both have a number of broods, which appear in different years, so that it may not be 13 or 17 years between cicada swarms in any given locality. The broods are numbered and it is possible to predict accurately when each will appear. Brood II was widespread over the eastern seaboard in 1945, its first appearance since 1928; it is expected next in 1962. Brood VI was present in some areas in 1949 and brood X was quite serious in Maryland and Pennsylvania in 1953. Brood XIV is due in 1957. Brood XIX of the 13-year race emerged in 1946 and XXIII in 1950.

50. Periodical cicada, "seventeen-year locust," laying eggs, and twigs showing bark torn in process.

The adult periodical cicada has a stout black body about 1 inch long with wings extending well behind the body when at rest. It has reddish-orange eyes, legs, and wing veins. It appears from mid-May to early June and is around for 5 or 6 weeks. A town may have cicadas in such abundance that life is made hideous with their shrill unending song, and people driving through sometimes stop their cars to see what is the matter with their engines. In some gardens tree trunks will be covered with cast shells of the nymphs and the ground under trees literally perforated with holes, ½ inch across. The next town, only a mile or so away, may be lucky and have almost no cicadas.

The female has a tough, horny ovipositor and the chief damage is the tearing of twigs as eggs are deposited in rows, the bark being pushed away and the wood raised into bundles of splinters. About 75 trees, shrubs, and herbaceous plants are used for egg-laying, but oak is preferred, with hickory and apple close seconds. Dogwood twigs are frequently injured. Twigs and small branches so punctured usually turn brown but hang on as an eyesore for weeks before breaking and falling to the ground. Eggs hatch in 6 or 7 weeks, the antlike young drop and enter the soil through cracks. They burrow down to the roots and stay 6 to 18 inches below ground level until the 17th spring. Then they burrow upward and crawl out when ready for the final molt. Sometimes, in moist places, they construct earthen cones or chimneys before coming out. They crawl to a tree trunk, stick, or other object, the thorax is split and the winged cicada emerges, leaving the hard, empty shell in lifelike position behind. From 20,000 to 40,000 cicadas may come out of the soil underneath a single large tree.

Control. The only insecticide yet proven to have any value against cicadas is the very dangerous TEPP, and this kills only on direct contact with the adults. Start spraying soon after cicadas appear, using only ½ teaspoon of a 20 per cent mixture per gallon (½ pint per 100 gallons) and observe all safety precautions. Young trees can be protected by mosquito netting and it would pay not to set out new orchards a year or two before a large brood is expected in an area. Avoid pruning young trees heavily the year before a brood is due. Cut off injured twigs as soon as possible.

CRAYFISH

Crayfish, or crawfish, are members of the animal class Crustacea, which also includes lobsters, crabs, and sowbugs. Crayfish are almost miniature lobsters, having the same horny shell; head and thorax united into one unjointed portion; and the hind portion, the abdomen, jointed and flexible. They have 2 big grasping pincers or claws and behind these, 4 pairs of walking legs. They are green to brown, 3 to 6 inches long, and molt frequently and periodically because the hard shell cannot grow.

In autumn the female curls up her tail to form a basket and carries her eggs there until the next summer. It seems strange to find such aquatic creatures as garden pests, but they live in burrows in wet soil. In places like New Orleans, where the soil surface is close to the water table, lawns are often dotted with crayfish mounds, round piles of mud 3 or 4 inches high, opening at the top like chimneys. The crayfish crawl out of the burrows at night to eat cotton and other plants as well as dead or live animal food.

Control. Use 2½ tablespoons coal-tar creosote emulsion to 1 gallon of water and pour ½ cup in each crayfish hole, or place 2 tablespoons carbon bisulfide (very inflammable) in each hole and cover with soil.

CRICKETS

Crickets are relatives of grasshoppers, order Orthoptera, family Gryllidae for tree and field crickets, Gryllacrididae for cave or camel crickets, Gryllotalpidae for mole crickets, and family Tettigoniidae for the Mormon cricket, which is really a long-horned grasshopper. Crickets have chewing mouth parts but incomplete metamorphosis. They are noted for the chirping notes produced by the males when they rub together specially modified parts of their front wings. They have long, filiform antennae, a spear-shaped ovipositor, and 2- to 4-segmented tarsi. The hardened horny fore wings are called tegmina; they are flat on the back but bent down abruptly along the sides. Most feed on plants; some are predaceous; some are both.

Black-horned Tree Cricket (*Oecanthus nigricornis nigricornis*)— Widely distributed, greenish yellow with head black or with 3 black stripes, destructive in berry-growing regions. It lays eggs in rows in pithy stems of raspberry, blackberry, loganberry, grape, elder, sometimes in woody twigs of elm, maple, peach, apple, and other trees. Canes die above the punctures or split and break off. Early spraying with lead arsenate is helpful.

Camel Cricket (*Daihinia brevipes*)—Found in the Great Plains states from North Dakota to northern Texas, reported as injurious in Oklahoma to tomatoes, watermelon, cotton, cowpeas, and other plants in the seedling stage. It feeds at night, is found mostly in sandy areas. Poison bran mash bait gives satisfactory control.

Changa (*Scapteriscus vicinus*)—Puerto Rican or West Indian Mole Cricket, an introduced species similar to the southern mole cricket. It is injurious to truck crops, pastures, lawns in the coastal plain of the Southeast. It is 1½ inches long, brown above, light brown underneath. See Northern Mole Cricket for control.

Coulee Cricket (*Peranabrus scabricollis*)—More nearly related to the katydids than crickets, very destructive in Montana and Washington. Feeding on sagebrush, dung, living and dead animals, it also eats nearly all field and garden crops, fruits, and shrubs. Adults are fat, soft-bodied, 1½ inches long, dark reddish brown. Females are wingless; males have short winged stubs. They are active in the daytime and move in migratory hordes, devastating everything in their path. Ditches can be dug to stop migrating swarms or poison bait used as for the Mormon cricket. Western meadowlarks are credited with stopping outbreaks.

Field Cricket (*Acheta assimilis*)—Present everywhere in small numbers, sometimes seriously abundant. They vary in color, often black or brown, ⅗ to 1 inch long, antennae and ovipositor of females longer than the body. They are indiscriminate feeders, eating plants in the garden, or paper, food, or clothing in the house. They injure seedling cotton and cereals, cucurbits, legumes, tomato fruits, strawberries. They hibernate in the egg stage in the North where there is one generation; in warm climates they winter as nymphs and there may be 3 generations. During the day they remain under trash, coming out in late afternoon to chirp, feed, mate, and lay banana-shaped eggs in damp soil. Use poison-bran baits or spray or dust with chlordane or dieldrin as for grasshoppers. Maintain a fine dust mulch; spade deeply in fall to bury eggs.

Four-spotted Tree Cricket (*Oecanthus nigricornis quadripunctatus*) —Like the black-horned tree cricket except for a dark spot in each of the 2 basal antennal segments.

Jerusalem Cricket (*Stenopelmatus fuscus*)—Sand cricket, a western species with legs adapted for tunneling in sandy soil. It is large, wingless, amber brown, does not have hearing organs on front tibiae. It is a useful predator, injurious to little except potato tubers in newly broken soil.

Mormon Cricket (*Anabrus simplex*)—Western, Great Plains, Idaho, or Black Cricket, found in most of the area west of the Rocky Mountains and in some of the Great Plains states. It is a very destructive species which migrates periodically from native breeding grounds in the hills to devastate garden crops, fruit, and grain. It is of great economic importance as a scourge of range grasses. Eggs are laid in late summer and fall in light, sandy loam soil, inserted singly just under the surface in bare spots between clumps of grass or sagebrush. Young crickets start hatching early in April and reach maturity in 6 to 8 weeks. There is 1 generation. Adults are 1 inch long, heavy-bodied, with small useless wings, antennae and ovipositor as long as the body, tarsi 4-segmented. They are active during the day and may travel ⅛ to 1 mile a day when they start migration.

Control. Metal barriers or ditches to stop migratory hordes have been used in the past. Now poison bait is used, often applied by airplane. There are several formulae. In one, 2 ounces aldrin, 100 pounds steam-rolled wheat, ½ gallon of diesel oil are mixed and applied by plane at the rate of 5 pounds per acre. Another dry formula calls for 100 pounds standard bran (no shorts or middlings), 1 pound toxaphene or ½ pound of chlordane, ½ gallon fuel oil or kerosene, applied at the rate of 10 pounds per acre.

For broadcasting by hand, a wet bait is made of 100 pounds of standard wheat bran, 4 pounds sodium fluosilicate, 12 to 15 gallons of water. This can be reduced proportionately for gardens. California gulls still feed on Mormon crickets in Utah.

Northern Mole Cricket (*Gryllotalpa hexadactyla*)—A native pest, known in damp, muddy places from Canada through Florida but a problem only in the South. A European species (*Gryllotalpa gryllotalpa*) has become established in a few places along the eastern coast and threatens nurseries. These crickets are large, 1½ inches long, brownish above, paler underneath, covered with velvety hairs. Their front legs are greatly enlarged, adapted for burrowing, and they terminate in 4 strong, bladelike teeth called dactyls (Plate XXI). They live deep in the ground during the day, coming out at night to pulverize a garden bed and the plants growing in it. Most injury comes from their tunnels in the upper inch or two of soil, which cut off the roots of seedlings, injure lawns. The mole crickets also eat pits in underground roots and stems, cut stems off above the ground, and eat seeds.

Control. Treating the soil with chlordane has now become rather standard procedure. A poison bait is used to some extent (5 pounds dry bran or corn meal, 5 pounds cottonseed meal, ½ pound calcium arsenate, 2 quarts of a solution of 1 part molasses mixed with 9 parts of water).

Snowy Tree Cricket (*Oecanthus niveus*)—Widely distributed throughout North America. Tree crickets are generally beneficial, eating aphids, treehoppers, and scales, but they do feed somewhat on flowers, fruit, and leaves; twigs may be broken by their egg punctures. This cricket is pale green, with slender body, ⅝ inch long, with a black spot on the first 2 antennal segments (Plate XXI). It lays eggs singly in a row down one side of a twig or cane of apple, ash, blackberry, cherry, loganberry, pear, plum, prune, peach, and other fruits and ornamentals. There is only 1 generation; egg-laying is in autumn. The songs of the males are short, clear, whistling notes. Control by pruning out and burning infested twigs or canes and spraying with lead arsenate in early spring.

Southern Mole Cricket (*Scapteriscus acletus*)—Much like the northern mole cricket, but with 2 dactyls instead of 4.

CURCULIOS

Curculios, order Coleoptera, family Curculionidae, are beetles with a pronounced snout, the head being prolonged forward and downward with the biting mouth parts at the end and elbowed antennae arising midway. This is the largest family of insects in any order, with more than 2000 species in North America. They all eat plants both as larvae and as adults. They are mostly small and dull-colored, with a habit of dropping from bushes and "playing dead" when disturbed.

Apple Curculio (*Tachypterellus quadrigibbus*)—A native insect found east of the Mississippi River. Preferred hosts are apple, cherry, haw, wild crab, quince, pear, and shadbush. Feeding and egg punctures result in knotty, misshaped, undersized fruit and premature drop. This curculio does not make crescent-shaped marks like the plum curculio but a large number of punctures close together. It is brown with 4 humps on the back, a long slender snout. It winters in leaves and rubbish on ground, feeding on buds, fruit spurs, and terminal shoots in spring and attacks fruit as soon as it is set. The larvae develop in June drops and in mummied apples left on trees, pupating inside. Adults emerge from the middle of June to early September.

There are two other apple forms: the larger apple curculio (*Tachypterellus quadrigibbus magnus*), from Illinois to Texas, and another species (*T. consors*), from the Rocky Mountains to the Pacific coast. Control measures are the same as for the plum curculio.

Black Walnut Curculio (*Conotrachelus retentus*)—A common pest of young walnuts in eastern United States. The curculios, pale reddish covered with gray pubescence, hibernate as adults, feeding on young shoots in spring and making crescent-shaped cuts for their eggs in very young walnuts, which drop to the ground half grown. They pupate in soil; beetles emerge in August and September to feed on leaf petioles before hibernating. Larvae in dropped nuts can be destroyed by burying deeply or putting nuts in water. Several parasitic wasps and flies aid in control.

Butternut Curculio (*Conotrachelus juglandis*)—Also known as Walnut Weevil, attacking native and Japanese butternuts and young English walnuts. The adult resembles the plum curculio but with white markings, ¼ inch long. It punctures nuts, tender tips, and leaf petioles, lays eggs in new growth and in young nuts through crescent-shaped slits. The grubs, dirty white with brown heads, burrow through the nut or down the twig for 4 or 5 weeks, then go below the soil surface to pupate. DDT applied to new shoots in early June should be effective; lead arsenate has been used in the past.

Cabbage Curculio (*Ceutorhynchus rapae*)—An ashy-gray weevil, 1/8 inch long, with a short snout. Adults and grubs gouge out stems and adults also work on leaves. They infest seedling cabbage, cauliflower, horseradish, mustard, radish, and turnip. Dust young plants with DDT.

Cambium Curculio (*Conotrachelus anaglypticus*)—The larvae feed on cambium and inner bark of many fruit, shade, and forest trees, working around the edges of wounds, retarding healing. They also work in the crowns and roots of columbine, causing wilting and dying, and produce wilting and dieback of young camellia shoots. The snout beetle is small, less than 1/4 inch long, reddish brown; the grubs are small, fleshy, legless. Remove and burn infested plant parts.

Clover Root Curculio (*Sitona hispidula*)—A common pest of clover and alfalfa, sometimes feeding on soybeans, cowpeas, and other legumes. Tiny grayish grubs score and furrow roots, nearly girdling them. Small gray or brown beetles with short, blunt snouts feed on foliage, sometimes eating off tops of young soybeans entirely. Crop rotation seems the most practical control.

Cowpea Curculio (*Chalcodermus aeneus*)—Also known as Cowpea Pod-weevil, injuring cowpeas, seedling cotton, beans, and strawberries. Most important in the cotton states, it occurs as far north as Iowa. Adults lay eggs in cowpeas or beans in the field and larvae destroy developing seeds. Dusting with fluosilicates, cryolite, 5 per cent DDT or TDE is helpful.

Grape Curculio (*Craponius inaequalis*)—A native pest of wild grape injuring berries of cultivated grape in some areas. It is reported as injurious in New England, Florida, Kentucky, Missouri, Ohio, and West Virginia. The small black beetles, just over 1/10 inch long, winter in sheltered locations and feed for a month or two in spring before laying eggs in cavities under skin of grape berries. Footless larvae feed on berry flesh and seeds, drop to the ground, and pupate by midsummer. Adults emerge and feed again before hibernation. Control measures are usually unnecessary.

Hickory-nut Curculio (*Conotrachelus affinis*)—Confined to hickories, pignuts preferred, then shagbark, whiteheart, and butternut. The beetles, reddish brown with a broad band of lighter gray across the back, appear when nuts are half formed to lay eggs in circular cavities in nuts and shells. Nuts drop in midsummer; larvae stay inside for about a month, then enter the soil to pupate. Spraying in early spring with DDT or lead arsenate helps to keep the beetles from feeding on foliage. Bury dropped nuts deeply or put in water to kill larvae. There are several parasites.

Plum Curculio (*Conotrachelus nenuphar*)—A native snout beetle, found east of the Rocky Mountains, a major pest of stone fruits—plum, peach, cherry, apricot, prune, nectarine—and next to codling moth in importance on apple, sometimes injuring pear and quince. The adult is dark brown with a grayish patch on the back, 4 definite humps on the wing covers, and a long, curved snout which projects forward and downward in an arc ⅓ the length of the body which is ¼ inch long (Plate XXII). It winters in stone walls, hedgerows, or other protected places, appearing on the trees at blossom time. The beetles feed on leaves and petals. They injure young fruits by feeding and laying eggs in small circular excavations marked by a crescent-shaped slot underneath. Feeding punctures may result in warts or scars, sometimes misshapen, knotty apples. Grubs in stone fruits render them unmarketable. Also, the punctures on peaches and plums afford entrance to brown rot spores. Economic losses for the country as a whole run between $8,000,000 and $17,000,000 a year.

Eggs hatch, about a week after being inserted in the fruit, into gray-white legless grubs with brown heads and curved bodies. They feed in the flesh for 2 weeks or more, by which time the fruit has probably fallen to the ground, although most cherries and some peaches remain on the tree until ripe. The larvae leave the fruit and enter the soil to pupate and the adults emerge in about a month. There are 2 generations in Virginia, sometimes a partial second in Delaware, but only 1 further north. Temperatures affect activity. Temperatures above 70°F. bring beetles out of hibernation, promote egg-laying, and usually mean severe damage from curculios.

Control. Spray apples with lead arsenate, at the rate of 3 pounds to 100 gallons, at petal fall, 7 to 10 days later, and again in 2 weeks. Schedules and poisons for peaches and other stone fruits vary widely. DDT and TDE are ineffective, but methoxychlor, 3 pounds per 100 gallons, applied as shucks push off and repeated 10 and 20 days later, has given good results in Connecticut. Gamma isomer of benzene hexachloride has given good control but may give an off-flavor to canned peaches though not to fresh fruit. Parathion is effective and gives no off-flavor but must be used with extreme safety precautions. Dieldrin is said to be excellent, at 1 pound of 25 per cent wettable powder per 100 gallons, at petal fall and 7 to 10 days later, but should not to be used near harvest. It, too, should be used following all precautions on the label. The New Jersey Experiment Station still suggests lead arsenate for home gardeners, even on stone fruits, ½ cup safened with 2 cups of hydrated lime used with sulfur in 5 gallons of spray, applied at shuck split and 10 days later.

It is always advantageous to pick up dropped fruits and destroy them by deep burial or soaking in waste oil, and to clean up possible winter shelters. It is also helpful to collect curculios during the season by placing a sheet under a tree and jarring off adults with a stick. There are several parasites and a useful fungus disease.

Quince Curculio (*Conotrachelus crataegi*)—The most serious pest confined to this host. It resembles the plum curculio but winters in the soil as a grub. The adult, broad, grayish brown without humps on its back, eats irregular cavities in the fruit, which may be knotty and misshapen. The white legless grubs feed in the fruit during summer but seldom cause it to drop. They leave the fruit before it falls naturally so that picking up fallen quinces is no help in control. Spraying with lead arsenate and lime, 4 pounds of each to 100 gallons, is recommended at petal fall and 10 days later.

Rhubarb Curculio (*Lixus concavus*)—Rhubarb Weevil, common from New England to Florida and west to Idaho. This is one of the largest of the snout beetles, ½ inch long, blackish but covered with a rusty yellow dust. It punctures rhubarb stalks and lays eggs in them but the larvae develop and feed on common curled dock. Hand-pick the beetles; destroy all dock plants growing near rhubarb.

Rose Curculio (*Rhynchites bicolor*)—Rose Snout Beetle, bright red with a black undersurface and black curved beak, ¼ inch long. Adults drill holes in buds of both wild and cultivated roses, the buds either not opening or producing petals riddled with holes. Small white larvae develop from eggs laid in hips but drop to the ground for pupation and hibernation. The rose curculio is particularly destructive in North Dakota and other cold regions, breeding in wild roses but swarming to cultivated roses in such numbers as to prevent almost all bloom. Western forms vary in color from black and red to black with a greenish luster. Spraying or dusting with DDT is recommended for control. See Plate XI.

CUTWORMS

High in the ranks of gardening headaches are the cutworms, smooth, fat, soft, repulsive caterpillars, larvae of night-flying moths, family Phalaenidae (formerly Noctuidae). Different species occur all over the world and injure almost all crops. The solitary or surface cutworms, including black, bronzed, and dingy, are most likely to harass the home gardener. They feed on plants near the surface of the ground, cutting off succulent stems of tomato, bean, cabbage, some other vegetables, and flowers soon after they are set out (Plate XXIII). Climbing cutworms go up the stems of herbaceous plants, shrubs, and vines, sometimes even climbing trees to eat buds, leaves, and fruit. Army cutworms work in large groups and are more prevalent in western gardens. Subterranean cutworms, including pale western and glassy, remain continuously in the soil, feeding on roots and underground stems.

Most surface cutworms have similar habits. They winter as partly grown larvae in cells in the soil, under trash or in clumps of grass. They start feeding in the spring, working only at night, and remaining coiled up in a ball just under the earth surface during the day. When full grown they dig down several inches in the soil to make a cell where they pupate from 1 to 8 weeks, or over winter. Southern species have several generations a year; most northern species have but 1, with moths appearing in summer.

51. Paper collar around a cabbage seedling—a simple way to foil cutworms.

Control. In the annual garden treat the soil before planting by dusting with 10 per cent toxaphene or 5 per cent DDT at the rate of ½ pound per 1000 square feet. If the cutworms are the type that do not feed above the surface of the soil, work the dust into the top inch. Instead of dusting you can spray with 2 ounces (6 level tablespoons) of 40 per cent toxaphene or 50 per cent DDT wettable powder in 2½ gallons of water for 1000 square feet.

Baits have long been used for cutworms. There are many on the market under different brand names, or you can mix your own by adding 6 tablespoons 40 per cent toxaphene wettable powder or 1½ tablespoons sodium fluosilicate or Paris green to 2½ quarts of bran, adding the poison slowly and stirring so every particle of bran is coated (wear leather or rubber gloves in the process). *Sprinkle* water on the mixture very slowly, stirring continuously, and stop when you have a crumbly mass. Spread the bait by hand late in the afternoon, ½ pound to 1000 square feet. If the garden is already planted, scatter it along rows or around newly set plants, but do not let it hit plants.

An old method of circumventing cutworms without chemicals is to place a collar of stiff paper or thin cardboard around each plant as it is set out. This should go down an inch or two into the soil to hold it in place and to foil worms working just under the surface.

Army Cutworm (*Chorizagrotis auxiliaris*)—A western species, appearing in armies, attacking all kinds of vegetation in Washington, Oregon, Wyoming, and Utah. Dieldrin is a possibility for control.

Black Cutworm (*Agrotis ypsilon*)—A surface cutworm, known also as the Greasy Cutworm. It is gray to brown to nearly black with a broken yellow line on the back and a pale line on each side, the whole appearance being shiny and greasy. The skin has convex granules, large and small. This species is widely distributed, is very fond of truck crops, and often cuts off tomatoes in home gardens. It is a restless feeder, cutting off many plants to satisfy its appetite. It lays eggs singly or a few together on leaves and stems, often on plants in new land. It winters as a pupa. Moths are reddish to brownish gray with silvery patches at bases and tips of fore wings. There are 2 generations in the North, often 4 in the South.

Bronzed Cutworm (*Nephelodes emmedonia*)—A northern species injurious to corn, grains, and grasses. The larva is dark bronzy brown, striped from head to tail with 5 clear pale lines about half as large as the brown area between, with a granulate skin. There is 1 generation, the winter being spent as a partly grown larva.

Dark-sided Cutworm (*Euxoa messoria*)—A common species that may climb to feed on tree foliage in the spring. The dull, pale green larvae also attack cultivated crops, wild grasses, and weeds. The moth is silver gray with dark mottled fore wings. DDT can be used as a spray for trees and some crops.

Dingy Cutworm (*Feltia subgothica*)—A northern species sometimes assuming climbing habit. Larvae are dull dingy brown with a broad buff-gray stripe down the back, divided into triangular areas on each segment, a narrow dark stripe on each side and coarse skin granules.

Glassy Cutworm (*Crymodes devastator*)—Widespread, except in the more southern states. It is a subterranean species preferring sod, and injurious to crops following sod. The larva is greenish white and rather translucent or glassy with a red head; the skin is not granulated.

Pale Western Cutworm (*Agrotis orthogonia*)—A subterranean form of great economic importance in the West, where it has destroyed millions of dollars' worth of small grains, beets, and alfalfa. The body is greenish gray, unmarked by lines or stripes, with a brown head and flat granules on the skin. The moth is mottled gray, nocturnal and diurnal; it appears in late August and September to lay whitish eggs in small batches just under the surface in soft soil. The larvae feed day and night, on cabbage, carrots, and onions as well as grains. Poison baits have no effect; the chemicals have to be washed into the soil.

Red-backed Cutworm (*Euxoa ochrogaster*)—Regularly destructive in many northern sections. Larvae are reddish on the back, feed on succulent plants, may be destructive to cereal, forage, and truck crops. They feed both above and below ground, hibernate in the egg stage. They succumb readily to poison bran bait.

Spotted Cutworm (*Amathes c-nigrum*)—Generally distributed, but rather scarce in the South, a surface feeder preferring garden crops. Larvae have wedge-shaped black dashes on each segment, a dark line through the spiracles, and a smooth skin. Eggs are laid singly, or in patches of 100 or more, on leaves. There may be 2 or 3 generations.

Variegated Cutworm (*Peridroma margaritosa*)—Probably the most widely known and important cutworm, present in many countries, damaging crops in the United States to the tune of several million dollars a year. The larva is ashy or light brown mottled with dark brown, a distinct yellow dot in the middle of each segment, often a dark W on the eighth segment, a smooth skin. The moth is grayish brown with dark mottled fore wings and a brassy luster. In early spring it lays small, white, ribbed eggs in large irregular masses on foliage and stems of plants or limbs of trees, or fences or buildings. The larvae eat foliage, buds, and fruits of garden crops, fruit trees, and vines; they injure flowers outdoors and in the greenhouse. There are 2 generations outdoors, more inside. Hand-picking, trapping under boards, poison bait, poison sprays or dusts are all used in control.

EARTHWORMS

Earthworms are friends of man! They are not insects but belong to the animal phylum Annelida, meaning rings, and are made up of many round segments. They are usually 2 to 10 inches long with slender, cylindrical soft bodies, bearing 8 bristlelike projections, setae, on each ring. They are hermaphrodites in that each worm produces ova and sperm cells, but they are not self-fertilized. They mate and the eggs are laid in a round case or capsule which eventually passes off over the head.

Earthworms have been considered by some people the most important of all animals. Charles Darwin estimated that earthworms bring up 7 tons of new soil for every acre of land, that good garden soil normally has about 53,000 worms per acre and poor field soil only half that many. There are earthworm farms raising worms to sell to gardeners with claims made for the wonders worked by so-called "hybrid" worms. However, if your soil is good enough to support earthworms you'll probably have plenty without having to buy them.

Earthworms live in moist soil containing decaying organic matter and crawl out at night to feed, or come out when their burrows are filled with water. They eat the soil and their digestive juices dissolve leafmold and other organic matter; then this digested earth is discharged in the form of castings, soil of the finest quality. Earthworms also drag leaves into their burrows, increasing the organic content of the soil in that way. Strong, healthy worms work from 3 to 8 feet underground, making the trip to the surface nightly to deposit castings. Their beneficial action may go much deeper than spade, plow, or rototiller.

Despite the fact that some gardeners want earthworms badly enough to support earthworm farms, others object to lumpy piles of castings on their fine front lawns. They can be a nuisance on golf courses and the rather recent oriental earthworm (*Pheretima hupeiensis*) is definitely a menace. It is known at scattered points from Connecticut to Miami but is concentrated in the Metropolitan New York area. It is light grass green, has a bad odor when crushed.

Older recommendations called for treating lawns with lead arsenate or Mowrah Meal, and lead arsenate is still good for common earthworms, at 5 to 10 pounds per 1000 square feet, but not for the oriental earthworm. Chlordane is better for the latter, 1 quart of 48 per cent chlordane emulsion in 10 gallons of water applied to 1000 square feet, or 3 pints of 20 per cent aldrin in 10 gallons. For the common earthworm chlordane can be used as a 50 per cent wettable powder at the rate of 1 pound per 1000 square feet. Toxaphene is also effective for earthworms, but DDT is not.

Earthworms in flowerpots are not welcome. Lime water is the time-honored remedy, either purchased at the drugstore or made at home by stirring 1 pint of freshly slaked lime into 2½ gallons of water and using it as soon as it clarifies. It is not a good idea to use this on potted azaleas or other plants preferring an acid soil. Treating the soil with chlordane is probably a better idea.

EARWIGS

Earwigs are beetlelike insects of the order Dermaptera, readily recognized by tail appendages which look like forceps. They have gradual metamorphosis, but biting mouth parts, feeding on decayed or living plant material and on other insects. They are nocturnal, living under bark or under stones or other debris on the ground during the day. They were named from the mistaken notion that they crawl into the ears of sleeping persons. There is only one species of much consequence to gardeners.

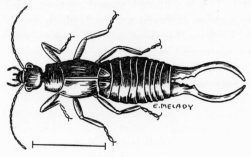

52. European earwig—large curved forceps denote male.

European Earwig (*Forficula auricularia*)—An introduced species, first discovered at Newport, Rhode Island, in 1911, with another colony appearing at Seattle, Washington, in 1915. Since then it has been reported as a garden pest from California, Colorado, Delaware, Idaho,

Maine, Massachusetts, New York, New Jersey, Oregon, Pennsylvania, and Utah. The insect is hard, dark brown, up to ⅘ inch long, with a pair of sharp pincers or forceps at the tip of the abdomen, protruding about ¼ the length of the body. These structures are larger and more curved in the male than in the female. The front wings are very short and the hind wings are folded up under them aided by the forceps. Earwigs seldom fly; they run.

The female lays a batch of smooth white eggs in early spring in the soil in any protected place and broods over them until they hatch. She watches over her young until the first molt, then leaves, often to lay another batch of eggs. Young nymphs feed on green plant shoots, eating holes in leaves of many different vegetables and flowers, and older earwigs work on blossoms, eating stamens and bases of petals, and often climb into fruit trees, especially apricot and peach, to dine on ripening fruit. They are quite a pest in houses, crawling over everything at night, hiding under cushions, dishes, or clothing, into crevices of various sorts.

Earwigs are more important in coastal areas. In California eggs are laid from December through February and the pest is most destructive from April through July. They are, however, beneficial as scavengers on decaying matter and in feeding on insect larvae, snails, and other slow-moving animals.

Control. A poison bait has been standard control: 6 pounds wheat bran mixed with ½ pound sodium fluosilicate and moistened with 1 pint of fish oil. This is scattered toward evening, thinly, over areas frequented by earwigs. It should not touch plants and is poisonous to pets and birds. Lindane, chlordane, or DDT dusts are now used, applied around hiding places and especially along fences and foundations of houses. To keep earwigs out of fruit trees dust the soil at the base of the trees and tree trunks with 10 per cent DDT about a month before fruit ripens.

EARWORMS

Corn Earworm (*Heliothis zea*)—Present practically everywhere that corn is grown, the worst corn pest in the United States, though more damaging to sweet corn than to field corn. The claim has been made that American farmers grow 2,000,000 acres of corn a year just to feed the earworm. It is damaging to other crops under different names, Tomato Fruitworm, Tobacco Budworm, Cotton Bollworm.

The caterpillars, larvae of moths, family Noctuidae, are nearly 2 inches long when full grown, yellowish or green or brown with lengthwise light and dark stripes (Plate XIII). In early plantings they attack buds and feed on unfolding leaves, giving a ragged appearance and possibly some stunting. They feed somewhat on tassels, but most of the damage is to the ear. The larvae feed from the tip, starting on fresh silk, then working down to the kernels, piling up masses of moist castings. Feeding on the silk prevents pollination, resulting in nubbins; feeding on the kernels introduces various mold fungi. Late season corn may be nearly 100 per cent infested.

As the tomato fruitworm, the larva begins feeding on foliage but soon works into green fruit, usually burrowing in at the stem end and sometimes destroying as much as 25 per cent of the tomatoes. They are restless caterpillars moving from one fruit to another and over to beans, cabbage, broccoli, and lettuce. As the cotton bollworm, the larva injures green bolls of cotton, and as the tobacco budworm, it works in tobacco buds. Other food plants include alfalfa and clovers, globe artichoke, chick pea, geranium, gladiolus, grape, mignonette, okra, peach, pea, peanut, pear, pepper, pumpkin, rose, squash, strawberry, sunflower, and vetch.

The earthworm winters as a pupa 2 to 6 inches below ground; the moths crawl out through exit holes prepared by the larvae. Adults vary in color; the front wings are grayish brown marked with dark lines shading to olive green; the hind wings are white with dark spots or markings; wingspread 1½ inches. They fly at dusk or on warm, cloudy days, feed on nectar of flowers, and lay 500 to 3000 eggs, yellowish, hemispherical, ridged, singly on host plants. There are 2 or 3 generations a season and moths of later generations often lay their eggs on corn silk. The newly hatched larva is very small, white with a black head, but grows rapidly, molting every 2 to 5 days. The pupae are seldom able to survive the winter north of Virginia, unless the weather is unusually warm and dry. Most northern infestations come from adults migrating from the South.

Control. There are some corn hybrids on the market partially resistant to corn earworm and there are many natural factors aiding in control, including the fact that one earworm will consume another. There are egg parasites; birds feed on earworm, often damaging ears in the process; moles destroy pupae; cold, moist weather reduces infestation. There is no practical chemical control for field corn, but sweet corn and corn grown for seed can be treated with an oil solution of

DDT (1½ pounds in 25 gallons of white mineral oil) applied to silks as a fine spray soon after silks appear. For a small quantity mix ¼ pint ready-made emulsifiable DDT solution with ¾ pint white mineral oil (procurable at a drugstore), add water to make 1 gallon, and shake in a covered container until the mixture is uniformly white. Use a small atomizer sprayer and only enough spray to wet the silks. This should be applied 2 or 3 days after silks appear, before they wilt. The worms can also be killed with a special corn earworm oil applied with a medicine dropper 3 to 7 days after silks first appear. Many such oils are on the market, some containing pyrethrins, some dichlorethyl ether, some DDT. Put the end of the medicine dropper ¼ inch into the mass of silk inside tip of the husk and squirt in about half a dropperful, 20 drops. Mark each treated ear with crayon or string to make sure it does not get a second dose. New suggestions are an endrin spray and turpentine dust.

On tomatoes, fruitworms can be controlled by applying pinches of bait, 1 part cryolite to 9 parts corn meal or cottonseed meal, to the fruit clusters, or tomatoes can be dusted with lead or calcium arsenate, 20 parts of either mixed with 80 parts hydrated spray lime, or with 5 per cent TDE, ending treatment when fruits are half grown. DDT is sometimes injurious to tomatoes. Dieldrin and Dilan are effective.

FLIES

Flies belong to the order Diptera, meaning 2-winged, the order including practically all insects with only 1 pair of wings—mosquitoes, gnats, and midges as well as flies. The second pair of wings is represented, if at all, by threadlike knobbed organs called halteres. There are some wingless flies and some with reduced wings, but the halteres are usually present. Fly mouth parts are adapted for piercing-sucking or for lapping. The compound eyes are very large and usually there are 3 simple eyes, ocelli. The larvae, called maggots, are footless, grublike creatures, usually soft, white or yellowish, with the head reduced. There is complete metamorphosis, with the pupal stage ordinarily passed inside the last larval skin, called a puparium.

There are a great many species of flies. Some are dangerous to man as carriers of human diseases and some are destructive to crops. But some flies are useful scavengers, cleaning up dead animals and plant wastes, and others are insect destroyers, either predators like the syrphid flies, or parasites, living in or on harmful insects.

Black Cherry Fruit Fly (*Rhagoletis fausta*)—Distributed through northern United States on cherry, wild cherry, pear, and plum. Except that the abdomen is entirely black and that it prefers sour cherries, this species is like the cherry fruit fly.

Carrot Rust Fly (*Psila rosae*)—A European pest first noticed in Ottawa in 1885, now rather generally present in northern states and quite injurious in gardens in the Pacific Northwest. Carrot is the most important host, with serious injury also to celery, parsnip, celeriac, and parsley. The damage is caused by maggots feeding on the root system, producing stunting, dwarfing, or complete destruction of plants. Larval excrement looks like iron rust in the root tunnels, whence the name rust fly. Soft-rot bacteria often follow the maggots, so that carrots decompose in a soft, vile-smelling mess.

The fly is small, ⅕ inch long, shiny dark green, with yellow hairs, legs, and head, black eyes. It lays eggs about the crowns of host plants. The yellowish maggots, ⅓ inch when grown, work down into the soil to the roots. They feed there for a month, then pupate in the soil to produce a second brood of flies in August. Sometimes a partial third brood damages late carrots and celery and injury may continue in storage. Brown puparia or maggots winter in soil.

Control. Carrots planted after June 1, and harvested early, may escape injury. Naphthalene flakes, 1½ pounds sprinkled along the row, have been recommended in the past, and gamma benzene hexachloride more recently, worked into the top 6 to 8 inches of soil before planting. Both may flavor the crop. Chlordane does not have that disadvantage and may be about as effective. Treating seed with calomel, as for the cabbage maggot, is helpful.

Cherry Fruit Fly (*Rhagoletis cingulata*)—A native, common in northern United States on cherry, wild cherry, pear, and plum; responsible for most of our wormy cherries. Adults are smaller than houseflies, black with yellow margins on the thorax, 2 white crossbands on the abdomen and dark band across the wings typical of fruit flies in the family Trypetidae. They emerge from brown puparia in the soil for a period of 5 or 6 weeks, starting in early June (about a week after the black cherry fruit fly). They fly to trees, feed 7 to 10 days by scraping surface of leaves and fruit, sucking up honeydew and sap, and lay eggs in young fruit through small slits cut in the flesh. The maggots, developing and eating inside the fruit, produce misshapen, undersized cherries, often with one side shrunken or decayed and turning red before maturity. When full grown, the worms eat their way out of the fruit, fall to the ground, and spend the next 10 months as puparia 2 or 3 inches below the surface.

Control. The only feasible method is spraying to kill the flies before they lay eggs. Cherries grown for canning, where fruit is washed by machinery, are sprayed with lead arsenate, 2 pounds, plus 2 pounds hydrated lime to 100 gallons of water. This dosage is increased to 2½ to 3 pounds in the West, but cut in half for the English Morello variety. Dusts containing 10 parts lead arsenate to 90 parts fine sulfur or hydrated lime are also used. The first application is applied when flies first appear, usually when Early Richmond cherries start to show color; the second is made 7 to 10 days later. Cherries grown commercially for sale as fresh fruit and those in home gardens are dusted with 75 per cent rotenone or sprayed with 3 pounds of a 4 per cent rotenone preparation in 100 gallons. Parathion is said to be as effective as lead arsenate and there is less of a residue problem, but it is far more dangerous in the application. EPN and Diazinon are also good.

Currant Fruit Fly (*Epochra canadensis*)—A native pest in many sections, common on currants and gooseberries in the West. The adult, yellow-bodied with dark-banded wings, about the size of a housefly, emerges from its puparium in the soil in April or May. It lays 100 to 200 eggs singly in fruit. Whitish maggots cause fruit to turn red and drop prematurely, feeding continuing for a few days in fruit on ground before maggots enter soil to pupate. There is 1 generation. Early-maturing varieties escape most of the damage. A spray consisting of 1 quart of syrup and 2 ounces of lead arsenate to 3 gallons of water, applied as soon as the flies emerge and before they can lay eggs, with a second spray in 10 days, is said to be the best control measure. Rotenone sprays or dusts might be wiser in home gardens.

Hessian Fly (*Phytophaga destructor*)—One of the most important world pests, causing great losses in wheat and some in barley and rye. The original home of the Hessian fly was probably Russia and it apparently came into this country in straw bedding used by Hessian troops during the Revolutionary War, being noted on Long Island in 1779. The flies are small, frail, black, the maggots greenish white, shiny. They draw sap from stems, causing them to break over, resulting in great reduction in yield.

Although the Hessian fly is not a problem in back-yard gardens, the method of control should interest all gardeners, for it uses forethought instead of toil and sweat. Entomologists in all the wheat states have worked out the life history of the fly so as to give a safe planting date in each location.

Lesser Bulb Fly (*Eumerus tuberculatus*)—Several small grayish or yellowish wrinkled maggots, up to ½ inch long, may be found in decaying bulbs of narcissus, hyacinth, amaryllis, onion, iris, shallot. The flies are blackish green with white markings on the abdomen, ⅓ inch long. They appear on flowers in late April or May and lay eggs at base of plants. The maggots can injure healthy bulbs but are more often found in sickly or injured stock. They pupate in the bulbs or in soil nearby; there are 2 generations a year. See Narcissus Bulb Fly for control.

Mediterranean Fruit Fly (*Ceratitis capitata*)—The most destructive member of the fruit fly family, a potential pest of many deciduous and citrus fruits, including peach, nectarine, plum, grapefruit, orange, apple, pear, quince, also coffee, and nearly a hundred other wild and cultivated fruits.

It was discovered in Florida in 1929, scattered over an area covering 10,000,000 acres. By a most remarkable eradication campaign, it was completely exterminated and no insects have been found in this country since 1930, although the fly is present in Bermuda and Hawaii and nearly all subtropical countries except North America. This is one of the few cases on record of actually eradicating a pest after it had become established over a rather wide area, but constant vigilance is needed to see that it does not re-enter this country in fruit or in luggage of travelers. More than 100 maggots have been found inside a single orange, though that is 3 or 4 times the usual number.

The promptness with which the eradication program was initiated, the fact that adequate state and federal funds were immediately made available, and the co-operation of all growers contributed to its success. The state was divided into infested zones, areas within a mile of property where the fly had been found, and protective zones, forming a 9-mile radius outside the infested zones. A host-free period was maintained from May 1 to October 1, prior to which time all ripe fruits had to be shipped or destroyed and during which time no vegetables could be grown which would reach a susceptible stage before October 1. That meant no vegetables or fruits which could be infested by maggots; adult flies were eliminated by sweetened poison-bait sprays.

Mexican Fruit Fly (*Anastrepha ludens*)—A Mexican pest, operating also over the border into Texas. This citrus insect is as serious in

Mexico as the Mediterranean fruit fly is in Mediterranean countries, but there are fewer host plants and not such wide distribution. It is primarily a pest of citrus fruits and mangoes, but sapotas, peaches, guavas, apples, pears, quinces, plums, apricots, and other fruits are included in quarantine regulations against the Mexican fruit fly. It is larger than a housefly, conspicuously marked in yellow or brown, and lays many long white eggs under the skin of fruits. Larvae take about 6 weeks for development, first in the rind, later in the pulp; pupation is in the ground and there are 4 generations a year. Fruit from the regulated area in Texas is treated, usually with vapor heat, to kill any possible larvae before being shipped.

Mushroom Flies (*Sciara* spp.)—Fungus gnats, often troublesome in potted plants in homes and greenhouses. The plants may lack vigor and lose color without visible injury to above-ground parts, though there may be small brown scars on the roots or fine roots may be eaten off. Small, active, threadlike white maggots are either in the root tissue or the soil around the plants. They may be followed by root rots. Adults, very small, sooty gray to black, long-legged, $\frac{1}{8}$ to $\frac{1}{10}$ inch long, deposit eggs in clusters which hatch in 4 to 6 days. Maggots feed for 5 to 14 days, pupate, and adults live about a week. Generations follow rapidly. Because they breed in manure and decaying vegetable matter potting soil rich in humus is very likely to have these flies.

Control. Drenching soil with bichloride of mercury will kill maggots but may injure a few plants; do not use in the same greenhouse with roses. Soil treatment with 1 per cent chlordane or lindane dust is good. Adults can be killed by dusting with DDT, lindane, chlordane, or pyrethrum.

Narcissus Bulb Fly (*Lampetia equestris*)—A European species introduced here in bulbs; a large, hairy, yellow and black fly about the size and appearance of a small bumblebee. It lays eggs on or near crowns of narcissus (preferred host), amaryllis (much favored), hyacinth, and other plants. Although hyacinths, lilies, scilla, tulips, and iris are often listed as hosts they are merely accidental hosts, with larvae failing to mature. The list of real hosts, according to observation in bulb fields, includes cooperia, eurycles, galanthus, galtonia, habranthus, hymenocallis, leucojum, pancratium, sprekelia, vallota, zephyranthes, and cipollini. Ordinarily but one maggot develops in each bulb. It is fat, white to yellow, wrinkled, $\frac{1}{2}$ to $\frac{3}{4}$ inch long. It soon reduces the bulb contents to a soft brown mass. Puparia are formed either in bulbs or in soil; there is usually 1 generation. Plants with infested bulbs have yellow stunted foliage or almost no growth. The bulbs feel spongy when squeezed.

Control. In home gardens discard all bulbs that feel soft to the touch. Protect amaryllis put out of doors for the summer with a covering of cheesecloth in early summer to keep the flies from laying eggs. Commercial growers have used hot-water treatment, fumigation with methyl bromide, and other means to kill larvae in the bulbs, but bulbs already infested may be of poor quality. Recent work indicates that preplanting treatments can give almost complete protection from attacks of the bulb fly in the field. Heptachlor, 25 per cent emulsifiable concentrate, used at the rate of ½ pound to 64 gallons of water, has been very satisfactory with bulbs dipped in the solution for only 10 minutes. Aldrin, dieldrin, and chlordane are also effective but require higher dosages and longer treatment.

Orchidfly (*Eurytoma orchidearum*)—Cattleya Fly, a serious orchid pest in greenhouses. The small, black, wasplike fly, ⅛ inch long, lays eggs in new growth and sometimes in pseudobulbs, causing swollen places; larvae feed in bulbs, stems, leaves, and buds of many kinds of orchids. Cut out the swollen areas; spray or dust with DDT to kill flies.

Syrphid Flies—These are the bright colored flower flies or hover flies, family Syrphidae. They resemble bees hovering over flowers to feed on nectar and are important in pollination. They are also attracted to tree sap and fermenting fruit. The larvae of a few species, including the narcissus bulb fly, feed on plants and some feed on decaying animal and vegetable matter, but the majority are predaceous on aphids, mealybugs, and other insects and are decidedly friends in the garden. Adults lay white, elongate eggs, singly, among groups of aphids. The larvae are footless, sluglike, tan or greenish; if you see some of these on your rosebuds, withhold sprays for a few days and give the maggots a chance to clean up. They have pointed jaws with which they grasp the aphid, raise it into the air, and suck out all body contents, leaving the empty skin. A single larva is credited with destroying an aphid a minute over long periods of time and there may be many larvae in a garden.

Tachinid Flies—A most beneficial group, family Tachinidae, with all species parasitic on other insects. Most resemble overgrown houseflies, bristly, gray or brown or black, mottled, without bright colors, usually found resting on foliage or flowers. Eggs are usually glued to the skin of the host insect, sometimes laid on foliage where the insect will eat them along with the leaf. The larvae feed internally on their hosts, which almost always die. Many species-have been imported for our benefit. One, brought in to help control gypsy and brown-tail moths, parasitizes over 100 species of caterpillars. Many are parasitic on cutworms and armyworms.

Walnut Husk Fly (*Rhagoletis completa*)—Native in central states on wild black walnuts, injurious to English walnuts on the West coast, causing a black staining of the shell. The adult is a little smaller than a housefly with transparent wings which have dark, transverse crossbars. The flies lay eggs in enveloping husks in July and August. The maggots hatch in 4 to 7 days, tunnel through the husks for several weeks, then drop to the ground, or fall with the nuts, and pupate in the soil. Some emerge as flies the next season, others remain in the ground for another year. The decaying husk stains the shell indelibly, making walnuts unsalable even though the kernels are sound. Cryolite applied as a spray or dust has been standard control.

FRUITWORMS

Fruitworms are caterpillars or grubs infesting fruit.

Cherry Fruitworm (*Grapholitha packardi*)—Larva of a native moth found from Colorado north and west. The worms hibernate in bark cells or stubs of pruned branches. Small gray moths deposit eggs singly on cherries in May or early June. Hatching in 10 days, the pinkish larvae, ⅜ inch long when grown, bore into the fruit, often causing large losses. There is 1 generation. Sprays for cherry fruit fly control the fruitworm in the Pacific Northwest. Parathion and methoxychlor sprays have been effective in Colorado.

Cranberry Fruitworm (*Acrobasis vaccinii*)—Present in nearly every cranberry bog; may also infest blueberries. The moth is ash gray mottled with black, has a ¾-inch wingspread. It lays eggs on berries in July; pale green larvae eat into berries near the stem, closing the hole with silk. One larva eats out the pulp of 2 or 3 berries before attaining full size, ⅞ inch. There is 1 generation. Infested berries shrivel and on Cape Cod nearly half the crop may be lost. Spraying or dusting with ryania or rotenone is quite effective. Control recommendations include flooding bogs for 10 to 14 days after harvesting and early in May. All infested berries removed by screening should be destroyed. Methoxychlor has controlled this fruitworm in blueberries.

Eastern Raspberry Fruitworm (*Byturus rubi*)—Most destructive to raspberry and loganberry in northern states. Light brown beetles, ⅛ to $\frac{1}{16}$ inch long, feed on buds, blossoms, and tender leaves, and lay eggs on blossoms and young fruits. Slender grubs, white with brown patches, bore into fruits, making them unfit for eating. As the fruit ripens larvae drop to the ground and pupate in soil. They winter as adults, still in the soil, emerging about mid-April. Dusting with 1 per cent rotenone or 5 per cent DDT just after blossom buds show and again just before blooms open is helpful. Cultivate the soil thoroughly in late summer.

Gooseberry Fruitworm (*Zophodia convolutella*)—Present in northern states on currants and gooseberries. The moth has ashy wings with dark markings; the larva is yellow green with a pinkish cast, darker lines along the sides. Pupae winter in the ground; moths lay eggs in flowers. Larvae completely hollow out fruit, one worm destroying several berries. Spray with arsenicals before the calyx closes. Destroy infested berries.

Green Fruitworm (*Lithophane antennata*)—Generally distributed over eastern states. The larvae feed on foliage of apple, ash, maple, and other deciduous trees, and in green fruits of apple, pear, and cherry. The grayish moths emerge in fall, hibernate in woodlands or sheltered nooks in the orchard, and lay eggs in early spring on twigs and branches. The larvae are apple green with white stripes and slightly raised tubercles, up to $1\frac{1}{2}$ inches long. They eat out the side or one end of young apples, destroying them entirely, or making them worthless. Spray with DDT or lead arsenate at the cluster bud stage, when fruit buds have separated but before they open; later sprays for codling moth have little effect on fruitworms.

Tomato Fruitworm—See Corn Earworm under Earworms.

Western Raspberry Fruitworm (*Byturus bakeri*)—Similar to the eastern raspberry fruitworm.

GALLS

Insect galls are swellings or deformities of plant tissues resulting from the irritation caused by the feeding of the insect or a toxin injected during the feeding process. Such plant deformities may be blisters or projections on the leaves, swellings on stem or twig, bud galls, flower galls, or root galls. The late Dr. E. P. Felt stated in *Plant Galls and Gall Makers* that there are more than 2000 American insect galls, 805 the work of gall wasps, nearly 700 caused by gall midges, 80 by aphids or psyllids, and the rest by sawflies, jointworms, beetles, moths, true bugs, and mites. Members of the beech family are favored by 740 of the 805 gall wasps and oaks by 731. Many galls have been included in this book under the name of the insect producing them; e.g., eastern spruce gall aphid, grape pylloxera, chrysanthemum gall midge, etc. A few others are given here. There is seldom any control except cutting out infested portions and most are not very important to gardeners.

Ash Flower Gall (caused by a mite, *Eriophyes fraxiniflora*)—The stamens and flowers of white ash are transformed into galls, ¼ to ¾ inch in diameter, drying and remaining on trees. Dormant applications of a miscible oil are supposed to give control.

Blackberry Knot Gall (due to a gall wasp, *Diastrophus nebulosus*)—Knotty, rounded, or elongate swellings, 2 to 6 inches long, often with deep longitudinal furrows, are formed in stems.

Blueberry Stem Gall (due to a gall wasp, *Hemadas nubilipennis*)—A kidney-shaped gall, first green then reddish brown, common on blueberry stems.

Dogwood Club Gall (caused by a midge, *Mycodiplosis alternata*)—Common on flowering dogwood, a club-shaped gall in twigs, ½ to 1 inch long. The reddish-brown midge attacks young shoots in late May; development of small orange larvae in galls is completed by September when they drop to the ground. Cut off and burn swollen twigs while larvae are present.

Grapevine Tomato Gall (caused by a midge, *Lasioptera vitis*)—A green or reddish swelling in new growth, leaf or tendril, ¼ to ¾ inch long, with pinkish maggots inside.

Hackberry Nipple Gall (caused by a psyllid, *Pachypsylla celtidis-mamma*)—Small round galls opening on underside of leaves look like nipples. Spraying with nicotine sulfate in a summer oil is suggested.

Maple Bladder Gall (caused by a mite, *Vasates quadripes*)—Bladderlike galls, first red, then green, then black, single or in clusters, on upper surface of leaves. They may be thick enough to deform leaves with injury worse on young silver or soft maples. The white or pinkish mites winter in bark crevices or bud scales and migrate in late April when the buds break. A dormant lime-sulfur spray will control this but is hard to use near houses. Malathion, 6 to 7 pints of an emulsion in 100 gallons of water, has been effective applied in April before buds open.

Mossy Rose Gall (caused by a gall wasp, *Rhodites rosae*)—A globular mass of mosslike filaments surrounding a cluster of hard cells, each of which contains one larva. The galls appear in June and July with larvae remaining in the cells until spring. There is no control except removal of infested canes.

Oak Galls. These are far too numerous to mention individually. There are a great many small leaf galls as well as the familiar round brown galls known as oak apples, each of which is really a leaf deformed by a gall wasp. An interesting gall on white, chestnut, and basket oaks is the wool-sower, a globular, white, pink-marked woolly growth, 1½ to 2 inches across, on twigs. There is nothing for the gardener to do about oak galls.

Rose Root Gall (caused by a wasp, *Rhodites radicum*)—A large conspicuous swelling, 1 to 2 inches across at the roots of cultivated roses. It is not very common.

Witch-hazel Cone Gall (caused by an aphid, *Hormaphis hamamelidis*)—Conical galls, ½ inch high, green sometimes tipped with red, growing out of upper leaf surface, very common. After developing in the gall, some of the aphids fly to birch for summer generations, but they return to witch-hazel in the fall.

GRASSHOPPERS

Grasshoppers belong to the order Orthoptera, family Acrididae. They are the locusts of the Bible and the locusts that even in our own time may measure 2000 square miles in a swarm over the Red Sea. In 1740, when they attacked crops in Massachusetts, the colonists, armed with bundles of brush, drove them into the ocean by the millions. In 1818, grasshoppers destroyed the crops of Montana settlers; in 1877 they halted the covered wagons rolling west. Yearly damages still run into many millions, but much better control measures have been developed in the last few years.

Grasshoppers are moderately long insects, slightly deeper than wide, usually dark, mottled, with prominent jaws and eyes, antennae always much shorter than the body and an "ear," hearing organ or tympanum, on each side of the first abdominal segment. Their hind legs are enlarged for jumping and the abdomen of the female ends in 4 hard movable prongs which function like a miniature posthole digger when she is inserting her eggs an inch or so into the ground. The eggs are laid in masses of 15 to 50 according to species and surrounded by a gummy substance which hardens to form a case, the whole being called an egg pod. Grasshoppers feed in the daytime in the sun. They are most numerous in states where the average annual rainfall is between 10 and 30 inches, attacking cultivated crops and range vegetation, destroying clothing and fabrics in houses, polluting water in wells and reservoirs, presenting a hazard to motorists.

There are about 600 species in the United States, 5 of them doing 90 per cent of the damage to crop plants.

American Grasshopper (*Schistocerca americana*)—Sometimes damaging field crops and fruits in Alabama, Georgia, Florida, Louisiana, and Mississippi. It is large, 2½ inches long with wingspread of 4 inches, colored tan, white, and pink.

Carolina Grasshopper (*Dissosteira carolina*)—Not very destructive but common through the country, numerous along roadsides in late summer. It is brown, mottled with gray and red, hind wings black with yellow margins, nearly 2 inches long, flies readily when disturbed.

Clear-winged Grasshopper (*Camnula pellucida*)—Variable in color, yellow to dark brown with black spots, 1 inch long, migratory habits. Generally distributed but most damaging in Utah, Wyoming, Montana, and Idaho on grains, grasses, garden crops, vineyards, orchards. Egg pods may be numerous in breeding areas and plowing up such areas is quite effective in controlling this particular grasshopper.

Differential Grasshopper (*Melanoplus differentialis*)—Usually yellow with contrasting black markings, clear, glossy outer wings, 1½ inches long; hind thighs with black bars like chevrons. Fairly rare in the East, it feeds on succulent field and garden crops, deciduous fruit trees in other sections. In dry years it persists only in irrigated areas or along streams.

Eastern Lubber Grasshopper (*Romalea microptera*)—Sometimes called Florida Lubber, a large, stout, short-winged, clumsy locust attacking grass, flowers, and ornamental trees and shrubs in Florida and other southern states.

Migratory Grasshopper (*Melanoplus mexicanus mexicanus*)—Named Rocky Mountain Grasshopper in its extreme migratory phase. Reddish brown with an irregular black patch on the collar, 1 inch long. Adults are strong fliers, migrating hundreds of miles, destroying crops wherever the swarm passes.

Red-legged Grasshopper (*Melanoplus femur-rubrum*)—Reddish brown above, sulfur yellow underneath, wings colorless, hind legs red, ¾ inch long. It is common along roadsides, injurious to legumes, particularly to soybeans in the Middle West, where it cuts through pods, causing seeds to mold. It also feeds on other truck crops, vines, and fruit trees.

Two-striped Grasshopper (*Melanoplus bivittatus*)—Common, widely distributed pest of grains, vegetables, fruit trees, all cultivated crops. It is stout, 1¼ inches long, greenish yellow with 2 light stripes down its back.

Control. Until the advent of chlordane, poison-bran baits were the chief means of fighting grasshoppers, but now dusting or spraying with new chemicals is considered more effective and economical. Insecticides in present use with recommended dosages of the actual chemical per acre are: aldrin, 1½ to 2 ounces; chlordane, ½ to 1 pound; dieldrin, ¾ to 1 ounce; heptachlor, 3 to 4 ounces; toxaphene, 1 to 1½ pounds. These can be applied as sprays or dusts, with ground equipment or by airplane. If used as dusts increase dosage per acre by 50 per cent. In formulating sprays figure the percentage of chemical in the concentrate purchased and the amount of spray your equipment delivers per acre.

For small home gardens, dust ornamentals with chlordane, lindane, or DDT. Use methoxychlor for fruits and vegetables near edible stage.

GROUND PEARLS. See under Scale Insects.

HORNWORMS

Hornworms are large caterpillars, larvae of sphinx moths, bearing a pointed projection at the end of the body that looks like a horn. The two hornworms commonly found in gardens feed rather interchangeably on tobacco, tomato, and other solanaceous plants.

Tobacco Hornworm (*Protoparce sexta*)—Sometimes called Southern Hornworm, distributed throughout the Americas. This is an awe-inspiring caterpillar, 3 or 4 inches long, green with 7 oblique white stripes and a red horn projecting at the rear (Plate XIX). It feeds voraciously on tomato, tobacco, eggplant, pepper, potato, groundcherry, and related weeds.

The hornworm winters in soil as a brown, hard-shelled pupa that has a slender tongue projecting down like a pitcher handle. The adult sphinx moth, also called a hawk or hummingbird moth, emerges in May or June to feed at dusk, hovering over petunias and similar flowers to sip nectar with its long tongue. It has a wingspread of 4 or 5 inches, is gray or brown with white and dark mottlings and 6 yellow spots on each side of the abdomen. The female lays greenish-yellow eggs singly on underside of leaves. Young larvae hatch in a week, feed for 3 to 4 weeks, molting 5 times, then pupate 3 or 4 inches deep in the soil. There is 1 generation in the North, 2 or more in the South.

Control. Picking off caterpillars by hand is often sufficient control in the small garden. If hornworms are too numerous, keep plants dusted with 5 per cent TDE (DDD) or with a mixture of 1 part calcium arsenate to 3 parts hydrated lime. Some states suggest 10 per cent TDE; some say equal parts of calcium arsenate and lime, others only 1 part to 4 or 5 of lime. Peppers can be dusted or sprayed with DDT, but this is not often recommended for tomatoes. Treatment should cease before tomato fruit is half grown to prevent toxic residues. Do not destroy caterpillars covered with oval white objects attached to the skin by one end. These are cocoons of a parasitic braconid wasp. The female thrusts her eggs inside the hornworm body; when the larvae hatch they feed for a while inside the caterpillar, then eat their way outside to spin cocoons. If left undisturbed more wasps will emerge to parasitize other hornworms. See Figure 86.

Tomato Hornworm (*Protoparce quinquemaculata*)—Almost identical with the tobacco species, feeding on the same plants, controlled in the same way. There are 5 instead of 6 yellow spots on each side of the abdomen of the moth, and 2 narrow stripes extending diagonally across each hind wing. The larva has 8 instead of 7 diagonal white stripes and they join a horizontal white stripe, forming a series of V's. The horn is green with black sides.

KATYDIDS

Katydids, order Orthoptera, family Tettigoniidae, are long-horned grasshoppers, characterized by long, hairlike antennae; 4-segmented tarsi; with auditory organs, when present, at the base of front tibiae (in true grasshoppers the "ear" is on the abdomen); and a swordlike ovipositor in the female. The males sing by rubbing front wings together, each species having a characteristic song. They are mostly plant feeders but cannot really be called garden pests. Control measures are unnecessary.

Broad-winged Katydid (*Microcentrum rhombifolium*)—Widely distributed in the East, leaf green, about 1½ inches long. It is best known for its eggs, grayish brown, oval, very flat, ¼ inch long, laid on twigs in double rows, each egg overlapping the next. Gardeners, astonished at the sight of such a prominent display of large eggs, often fear they have a new garden menace.

Fork-tailed Bush Katydid (*Scudderia furcata*)—Widely distributed, taking its name from forked appendages at the tip of the male abdomen; arboreal in habit, pale green, medium size, with long, narrow tegmina (wing covers). Eggs are laid in the edges of the leaves between upper and lower leaf surfaces.

Northern Katydid (*Pterophylla camellifolia*)—True Katydid, also called Eastern Katydid, heard after dusk in late summer saying "Katy did, Katy didn't." The song is made by special stridulating organs on the wings of the males, though the females can make faint sounds. Adults have dark gauzy green wings, live in colonies in highest treetops in the North. Eggs are laid in crevices of bark of trees or soft shrubbery, hatch in the spring, and reach adult form by July or August. There is only 1 generation. The range extends from New England to Georgia and west to Illinois.

LEAF CRUMPLER

Leaf Crumpler (*Acrobasis indigenella*)—Abundant in upper Mississippi Valley and some other northern states on apple, plum, prune, crabapple, quince, cherry, wild cherry, wild plum, and pear. The caterpillar is dark brown, somewhat hairy, ⅓ to ½ inch long. It winters in cocoons, ¾ to 1½ inches long, made by crumpling dead leaves and tightly fastening them to an apple twig. In spring, as apple buds open, the worms loosen their cases and feed on buds, fastening new leaves together with silken threads. They pupate in May and June. The moths, with brown, white-mottled wings, expanding only ¾ inch, lay eggs on new leaves. Young caterpillars, hatching in 2 or 3 weeks, make curved, cornucopia-shaped cases in which they feed for the rest of the season, then use for winter quarters.

Control. If trees are sprayed regularly for codling moth and other pests, leaf crumplers will not be much of a nuisance. If present, lead arsenate should be applied at cluster bud, calyx, and 3 weeks after calyx stages. If young trees are infested, spray in August with lead arsenate and soybean flour.

LEAF CUTTERS

Maple Leaf Cutter (*Paraclemensia acerifoliella*)—Also called Maple Casebearer, a native pest of sugar maple, sometimes beech, rarely on red maple and birch. The small caterpillar, not over ¼ inch long, dull white with rusty head and thorax, eats as a leaf miner for 10 to 14 days, then cuts out oval sections, up to a half inch in size, to make a case for wintering in leaf litter. Foliage may be nearly destroyed. The moth, with iridescent blue fore wings, fringed, smoky brown hind wings, emerges in May. Control by raking and burning fallen leaves in autumn, spraying with lead arsenate and fish oil in June.

Morning-glory Leaf Cutter (*Loxostege obliteralis*)—A greenish caterpillar with dark spots, ¾ inch long, resembling the garden webworm. It cuts off stalks as leaves wilt and eats large holes in leaves, hiding during the day in shelters made by rolling and folding wilted leaves. The adult is a yellowish moth with faint brown markings. Other hosts include dahlia, mint, sunflower, violet, wandering Jew, and zinnia. Spray or dust with lead arsenate to kill young caterpillars; handpick others.

Waterlily Leaf Cutter (*Nymphula obliteralis*)—The larvae of this moth are aquatic, breathing by means of gills, feeding on waterlily and other plants (often in greenhouses) in boatlike cases made by cutting oval pieces out of the leaves and fastening them together with silk. Wind, blowing the cases about a pool, helps to spread the infestation. Foliage is reduced to a ragged, rotten mass. Gather and destroy cases. If infestation is severe, lower water in pool and dust with equal parts pyrethrum powder and tobacco dust. Repeat in 20 minutes. The first application drives the caterpillars out of their cases; the second kills them. Fish must be removed from the pool before treatment and not returned until the water has been changed.

LEAF FOLDER

Grape Leaf Folder (*Desmia funeralis*)—Generally distributed east of the Rocky Mountains, also found in California, on wild and cultivated grapes, Virginia creeper, and redbud. The caterpillar is glossy, translucent yellow green on the sides, darker above, with brown head, 1 inch long. It feeds inside folded leaves. In the East, injury is little more than ragged foliage, but in California there may be extensive damage to late-maturing grape varieties. Larval attacks are followed by decay of fruit; leaves are rolled tightly instead of being folded over. The moths, black with white markings, wing expanses ¾ to 1 inch, emerge from inside rolled or folded leaves for a summer brood. There are 2 generations in warm climates, but only 1 in New England where pupation is in the soil. An arsenical spray is effective if applied before larvae are protected by folded leaves. There are a number of parasites.

LEAFHOPPERS

Leafhoppers belong to the insect order Homoptera, family Cicadellidae. There are around 175 genera and 2000 species in our country. Most of them are small, not over ½ inch long, and they feed on foliage of almost all types of plants, usually sucking from the undersurface and hopping away quickly when disturbed. They have piercing-sucking mouth parts and gradual metamorphosis, nymphs resembling adults except for wings. The two pairs of wings are of uniform texture and are held in a rooflike position when at rest. Leafhoppers have a long, wedge-shaped appearance, and the front margin of the head, as seen from above, is either triangular or broadly curved. The large eyes are at the side of the head and small, hairlike antennae arise in front of the eyes. There are 2 ocelli between the eyes and a double row of spines on the underside of the hind tibiae. They expel honeydew.

Withdrawal of plant sap from the host causes loss of color, often in a stippled pattern, sometimes stunting and general decline in vigor. Some leafhoppers cause a diseased condition in the plant known as hopperburn, which may be due to a toxin injected during the feeding process. Leafhoppers act as vectors of many important virus diseases: aster yellows, elm phloem necrosis, curly top of sugar beets and other plants, Pierce's disease of grapes, yellow dwarf of potatoes, peach yellows, cranberry false blossom, and many others.

Leafhoppers are controlled by contact insecticides, formerly nicotine sulfate or pyrethrum, now largely by DDT, which has proven particularly useful because of its residual action.

Apple Leafhopper (*Empoasca mali*)—Present east of the Rocky Mountains, except in the lower Mississippi Valley. During late summer and fall apple foliage turns pale, the green upper surface flecked with many small white spots, the underside covered with dark bits of excrement, often white cast skins. Nymphs and adults are greenish white. There is 1 generation a year and no migration to another type of host, as with the potato leafhopper, but this species has been recorded on roses as well as apple. Hibernation is in the egg stage under loose bark.

Beet Leafhopper (*Circulifer tenellus*)—A western species, found eastward to Illinois and Missouri, dangerous as a vector of curly top, a virus disease (Plate XXIV). The pale greenish or yellowish leafhoppers, ⅛ inch long, are darker toward winter, which they spend as adults on salt bush, Russian thistle, greasewood, filaree, and other wild hosts in arid foothills or desert. Egg-laying takes place in March and the first generation matures on these wild plants. From early May to June adults of this generation fly in swarms, often hundreds of miles, to sugar-beet fields. As they feed they introduce the curly-top virus. They are the only known vectors of this disease, which makes the leaf veins warty, petioles kinked, leaves rolled and brittle on the edges, plants stunted and finally killed.

The leafhoppers insert their eggs in veins, leaf petioles, or stems. Nymphs hatch in 2 weeks, become adult in 3 to 8 weeks more. There may be 3 or more generations. When the sugar beets are plowed out, the leafhoppers, carrying the virus, swarm to neighboring gardens, infecting tomato, table beets, cantaloupe, celery, cucumber, pepper, spinach, squash, and other vegetables, and many flowers—geranium, nasturtium, pansy, zinnia, among others. Symptoms in all plants are the same—curled leaves, stunting, often death.

Control. Although the leafhoppers can be killed by dusting or spraying with DDT, they have probably already spread the disease. Rogue out plants with curly top as soon as noticed; eliminate winter weed hosts as far as possible. The fog belt along the coast of California is fairly free from leafhopper attack and there are a number of natural enemies.

Blunt-nosed Cranberry Leafhopper (*Scleroacus vaccinii*)—Famous as the vector of cranberry false-blossom disease, found from Wisconsin east. The hopper is light brown, short, with a rounded blunt nose. It winters in the egg stage and hatches in May; there is 1 brood a year. Flooding the bogs in late June when young nymphs are present, spraying or dusting with pyrethrum, and use of resistant varieties give fair control of the disease and its vector.

Clover Leafhopper (*Aceratagallia sanguinolenta*)—Vector of yellow dwarf of potatoes, prevalent when potatoes are grown next to clover. The virus winters in the adult leafhopper.

Elm Leafhopper (*Scaphoideus luteolus*)—White-banded Elm Leafhopper, vector of elm phloem necrosis, which has killed so many elms in Ohio and neighboring states. Eggs wintered on elm bark hatch about May 1; nymphs crawl to leaves and feed on veins; adults move from diseased to healthy trees. DDT-xylene sprays are used as for elm bark beetles.

Grape Leafhopper (*Erythroneura comes*)—A native leafhopper occurring in all grape-growing regions. Adults, slender, ⅛ inch long, yellowish with red markings, winter in weeds and refuse and fly to the vines when grape leaves are half grown, feed for 2 or 3 weeks, and insert eggs into leaf tissues. Pale greenish nymphs start sucking in May, are full grown in 3 to 5 weeks. There are 2 generations in the North, usually 3 in California and the South.

Grape is the principal host, but feeding may occur on apple, beech, blackberry, currant, dewberry, gooseberry, grasses, maple, plum, raspberry, strawberry, Virginia creeper, Boston ivy. Small white spots appear all over grape and other vine leaves; they later turn brown and fall prematurely, interfering with proper ripening of berries.

Control. Spray thoroughly with DDT immediately after bloom, at rate of 1½ pounds 50 per cent wettable powder to 100 gallons of water, or 1½ tablespoons per gallon.

Japanese Leafhopper (*Orientus ishidae*)—An introduced pest reported in 1919, now well distributed in northeastern fruit districts, known on apple, aralia, and hazel. It is larger than the apple leafhopper, ⅕ inch long, dark gray, wings milky with brown veins, legs black; nymphs brown with white spots. Leaves turn yellow where nymphs first congregate, often near watersprouts; later triangular sectors of leaves all over tree are killed. Damage may be extensive with weakening of tree. Eggs winter near base of trunk, being hatched in late May or early June. Spraying with DDT or parathion is effective.

Norway-maple Leafhopper (*Alebra albostriella*)—Causing some injury near New York City. Swollen twigs on Norway maple, looking as if diseased, are produced by eggs laid under bark. Foliage is infested with numerous small, yellowish hoppers. Another leafhopper infests Japanese maples.

Plum Leafhopper (*Macropsis trimaculata*)—An eastern pest important as the vector of peach yellows and little peach, virus diseases affecting peaches, nectarines, plums, almonds, apricots. The leafhoppers, blunt, short, with 3 dark spots, are strong fliers and may travel long distances, although usually staying near the tree where they were hatched. There is 1 generation, eggs laid on peach twigs in July and August not hatching until the next May.

Poplar Leafhopper (*Idiocerus scurra*)—Occasionally abundant on poplar, also found on willow and hawthorn.

Potato Leafhopper (*Empoasca fabae*)—The most injurious potato pest in eastern United States, found in some western states, although there its place is usually taken by other species (intermountain, arid, and western potato leafhoppers). This small, ⅛ inch long, wedge-shaped green leafhopper, with white spots on head and thorax, plays many roles (Plate XIV). Down South where it shines as a bean pest it is called the "bean jassid." It is responsible for dahlia stunt, potato tipburn or hopperburn, peanut pouts, and other "diseases," as well as normal leafhopper injury.

Instead of hibernating in the North the potato leafhopper winters in the Gulf states, breeding on alfalfa and other legumes and weeds. Coming north in the spring, it feeds first on apple foliage, migrating to beans as soon as the plants are up, often migrating suddenly in swarms. When potatoes are several inches high the hoppers move over to them, laying eggs in main veins and in petioles, each female laying 2 or 3 eggs a day for 3 or 4 weeks. The eggs hatch in 10 days with nymphs full grown in about 2 weeks, at the fifth molt. There are 2 generations in Middle Atlantic states, so that both early and late potatoes are infested.

On potato, eggplant, rhubarb, horsebean, dahlia, and sometimes rose the condition known as hopperburn is prevalent. First a triangular brown spot appears at the tip of the leaf, then similar triangles at the end of each lateral leaflet, then the entire margin rolling inward and turning brown, often appearing scorched, and with only a small part of each leaf along the midrib staying green. The yield of potatoes is cut enormously; dahlias may be so stunted they do not flower. I often find the tipburn effect on rose foliage in August but seldom any rolling. Authorities are not too clear on how this effect is produced. Some state that the potato leafhopper mechanically plugs the phloem and xylem vessels in the leaves so that transport of food materials is impaired.

On bean and apple, leafhopper feeding produces whitening of foliage and sometimes stunting, crinkling, and curling, but not the browned, burned effect. In California the potato leafhopper punctures and blemishes the rind of citrus fruit.

Control. Spray potato fields with DDT, 2 to 3 pounds 50 per cent wettable powder to 100 gallons of water or bordeaux mixture, starting when plants are 4 to 8 inches high; repeat at 7- to 10-day intervals.

Some recommend that the dosage of DDT be doubled if it is added to bordeaux, for the lime has some inhibiting effect. A 5 per cent DDT dust is satisfactory, but talc or pyrophyllite should be used as the diluent, not lime. In spraying ornamentals in small gardens use 2 tablespoons 50 per cent DDT wettable powder per gallon or DDT dust, being sure to cover undersurface of dahlia leaves very thoroughly and to start before the leaves curl. Use pyrethrum spray or dust for edible plants near harvest.

Red-banded Leafhopper (*Graphocephala coccinea*)—Probably our most conspicuous leafhopper, with its wings gaudily decorated with alternate bands of magenta and green or blue. It is common on garden flowers, including aster, calendula, gladiolus, hollyhock, rose, and zinnia, but the injury is not serious.

53. Rose leafhopper, and feeding pattern caused by sucking.

Rose Leafhopper (*Edwardsiana rosae*)—Imported from Europe, attacking most plants of the rose family but primarily apple and rose, being especially serious on apple in the Northwest. It hibernates in the egg stage, usually on rose canes or apple bark. The adults, creamy white to light yellow, produce characteristic light stippling and sometimes a yellowing and slight curling of foliage but no hopperburn. Eggs for the second generation, which defaces rose foliage late into the fall, are laid in July in leaf veins and petioles. DDT is very effective in controlling this leafhopper, but it so enhances the mite problem on roses I personally do not use it for the spring generation, getting along with pyrethrum and rotenone in my combination spray. But for the late fall brood, which is much more serious in New Jersey, I do add 1 tablespoon of 50 per cent DDT wettable powder to each gallon of rose spray. Nicotine sulfate will kill those hoppers hit with the spray.

Six-spotted Leafhopper (*Macrosteles fascifrons*)—Aster Leafhopper. This species is tremendously important to gardeners because it transmits the virus disease known as aster yellows, not only to asters but to many other ornamentals, among them alyssum, anchusa, browallia, capemarigold, cornflower, calendula, chrysanthemum, cineraria, clarkia, coreopsis, cosmos, gaillardia, gypsophila, lobelia, mignonette, petunia, phlox, poppy, rudbeckia, scabiosa, schizanthus, strawflower, sweet william, vinca, and zinnia. Lettuce and celery are particularly subject to yellows, and the virus may also cause disease symptoms on carrot, parsnip, parsley, and other vegetables as well as grain crops. Symptoms vary with the different plants, but there is usually a general yellowing of foliage rather than a mottling or mosaic. There is a clearing of affected veins, plants are always stunted and usually distorted, with excessive branching and shortening of internodes, and virescence (greening) of the flower petals. Lettuce develops a condition known as rabbit ear.

The leafhopper responsible for all this trouble is greenish yellow with 6 black spots. It winters in the egg stage on perennial weeds or flowers. The virus is not carried in the egg and the hoppers have to feed on infected plants in spring and then hold the virus 10 to 18 days before it can be transmitted to asters and other garden plants. Nymphs in early instars do not transmit the disease because the period between each molt is shorter than the latent period of the virus. At normal summer temperatures the life cycle is about 40 days, so there may be several generations a season.

Control. DDT sprays or dusts will reduce leafhopper populations but not entirely eliminate aster yellows. Commercial growers protect their asters with cheesecloth or muslin, not coarser than 20 threads to the inch, on wooden frames. In home gardens all diseased plants should be rogued immediately, before the virus can be spread. Pyrethrum sprays or dusts will kill hoppers actually hit, and are advised for vegetables near the edible stage.

Southern Garden Leafhopper (*Empoasca solana*)—Similar to the potato leafhopper but with a more southern distribution, although occurring in New York. It infests flowers and other ornamentals, aster, dahlia, willow, amaranthus, tamarix, and potato, peanut, grape, cantaloupe, sweetpotatoes and other fruits and vegetables.

Three-banded Leafhopper (*Erythroneura tricincta*)—On grape, Virginia creeper, apple, and other plants, much like the grape leafhopper and more injurious in some states. It makes a very coarse stippling on foliage.

Virginia-creeper Leafhopper (*Erythroneura ziczac*)—Another species similar to the grape leafhopper, feeding on grape, elm, Boston ivy, and Virginia creeper, which may have foliage almost completely whitened, and rose.

White Apple Leafhopper (*Typhlocyba pomaria*)—On apple, rose, sometimes currant, gooseberry, raspberry. Winter is passed in the egg stage underneath bark of smaller apple branches and the small greenish nymphs hatch when apple blossoms are at the pink stage. Adults lay eggs in July and second-generation nymphs feed in August and early September, adults being most numerous in late September and October. Apple foliage is blanched white and after that the hoppers move in great numbers to nearby rose gardens. The foliage shows a rather coarse stippling and the undersurface is covered with shining black dots of fecal deposits. DDT and parathion are both effective on apple. Home gardeners should stick to DDT for roses.

LEAF MINERS

Leaf miners are insects which feed between the two surfaces of a leaf. They may be larvae of flies, moths, sawflies, or beetles. They make blisters or blotch mines or serpentine tunnels and, because they are protected by the host plant most of their lives, control has been hard, depending on an exact knowledge of the life history of each individual miner. New chemicals have provided more effective control methods, but detailed knowledge is still necessary as to chemical required and best time of application. DDT has been very satisfactory for some leaf miners, less effective for others. Lindane is good in many instances.

Apple Leaf Trumpet Miner (*Tischeria malifoliella*)—On apple (preferred), blackberry, raspberry, and hawthorn. Numerous trumpet-shaped mines are made in leaves, pupation taking place there. Very small moths, dark, with narrow fringed wings, emerge through slits in the leaves. There are 2 or more broods. Special control measures are not always needed; DDT or parathion is effective.

Arborvitae Leaf Miner (*Argyresthia thuiella*)—Distributed from Maine to Missouri, common in home plantings. Very small larvae, ⅕ inch long, green with a reddish tinge and black head, short bristles across the back of each segment, mine in the terminal leaves, eating out the inside. The mined tips turn yellow or whitish, finally brown, and stand out prominently against normal green foliage. In the most severe cases, all the foliage is mined and the shrubs turn brown all over. Small gray moths, wingspread only ⅓ inch, emerge from mined leaves in May and June to lay eggs which hatch in late June. For a few plants the easiest control is to cut off and burn discolored tips. DDT sprays are effective but followed by serious mite infestations. Spraying with nicotine sulfate, 2½ teaspoons per gallon of slightly soapy water, in July, helps to kill newly hatched larvae.

Two other leaf miners also infest arborvitae.

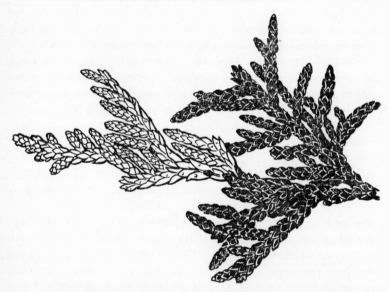

54. Twig mined and discolored by arborvitae leaf miner.

Asparagus Miner (*Melanagromyza simplex*)—Present through the Northeast and in California on asparagus but rather a minor pest. Maggots of a small fly mine in the stalks just below soil surface. The foliage may turn yellow and die prematurely. Puparia winter in the larval tunnels and the flies appear in late May to lay eggs, with adults of a second generation abroad in July. Pull up and burn old stalks to destroy puparia. Spray with nicotine sulfate, 1½ teaspoons per gallon. Plant rust-resistant strains which are also more resistant to the miner.

Azalea Leaf Miner (*Gracilaria azaleella*)—Also called Azalea Leaf Roller, largely a greenhouse pest, sometimes in nurseries and gardens. Eggs are laid in leaves by a small moth, marked with purple and yellow, wing expanse ½ inch. Small yellow caterpillars hatch in 4 days, enter the leaves, and feed between surfaces, causing blisters. When partly grown the larvae emerge and start to roll leaves at the tip, feeding inside the protection of the roll. A cocoon is made inside a leaf rolled in from the margin. A lindane-DDT emulsion applied with a mist blower has given control in a nursery. Other recommendations have been lead arsenate applied before leaves roll; TEPP, very poisonous to operator; and pyrethrum, non-poisonous, applied twice with a 30-minute interval.

Basswood Leaf Miner (*Baliosus ruber*)—A pest of basswood throughout its range, known also on oak, linden, and apple. The adult is a reddish-yellow wedge-shaped beetle which winters under leaves and trash, becomes active in May, skeletonizing the foliage. Eggs are laid singly in feeding areas and covered with excrement. The larvae start feeding into the leaves in single mines, then several join together in a common mine. Spiny pupae appear in the mines in August; beetles emerge to do more feeding before hibernation. Spray in spring or fall when beetles are feeding with lindane or lead arsenate.

Birch Leaf Miner (*Fenusa pusilla*)—An imported sawfly, first discovered in Connecticut in 1923, and now a major scourge in New England, New York, New Jersey, and Pennsylvania. Infested trees look as if they had been blighted by a disease. Gray, paper, and European white birches are most favored, in woods and in home plantings. The mature larva, whitish, rather flat, with black spots on underside of thorax and first abdominal segments, ½ inch long, winters in a cell in the soil. The black sawfly, $\frac{1}{16}$ inch long, emerges in early May about the time leaves are half open and lays eggs in these new leaves. The larvae first make small, gray, kidney-shaped blotches in a leaf, but gradually half the leaf turns brown. There are several generations, with flies laying eggs always in newly developing leaves. Hence the first brood is the worst, when all the leaves are new; later broods mostly infest ends of branches or watersprouts.

Control. Nicotine sulfate was recommended for many years, but it was difficult to time the spray properly; DDT proved only partially successful. Now excellent control is obtained by spraying in May as soon as the small blotches can be seen with malathion or lindane emulsion, 1 to 2 teaspoons in 1 gallon of water. For the second brood spray around July 1 and repeat 10 to 14 days later. Wettable powders, 2 teaspoons per gallon, can be substituted for emulsions. Chlordane is also effective but has caused a little defoliation on river birch (*Betula nigra*).

Blackberry Leaf Miner (*Metallus rubi*)—Sometimes important in the Northeast. Whitish sawfly larvae, with brown heads, make blotch mines between leaf surfaces; plants appear scorched by fire. There are 2 broods a year.

55. *Boxwood leaf miner: flies laying eggs, maggots inside blistered surface, pupa cases protruding from mines.*

Boxwood Leaf Miner (*Monarthropalpus buxi*)—The most commonly destructive boxwood insect. It is a European fly, established in the East in 1910, not as much of a problem in Virginia and the Carolinas as in more northern states. The mines are small blotches or blisters in which yellow to orange maggots feed, 2 or 3, sometimes more, to a blister. In spring, some days before emergence, a small opaque window is formed on the underside of the leaf, in the middle of the blotch, and, on tearing open the leaf, the maggots are found to have pupated and acquired dark heads. Shortly after that, the windows are broken, the pupae push part way through the leaf, and when the small orange midges or flies emerge they leave white pupal skins protruding from the leaves. Appearing in swarms, usually early in the morning, the flies continue to emerge over a period of 10 days to 2 weeks. Each particular female, however, emerges, mates, inserts its eggs through upper epidermis of new leaves, and dies in about 24 hours.

Time of emergence varies with the location and the season. In Maryland and Cincinnati, Ohio, it is late April. In New Jersey my earliest record is May 8, the latest May 20, with May 14 a good average. New blisters show up in the leaves by midsummer, the tiny maggots having started to feed about 2 weeks after egg-laying. Infested plants are not killed, at least for several years, but they have a most unthrifty appearance, yellow with sparse foliage, and are very much of an eyesore in a lovely garden.

Control. The old molasses and nicotine concoction has given way to DDT, one teaspoon of an emulsion in a gallon of water or 1 to 2 tablespoons of 50 per cent wettable powder. It is essential, because the fly lays its eggs immediately, that this spray be on the plant in advance of emergence. With proper timing, 1 spray is sufficient. If there is a long period after application before actual emergence a second treatment may be desirable. Until very recently the time of fly emergence was thought to be the only point of attack, but now we are learning that it is possible to kill young larvae in the mines by spraying with lindane emulsion, 1 to 800 dilution, twice in early summer. Other chemicals are promising along this line.

Chrysanthemum Leaf Miner (*Phytomyza atricornis*)—Marguerite Fly, rather common in gardens and greenhouses. Leaves and petioles of chrysanthemum, marguerite, cineraria, eupatorium, daisy, Shasta daisy, and other composites are mined by a pale yellow larva of a minute black fly. The mines are irregular, light-colored, extending over the surface just under the epidermis. Larvae feed on parenchyma cells; badly infested leaves dry up and hang on plants; tunnels are filled with black specks of excrement; pupation is inside mines. The larvae are so close to the surface they can be killed with a strong nicotine sulfate ($1\frac{1}{2}$ to 2 teaspoons per gallon) and soap spray, but DDT or lindane may be preferable.

Columbine Leaf Miner (*Phytomyza minuscula*)—Very common in gardens. Striking white winding tunnels, filled with black bits of excrement, are seen on leaves in almost every clump of columbine. The adult is a small brownish fly which lays eggs on underside of leaves. When the pale maggots are grown they emerge through crescent-shaped slits and attach brown puparia to the leaf; the flies emerge in about 2 weeks. There are several generations, with pupation of the last brood in the soil. Another species causes a blotch instead of a serpentine mine on columbine. Nicotine sulfate has been recommended in the past, spraying early and removing all infested leaves. Lindane will probably be more effective.

Corn Blotch Leaf Miner (*Agromyza parvicornis*)—Wheat Leaf Miner, an eastern species ranging west to Utah. The adult is a small, black fly whose maggots make irregular blotch mines in corn and grains, injury being worse in young corn. There are several generations in Florida with breeding through the winter. Pull up and destroy seriously infested plants; plant an excess of corn, to have a good stand left after the miners get their share.

Eggplant Leaf Miner (*Keiferia glochinella*)—Attacking eggplant and other solanaceous plants in the South. Larvae and moths are like those of the potato tuberworm (see under Borers) but a little smaller. There are several parasites which make this a relatively unimportant pest.

Elm Leaf Miner (*Fenusa ulmi*)—An imported species attacking English, Scotch, and Camperdown elms, sometimes American. Small, shiny black sawflies lay eggs through slits in upper leaf surfaces. In late May white legless larvae, 1/3 inch long, make blotch mines in leaves, often 15 to 20 larvae working in one leaf, which turns brown and shrivels. Leaves may drop prematurely. There is only 1 generation; after about 3 weeks the larvae remain in papery brown cocoons in the soil until pupation the next May. Spraying for young larvae with nicotine sulfate and soap has been recommended in the past, but lindane as for the birch leaf miner would probably be more effective.

European Alder Leaf Miner (*Fenusa dohrnii*)—Distributed through the Northeast on alder. Whitish larvae, 1/3 inch long, winter in papery cocoons in the soil and pupate in spring. Small black sawflies emerge in May to lay eggs in slits in upper leaf surfaces. Ten or more yellow blister mines may be present in a single leaf. There is a second generation in July and sometimes a third in September. See Birch Leaf Miner for control.

Holly Leaf Miner (*Phytomyza ilicis*)—A European species very common on our native holly, sometimes on English holly, causing conspicuous blotch mines on the upper surface, often several on a leaf. A native species, the American or serpentine holly leaf miner (*Phytomyza ilicicola*), produces very slender sinuous mines packed with frass. It is not so common, but sometimes the two kinds of mines are seen in the same leaf. The European miner winters in the mines, a yellow-green larva, 1/8 inch long, and pupates there in spring. Small black flies, 1/16 inch long, emerge about the time holly twigs have 3 or 4 new leaves. This may be late April in Maryland, early May in New Jersey, and mid-May in Connecticut. They feed for about 10 days before egg-laying. The female makes feeding punctures in foliage with her ovipositor, but both males and females lap the exuding sap. These feeding punctures look like pinpricks and may be so numerous, up to 50 on a leaf, the leaf is distorted. Eggs are laid singly in lower surface of new leaves, small larvae starting to feed in about a week, but the mines are not noticeable until late summer.

Control. DDT applied at the beginning of emergence, with usually a second spray 10 days later, gives satisfactory control. Use 2 level tablespoons 50 per cent wettable powder to a gallon of water and spray as soon as you see black flies around new growth. Nurseries and holly plantations often use a DDT emulsion applied with a mist blower. Dieldrin is also effective applied in May. If you miss spraying for adults, young larvae can be killed in the mines by spraying with lindane or dieldrin in late July.

56. Work of holly leaf miner.

Larkspur Leaf Miner (*Phytomyza delphiniae*)—A fly common on delphinium, larkspur, aconite. Several larvae feed together to form tan to brown blotch mines filled with dark flecks of excrement. The flies puncture the leaves from the underside, making them turn brown. The foliage often appears more blighted by disease than injured by an insect. There are several generations, with pupation in summer on the outside of a leaf near a mine. Spray with lindane, DDT, or nicotine sulfate. Remove infested leaves.

Lilac Leaf Miner (*Gracilaria syringella*)—Lilac Leaf Roller, a European moth first known in America in 1925. It is reported from eastern states and the Puget Sound area on lilac, ash, privet, euonymus, and deutzia. The moths, brownish, with 6 yellow lines on the fore wings, lay eggs in vein axils on underside of leaves. The faint yellow larvae, ¼ inch long, first mine and then roll and skeletonize the leaves. There are 2 generations, larvae of the second hibernating in cocoons in the soil. Moths emerge in May and July. When this miner is abundant the beauty of lilacs and other shrubs is spoiled. Probably much browning of lilac foliage thought due to disease is caused by the lilac leaf miner. Spraying with lead arsenate and nicotine sulfate before larvae curl the leaves has been standard control.

Locust Leaf Miner (*Chalepus dorsalis*)—Locust Leaf Beetle, distributed through eastern states south to Mississippi and west to Missouri, feeding principally on black locust. The beetle, ¼ inch long, is orange yellow with a broad black stripe down the back, black head and appendages. It is active in spring when locusts are coming into leaf and lays eggs on underside of leaves, 3 to 5 in a pile, covered with excrement. The larvae, yellow white with black heads, burrow from the bottom of this mass into the leaf, making a common circular mine. As they grow older each larva makes a separate new mine. After feeding for a month, the larvae pupate inside the mines; the leaves turn brown and drop. There may be a second generation of the beetles and it is not uncommon for locusts to lose all their foliage twice in a single season. In most seasons they make a brown eyesore on hillsides or along roadsides unless they are sprayed.

Control. Lead arsenate has usually been recommended in preference to DDT, applied in early May or when beetles are active and leaves expanded, at the rate of 4 pounds to 100 gallons plus 1 pound of sticker, but it was found in Rhode Island spray tests that it took 3 applications of lead arsenate to give 90 per cent control and this was injurious to the locusts. Three applications of DDT were effective but resulted in some yellowed leaflets. Many arborists now use lindane, at the rate of 1 pound 25 per cent wettable powder to 100 gallons of water.

Lodgepole Needle Miner (*Recurvaria milleri*)—An important pest of lodgepole pine in California, Idaho, Montana, also mining needles of western white and Jeffrey pine in epidemic areas. In Yosemite National Park and other recreational areas it has killed up to 80 per cent of mature trees in epidemic years. Moths, very small, white or gray, appear every other year to lay eggs behind twig and needle scales and around buds. The greenish larva mines one needle the first year, moves to another for the second year. Lindane emulsion sprays are promising, but outbreaks of needle miners are eventually brought under control by parasites and climatic conditions.

Morning-glory Leaf Miner (*Bedellia somnulentella*)—Convolvulus Leaf Miner. Small, pale caterpillars, larvae of gray moths, make irregular blotch mines in leaves, first serpentine, then widening into blistered blotch mines. Pupation is in cocoons attached to leaves.

Pine Needle Miner (*Exoteleia pinifoliella*)—Common in eastern states, sometimes abundant on ornamental pines. Brown larvae, ⅕ inch long, mine tips of needles, entering at some distance from the tip, and then excavate the whole leaf. Injured tips turn yellow, dry up. There is usually 1 generation in the Northeast. Yellow-brown moths, marked with white or gray, lay eggs in June and July. There may be more broods further south. A lead arsenate-fish oil spray applied the first warm days in late March or early April or a lead arsenate-nicotine spray when moths are flying in summer has been recommended.

Privet Leaf Miner (*Gracilaria cuculipennella*)—A European moth sometimes destructive here. Whitish caterpillars, ⅞ inch long when mature, make blotch mines in leaves, then feed externally in rolled leaves. See Lilac Leaf Miner for control.

Serpentine Leaf Miner (*Liriomyza pusilla*)—Common throughout the country, more devastating in the South and California. The yellow maggots, larvae of minute black and yellow flies, make long, slender, winding white mines under epidermis of bean, beet, cabbage, cowpea, cress, nasturtium, sweet pea, pepper, potato, radish, spinach, turnip, watermelon, and field crops. Pupation is in the mines or in brown puparia in the soil. There are several generations. In addition to decreasing the attractiveness of green vegetables for food, the mines afford entrance to disease and decay organisms. Chlordane or lindane dust, 3 to 5 applications, is said to be helpful. In the small garden remove infested leaves by hand.

Solitary Oak Leaf Miner (*Cameraria hamadryadella*)—Disfiguring many species of oak. The pale blotch mines, several on a leaf, each contain a single larva. A related species, the **Gregarious Oak Leaf Miner** (*Cameraria cincinnatiella*) makes similar mines, mostly on white oak, with 10 or more larvae in the mine. The solitary miner may have 5 or 6 generations, the gregarious has 2 near Washington, D.C. They winter in the mines, so raking up and burning leaves from infested trees in autumn is helpful in control. Lindane, parathion, and EPN are effective sprays.

Spinach Leaf Miner (*Pegomya hyoscyami*)—Generally distributed on spinach, beet, sugar beet, chard, and many weeds, especially lambs-quarters. Slender, gray, black-haired flies, ¼ inch long, lay oval white sculptured eggs, singly or in small groups, on underside of leaves. These hatch in 3 or 4 days into pale green or whitish maggots which first eat slender winding mines but then widen these and join them together to make large, light-colored blotches filled with dark excrement. Maggots may migrate from leaf to leaf; they are full grown in 1 to 3 weeks and pupate usually in the soil. Adults appear in 2 to 4 weeks and there may be 3 or 4 generations in a season. Leaf vegetables are unfit for greens; seed and root development are checked.

Control. In home gardens remove infested leaves; keep weed hosts destroyed; dust with pyrethrum. Parathion (1 per cent dust) is sometimes recommended for commercial growers.

Spotted Tentiform Leaf Miner (*Lithocolletis crataegella*)—Rather common in the East, known in the Northwest, and recently reported damaging in California. Leaves of apple, quince, plum, cherry, wild haw, sweet-scented crab may have up to 15 blotch mines apiece and may be buckled like a tent. The adult is a very small moth with spotted wings. There may be 3 generations with leaves sometimes losing most of their function, but outbreaks are very irregular, probably due to parasites. Spraying with parathion or DDT is considered effective.

Spruce Needle Miner (*Taniva albolineana*)—On blue, Norway, and Engelmann spruce from Maine to North Carolina and west to Colorado and Idaho. Dark brown moths, wingspread ½ inch, lay eggs on needles from mid-May to mid-June. Larvae bore into needles at base and make webs from entrance holes in needles to twigs. Each larva destroys an average of 10 needles. The entire crown of small ornamental spruces can be webbed; on larger trees heaviest infestation is on lower branches. A simple control is to wash off all loose needles and webs with a hose in March and early autumn, cleaning up and burning the trash on the ground afterward.

Two other species also mine spruce needles. *Epinotia nanana* webs dried mined needles together to give the tree an unsightly, unhealthy appearance. *Recurvaria piceaella* attacks Norway, blue, red, and white spruces from Maine to Colorado.

Strawberry Crown Miner (*Aristotelia fragariae*)—Reddish larvae, ¼ inch long, burrow in crowns of plants, causing stunting and poor foliage, and offering entrance to disease organisms. In the Northwest moths emerge in June and July and lay eggs about the crown. Larvae are full grown by October. Crop rotation is recommended, as well as cleaning up all old plants.

Sycamore Leaf Miner (*Lithocolletis felinella*)—The moth lays eggs beneath leaf hairs on lower leaf surface, and larvae, yellowish, ¼ inch long when grown, enter leaf directly. The mines are brownish with black fecal pellets. Raking and burning fallen leaves is helpful; a DDT spray might be effective if properly timed for the adult stage.

Tupelo Leaf Miner (*Antispila nyssaefoliella*)—Sour-gum Casecutter. The larvae of this tiny moth mine in the leaves of tupelo, sour-gum, and when mature cut oval cases out of the leaf, falling with them to the ground. The larva attaches its case to some object by a silken thread and pupates inside. Although it is reported abundant in some years, causing browning of leaves by late summer, my only experience with it was on an estate in Pennsylvania a few years ago, when all the gardeners stopped working to wonder at the bits of leaves walking around on the ground. In that instance every leaf on the tree seemed to have been infested. Recommended control is a lead arsenate-nicotine spray in May when moths emerge.

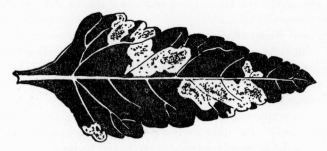

57. Blotch mines caused by verbena leaf miner.

Unspotted Tentiform Leaf Miner (*Callisto geminatella*)—On apple, pear, crabapple, haw, plum, wild cherry. Greenish-gray larvae mine leaves and buckle them as do those of the spotted tentiform miner. Moths are gray without spots. Hibernation is in the pupa state inside folded edges of the leaf. Destroy fallen leaves in autumn. Spray as for the spotted miner.

Verbena Leaf Miner (*Agromyza artemisiae*)—Practically inevitable in any garden growing verbenas. Each maggot feeds singly, making a blister or blotch mine, but several mines can run together to make the foliage most unsightly. The adult is a tiny midge. Try spraying or dusting with lindane. Rake and burn all plant trash in fall.

Wild Parsnip Leaf Miner (*Phytomyza albiceps*)—A European species generally distributed, making serpentine mines in aster and columbine. The larvae are white, puparia black, flies small, black or metallic blue. Pupation is in the soil.

LEAF ROLLERS

Leaf rollers are caterpillars which feed protected by the rolled-up leaf of the host plant but not between the two leaf surfaces as do leaf miners.

Basswood Leaf Roller (*Pantographa limata*)—General through eastern states. The moths, straw-colored with intricate olive-purple markings, $1\frac{1}{2}$-inch wingspread, emerge in June and July. The larva, bright green with a black head, 1 inch long, lives inside the apical half of a leaf rolled into a tube, and feeds from July to September. When full grown it leaves this nest and makes a small one lined with silk, in a fold from one edge of the leaf, spending the winter in fallen leaves inside this protection. Raking and burning leaves in autumn may be sufficient control.

Bean Leaf Roller (*Urbanus proteus*)—A southern pest troublesome to early fall crops of beans. The caterpillar is greenish yellow, velvety, with a brown head and constricted neck, 1 inch long. It rolls up edges of leaves after cutting slits in them. The adult, a blue skipper butterfly, 2 inches across, with long tails on hind wings, lays eggs on beans in summer. In warm weather larvae take 14 days to mature, a month when it is cooler. Pupation is on the plants. By September beans in Florida may be so heavily infested no pods can be formed.

Boxelder Leaf Roller (*Gracilaria negundella*)—Boxelder leaves whitened and rolled.

European Honeysuckle Leaf Roller (*Harpipteryx xylostella*)—On Tartarian honeysuckle. Leaves are rolled and ragged. Larvae are leaf green with 2 brown median stripes outlined with blue-green stripes, ¾ inch long, tapering to a narrow head and tail. The white cocoon, pointed at both ends, is fastened to a leaf. The moth is chestnut brown with cream-colored lower markings on fore wings, which expand to ¾ inch. Spray with lead arsenate to prevent defoliation.

Fruit Tree Leaf Roller (*Archips argyrospila*)—Present from coast to coast, capable, in occasional years of abundance, of ruining 90 per cent of an apple crop. This is a general feeder on most deciduous fruits—apricot, blackberry, cherry, currant, gooseberry, loganberry, pear, plum, quince, raspberry, and has been damaging citrus in California. It may also infest ash, boxelder, elm, horsechestnut, hickory, locust, oak, osage-orange, poplar, rose, sassafras, English walnut, and willow. It winters in the egg stage, in masses of 30 to 100 plastered on twigs, branches, and tree trunks, covered with a brown or gray varnish. They hatch about the time apple buds separate in spring, the young worms, pale green with brown heads, crawling to feed on leaves, buds, and small fruits for about a month. They spin a light web around several leaves, roll these together, often enclosing a small cluster of young apples. Cavities eaten in fruit show as deep russeted scars at harvest. When the caterpillars are full grown, 3/4 inch long, they pupate inside rolled leaves or make a flimsy cocoon on trunk or branches. Moths emerge in late June or July. They are brown with gold markings, wing expanse 3/4 inch. There is only 1 generation.

Control. A heavy application of a dormant oil spray put on before the buds break and applied to cover every egg mass has been effective. Spraying with lead arsenate to kill very young larvae is fairly successful, and some recommend DDT, 2 pounds 50 per cent wettable powder to 100 gallons, in early sprays. There are many parasites which probably account for the fluctuating abundance of this pest.

Hickory Leaf Roller (*Argyrotaenia juglandana*)—Found in the Northeast and west to Wisconsin. The larvae, pale green, semi-translucent, 3/4 inch long, roll hickory leaves and feed inside the rolls in May and June. The moths, appearing in June and July, have dark brown fore wings marked with black; gray hind wings.

Larger Canna Leaf Roller (*Calpodes ethlius*)—Ranging through the South and north to Washington, D.C. The caterpillar, which is green, semi-transparent with a dark orange head set off by a narrow neck, up to 1 3/4 inches long, cuts off a strip from the margin of a canna leaf and folds it over, feeding above and below from within this protection, eating larger irregular holes as it grows. Damage can be extensive. The adult is a skipper butterfly, brown with white spots. Spray or dust with lead arsenate or DDT before leaves are rolled.

Lesser Canna Leaf Roller (*Geshna cannalis*)—Also serious on canna in the South. The caterpillar, yellow white but with a green tinge after feeding on foliage, 1 inch long when grown, fastens young leaves together before they have unrolled. They are ragged, often turn brown and die. The moths, uniform light brown, appear in February and March in Florida. It may be possible to kill the larvae inside rolled leaves by pressing with the fingers. Clean off and burn dead trash from beds and infested plant parts.

Locust Leaf Roller (*Nephoteryx subcaesiella*)—Found from Maine to West Virginia and Colorado on locust and wisteria. The larvae, green with faint stripes, black head, up to 1 inch long, feed inside 2 or 3 leaves spun together with silk. They winter as pupae in silken cocoons among leaves on ground. Gray moths, shaded with red, emerge from May to July. In some states there is a second generation with moths again in August and September. The injury is rather common but probably not serious enough to call for control measures.

Oblique-banded Leaf Roller (*Archips rosaceana*)—Rose Leaf Tier. The omnivorous larvae of this moth feed on flowers in greenhouse and garden, chewing holes in rosebuds, rolling up leaves and tying them together, feeding on aster, carnation, geranium, sunflower, verbena. They also feed on vegetables, fruits, ornamental trees and shrubs including apple, apricot, ash, basswood, bean, birch, blackberry, boxelder, celery, cherry, currant, dewberry, dogwood, gooseberry, hawthorn, hazelnut, honeysuckle, horsechestnut, lilac, loganberry, maple, oak, peach, pear, plum, poplar, prune, raspberry, spirea, strawberry, sumac, thistle.

The pale green, black-headed larvae mine the leaves first, then work inside rolled areas, often tying several leaves together. They may also infest fruit. Eggs are laid in overlapping green masses on branches of host plants or on rose leaves in greenhouses.

Control. Parathion or DDT aerosols will control in greenhouses. Fruit trees can be sprayed with lead arsenate or DDT, flowers dusted with 5 per cent DDT or with pyrethrum. There are a number of natural parasites.

Red-banded Leaf Roller (*Argyrotaenia velutinana*)—A native insect, widely distributed in the Northeast, and ranging to North Carolina and Texas, that has increased in importance since DDT has been used in orchards. It feeds on apple, cherry, plum, some small fruits, vegetables, ornamental trees and flowers—chrysanthemum, geranium, hollyhock, honeysuckle, lobelia, rose, violet, zinnia. The moth, brownish with red bands across the wings, which spread only ¾ inch, appears in spring soon after apple buds break. The larva is slender, greenish, just over ½ inch long, and pupates in fall inside a half cocoon on trees or other objects. There may be 3 generations. Eggs of the first are placed on bark, those of the second on foliage or fruits. Early-season larvae feed on leaves, spinning light webs, but late-season larvae feed on fruits, eating patches off the surface. On ornamentals they roll and tie leaves and terminal growth.

Control. DDT is not satisfactory for this leaf roller; it kills the parasites and increases the rollers. TDE, 2 pounds 50 per cent wettable powder per 100 gallons, has given quite good control in apple orchards, but the usual spray is lead arsenate applied at petal fall and first cover.

Strawberry Leaf Roller (*Ancylis comptana fragariae*)—On strawberry, dewberry, blackberry, and raspberry in northern United States, Louisiana, and Arkansas. The caterpillars, greenish or bronze, up to ½ inch long, fold or roll and tie the leaves into tubes, feeding from within. Plants are weakened, leaves turn brown and die. Fruits are withered and deformed; infested beds appear white or gray from a distance. Small gray moths with light waxy markings across the fore wings, ½-inch wing expanse, appear in large numbers near the strawberry patch in May to lay eggs on underside of leaves. The larvae feed for 25 to 50 days, first on underside of leaf, then on upper, then pupate inside folded leaves. There are 2 or more generations.

Control. Spraying plants with lead arsenate or TDE when first blooms appear is fairly effective. Spraying with DDT after harvest is sometimes recommended. In Wisconsin tests, parathion was effective in killing rollers already inside folded leaves but cannot be used within 2 weeks of harvest. Pyrethrum and rotenone dusts are safer, if less effective. It is sometimes advisable to mow strawberry beds close to the ground and burn over right after harvest.

Sweetpotato Leaf Roller (*Piloceris tripunctata*)—Bluish-green caterpillars, up to 1 inch long, feed inside folded leaves, eating holes through leaves and skeletonizing. Injurious in the Gulf states.

Western Strawberry Leaf Roller (*Anacampsis fragariella*)—Occurring in Washington and Oregon along with the strawberry leaf roller. The caterpillars are creamy pink, ½ inch long. Leaves are rolled in May and June, moths emerge in July; hibernation is in the egg stage on old strawberry leaves. There is only 1 generation. A nicotine and oil spray applied when eggs are on foliage is effective. Top plants after harvest.

LEAF SKELETONIZERS

Leaf skeletonizers are caterpillars like leaf rollers, but they feed more openly, eating out everything except epidermis and veins, without the protection of conspicuously rolled leaves.

Apple Leaf Skeletonizer (*Psorosina hammondi*)—On apple, sometimes plum and quince, most abundant in central states, where it is of fluctuating importance. The green upper surface of the leaf is eaten off entirely or in part, making the foliage look brown and dead, and trees appear to have been struck by fire. Leaves at end of branches may be lightly folded with 2 or 3 lightly webbed together. Brown pupae winter in fallen leaves; dark brown moths, wings mottled with silver, lay eggs on leaves in late spring. Brownish-green caterpillars, with 4 black tubercles on the back, ½ inch long, feed in June and July, then pupate on leaves; second generation feeds in late August and September. The ordinary spray schedule, if it includes summer sprays for codling moth, will control leaf skeletonizers.

Apple and Thorn Skeletonizer (*Anthophila pariana*)—A European pest, first found in New York in 1917, now present from Maine to New Jersey and in the Pacific Northwest, feeding on apple, pear, cherry, and hawthorn. It hibernates as a small, dark brown moth, lays eggs in spring. The caterpillars, yellow green with black tubercles, brown head, feed on underside of leaves first, then make shelters by drawing upper surfaces together with silk, leaves becoming a mass of webbing and frass. There are several generations. Spraying with lead arsenate or DDT is effective.

Birch Skeletonizer (*Bucculatrix canadensisella*)—General in the Northeast, found as far west as Wisconsin and south to higher altitudes in North Carolina, on gray, paper, yellow, and European white birches. The moths, ⅜ inch across the wings, which are brown crossed with silver, appear in July to lay eggs singly on leaves. The young larva, yellow green, bores directly from the bottom of the egg into the leaf, mines it in 2 to 5 weeks, then cuts a crescent-shaped opening through the lower side of the leaf and spins a molting cocoon. After molting, it skeletonizes the leaf from the underside, molts again, feeds for another week, then drops to the ground and makes a brown ribbed pupal cocoon for the winter. There is 1 generation. Spraying with lead arsenate (at rate of 3 pounds to 100 gallons of water) about the middle of August will prevent defoliation, but this happens so late in the season the expense of spraying may not be justified. The pest is serious for 2 or 3 years out of every 10. There are many parasites.

Cotton Leaf Perforator (*Bucculatrix thurberiella*)—Hollyhock Leaf Skeletonizer, a cotton pest, larva of a small gray-and-tan moth; mines in and completely skeletonizes foliage of hollyhocks in California. Spray or dust with lead arsenate.

Grape Leaf Skeletonizer (*Harrisina americana*)—Common on wild grapes, sometimes injuring cultivated varieties. The larvae feed in groups, side by side across a leaf, eating the upper surface only. Adults are small, smoky-black, narrow-winged moths. The insect is so heavily parasitized no other control is required.

Maple Trumpet Skeletonizer (*Epinotia aceriella*)—The leaves of red maple, sometimes sugar maple, are folded loosely in July and August; the small green larva lives inside a long, dark, trumpetlike tube near the skeletonized areas. The injury is more spectacular than serious.

Palm Leaf Skeletonizer (*Homaledra sabalella*)—Palm Leaf Miner, the major pest of palms in Florida, feeding on saw, cabbage, dwarf and sabal palmettos, on coconut palm, and various date palms. The caterpillars are gregarious, living in colonies of 35 to 100, feeding under a protective web of silk and depositing their excrement in the upper surface of this web. Continued feeding causes dark brown blotches on leaves, followed by shriveling and death. In heavily infested areas every frond and leaflet may be attacked. The moths, which are rarely seen in the day, are attracted to lights at night. They lay eggs on the brown papery husk which encloses young leaflets. Larvae start to feed directly from the bottom of the eggs on leaf tissue, keeping the eggshells as protection until the silken web is formed. There are often 5 broods, with the winter passed in egg, larval, or pupal stages.

Control by spraying repeatedly, perhaps every 2 months, with 50 per cent wettable DDT (2 tablespoons per gallon or 2 pounds per 100 gallons) or with chlordane (1⅔ tablespoons per gallon) or lindane. The addition of a dye, malachite green, was added to the older lead arsenate spray to make it less objectionable. Cut out and burn infested fronds; remove interleaf husks that may bear eggs.

Western Grape Leaf Skeletonizer (*Harrisina brillians*)—Occurring in Arizona, California, New Mexico, and Texas. Black and yellow larvae feed on leaves of wild and cultivated grapes in late summer. They move in compact colonies as they completely skeletonize leaves. Moths are metallic black or green. Dusting with 50 per cent cryolite, 5 per cent DDT, or with methoxychlor is effective.

LEAF TIERS

Leaf tiers are much like leaf rollers, caterpillars tying leaves together with strands of silk and feeding inside that protection.

Celery Leaf Tier (*Udea rubigalis*)—**Greenhouse Leaf Tier.** Present throughout North America, a special pest of celery, feeding on a great many garden and greenhouse vegetables and ornamentals—ageratum, anemone, aster, bean, beet, cabbage, carnation, cauliflower, cineraria, chrysanthemum, cucumber, dahlia, daisies, geranium, heliotrope, kale, Kenilworth ivy, lantana, lettuce, lobelia, nasturtium, parsley, passionflower, pea, sweet pea, rose, spinach, snapdragon, strawberry, thistle, wandering Jew, to give a partial list.

The moths are brown, fore wings crossed by dark wavy lines, spreading ¾ inch. They are quiet during the day; fly at night. The female lays flattened, scalelike translucent eggs singly or in overlapping groups on underside of leaves, usually close to the soil. They hatch in 5 to 12 days into pale green caterpillars, turning yellow when grown, ¾ inch long with a white stripe down the back and a dark green line in the center of the white stripe. As they feed, they web foliage together in large masses, filling it with frass, and they mine into soft stems and hearts of plants, especially celery. When disturbed they wiggle violently in their webs or drop to the ground. They pupate in silken cocoons inside the webs. The life cycle takes about 40 days; there may be 7 or 8 generations a year in greenhouses and 5 or 6 outdoors in warm climates.

Control. Spray young plants with DDT or use 5 per cent DDT dust. On older plants use 2 sprays of pyrethrum, ½ hour apart, or use pyrethrum dust. Parathion or DDT aerosols can be used in greenhouses, or nicotine fumigation.

Hydrangea Leaf Tier (*Exartema ferriferanum*)—A small green caterpillar with a dark head sews terminal leaves of hydrangea tightly around the bud, the effect being that of little pocketbooks. It is often possible to tear open these tied leaves and kill the worm before it destroys the flower bud. DDT or lead arsenate applied early enough should give control, but the leaves are usually tied together before one thinks to spray.

Omnivorous Leaf Tier (*Cnephasia longana*)—Strawberry Fruitworm, a European pest destructive in California and the Northwest, first found in Oregon in 1929 on strawberries and Dutch iris. The lar-

58. Hydrangea leaves fastened together by leaf tier, which is eating the flower bud enclosed.

vae also feed on flax, peas, and other legumes, and many cultivated flowers, including calla lily, bachelor's button, gladiolus, heather, marguerites. Both flowers and foliage are webbed and eaten, and fruit of strawberries. The moth lays its eggs on rough bark of trees, many kinds, or rough wooden objects, and the larvae are carried to food plants by wind. In strawberries a dust of 5 per cent DDT mixed with 10 per cent sulfur applied in early bloom stage has given commercial control. DDT should be satisfactory for most ornamentals if a miticide is included.

MAGGOTS

Maggots are the larvae of flies. Those that are commonly known by their adult name have been treated under Flies; those that normally go under the name of maggot are considered here.

Apple Maggot (*Rhagoletis pomonella*)—Also known as Railroad Worm, Apple Fruit Fly, a native pest injurious to apples from the Dakotas east and Arkansas north (Plate XXV). It probably fed originally on wild haws and wild crabs; now it eats apples, blueberries, European plum, cherries. A smaller variety of this species breeds on snowberry in the West, but there it is not an apple pest. In Connecticut the maggot is considered the number-1 apple pest, wormy fruit in unsprayed orchards often reaching 100 per cent.

Hibernation takes place inside a small brown puparium buried 1 to 6 inches deep in the soil, but flies do not emerge until summer— late June in some sections, early July in most. They are slightly smaller than houseflies, black, with white bands on the abdomen and conspicuous zigzag black bands on the wings. The females lay their eggs singly through punctures in the apple skin; in 5 to 10 days these hatch into legless whitish maggots which tunnel through the fruit by rasping and tearing the pulp into brown winding galleries. Early varieties soon become a soft mass of rotten pulp; later varieties have corky streaks through the flesh and a distorted, pitted surface. Completing their growth about a week after apples have fallen to the ground, larvae leave the fruit and burrow in the soil to pupate. Ordinarily pupation continues until the next summer, but in its southern range the apple maggot may have a partial second generation.

Control. Two sprays of lead arsenate, 3 pounds to 100 gallons, the first when flies appear, the second 2 weeks later, effectively control maggots but may leave excessive arsenical residue on fruit. Home gardeners in New Jersey are advised to put on one special maggot spray, the last of June in central Jersey, early June in north Jersey, using ¾ cup of lead arsenate and ¾ cup of wheat flour to 5 gallons of water. DDT, at rate of 2 pounds 50 per cent wettable powder to 100 gallons of water, is preferable to lead arsenate from the standpoint of residue but may have to be applied 3 times, and this may mean too much poison on early varieties. Methoxychlor at the same rate is safer and fairly effective. Very important in control is cleaning up and disposing of dropped fruit, twice a week for summer varieties, before maggots leave the apples to pupate.

Blueberry Maggot (*Rhagoletis pomonella*)—A form of the apple maggot, most injurious to blueberries and huckleberries. Eggs are laid in ripe berries, maggots eat the pulp, and there is much fruit drop. Dust with rotenone or malathion.

Cabbage Maggot (*Hylemya brassicae*)—Introduced from Europe more than a century ago; a serious pest in northern states, of little consequence south of Pennsylvania. Early cabbage and broccoli after transplanting, late cabbage in the seedbed, early turnips, late spring radishes are most severely injured by maggots, but other crucifers, Brussels sprouts, cauliflower, cress, mustard, and sometimes beet, celery, and a few other vegetables, may be attacked (Plate XXVI).

The winter is spent in puparia, 1 to 5 inches deep in the soil. About the time sweet cherries bloom and young cabbage plants are set out, a small fly, ¼ inch long, dark gray with black stripes on thorax and black bristles, crawls out of the soil to lay white, finely ridged eggs at the base of the stems and on adjacent soil. These hatch in 3 to 7 days into small, white, legless maggots, blunt at the rear end, which enter the soil to feast on roots and stems just under the surface, riddling them with brown tunnels. Seedlings wilt, turn yellow, and die. Maggot abundance fluctuates from year to year but often 40 to 80 per cent of young plants are lost. After 3 weeks the maggot forms a puparium from its larval skin, producing another fly in 12 to 18 days. The number of generations is indefinite; ordinarily the first is important on cabbage and its relatives, while late broods menace fall turnips and radishes. In addition to its own feeding injury the maggot is credited with introducing the fungus causing cabbage blackleg.

59. Tar-paper square protecting cabbage seedling from maggots.

Control. Protect seedbeds with a cheesecloth cover to prevent egg-laying. Place a 3- to 4-inch square of tar paper on the ground around the stem of each seedling when it is transplanted and don't let it get covered with soil in cultivating. Dusting stems before setting with calomel, 1 pound mixed with 6 ounces of cornstarch, is still recommended in some states. Benzene hexachloride or lindane worked into the soil before planting is very effective against the maggot but may give an off-flavor to some root crops. Chlordane does not have that disadvantage but may be less effective. It is recommended at the rate of 2½ tablespoons of wettable powder to 4 gallons of water, with ½ cup poured around each plant. Aldrin, dieldrin, and heptachlor are being used for cabbage maggot control, applied to the row at the time of seeding.

Onion Maggot (*Hylemya antiqua*)—A northern onion pest, rarely injurious in the South. In dry years the onion maggot is of little importance, but in a series of wet springs 80 per cent or more of the crop may be destroyed, larvae tunneling in bulb and crown so thoroughly that the onion dies or is worthless. One small maggot can kill a seedling onion; early plantings are most injured.

The winter is spent in chestnut-brown puparia, resembling grains of wheat, several inches deep in soil or piles of cull onions or trash. The flies, gray or brown, bristly, ¼ inch long, with large wings, 4 dark stripes on the thorax and a slightly humpbacked appearance, emerge in May or June and lay sausage-shaped white eggs at the base of plants or in cracks in soil. They hatch in 2 to 7 days. Dirty-white, cylindrical maggots, ¼ inch long, feed for 2 or 3 weeks behind leaf sheaths and in bulbs, then pupate in soil. There are 2 or more generations. The third brood often attacks onions just before harvest and causes storage rot.

Control. Destroying all cull onions immediately after harvest is most important. Seed treatment with calomel, 1 pound to 1 pound of seed moistened with gum arabic, just before planting, is an old control still recommended. More modern is seed pelleted with an insecticide-fungicide mixture: 4 ounces 25 per cent heptachlor, or 2½ ounces 40 per cent dieldrin, or 2 ounces 50 per cent dieldrin, mixed with 4 ounces 50 per cent thiram and pelleted on 1 pound of seed with 3½ ounces 4 per cent methyl cellulose. Back-yard gardeners growing onions from sets will probably be content to dust plants with 5 per cent chlordane, though this will not be entirely effective in serious infestations.

Pepper Maggot (*Zonosemata electa*)—First noticed in New Jersey in 1921, also present in New York, Connecticut, and Mississippi, most injurious on peppers, sometimes infesting eggplant. Yellow-striped flies, ³⁄₁₀ inch long, lay eggs on young peppers in late June. The yellow-white maggots feed on the core and spoil the pods. Pupation is in soil; there is 1 generation. Dust with 1 per cent rotenone or 5 per cent chlordane starting when first flies appear and repeating at 5-day intervals. Another remedy is to keep fruits thoroughly dusted with talc during the summer. This prevents the females getting a foothold on the skins for ovipositing.

Raspberry Cane Maggot (*Pegomya rubivora*)—A northern insect found from coast to coast on blackberry, dewberry, loganberry, raspberry, rose. The tips of new shoots wilt, sometimes with a purplish discoloration at the base of the wilted part, or are broken off clean as though cut through with a knife. Sometimes galls are formed in the canes. The white maggots, 1/3 inch long, tunnel down in the pith after they have girdled the cane and caused the break. Pupation is in canes. The flies, half the size of houseflies, emerge in spring to lay eggs in leaf axils of tender shoots. Cut off infested tips several inches below wilted portion.

Seed-corn Maggot (*Hylemya cilicrura*)—A European insect that arrived in New York 100 years ago and is now general over the country. Chief injury is to germinating seed, with peas and beans often more seriously injured than corn. Melon, cucumber, and potato sprouts are often killed; young plants of cabbage, beet, bean, pea, onion, turnip, spinach, radish, sweetpotato are frequent victims, sometimes gladiolus and coniferous seedlings.

Yellow-white maggots, 1/4 inch long, sharply pointed at head end, burrow in seed so that it fails to sprout or produces a weak, sickly plant. Injury is worst in cold, wet seasons on land rich in organic matter. The winter is spent in puparia in soil or as free maggots in manure. Grayish-brown flies, 1/5 inch long, emerge in early July to deposit eggs in rich soil or on seeds or seedlings. There may be 3 to 5 generations.

Control. One method is to wait to plant, or to replant, until the ground is warm enough to allow quick germination and rapid growth. Chlordane or lindane dust can be worked into soil before planting. Gladiolus corms can be sprayed in the trench at planting time, before covering, with lindane or chlordane. Seeds, especially lima beans, can be treated with a slurry of aldrin, dieldrin, heptachlor, or lindane before planting.

Sunflower Maggot (*Strauzia longipennis*)—Sunflower Peacock Fly, present in many parts of the country, infesting stems of wild and cultivated sunflowers. The flies are a gay yellow. The female has an orange ovipositor and the male a tuft of black spines on the head.

Turnip Maggot (*Hylemya floralis*)—Similar to the cabbage maggot. Aldrin and heptachlor have given effective control.

MAMMALS

A group of miscellaneous warm-blooded animals are, at times, garden pests. They are not all rodents (squirrels, rats, mice, rabbits, and other animals characterized by chisel-like teeth for gnawing) and some of them are as useful as they are destructive. Their young are born alive; they possess mammary glands and they suckle their young; they have

hair, even though it may be so modified as to be almost unrecogniz-
able; the body is kept at constant temperature regardless of the environment.

Armadillos (Nine-banded Armadillo, *Dasypus novemcinctus* and
other species)—In parts of Florida and Louisiana, most of Texas,
and increasing its range. A burrowing, chiefly nocturnal animal, house-
cat size, brown, stout, encased from head to tail in an armor of small,
bony plates but with ears and under parts naked, giving birth to an
annual litter, February to April, of identical quadruplets. It travels in
fairly well-marked trails scattered with marble-size droppings and has
den holes 7 to 8 inches across. Some species roll into a ball when disturbed. Armadillos eat insects, snails, worms, small reptiles, sometimes
carrion, but often their burrowing is as distressful to Florida or Texas
gardeners as that of woodchucks in the North. The porklike meat is
said to be good eating and the shells are made into baskets and other
novelties. Control is difficult. Try a 2-foot fence around the garden
as for rabbits, or place rabbit traps across their trails, or, as a last resort,
shooting, if permitted in your locality.

Cats (*Felis domesticus*)—Carnivorous mammals long kept by man
as pets or for catching rats and mice. That's the dictionary definition,
implying that cats are generally useful members of a community, but
people are seldom dispassionate about cats. Some are cat lovers, some
violent cat haters. Except in small city gardens where a lot of cats
congregate and dig, cats do little damage to garden plants and are
very useful in keeping down the population of field mice, moles, and
baby rabbits. Their chief offense is against birds and although cats
vary, some of them being pretty lazy, there is hardly any cat blameless
in this respect. Many years ago in Massachusetts 226 observers each
watched a single cat for 1 day. The cats killed an average of 2.7 birds
each, though perhaps a more general average would be 1 bird a day
per cat. However, birds make up not more than 25 per cent of the diet
of vagrant cats, with rodents and insects making up the balance, so
they can still be considered partially beneficial.

Belling a cat gives the birds a better break and keeping a cat indoors
during early morning hours helps a lot. Every cat owner should take
these precautions. I like cats and I used to keep one, for company and
for mice in my old house. Then I decided that birds at my window sill
were more fun than a cat indoors on the window seat. I don't think
it is fair to have both, any more than it is fair for bird lovers to try
to have all cats abolished. Vagrant alley cats that obviously have no

home can be caught in box traps and humanely put to death, but no one should ever leave poison around for animals.

Chipmunks (*Tamias,* eastern form; *Eutamias,* western)—Small, ground-dwelling squirrels, with a general grayish or tawny color and 5 dark and 4 light stripes that appear about equal in width, often found near stone walls. They dig burrows straight down, and then dig laterally, ending in a nest lined with vegetation. They may have 2 litters of young a year. They feed on grains, nuts, bulbs, planted seeds, and also on many injurious insects, so they are both helpful and harmful. Most of us enjoy seeing them in the garden, hate to have them ruin our bulbs.

The best protection for bulbs is planting in special wire baskets sold for the purpose. Naphthalene flakes in the soil will discourage chipmunks, but too much naphthalene too close to the bulb gives stunted growth or none at all. If chipmunks are too much of a problem they can be caught in box traps baited with grain or nuts and carried to woods for release.

Deer (White-tailed, *Odocoileus virginianus;* mule, *O. hemionis*)— Increasing as garden pests, even in highly populated suburban areas if there are any woods nearby. They feed on a wide variety of vegetables, fruits, and other farm crops, with some states paying farmers for damage claims. They may also ruin all the bulbs and various other ornamentals in home gardens with no one to pay for the damage. In some of my clients' gardens (less than 20 miles from New York City) the state has caught deer in huge traps and transported them to the woods, but they come back again. This spring deer found tender young rose shoots very much to their liking.

Other clients keep their plants protected with Goodrite Z.I.P. (zinc dimethyldithiocarbamate-cyclohexylamine complex). This is a good repellent but it does not add to the attractiveness of plants and applications have to be repeated. It can also be used on small dormant trees for winter protection. A repellent used somewhat in the Northwest on orchard trees is carbolineum and nicotine sulfate. The basic problem of overpopulation of deer in many agricultural communities may have to be solved by reducing the protection given them.

Dogs (*Canina familiaris*)—Most everyone likes dogs, but not too many people care to have brown patches on their front lawns or the border shrubbery dying. The first step in dog control is owner education. Owners should keep their dogs curbed, as required by some city ordinances, and not allow them to run loose. Shrub-guards, units of flexible steel wires bent out at right angles, give almost complete protection. Barberry and rose hedges deter dogs. There are many dog repellents on the market which probably have some effect for a short period. Nicotine is supposed to be a dog repellent, but when I spray with Black Leaf 40 dogs follow me around gardens.

Gophers. The term is used in Florida for land tortoises and sometimes in the Middle West for squirrels, but it usually means the pocket gopher (various species of *Thomomys, Geomys,* and *Cratogeomys*). This is a burrowing rodent, size of a large rat, with small eyes, short ears, strong claws on the front legs, a short, nearly naked tail, and large cheek pouches which are the "pockets." Gophers are widely distributed from Michigan to the Pacific coast, with more than 30 species in California and some in the Southeast, but they are not a problem in the Northeast.

They are active day and night at all seasons, with 1 litter of 4 or 5 young in colder parts of the range, 2 or 3 litters in mild climates. They dig clean-cut round tunnels, about 2 inches in diameter, parallel with the surface of the ground and 8 to 24 inches below it, throwing out rounded surface mounds of earth at intervals through short lateral tunnels and making other laterals to feed on surface vegetation. A single gopher may make 100 yards of tunnels. Meadow crops, truck crops, and ornamentals, especially those with bulbous roots, are injured, roots of trees and vines cut, and trees girdled.

Trapping and poisoning are both used in gopher control and are easiest in spring when gophers are active and ground soft. There are 2 kinds of special gopher traps, one with a flat trigger pan, one with a bait trigger, and they have to be set according to directions. Poison bait is easier. Dilute powdered strychnine with an equal amount of baking soda and dust over small sticks or cubes (1 x ½ inch) of fresh-cut potatoes, sweetpotatoes, carrots, or parsnips. Poke holes in the main tunnels with a stick, drop in 2 or 3 pieces of bait per hole and close openings with soil. For small areas a wire fence of not over 1-inch mesh can be embedded 2 feet in the earth.

Ground Squirrels (*Citellus* spp.)—Found from the West coast to Michigan and Ohio in the North, the Mississippi River in the South. They are shorter and stouter than tree squirrels, with less bushy tails, low, rounded ears. They may be plain gray or brown or mottled, spotted, or striped. They live on the ground or in burrows varying from a few to 100 feet long and as much as 6 feet below the surface. The main entrance is usually marked by a soil heap. Most species hibernate for half the year with 1 litter a year, but during their active period they cause extensive damage to grains, pasturage, garden vegetables, nut and fruit trees. They may eat insects, mice, and small birds. Some are useful at times, the striped ground squirrel getting half its food from grasshoppers, crickets, caterpillars, beetles, ants.

Two effective poisons, thallium sulfate and 1080, can be used only by official agencies, for they are too dangerous to all life. Strychnine baits are allowed and these vary according to the species. For the California ground squirrel the directions are as follows: Make a starch paste by dissolving 1 heaping tablespoon of dry gloss starch in cold water, add ¾ pint boiling water and boil and stir until clear. To this add 1 ounce strychnine (powder alkaloid) mixed with 1 ounce baking soda and $\frac{1}{10}$ ounce saccharin. Then add, stirring, ¼ pint glycerin and ¼ pint heavy corn syrup. Pour this over 16 quarts of barley (clean whole grain) and coat each kernel. Spread in a thin layer to dry. This is POISON; containers should not be reused for other purposes. Place 1 to 3 teaspoons of the mixture at the entrance of burrows. It can be dyed an abnormal green or yellow so it will not attract birds. In many states the U. S. Fish and Wildlife Service provides poison bait already prepared. For the Oregon ground squirrel, 16 quarts of clean whole oats are substituted for barley and for the Columbian ground squirrel, 10 quarts of steam-rolled oats.

Man. *Homo sapiens* can be more injurious to home gardens than all the other pests put together, especially with all these tricky new chemicals to play around with. I have a lecture called, "Are You Your Garden's Biggest Pest?" which I have given to garden clubs across the country the past dozen years, changing the content as I continue to observe gardeners and their gardens. Mistaken kindness accounts for more damage than neglect. The general cry is, "But I've got to do *Something!*" You don't have to do anything until you have studied the problem and found the right answer. Please reread pages 28, 29.

Mice. Meadow mice and pine mice are very hard on plants.

Meadow or Field Mice, Voles (*Microtus pennsylvanicus,* eastern meadow mouse and related species)—Blunt-nosed, blocky in form, 7 inches from head to end of tail, with long fur, short ears, small, beady eyes, dark gray or yellow brown with scattered black hairs. Preferring moist grasslands but living wherever there is food, meadow mice are active day and night at rhythmic intervals. They make runways on the surface of the ground and sometimes tunnels in the ground with summer nests. Winter nests are usually above ground, woven of grass. They eat seeds, fruits, stems, leaves, roots, bark of trees and shrubs in winter, occasionally insects. They have 5 to 10 litters a year, averaging 5 young per litter.

Mice can be controlled by snapback traps placed in runways or by poison bait. Zinc Phosphide Rodenticide may be obtained from regional offices of U. S. Fish and Wildlife Service. Apple bait is prepared by mixing 1 quart of fresh apple cut into half-inch cubes, without peeling or coring, with 1 level teaspoonful of the rodenticide. The grain bait formula is given in large quantities for farmers. Warm 10 ounces mineral oil with 10 ounces amber petroleum jelly, add 1 pound zinc phosphide and stir; pour over 98 pounds of steam-rolled oats, and mix thoroughly.

Protect orchard trees in winter with wire hardware cloth, 1/4-inch mesh. Avoid salt hay, leaves, straw, and other protective material that would encourage mice to nest in rose beds.

Pine Mice (*Pitymys* spp.)—Abundant and most destructive in the Southeast. They resemble meadow mice but have very small ears and eyes, dense, glossy short fur, short tail. They are bright brown to chestnut in color, 4 to 5 inches long. They spend almost all their lives underground in their own tunnels or those of moles and feed all year on roots and tubers, killing orchard trees, nursery stock, small fruits, azaleas, camellias, gardenias, and other shrubs; very common on roses.

Pine mice can be trapped with wooden-base snap traps, set with the trigger crosswise in an opened tunnel and a sprinkle of oat flakes for bait. The poison apple bait described under meadow mouse can be used, or poisoned peanuts, prepared by dissolving 1/8 ounce strychnine and 1/8 ounce baking soda in 1/2 cup of water and pouring over 2 quarts of shelled peanuts. They are dropped into the runs and covered with squares of roofing paper.

Moles (western *Scapanus*, eastern *Scalopus, Condylura, Parascalops*) —Found from the Atlantic coast to Colorado and west of the Sierra Nevada Mountains. They have enlarged forefeet for digging, a long-pointed snout, extremely small eyes, soft silky fur. The western mole eats a fair amount of vegetable material and may damage bulbs and other plants, but the eastern mole dines mostly on beetle grubs, cutworms, wireworms, and other insects, earthworms, millipedes. It becomes obnoxious to gardeners by the ridges made in lawns by its tunneling just under the surface and sometimes the disturbance to roots in garden beds, although actual feeding on roots is probably by mice using the mole runs. The large western Townsend mole and the eastern star-nosed mole make large mounds as well as runs.

Treating lawns with chlordane to kill grubs also discourages moles. There are many baits on the market, to be dropped into runs, and sometimes these are fairly satisfactory. A commercial preparation of peanuts poisoned with thallium sulfate is said to work well for some moles. Traps are more highly rated. The harpoon type kills the mole with needle-sharp tines; the choker-loop squeezes it. Both have to be set properly in tunnels in daily use. Such measures as flooding tunnels with the hose, gassing the moles with automobile exhaust, or putting naphthalene flakes or carbon bisulfide in tunnels have only a minor, temporary effect. Some cats are very efficient molers, bringing home at least one a day; other cats are completely indifferent.

Porcupine (*Erethizon dorsatum*)—Distributed through most northern woody sections, known for its coat of barbed spines, clumsy thick body, weighing 10 to 20 pounds, slow moving but capable of climbing trees. Porcupines get much of their food from trees—bark, twigs, and leaves, with evergreen needles in winter—and fresh green vegetables and fruits in season. They can be trapped with the aid of salty baits, or a strychnine-salt poison bait can be placed high in trees above the reach of livestock.

Rabbits (Jack rabbits, *Lepus* spp.; cottontails, *Sylvilagus* sp.)—Jack rabbits, from Wisconsin west, eat all kinds of farm and garden crops, trees, shrubs, and vines. Cottontails, small to medium with a white undertail, are found in almost all states. They have 2 to 5 litters a year, averaging 4 or 5 young per litter. They love early vegetables in the garden but eat all succulent plants in summer and twigs and bark in winter.

Of the many remedies suggested, the best is still a fence of 1-inch chicken wire, stretching at least 24 inches high (48 for Jack rabbits) and nearly 6 inches into the ground. A repellent, Goodrite No-Nib'l, is quite effective. Others are moth balls scattered along plant rows; dried blood; tobacco dust; nicotine sulfate, 1–400 dilution with soap sprayed on plants; red pepper mixed with same amount of flour dusted on plants when damp with dew; powdered alum mixed with flour or tobacco dust; sulfur dust; spray of 3 ounces Epsom salts to 1 gallon of water. Cats kill many baby rabbits.

A repellent to be sprayed on tree trunks in fall is made of 3 parts powdered rosin dissolved in 2 parts denatured ethyl alcohol (it takes a day or two for the rosin to dissolve). Wrapping trunks with hardware cloth is better; aluminum foil or plastics can be substituted.

Raccoon (*Procyon lotor*)—Found in most sections, more abundant in the Southeast. Like deer, this intriguing animal with its heavy stocky body, long fur, black face, and dark-banded tail, is invading our suburbs in increasing numbers. It adores the fish in pools in my clients' gardens, loves corn, and even eats rosebuds and hips. It can be caught alive in very sturdy box traps and released miles away, perhaps to invade some other garden.

Rats (*Rattus norvegicus*)—The house, brown, or Norway rat is found in exclusive suburbs as well as in city slums and on farms. Kitchen garbage added to the compost pile will attract rats unless it is immediately covered with a thick layer of earth. Rats will eat plants or seed, in house and greenhouse, and of course they are dangerous as disease carriers. Rat killer 1080 is too poisonous for amateur use. Warfarin is sold but if it is consumed in large enough doses it will kill any warm-blooded animal. Pets that eat rats poisoned by warfarin may be affected. Red Squill is much safer; if domestic animals get it by mistake, it acts as an emetic. Rats cannot vomit and so must retain the poison and die. Red Squill is mixed with cereals, meat, apples or bananas for bait, according to the food preference of rats in each section.

Skunks (*Nephytis*)—Widely distributed and moderately helpful in that they live largely on injurious insects and mice, sometimes other rodents. When they go after grubs in lawns they leave conspicuous holes and you may prefer to grubproof your lawns with chemicals before the skunks start operations.

Tree Squirrels (gray, *Sciurus,* and red, *Tamiasciurus*)—Building nests in trees with leaves and twigs or using natural hollows. There are 1 or 2 litters each year with 4 or 5 young per litter. Squirrels eat corn, wreck pears just to get the seeds, eat up sunflower seed put out for birds, and sometimes get into houses and make rather a mess—still they are a natural part of the garden picture and I, for one, would not have them shot, even if shooting were permitted in my town. Peter, the friend who kept me company on the outer window sill while I wrote the first edition of this book, is no more, and the present squirrels regard me merely as a source of food. Even so, their antics amuse me.

If you don't want to feed squirrels along with birds you can suspend the feeding station on a wire and have great metal guards fore and aft. You'll have to plant an extra row of corn for them, but usually they will be satisfied with the outer row and let you have the rest.

Woodchucks, Groundhogs *(Marmota)*—In most regions, except the extreme South. They have short legs and tail, large, thick bodies, broad, blunt head, coarse fur, weigh 6 to 10 pounds. They dig tunnels 10 to 30 feet long, down 4 or 5 feet, with 2 entrances. They hibernate in winter, produce 1 litter in spring. They destroy crops in field and garden, eating a pound of vegetation a day to keep alive. They can be killed in their burrows with a special cartridge for fumigation obtained from the U. S. Fish and Wildlife Service or with carbon bisulfide, 3 tablespoons poured on a rag and thrown into the burrow entrance which is closed with sod. The second entrance must also be located and closed.

MANTIDS

The praying, or preying, mantis and its relatives are very definitely our friends in the garden. They belong to the grasshopper order, Orthoptera, and the family Mantidae. They are all predaceous on other insects, capturing their prey with marvelous front legs, long and muscular, fitted with grooves and spines for grasping and holding. While waiting for some unwary insect they sit in an attitude of prayer. Baby mantids, looking ridiculously like their elders except for wings, are cannibals from the day they are born. They start with aphids, or perhaps one another, going on to larger insects as they grow. A full-grown praying mantis is not afraid to strike at a frog, a lizard, or a hornet. There are about 20 species known in North America; 3 are common in the East.

Carolina Mantis *(Stagmomantis carolina)*—A southern native, found as far north as southern New Jersey, Pennsylvania, and Ohio. It has uniformly green wings, is about 2½ inches long.

Chinese Mantis *(Tenodera sinensis)*—The common form in Middle Atlantic states. It was introduced accidentally from Asia about 1895, in nursery stock sent to Philadelphia, and was not imported later to fight Japanese beetles as some believe. In fact, praying mantises don't even like the beetles particularly, though they sometimes eat them. The Chinese mantis has spread to Ohio and southern New England and is often seen in gardens in late summer. It is large, 4 or 5 inches long, and the broad green front margin of the wings is sharply separated from the larger brown portion. Its triangular head is highly movable and it has very large, highly intelligent eyes. In egg-laying the female hangs head down and produces a gummy fluid which she beats into

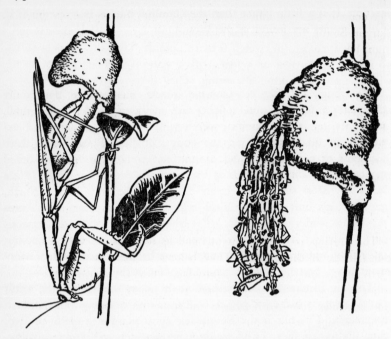

60. *Praying mantis making her egg mass as she hangs head down,*
and young mantids emerging (Drawn from photograph by Teale).

a froth the color of ripe grain to make her egg mass. This is made up
of a series of plates providing chambers for 100 or more eggs and is
attached to any shrub or tall grass around the garden or in a field.
It looks like a short, broad cornucopia of brown and tan dried foam.

If you accidentally cut off egg masses during fall cleanup or spring
pruning, simply tie them on to other shrubs and the babies will hatch
later. Don't try to keep the egg masses in the house; they will hatch
too soon. I had a female mantid on a spray of goldenrod in my office
one September; she was most appealing as she followed my every
movement with her great big eyes. But she disappeared to lay her eggs
and I never did find the cocoon until Christmas Eve when the babies
started marching down from the top of the curtain and across my
desk. That was a waste of mantids, for I could not find enough insects
to keep them alive until spring.

European Mantis (*Mantis religiosa*)—Another accidental importation, found near Rochester, New York, in 1899 and established in that

section. It is a little larger than the Carolina mantis but resembles it. Other species are found in the West.

MEALYBUGS

Mealybugs are relatives of scale insects, members of the family Coccidae, order Homoptera. They are really soft scales, with small, oval, soft, segmented bodies covered with a white powdery wax extending in filaments beyond the body. Most mealybugs have these filaments of equal length all around the body, but the long-tailed mealybug has longer threads at the posterior end of the body (Plate XXVII). Most species are house or greenhouse pests in the North, garden pests only in subtropical regions, but Comstock and Taxus mealybugs winter out-of-doors as far north as New York and Connecticut. Mealybugs injure plants by sucking sap and producing copious honeydew, which attracts ants and forms a medium for growth of sooty mold fungi. Some species disseminate plant-disease organisms.

The life history of most mealybugs is about the same. The adult female deposits her eggs, 300 to 600, in a compact, waxy sac beneath the rear end of her body. Egg-laying continues for a week or two, then the female dies. These conspicuous egg sacs, well known to anyone who has grown house plants, are chiefly at axils of branching stems or leaves but sometimes on other plant parts. Indoors, eggs hatch in about 10 days; the young nymphs remain in the case for a short period, then crawl over the plants. As crawlers, they are oval, light yellow, 6-legged insects with smooth bodies, feeding like aphids by inserting their beaks into plant tissue and sucking out the sap. Soon after feeding begins, waxy filaments start forming, covering the bodies and radiating out in 36 leglike projections. The bugs get more sluggish but do not entirely stop moving. The mature female is much like the nymph, up to ¼ inch long, but the male forms a white case within which it changes to a minute, active, 2-winged insect like a fly. It mates with the female and dies soon after, being unable to feed in the winged state. The long-tailed mealybug differs by giving birth to living young instead of forming an egg sac.

Mealybugs outdoors were formerly controlled by oil sprays, but now parathion and other phosphate aerosols are widely used in greenhouses, and malathion sprays in homes. Outdoors, much reliance is placed on biological control.

Azalea Mealybug—See Azalea Bark Scale.

Citrophilus Mealybug (*Pseudococcus gahani*)—First observed in California in 1913. It attacks apple, azalea, blackberry, citrus, climbing fig, cherry, columbine, cyclamen, English ivy, eugenia, foxglove, heliotrope, mallow, Mexican orange (Choisya), mustard, nightshade, peach, pear, pittosporum, plum, prune, potato, pepper-tree, privet, raspberry, rhubarb, rose, grevillea, sunflower, walnut. It differs from the citrus mealybug in having 2 tapering filaments at the end of the body and 1/3 the length of the body. The body fluid is darker than in other species and the waxy coating is scarce in 4 areas which look like 4 longitudinal lines. For many years it was kept under control by an Australian beetle, Cryptolaemus, which was reared on potato sprouts and distributed to growers, but in 1928 2 internal parasites from Australia were released and inside 2 years they had the citrophilus mealybug under commercial control.

Citrus Mealybug (*Planococcus citri*)—Distributed throughout the world in greenhouses and outdoors in subtropical climates, an omnivorous feeder. As a greenhouse and house-plant pest it is especially troublesome on soft-stemmed foliage plants such as African violet, coleus, begonia, fern, fuchsia, is almost always present on gardenia, readily infests amaryllis, avocado, bignonia, camellia, crassula, cineraria, cycas, cactus, chrysanthemum, croton, daphne, dracaena, heliotrope, ivy, lantana, oleander, orchids, poinsettia, rubber plant, umbrella plant, yucca. It is an outdoor pest of citrus trees in California and Florida and in the latter state is troublesome on sprouts of spring-grown potatoes kept through the summer for planting the fall crop. In southern California the citrus mealybug is found in the open on most of the plants mentioned above and also on bottlebrush, bouvardia, palms, moonflower, passion-flower, plumbago, strelitzia, and wandering Jew. It can also live outdoors in Arizona and parts of New Mexico but is not so much of a pest there. The white powder over the back of the citrus mealybug is very dense and the filaments are about equal length around the body.

Control. A few mealybugs on house plants can be picked off with a toothpick or killed with a small cotton swab dipped in alcohol. Keeping foliage washed or syringed off frequently will prevent mealybug infestation. An aerosol bomb containing rotenone and pyrethrum will keep down light infestations, but spraying with malathion is more effective. Spraying with a white-oil emulsion such as Volck, using 3 to 5 tablespoons per gallon, has long been recommended. Plants should be kept out of direct sun during and after treatment and syringed off with water several hours later. Parathion or TEPP aerosols are often used in commercial greenhouses as well as a malathion spray. Natural enemies play an important part in mealybug control.

Coconut Mealybug (*Pseudococcus nipae*)—Palm Mealybug, common in greenhouses, sometimes in lath houses, sometimes heavily infesting tree palms in southern California. The brown or yellow body is covered with thick plates of creamy, cottony wax. Parathion has given good control.

Comstock Mealybug (*Pseudococcus comstocki*)—Catalpa Mealybug. A Japanese pest distributed from Massachusetts to Florida, known in Ohio, Indiana, Louisiana, and also in California. One of the few mealybugs to winter outdoors in temperate climates, it feeds on apple, boxwood, catalpa, holly, grape, horsechestnut, Japanese honeysuckle, magnolia, maple, mulberry, osage-orange, peach, pear, Monterey pine, poplar, and weigela. It has long been known as a serious pest of umbrella catalpa, but it has been actively injurious to apple only in recent years. In addition to the injury from sapsucking the fruit is greatly disfigured with sooty mold growing in honeydew, often coincident with a soft rot. When the mealybugs congregate at a split in the tree, or at a pruning scar, knotty galls are formed.

The Comstock mealybug winters in the egg stage in bark crevices, hatching when leaves are about an inch long. There is a second generation maturing in late summer in Connecticut, with 3 broods in Virginia. This is one of the species with 2 longer filaments at the end of the body.

Control. Chief dependence is on parasites. Parathion kills some parasites without reducing the mealybugs. DDT has been more effective on apple in Connecticut. On catalpa and other ornamentals some control is obtained by cleaning all old leaves from the trees and brushing out mealybugs from crotches and crevices with a stiff brush. Thorough washing of trunk and branches with the hose is helpful, as is spraying with nicotine sulfate and soap. Sometimes a dormant spray of oil or lime-sulfur is used.

Cypress Mealybug (*Pseudococcus ryani*)—Present throughout California, most common on Monterey cypress, but feeding also on other cypress, arborvitae, araucaria, Norfolk Island pine, incense cedar, redwood. This species has short lateral filaments and a pair of tail filaments 1/3 to 1/2 the length of the body.

Golden Mealybug (*Pseudococcus aurilanatus*)—Introduced into California from Australia and New Zealand on Norfolk Island pine and the monkeypuzzle tree. It is common in southern California and is found up to San Francisco. The body is reddish purple, covered with yellow wax; eggs are purple in a yellow sac.

Grape Mealybug (*Pseudococcus maritimus*)—Another omnivorous feeder, but mostly underground. It was originally found on roots of buckwheat in California; it also occurs on roots or tops of clover, elder, buckeye, willow. From these it has gone over to cultivated plants, including apple, century plant, California poppy, coleus, columbine, Canary date palm, carnation, grevillea, lima bean, English ivy, ginkgo, grape, laburnum, lemon, orange, Mexican orange, passion-flower, pear, potato, Japanese quince, strawberry, English walnut, and Japanese yew.

The grape mealybug is present generally in California where it is most important on grapes and pears in the Santa Clara Valley, on citrus and English walnut in the coastal section, and in Florida where it injures avocado, sweetpotato, and tomato. It has also been recorded from scattered localities in Oregon, Michigan, Missouri, and New York. It may be present in quantity on stored gladiolus bulbs, is carried over in calla lily corms to infect foliage later, and spreads a fungus disease of Texas bluebell.

On grape, the mealybug winters as eggs under loose bark, the spring generation developing on buds, leaves, young fruits. The second generation congregates on grape clusters where excessive honeydew encourages black sooty mold, making grapes entirely unappetizing. Ants help the mealybugs to get about.

Control. Parathion applied in February as a dormant spray is effective and can be used by commercial growers; malathion is better suited to gardeners. Chlordane to control ants will indirectly reduce mealybugs. Spraying grapes and pears before buds open with a dormant oil emulsion has been recommended. There are efficient natural parasites.

Ground Mealybug (*Rhizoecus falcifer*)—Root Mealybug. A European species living on terminal or outer roots of potted plants, especially cacti. It also feeds outdoors in California on roots of grasses, acacia, boxwood, chrysanthemum, currant, Shasta daisy, gooseberry, grape, larkspur, marguerite, orange, peach, pepper, petunia, plum, California privet, thyme, among others. There is no entirely satisfactory control around growing plants. It helps to build a basin around an infested plant and pour in a solution of nicotine sulfate (2 teaspoons per gallon) and soap. Before planting, soil can be spaded and treated with dichloroethyl ether emulsion, 3 tablespoons per gallon, applied at the rate of 3½ gallons per square yard. The soil should be moist when the application is made and no planting should be done for at least 3 weeks. Be sure the mealybugs are not brought into the garden on potted plants.

Japanese Mealybug (*Pseudococcus krauhniae*)—Closely related to citrus mealybug but with an elongated or serpentine egg sac. It infests orange, wisteria, and Japanese persimmon in the Ojai Valley, California. It was also reported on western yew in New Jersey but that was probably the Taxus mealybug.

Long-tailed Mealybug (*Pseudococcus adonidum*)—Widely distributed in greenhouses and outdoors in warm climates. This species has 2 pencil-like filaments at the tail as long as, or longer than, the body. Living young are produced instead of eggs. It is the most important mealybug on avocado, killing the scions after grafting, and infests a long list of other plants. It occurs on citrus—orange, grapefruit, lemon—and on banana, begonia, cactus, calla, cineraria, coleus, croton, dracaena, eucalyptus, ferns, fig, fuchsia, gardenia, guava, honeysuckle, mango, moonflower, oleander, Guadalupe palm, pandanus, plum, poinsettia, primrose, rubber plant, sago palm, strelitzia, umbrella plant, carob, zamia.

Control. On avocado, after grafting, dust top 6 inches with 5 per cent chlordane, or paint the area with a slurry made of 2 pounds 50 per cent wettable powder to 1 gallon of water. This controls ants that bring mealybugs. For this species on other plants spray with malathion or parathion or use parathion or TEPP aerosols in greenhouses.

Mexican Mealybug (*Phenacoccus gossypii*)—Introduced from Mexico on cotton and now a general greenhouse pest and an outdoor problem in warm climates. It is often serious on chrysanthemum. Hollyhock, geranium, English ivy, lantana, and stock are other favored food plants. It is not much of a pest on citrus. This is a short-tailed mealybug, blue gray, covered with thin powder, with posterior filaments ¼ the length of the body. It attacks leaves, stems, flowers in all stages of growth and causes stunting of chrysanthemums with distortion of foliage.

Control. I have had good success spraying chrysanthemums with TEPP in a private greenhouse and TEPP aerosols are used commercially. Fumigation with hydrogen cyanide is more effective against the Mexican mealybug than other species. Low-dosage soil treatment with sodium selenate has controlled this species on chrysanthemums.

Pineapple Mealybug (*Pseudococcus brevipes*)—Chiefly a tropical species, sometimes occurring on pineapple, banana, and sugar cane in

Louisiana and Florida. This is a toxicogenic insect which causes, by its feeding on plants, a condition known as pineapple wilt.

Redwood Mealybug (*Pseudococcus sequoiae*)—On redwood.

Solanum Mealybug (*Phenacoccus solani*)—On paper-white narcissus bulbs in storage, especially in Florida, migrating to roots of the bulbs in the field from ambrosia, aster, malva, pansy, peanut, potato, tomato, and other plants. Growers can fumigate the bulbs with calcium cyanide after harvesting and curing.

Striped Mealybug (*Ferrisiana virgata*)—A tropical species, recorded in Texas in 1895 but only recently in Maryland (1953) and Virginia on azaleas and many other flowering plants. The nymphs are light yellow, the adults covered with glassy threads several times as long as the body. They do not secrete honeydew. There are at least 2 generations with nymphs wintering on seed tassels. Spraying with malathion has given satisfactory control.

61. Taxus mealybug on yew.

Taxus Mealybug (*Pseudococcus cuspidatae*)—First reported from a New Jersey nursery in 1915, now common in New Jersey, New York, Connecticut, and probably present on yew over much of the Northeast. All species of Taxus are infested, those with dense foliage, like *Taxus caspidata nana* and *T. wardi* being preferred. This species has been collected from apple, basswood, cedar, maple, and rhododendron, but probably does not breed on these plants. It is very abundant on yew in home gardens. I have treated a hedge 100 feet long with trunks and branch axils of every bush completely covered with the mealybugs. But because they are on the interior, infestations usually go unnoticed until general poor health causes a close examination.

The female is about ⅜ inch long and half as wide, covered with white wax so distributed that the reddish body fluid shows through in 4 longitudinal lines. There are 15 filaments on each side of the body and tail filaments about ⅓ body length. This species gives birth to living young. Nymphs winter in bark crevices and are mature by June. There are 2 or 3 broods; adults disappear in early fall.

Control. I have had excellent luck with nicotine sulfate, 1 to 400 dilution (2 teaspoons per gallon), spraying with sufficient pressure into the interior of the bushes. Malathion may be even more effective.

Yucca Mealybug (*Puto yuccae*)—Found in California, Arizona, and New Mexico. This species has a pale body entirely covered with thick plates of white cottony wax. Besides yucca, food plants include artemisia, aster, banana, black sage, ceanothus, eriophyllum, evening primrose, iceplant, lantana, lemon, lime, monkeyflower. Roots, crowns, or tops may be infested.

MIDGES

Midges are very small flies, 2-winged insects of the order Diptera. The biting midges, punkies and no-see-ums, make the gardener miserable when he takes to the woods for a vacation. The gall midges or gall gnats, family Cecidomyiidae (Itonididae) make the gardener miserable when he stays home and worries about his rosebuds or galls on the chrysanthemums. Many of the galls on trees are caused by midges. DDT is effective for control of some midges of economic importance.

Apple Leaf-curling Midge (*Dasyneura mali*)—An apple pest in New England and New York. Small orange maggots live inside curled edges of leaves on new shoots. The fly is red with iridescent wings. Spraying with DDT or nicotine sulfate near petal fall gives control.

Artemisia Gall Midges (*Diarthronomyia artemisiae* and other species). In Utah and Colorado, globose bud, rosette, or bladder galls are formed on artemisia. In California, brown or reddish subconical galls form on underside of leaves, or white confluent galls on stems, or small, oval, thin-walled hairy galls on leaf surfaces.

Cactus Fruit Gall Midge (*Asphondylia opuntiae*)—A small gray midge with white larvae, often present in great numbers on green and ripening fruit of opuntia cactus, leaving brown pupal skins protruding from exit holes. Common in California, Colorado, New Mexico, Texas.

Catalpa Midge (*Itonida catalpae*)—A yellow fly, $\frac{1}{16}$ inch long, appearing in late May or early June lays eggs on unfolding catalpa leaves. Whitish to orange maggots occur in great numbers close to midrib and large veins on underside of leaves. There are several generations. Maggot injury looks like a fungus disease, with circular dead spots on the leaves and later wilting, browning, crumpling, defoliation. Late in the season maggots enter pods and destroy seeds. Persistent killing of terminal buds stunts and dwarfs trees. Spraying with nicotine sulfate in May has been suggested in the past; DDT would probably be more effective.

Cattleya Midge (*Parallelodiplosis cattleyae*)—Yellowish maggots, $\frac{1}{8}$ inch long, feed in tips of roots of many kinds of orchids, causing nutlike galls. Cut off and destroy galls. Repot plants and spray with lindane or DDT when midges come out.

Chrysanthemum Gall Midge (*Diarthronomyia chrysanthemi*)—Limited to chrysanthemums, all varieties in greenhouse or garden. The frail, long-legged orange gnat, $\frac{1}{14}$ inch long, lays about 100 minute orange eggs on new shoots (Plate XXVIII). Hatching in 3 to 16 days, white, yellow, or orange maggots bore into tissues. The irritation of their feeding causes many cone-shaped galls on upper surface of leaves and on stems, where a number together often form knots. Developing buds are distorted and ruined; stems are twisted. When flies emerge from the galls, usually between midnight and 4 A.M., they leave protruding empty pupal cases. The life cycle is about 35 days with 5 or 6 generations a year on greenhouse chrysanthemums. I usually find 2 in gardens.

Control. Pick off and burn infested foliage. Spray with 25 per cent lindane emulsion, 1 teaspoon per gallon, or with 1 tablespoon of wettable powder per gallon, 2 or 3 times at 5-day intervals. Make the application toward evening to kill flies coming out at night. A DDT spray or aerosol will kill adults but is not so effective as lindane for the insects inside galls.

False Leaf Mining Midge (*Cricotopus ornatus*)—Sometimes present on waterlily. Larvae of a small fly mine in serpentine tunnels, followed by bacteria; new leaves turn brown and rot.

Grape Blossom Midge (*Contarinia johnsoni*)—Sometimes attacking blossoms and buds and preventing fruit development. Eggs are laid in buds, reddish maggots develop, feed, drop to the ground to pupate in a little more than 2 weeks, remaining there until the next spring.

Juniper Midge (*Contarinia juniperina*)—Yellow maggots cause blisters at base of needles, which may drop; tips die. Larvae winter in the soil and flies lay eggs on needles in April. Control by pruning dead tips and cultivating soil or treating it with lindane.

Monterey Pine Midge (*Thecodiplosis pini-radiatae*)—A common, serious pest of Monterey pine in California, also present on other pines and Monterey cypress. Minute dark flies lay orange eggs in masses on terminal buds from January to March; orange maggots feed at base of needles until November or December, then pupate in soil. Needles are shortened, yellow, swollen at base. Trees are weakened, look as if swept by fire, with needle drop; some die. Cultivate around trees in early winter to destroy pupae.

Pear Midge (*Contarinia pyrivora*)—The fly deposits eggs in pear blossom buds in late April or May. When full-grown the maggots drop to the ground or remain in fruit, which becomes bloated, lopsided with dark blotches, drops early.

Rhododendron Midge (*Giardomyia rhododendri*)—Young leaves are rolled and margins browned by small, whitish maggots. New growth does not develop properly. Spray tips with lindane or DDT.

62. Rose shoots injured by rose midge.

Rose Midge (*Dasyneura rhodophaga*)—Confined to roses, a greenhouse pest since 1886, first reported in gardens in 1916, and now found in scattered localities in many states. It arrives in a garden with unbelievable suddenness and works with devastating thoroughness, more often in mid- or late summer. A flower garden is changed almost overnight into a green garden with every potential bud in a leaf axil black and crisp, every tiny new shoot dead, buds on pedicels twisted, deformed, blackened.

The adult, minute, $\frac{1}{20}$ inch long, reddish or yellow brown, lays small yellowish eggs on succulent growth, under sepals of flower buds, in unfolding leaves. In warm weather they hatch in 2 days and young whitish maggots feed at base of flowers, often 20 or 30 to a bud, or on upper side of leaves and leaf petioles, causing them to become distorted, turn brown, and die (Plate XXVIII). They reach maturity, orange, $\frac{1}{12}$ inch long, in about a week. They fall to the ground to pupate in small white cocoons and new adults appear in 5 to 7 days. The life cycle takes 12 to 16 days in greenhouses, longer out-of-doors.

Control. DDT, which is very effective, has replaced ineffective tobacco sprays, mulches, etc. At the first indication of infestation spray with 50 per cent wettable DDT, 2 tablespoons per gallon, or at the rate of 2 pounds per 100 gallons. Cover bush and ground underneath thoroughly. Repeat twice at 7 to 10 day intervals. Prune off into a paper bag and burn all infested buds.

Violet Gall Midge (*Phytophaga violicola*)—The small fly lays white eggs in curled margins of unfolding new violet leaves. The maggots cause curling, distortion, twisting of leaves, followed by a wet rot. Infested plants are dwarfed; blossoming is limited. Gather and burn fallen leaves frequently.

MILLIPEDES

Millipedes, "thousand-legged worms," class Diplopoda, are long, hard-shelled, cylindrical, with 2 pairs of legs on each of their many segments. They are brown or pinkish brown, occasionally grayish, about an inch long, rarely up to 2 inches, and are usually found coiled up like a watch spring. Most gardeners confuse them with wireworms, which are also hard-shelled but are flat, not round in cross sections, have only the 6 legs of a true insect, and do not coil up like a spring (compare Plates XXIII and XXIX). Millipedes have 100 to 400 legs, not 1000. They are useful as scavengers, feeding on decaying vegetable matter and manure, but they do sometimes eat small roots or seedlings, bean, corn, or pea seed. They slide into cabbage heads to horrify the cook, tunnel into potato tubers or into carrots, beets, parsnips, or turnips. Fruits that touch damp ground, especially muskmelon, tomatoes, or strawberries, are often entered by these wiry worms. They are frequently found in decaying bulbs but are seldom the original cause of decay. Chief injury is in greenhouses in soil rich in organic matter.

Each female deposits about 300 eggs, in clusters of 20 to 100, in the soil or on the surface. They are nearly translucent and covered with a sticky material. They hatch in about 3 weeks. Young millipedes have only 3 pairs of legs at first, with fewer segments than the adult; they grow slowly and there is probably 1 generation a year.

Control. Poison bait has been largely replaced with sprays or dusts of lindane, DDT, or chlordane, treating surface of the soil and benches and all hiding places in greenhouses. In gardens, protect ripening fruits with salt hay or other mulch. Destroy refuse.

MITES

Mites are not true insects. They belong to the animal class Arachnida, which includes spiders, scorpions, harvestmen (daddy longlegs), and ticks, all grouped together by having 4 pairs of legs instead of the 3 pairs of members of the insect class Hexapoda. They also differ from insects in lacking antennae, true jaws, and compound eyes, and in having only 2 body regions, head and thorax being joined together. Mites, members of the order Acarina, differ further in having the body seemingly all one piece, without segments, and the young with only 3 pairs of legs, the fourth added at maturity. Ticks are the large members of this order, mites the very small, almost microscopic forms.

Many mites injure man or animals. The plant pests can be divided into the spider group, family Tetranychidae, including 2-spotted mite and other common red spiders, European red mite, spruce mite, etc.; the soft-bodied mites, family Tarsonemidae, with cyclamen mite the most important member; root mites, family Tyroglyphidae, including the bulb mite; and the blister or gall mites, family Eriophyidae, with the pear leaf blister mite. There are also running mites, active on or in the ground, larger than red spiders, very red, but these are friends, preying on other mites and small insects.

Since the advent of DDT and some other chlorinated hydrocarbons mites have increased enormously in importance. This has been due to the killing off of beneficial predators and parasites and apparently, in some cases, to a direct effect of DDT on plant tissues, predisposing them in some way to mite injury. In the past decade many excellent new miticides have been developed, some very toxic to humans and to be used with caution, others relatively safe. Among the latter are Aramite, malathion, Ovotran, Dimite.

Avocado Brown Mite (*Oligonychus punicae*)—On avocado in California, sometimes causing defoliation, but not as serious as other mites.

It is dark brown, makes only light, delicate webbing, has stalked amber eggs. This mite is readily controlled with dusting sulfur.

Avocado Red Mite (*Oligonychus yothersi*)—A Florida pest of avocado, mango, and camellias, also occurring on camphor, Australian silk oak, and other trees, and in some states on boxwood. The mites are reddish purple, oval, immature states greenish. Eggs are laid singly on both leaf surfaces. Leaves are speckled or russeted along the midrib and may drop off. Dusting with sulfur has been quite satisfactory. On avocado, parathion has given a good initial kill but is followed by an increase in mites. TEPP and Aramite have controlled the mites on camellias.

Blueberry Bud Mite (*Aceria vaccinii*)—Blossom buds may be so deformed they do not set fruit or the berries have rough blistered skin. The mites live all year under leaf or fruit bud scales but can be controlled with a post-harvest spray of a summer oil, 3 per cent dilution.

Boxwood Mite (*Eurytetranychus buxi*)—Rather general on boxwood, especially where DDT has been used to control leaf miners. Injury shows as a light mottling of leaves early in the season, followed by a general grayish, dingy, unhealthy appearance. What appear to be minute hen scratches on foliage are an early indication of mites at work. The mites are yellow green or reddish, $\frac{1}{64}$ inch long. Yellow eggs winter on leaves, hatch in April. The mites breed rapidly with 5 or 6 generations in a summer. Dusting with sulfur has been recommended control until recently, or a dormant oil spray before growth starts. Aramite is now effective, 1 tablespoon of 50 per cent wettable powder to a gallon of water. Ovotran and Dimite are good.

Broad Mite (*Hemitarsonemus latus*)—Often associated with cyclamen mite and causing similar injury in greenhouses and sometimes in gardens. The broad mite is pale, almost transparent, slightly smaller and wider than the cyclamen mite. It moves more rapidly and feeds exposed on the undersurface of leaves, completing its life cycle in 7 or 8 days. The injury is a blistered and glassy or silvery appearance to the leaf, which may become rather brittle, and sometimes a puckering downward. It attacks many ornamentals—cyclamen, delphinium, snapdragon, African violet, begonia, china aster, marguerite, chrysanthemum, fuchsia, lantana, gerbera, geranium, marigold, verbena, zinnia—also avocado seedlings in greenhouses, peppers, and a few other vegetables.

Control. Sulfur dust has been effective for this species.

Bulb Mite (*Rhizoglyphus echinopus* and *R. solani* complex)—Injuring bulbs or corms of amaryllis, crocus, freesia, gladiolus, hyacinth, lily, narcissus, onion, tulip, and underground stems of asparagus, peony, a few other plants. The mite is whitish, often with 2 brown spots on the body, $\frac{1}{50}$ to $\frac{1}{25}$ inch long, slow moving, found in colonies. It is abundant on rotting bulbs and decaying plant material, but it can also burrow into healthy bulbs and carry bacteria and fungi that produce rots. The mites spread infection from diseased to healthy bulbs in field, greenhouse, and storage.

The egg develops into a 6-legged larva, lasting 3 to 8 days, ending in a quiescent state. It molts into a protonymph with 8 legs, feeds for 2 to 4 days, has a second resting period, and molts into a tritonymph, then finally into the adult form. If conditions are unfavorable after the second molt the mite goes into a heavily chitinized, non-feeding but active stage, the hypopus, in which it attaches itself to any moving object, perhaps a mouse or a fly, and so is transported to a new breeding place.

Control. Burn all infested (soft mushy) bulbs. Treat others for 10 minutes in a 1 to 400 solution of nicotine sulfate at 122°F.; or in 2 to 4 per cent lime-sulfur held at 125°F. for 1 minute; or in hot water held at 110° to 111.5°F. for 3 hours; or store in tight containers with 2 per cent nicotine dust. Predaceous mites attack the bulb mite.

Bulb Scale Mite (*Steneotarsonemus laticeps*)—Related to the cyclamen mite and not associated with rots as is the bulb mite. The mites feed between leaves and flowers in neck region of the bulb, which becomes soft and spongy. Bulbs have yellow-brown scarlike streaks, and resulting flowers and foliage are severely injured. Store bulbs in a cool place. If necessary, treat as for the bulb mite.

Citrus Bud Mite (*Aceria sheldoni*)—On lemons in California, causing blasted or multiple buds, deformed twigs or leaves, blossoms, or fruits, bunched growth, blackening of the rind beneath the fruit button. Oil sprays are fairly effective.

Citrus Red Mite (*Metatetranychus citri*)—Purple Mite in Florida, Red Spider to many citrus growers, more serious in arid California than in moist Gulf states. This mite prefers lemons in California, satsuma oranges along the Gulf, but infests other oranges and grapefruit. Foliage is speckled silver, may turn brown and drop; fruit is gray or yellow and the crop light. Eggs are red, with a vertical stalk, laid on fruit, twigs, leaves. Larvae are at first orange, later dark red; adult females are almost black, males are lighter red but with a dark band around the body. They have red tubercles with white bristles.

Citrus Rust Mite (*Phyllocoptruta oleivora*)—More serious in the Gulf states than California, on oranges, grapefruit, lemons, limes, and other citrus fruits. Chief injury is the russeting of oranges, a silvering of lemon fruit. A severe attack starts as faint black areas on green oranges, increasing until the whole fruit looks rusty, dry, rough. Outer cells are killed, size is reduced, rind thickened, quality impaired. The mite is long, wedge-shaped, orange as an adult, only $\frac{1}{150}$ inch long. Yellow eggs are laid in depressions on fruit or on leaves. Cycles are completed in 10 days or less and mites are present through the year in Florida but least numerous in January and February. Sulfur is a specific for rust mite. It may be applied as lime-sulfur, 1 to 50 or 1 to 100 dilution, or as a wettable sulfur spray, but sulfur dust is very effective, with 3 to 6 applications a year.

Clover Mite (*Bryobia praetiosa*)—Almond Mite, Brown Mite, distributed throughout the United States. Hosts include fruits—apple, apricot, almond, cherry, peach, pear, prune, raspberry—many shade trees and herbaceous plants, lawns and shrubbery around houses. This mite has become an annoyance indoors, entering houses in large numbers in fall but not actively injuring furnishings. In southern states the mite winters on various clovers and malva, but in the North it winters as small red eggs, looking like brick dust, on bark and around buds. They hatch in early spring. Young mites are red, adults rusty brown, larger than other mites, with front legs longer than the others. Their feeding causes foliage to turn yellow and drop.

Control. Spraying grass and shrubs near houses, along with base walls and doorways, with malathion, 1 per cent emulsion, helps to keep clover mites from entering.

Currant Bud Mite (*Cecidophyes ribis*)—Injurious to black, native, and flowering currants. The buds swell and die before opening, after which mites emerge to infest buds on normally developing canes. Cut and burn infested shoots; dust with sulfur in early spring.

Cyclamen Mite (*Steneotarsonemus pallidus*)—Pallid Mite, Strawberry Crown Mite, first noted in New York in 1898 and now present throughout the country as a greenhouse and garden pest. It is particularly injurious to cyclamen, snapdragon, and African violet indoors, but the greenhouse list includes ageratum, azalea, begonia, gerbera, marguerite, lantana, marigold, verbena, zinnia. Outdoors this mite is probably the worst enemy of delphinium, deforms aconite and snapdragon, is often the limiting factor in strawberry production, may infest peppers and tomatoes.

The mite is too small to see with the naked eye, but it can be readily identified by the characteristic reaction of the plants on which it feeds. Cyclamen infested early does not flower; later infestation produces distorted, streaked, or blotched blooms that fall early, with foliage curled into cups, wrinkled, purplish (Plate XXX). African violets are stunted, have twisted stems. Delphinium leaves are thickened, puckered, without normal indentations; flower stalks are gnarled, twisted, darkened; buds turn black and seldom open; the whole plant may be stunted to less than a fourth normal height. Mite work on delphinium is often known as "blacks" and thought to be a real disease. Mites feeding in young, unfolding leaves of strawberries cause stunting, distortion, chlorosis, browning, and shriveling of flowers, no fruit.

The young cyclamen mite is glassy white or transparent pale green, $\frac{1}{100}$ inch long, slow moving; the adult is pale brown. The female lays 5 or 6 eggs a day for 2 or 3 weeks at the base of the plant or in crevices about leaves and buds. They hatch in a week into 6-legged larvae which are active for 7 days, then quiescent for 3 before changing to the 8-legged adult. This is a cool-weather mite, injuring delphinium from early spring to June and in late summer but seldom active in the heat of midsummer.

Control. Keep this pest out if you can. Purchase only perfect, healthy specimens, whether delphiniums for the garden or African violets for the house. Buy certified strawberries where possible. Space plants indoors so they do not touch; avoid handling clean plants after touching those possibly infested. Discard heavily infested plants. Valuable plants lightly infested can be immersed in hot water at 110°F. for 15 minutes. For African violets a capsule of sodium selenate (sold as Kapsulate and under other trade names) can be laid on the surface of the pot, which is then filled to the rim with water. Phosphate systemics are not successful, nor are the phosphate sprays, so effective for other mites, of much help for the cyclamen mite. Dimite, used at 1 teaspoon per gallon, is quite effective, if started very early in the season outdoors on delphinium. Repeated applications of rotenone at 5-day intervals give reasonably good control.

Date Mite (*Oligonychus pratensis*)—An important pest of date palms in California, also on Washingtonia and Canariensis palms near date gardens and on grasses, occasionally on maple, cypress, and various ornamental trees. The mite is pale yellow. Leaves and fruits are webbed together; the fruit is scurfy, shriveled, cracked, yellow. Dusting with sulfur is effective.

European Red Mite (*Metatetranychus ulmi*)—An imported species first noted in 1911, now serious in the Northeast and Northwest, particularly damaging following use of DDT in orchards. It is most injurious to apple, pear, plum, prune, but may infest almond, walnut, citrus, and ornamental trees and shrubs, including mountain-ash, elm, black locust, and rose. Bright red to orange eggs, each with a stalk, winter on twigs and branches, often in crevices of fruit spurs. They hatch in spring just before blooming. The first nymphal stage is bright red, the second and third dull green or brown. The adult female is velvety red with 4 rows of curved spines arising from white tubercles, $\frac{1}{50}$ inch long. Foliage is speckled and turns a sickly bronze, looking as if covered with dust, but there is not much webbing. Fruit buds are weakened, many leaves drop, and fruit is undersized, of poor quality.

Control. Very thorough spraying with a 2 or 3 per cent dormant oil emulsion (1 pint 83 per cent petroleum emulsion to 5 gallons of water), applied at the delayed dormant stage, gives fair control. Summer miticides, Aramite, TEPP, or parathion may have to be added to DDT sprays.

Filbert Bud Mite (*Phytoptus avellanae*)—Filbert Big-bud. Buds are swollen to 2 or 3 times normal size, with no further development into foliage. In May when mites leave swollen buds and start crawling to normal buds some can be killed with a miticide.

Oak Mite (*Oligonychus bicolor*)—Important on oak, elm (especially where heavy dosages of DDT have been used for bark beetles), sometimes on birch, hickory, maple, and other shade trees. The mite is dark green to black with forward part of body lighter and brownish; dorsal spines are slender with no spots at the base; eggs are brown, flatted on top. The foliage looks very dusty. Aramite or some other miticide should be added to DDT sprays.

Pacific Mite (*Tetranychus pacificus*)—Important along the Pacific coast from California to Washington on apple, pear, cherry, grape, plum, prune, almond, walnut, beans, and various ornamentals. Foliage is heavily webbed, turns bronze, and there may be extensive defoliation; fruit fails to color properly, often with heavy drop before harvest. This species looks like the two-spotted spider mite and makes similar webs. Adults winter in trash on ground, migrating to trees in spring and feeding on lower foliage first. Eggs are laid in webbing. There are several generations with peak of abundance in late summer, when many mites spin webs at calyx end of fruit. Grape leaves turn prematurely red or brown, bean leaves are webbed.

Control. Dusting with sulfur or spraying with a 1½ per cent summer oil emulsion is fairly effective, but more potent miticides may be necessary if DDT is used to control codling moth. Parathion is effective but should be left to the commercial grower, also TEPP. Rotenone in a summer oil emulsion is safe; DN-Dust D-4, or DN-111 spray, or toxaphene are other possibilities.

Pallid Mite (*Tydeus californicus*)—Sometimes abundant on avocado. It is white, a little larger than the six-spotted mite, without spots.

Pear Leaf Blister Mite (*Eriophyes pyri*)—Present wherever pears are grown, sometimes on apple, mountain-ash, shadbush, and cotoneaster. Brownish blisters appear on underside of apple and pear leaves, each about ⅛ inch across but often massed together to nearly cover the leaf. When the blisters are opened, small elongated pinkish or white mites, 1/125 inch long, can be seen with a hand lens. Adults winter under scales of fruit and leaf buds, often hundreds in a single bud. They lay eggs in the buds as they swell in spring, and the young burrow in unfolding leaves, feeding entirely inside the blisters. Successive generations develop in the leaves, but they migrate to buds at the approach of cold weather.

Control. Apply a dormant lime-sulfur spray, 1 to 15 dilution, before buds open, or an oil emulsion just as buds begin to swell. The weather has to be warm enough for the oil to penetrate.

Pecan Leaf Roll Mite (*Aceria caryae*)—Feeds on margin of leaflets, causing them to roll into a thickened gall-like growth parallel to the midvein. Another mite (*Eotetranychus hicoriae*) seems to be even more important on pecan, causing a scorching of leaves and defoliation. Parathion has given effective control.

Platani Mite (*Oligonychus platani*)—Serious on loquats in California, also on avocado, camphor, cotoneaster, cypress, eucalyptus, oak, pyracantha, sycamore, toyon, walnut, and willow. It feeds on upper surface of leaves, causing a brownish discoloration. Natural enemies keep it under fair control.

Privet Mite (*Brevipalpus inornatus*)—False Spider Mite, widely distributed, injuring privet, azaleas, and other flowering shrubs, palms, ivy, chrysanthemum, coleus, fuchsia, and many others. It was first described from goldenrod. The egg is elliptical, bright orange red at first, then slightly darker. The mites are bright orange to dark red with various dark pigmentations. They feed on underside of leaves, on stems, and petioles. Leaves turn bronze underneath and deep red on upper surface of some plants, yellow on others. Privet turns yellow, azalea leaves brown or bronze and drop off. In experiments on control, chlorobenzilate, Dimite, and Diazinon have given best results with Aramite and Ovotran next. Malathion was not so effective.

This species is apparently identical with the bioculatus mite, said to be the most serious pest of fuchsia in California, pitting underside of leaves and causing heavy leaf drop.

Redberry Mite (*Aceria essigi*)—Blackberry Mite, a western species on blackberry, microscopic in size. Mites feed near the base of drupelets, preventing fruit from ripening in whole or in part, causing "redberry disease." Affected fruit stays bright-colored, hard, clings to bushes. Mites winter in buds. Use a dormant lime-sulfur spray, 1 to 15 dilution, in March as buds are opening, and a second spray, 1 to 40 dilution, when fruiting arms are about a foot long.

Six-spotted Mite (*Eotetranychus sexmaculatus*)—Yellow mite, a citrus pest in the Gulf states and parts of California. The adult is pale yellow, feeds on underside of citrus leaves in very definite areas, often near veins, which are depressed and covered with webs. The upper surface of the leaf has yellowish blisters with a smooth shiny surface. Oil sprays, DN or sulfur dusts have been used for control.

Southern Red Mite (*Oligonychus ilicis*)—The red spider of the South, but also injurious to holly, azalea, and some other shrubs in the North. Camellia, camphor, cypress, eucalyptus, loquat, live oaks, plane, English walnut, rose are among ornamentals infested. The mites feed on both leaf surfaces, rasping the epidermis. Leaves turn gray or brown as feeding continues. Adult females are nearly black, males and nymphs light red. Both have spiny hairs curving backward. Red eggs are laid on both leaf surfaces and heavily infested leaves look as if they had been dusted with red pepper. There may be extensive defoliation. There are many generations, but in the South most damage is in the fall or spring with low populations in midsummer. In the North mites start feeding on holly at the end of April and populations increase rapidly in summer.

Control. Parathion is very effective, but home gardeners can get good control with the safer Aramite, Ovotran, chlorobenzilate, or Dimite.

Spruce Spider Mite (*Oligonychus ununguis*)—A most important evergreen pest. Arborvitae turns brown, spruce grayish, juniper yellow, hemlock nearly white from the sucking of these very small mites. They are dark green to nearly black, with spines on the back, salmon-pink legs. Spherical eggs, wintering at the base of needles, hatch in April or May, complete a generation in 4 or 5 weeks, and go on building up populations until winter eggs are laid in October. The mites spin a quantity of webbing between the needles. Injury is worse in hot, dry seasons, and following use of DDT. Young spruces may die the first season; older trees die progressively, from lower branches upward, over a period of years.

Control. Syringing with a hose to break webs is helpful and sulfur dust has been much used in the past. Now Aramite, 1 tablespoon 50 per cent wettable powder to a gallon of water, or Ovotran gives excellent control. The latter is more effective against the egg stage.

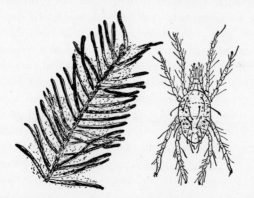

63. Spruce twig webbed by spruce spider mite and mite as seen under a microscope.

Strawberry Spider Mite (*Tetranychus atlanticus*)—A pest of vegetable and field crops as well as strawberry in California; a major strawberry pest in Virginia, causing loss of vigor, reduced yield, stunting, sometimes death. This species is quite susceptible to sulfur, but it may be injurious in cool weather when sulfur is less effective. Aramite as a 3 per cent dust gave good results in Virginia, also Systox as a systemic insecticide.

Tomato Russet Mite (*Vasates lycopersici*)—First found in California in 1940, now an important tomato pest in many other states. It also feeds on potato, petunia, groundcherry, datura, and other solanaceous hosts. Typical injury is a bronzing or russeting of surface of stems and leaves, with feeding starting at base of the main stalk. Leaves turn brown 3 or 4 weeks later. Fruit is attacked only in severe cases, but loss of foliage results in sunburned fruit. Sulfur dust has given good control. Predaceous mites and thrips help.

Two-spotted Spider Mite (*Tetranychus telarius*)—A pest in every garden, probably the most common of the mites we call red spider. The mites turn rose leaves gray or reddish or yellow or brown, with defoliation by midsummer. Leaves of phlox, hollyhock, primrose, violet, and many, many other flowers turn yellow, as well as foliage of beans and other vegetables and that of many fruits. Ivy in the house is a sickly gray from red spiders. Nearly all greenhouse plants are subject to infestation.

Red spiders are very small. The female is less than $\frac{1}{50}$ inch, the male even smaller. The body is oval, yellow or greenish with 2 dark spots on the back, sparsely covered with spines. In some strains the adults are red. The young, 6-legged mite feeds for a day or two after hatching, then enters a resting stage; it molts into a second active stage and again rests. The female goes through a third such period before becoming adult, the male only 2 periods. Mating takes place a few minutes after the female reaches adult form, and she lays 100 to 200 eggs on underside of leaves in 3 or 4 weeks. Eggs from unmated females develop into males only. The mites make mealy cobwebs on the underside of leaves, from one leaf to another, sometimes entirely covering a new shoot, flower buds and all.

The number of generations increases with the temperature. At 75°F. the adult stage is reached in 5 days; it takes 40 days at 55°F. In greenhouses there is a new generation every 20 to 30 days. Outdoors, mites hibernate as adults in soil, on tree bark, on leaves of plants retaining foliage, starting activity quite early in spring but usually reaching peak of abundance in July. In situations of high humidity where air is stagnant, mites are always serious. Plants under overhanging eaves, in a walled garden, in dense clumps, or a thick hedge are most susceptible. Where DDT is used in mist blowers for mosquito control red spiders build up enormous populations in gardens.

Control. There are many excellent new miticides. Aramite and malathion both give excellent control in home gardens if applied early enough and often enough. In greenhouses commercial growers have used parathion or TEPP bombs, but some resistant strains of mites have developed and it may be necessary to change chemicals rather frequently. Chlorobenzilate as a spray, Aramite as a spray or dust, parathion as a spray, aerosol, or dust, dithione (sulfotepp) as an aerosol or smoke, Ovotran as a spray or dust, malathion as a spray, TEPP as an aerosol are all possibilities. Application of systemic insecticides started with sodium selenate applied to the soil, still recommended for carnations and chrysanthemums, and now includes demeton (Systox) and schradan (OMPA, Pestox III) applied as a spray or aerosol. Syringing plants with the hose is still a good idea for red spiders; use force enough to break the webs.

Walnut Blister Mite (*Aceria erinea*)—Yellow or brown feltlike galls on underside of leaves, not very injurious. It can be controlled with a dormant lime-sulfur spray, 1 to 10 dilution, when buds swell in spring.

Willamette Mite (*Eotetranychus willamettei*)—On apple, pear, cherry, raspberry in Pacific Northwest. It is similar to the Pacific mite but spins less webbing. Summer sprays of parathion, rotenone and oil, or TEPP are used by fruit growers.

MOTHS

Moths belong to the insect order Lepidoptera, having wings covered with scales. They differ from butterflies in being mostly night fliers, not holding wings vertically when at rest, in having a heavy, hairy body, antennae that may be feathery but not knobbed, in laying eggs in large clusters often coated with hairs, and with pupae usually inside a cocoon. There are many families, with different workers not always in agreement. The list below, in alphabetical order, includes only families with members injurious to cultivated plants. Species commonly known by their adult stage are treated in this section; those best known for their caterpillar stage will be found under Borers, Budworms, Cankerworms, Casebearers, Caterpillars, Cutworms, Earworms, Fruitworms, Hornworms, Leaf Folders, Leaf Rollers, Leaf Skeletonizers, Leaf Tiers, Spanworms, or Webworms.

Aegeriidae. Clear-winged moths; wasplike, wings mostly without scales; rear edge of fore wings locks over front edge of hind wings; mostly day fliers; larvae are borers in woody and herbaceous plants. Peach tree, squash, and currant borers.

Arctiidae. Tiger moths; nocturnal; wings held rooflike over body when at rest; brightly spotted or banded; larvae very hairy. Woollybears; fall webworm.

Citheroniidae. Royal moths; stout-bodied with large wings; larvae have horns or spines, feed on trees, pupate in ground without a cocoon. Hickory horned devil or regal moth.

Coleophoridae. Casebearers; small, brown or gray with narrow pointed wings, fringed along hind margins; larvae leaf miners when young, then making cases.

Cosmopterygidae. Small moths, wings long, narrow, sharply pointed at apex; larvae are leaf miners. Palm leaf skeletonizer.

Cossidae. Large, heavy-bodied, with spotted or mottled wings; larvae are wood-borers. Carpenterworm; leopard moth.

Dioptidae. Only 1 species in the United States, the California oakworm.

Gelechiidae. Gelechiid moths; small, dull-colored; narrow fore wings; long, upcurving labial palps; hind wings often with a curved outer margin. Pink bollworm; potato tuberworm.

Geometridae. Measuring worms, geometers; small, slender-bodied; some species with wingless females; larvae have 2 or 3 prolegs at the end of the body, move with a looping motion. Cankerworms; spanworms; loopers.

Gracilariidae. Leaf miners; very small moths with tapering wings; larvae make blotch mines. Gregarious oak leaf miner.

Incurvariidae. Small moths with minute spines on wing membranes; female with piercing ovipositor. Maple leaf cutter; yucca moth.

Lasiocampidae. Tent caterpillars; robust, very hairy, antennae feathery; larvae hairy, living in webs.

Limacodidae (Eucleidae). Slug caterpillars; larvae short, fleshy, sluglike, without prolegs. Saddleback caterpillar.

Liparidae (Lymantriidae). Tussock moths and allies; medium size, hairy, males with plumose antennae, females wingless in some species; larvae hairy, some with tufts (tussocks) of hairs. Gypsy moth, browntail moth, white-marked tussock moth.

Lyonetiidae. Ribbed cocoon makers; small, with very narrow wings; larvae leaf miners. Birch and oak skeletonizers.

Megalopygidae. Flannel moths; medium-sized with a dense coat of scales mixed with fine curly hairs; larvae hairy, sometimes stinging. Puss caterpillar; crinkled flannel moth.

Nepticulidae. Minute moths; spinelike hairs on surface of wings; larvae are leaf miners in trees and shrubs.

Notodontidae. Prominents; brown or yellow with prominently projecting tufts on hind margins of wings; larvae have conspicuous tubercles. Yellow-necked, red-humped, and walnut caterpillars.

Oecophoridae. Small, flattened moths, brownish, wings broad, rounded apically; larvae web plants. Parsnip webworm.

Olethreutidae. Small, brown or gray, banded or mottled, fore wings rather square-tipped, fringe of long hairs on basal part of hind wings; larvae smooth-skinned, pale, feed on foliage, fruits or nuts. Codling moth; oriental fruit moth; grape berry moth; strawberry leaf roller.

Phalaenidae (Noctuidae). Noctuid moths, largest family in the Lepidoptera with 2700 species; nocturnal, mostly medium size, dull color, heavy-bodied, front wings narrow, hind wings broad; larvae are smooth, dull, very destructive. Armyworms; cutworms; corn earworms; cabbage looper, celery looper.

Plutellidae. Yellow marks look like diamonds when male folds its wings. Diamondback moth.

Psychidae. Bagworm moths; females wingless; larvae live in baglike cases.

Pterophoridae. Plume moths; small, slender, gray or brown with wings split into 2 or 3 featherlike divisions, legs long; larvae are leaf rollers and stem borers. Grape plume moth.

Pyralidae (includes Pyraustidae, Phycitidae, Crambidae). Snout moths; small, delicate, with projecting labial palpi looking like a snout. European corn borer; grape leaf folder; melonworm; pickleworm; garden webworm; waterlily leaf cutter; crambid moths (sod webworms).

Saturniidae. Giant silkworm moths; very large, brightly colored; wings with transparent eye spots. Cecropia, luna, promethea, polyphemus moths.

Sphingidae. Sphinx or hawk moths; medium to large; body heavy, spindle-shaped; feed at dusk, looking like hummingbirds; larvae large, with a horn at the rear. Tomato and tobacco hornworms.

Tortricidae. Tortricid moths; wingspread not over an inch, gray, tan, or brown, spotted or mottled, front wings square cut; wings at rest are bell-shaped; larvae are leaf rollers or tiers. Spruce budworm; fruit tree leaf roller.

Yponomeutidae. Ermine moths; small, brightly patterned, with broad wings; larvae web or mine leaves. Ailanthus webworm; arborvitae leaf miner.

Abutilon Moth (*Anomis erosa*)—Okra Caterpillar, feeding on abutilon, okra, hollyhock, hibiscus, and mallow. It is a light green semilooper, similar to the cabbage looper, growing to 1⅜ inches long, pupating in a folded leaf. It can be controlled with lead arsenate or DDT if its parasitic wasp does not do a good enough job.

Achemon Sphinx (*Pholus achemon*)—A large moth, wings expanding to 3 or 4 inches, fore wings gray with brown marks, hind wings pink, high flier. It lays pale eggs on upper surface of leaves; pupation is in mahogany-brown chrysalids in soil. The caterpillars are large, 2 to 3½ inches, green or pinkish, with oblique white bars on the sides; the young larva has a black horn, but this disappears with the first molt. Cultivated grapes, wild grapes, and Virginia creeper may be defoliated. There are 2 generations. Spray or dust with lead arsenate or DDT when young caterpillars appear.

Apple Fruit Moth (*Argyresthia conjugella*)—Larvae burrow into apple fruit in northern California. Moth is pale yellow with purple-brown fore wings marked with dark bands.

Artichoke Plume Moth (*Platyptilia carduidactyla*)—The adult has big brown divided (plumed) wings, 1-inch wingspread. Caterpillars feed on new foliage and mine inside stems, leaf stalks, buds, with noticeable damage to the head. There are 3 overlapping generations in California, with worst injury in spring. Pick and destroy all wormy artichokes; bury all old plant tops under 10 inches of soil; remove nearby thistles. Use a pyrethrum-oil spray (2 teaspoons pyrethrum extract to 1 gallon 2 per cent oil emulsion).

Brown-tail Moth (*Nygmia phaeorrhoea*)—Introduced into Massachusetts on nursery stock prior to 1897 and now present in all New England states. It is common on apple, cherry, oak, pear, plum, hawthorn, rose, willow, occasional on elm and maple. The caterpillars, 1½ inches long, are reddish brown to nearly black, with a broken stripe along each side, a red tubercle on segments 11 and 12, and covered with tufts of brown hairs. These are barbed and poisonous, causing a severe rash when they touch the skin, even death if large numbers of small hairs are breathed into the lungs. They winter as young larvae, several hundred webbed together in a nest, feed during the spring, and in June pupate in a cocoon among webbed leaves.

The moths are pure white except for brown scales at the tip of the abdomen, have a 1½-inch wingspread, are active fliers. They appear in July to lay eggs in globular yellow clusters, covered with light brown hairs, on underside of leaves. There is 1 generation a year.

Control. Cut off and burn winter webs; spray trees with DDT or lead arsenate or methoxychlor in early spring when leaves come out or in August when young caterpillars appear. A fungus disease kills many caterpillars. Brown-tail moths are included in quarantine regulations for the gypsy moth. See Puss Caterpillar for a recipe to soothe the rash.

Buck Moth (*Hemileuca maia*)—Ranging from southern New

Hampshire to Georgia and Oklahoma, named because it appears in autumn when deer run. The caterpillars feed gregariously on oak, sometimes on willow. They are brownish black, covered with pale yellow papillae. Each segment bears 6, 7, or 8 tufts of spines, except segment 11 which has only 5. They are irritating when they touch the flesh. The moths are brown or blackish except for a wide white band extending across both pairs of wings and enclosing ring spots. Eggs, laid in autumn in a ring around a branch, pupate in May. Larvae eat enormously until July, when they pupate in the ground. Spray with lead arsenate or DDT when caterpillars are young.

Catalpa Sphinx (*Ceratomia catalpae*)—On native species of catalpa from New Jersey to Florida and west to Illinois and Texas. Early fishermen in Georgia and Florida cultivated catalpas to get the sphinx caterpillars for fish bait. They are about 3 inches long, with a black horn, variable in color from nearly black on top to pale yellow. The hawk moths are gray with irregular light and dark markings, 3-inch wing expanse. Naked brown pupae winter in the soil under or near catalpa trees, and moths fly as soon as trees come into leaf, laying up to 1000 eggs in white masses on underside of foliage. Young caterpillars start feeding in 2 weeks, first in groups, then separately. There are 2 generations in the North, 3 or 4 in the South. Outbreaks are periodic, with defoliation and sometimes death for a period of about 3 years before parasites get it under control again.

Cecropia Moth (*Hyalophora cecropia*)—More conspicuous than destructive, a huge silkworm moth, wing expanse 5 or 6 inches, dusky brown, with a white crossband bordered with red and a red spot near the apex of each fore wing, a white crescent-shaped spot in the center, and coral-red, blue, and yellow tubercles on the body. The caterpillars are pale green, ornamented with blue, red, and yellow tubercles, 4 inches long. They feed on oak, linden, maple, boxelder, elm, birch, willow, poplar, and other trees. Large gray-brown silk cocoons are conspicuous on bare trees in winter. Control by removing and destroying cocoons.

Codling Moth (*Carpocapsa pomonella*)—Apple Worm, a European species distributed throughout apple-growing sections of the world (Plate XXV). It came to this country prior to 1819 and is the most serious pest on apple and pear fruit that we have. Crabapples, apricots, cherries, loquats, peaches, plums, haws, and similar fruits are occasionally attacked, and green nuts of English walnuts commonly infested on the Pacific coast. Unsprayed apples are sure to be 20 to 95 per cent infested. Crop reductions come from wormy fruit, from early drop of immature apples, and from "stings," small holes surrounded by dead tissue which lower fruit value even though the worms are poisoned before doing further damage.

The insect winters as a full-grown larva, a pinkish-white caterpillar with a brown head, 1 inch long, inside a silken cocoon under loose scales on apple bark or in other sheltered places. In spring the worms change to brown pupae and the moths emerge in 2 to 4 weeks. They are grayish brown, with irregular golden-brown lines on the fore wings and paler, fringed hind wings, spreading ½ to ¾ inch. They lay flat white eggs, singly, on upper surface of leaves, on twigs, and on fruit spurs. They work at dusk, when the weather is dry and the temperature fairly high, above 55°F. A cold, wet spring at time of egg-laying means less trouble with wormy apples.

Hatching in 6 to 20 days, small worms crawl to young apples, entering by way of the calyx cup at the blossom end. They tunnel to the core, often eating the seeds, then burrow out through the side of the apple, leaving a mass of brown excrement behind, and crawl to the tree trunk to pupate in cocoons for the next generation. Some infested fruits drop, the worms completing development in apples on the ground. There are usually 2 generations, with the second working from late July to September. Second-brood larvae enter the fruit at any point without preference for the blossom end.

Control. Lead arsenate has been the standard spray, with the calyx or petal-fall application very important. DDT has proved far superior to lead arsenate with the calyx spray less important. Many spray schedules still call for lead arsenate as a calyx spray but DDT, 2 pounds 50 per cent wettable powder per 100 gallons (½ cup to 5 gallons), at first cover spray, 1 to 3 weeks after calyx, and in later applications. Three cover sprays for the first brood and two for the second are usual. Attractant baits are used to check emergence of moths and to time sprays properly. Information on exactly what to use in your locality and when to apply it must be obtained from your local county agent. The all-purpose fruit sprays for home gardens usually contain DDT for codling moth. There is some indication that codling moths may be developing a little resistance to DDT and it does increase mites and red-banded leaf rollers. Some spray schedules include parathion to help with these pests and because it is somewhat effective for codling moths. Methoxychlor is more effective than lead arsenate, less effective than DDT.

Crinkled Flannel Moth (*Megalopyge crispata*)—Cream-colored with black and brown markings on wings. The poisonous caterpillar is thick, fleshy, up to 1 inch long, covered with long silky brown hairs which project upward to form a crest along the middle of the back. It feeds on apple, bayberry, birch, cherry, locust, oak, raspberry, and sweetfern in northern states.

Cynthia Moth (*Philosamia cynthia*)—Ranging from southern Connecticut to Virginia, one of the few known to feed on ailanthus and often completely defoliating it. The caterpillars, green with black dots and blue tubercles, 3½ inches long, may also feed on wild cherry and plum, have been reported on linden, sycamore, and lilac; they are found mostly near cities. The moth is a beautiful brown with white markings, wing expanse 6 to 8 inches. It was introduced here in the hope of making silk from its cocoons.

Cypress Moth (*Recurvaria apicitripunctella*)—Found in the Northeast on bald cypress and hemlock. The moth is yellow with black markings, very small, with fringed wings; the larvae mine leaves and web them together in late summer and early fall, hibernate, resume feeding in spring. Lead arsenate with fish oil has been recommended.

Cypress Tip Moth (*Argyresthia cupressella*)—Common on Monterey and other cypresses from California north into Washington. The adult is small, golden with brown markings, only ⅓ inch across; the larva is yellow green with a brown head, ¼ inch long. It winters in mined twigs, then makes papery white cocoons on foliage. Spray with DDT or nicotine-oil in early spring.

Cypress Webber (*Epinotia subviridis*)—Found with cypress tip moth. Brownish-green larvae with light tubercles, ⅖ inch long, eat leaves and tie them up with twigs into a nest; foliage may turn brown. Chief injury is in February and May.

Diamondback Moth (*Plutella maculipennis*)—Considered a minor cabbage pest, though sometimes damaging to any crucifer, it may also attack sweet alyssum, candytuft, stock, and wallflower in gardens and greenhouses. The moths, which winter in cabbage debris, are small, ¾ inch across, with gray or brown wings and white marks which make a diamond when the fore wings are folded; hind wings are fringed. Young larvae, greenish yellow with black hairs, ⅓ inch long, at first mine the leaves, later feed externally. Pupation is inside a lacy cocoon on a leaf; moths emerge in a week. There may be 2 to 6 generations. Spray or dust with DDT, DDD, or rotenone.

Douglas-fir Tussock Moth (*Hemerocampa pseudotsugata*)—De-

foliating and killing Douglas-fir and true fir in the Northwest. Caterpillars, up to an inch long, have bright-colored tufts of hairs and 2
black pencils of hairs at head and 1 at posterior. Moths are dull, brownish gray; females are wingless. Young larvae are carried by wind and
defoliate tops of trees first. Spray with DDT.

Eight-spotted Forester (*Alypia octomaculata*)—Ranging from New
England to Colorado and Texas, feeding on grape, Virginia creeper,
and Boston ivy, sometimes defoliating. The moth is black, wingspread
1½ inches, with 2 yellow spots on each fore wing and 2 white spots
on each hind wing. The caterpillar is bluish white, banded with orange,
with black lines and dots, orange head with black spots, orange prolegs,
black legs, 1½ inches long. Spray with DDT or lead arsenate; or pick
off larvae by hand.

European Pine Shoot Moth (*Rhyacionia buoliana*)—First discovered on Long Island in 1914, now present from Massachusetts to Virginia and west to Illinois and Michigan, a serious problem in home
gardens, nurseries, pine plantations. Red, mugho, Scotch, and Austrian pines are favored, others may be attacked (Plate III). Hibernation is as a partly grown larva, brown with a black head, in a bud
or mass of pitch on a bud. Becoming active with warm weather in
spring, the caterpillar leaves its winter bud and bores into an uninfested
bud on a new shoot. The shoot grows 1 or 2 inches, becomes crooked,
straw-colored, dead, usually with a mass of pitch at the point of larval
entrance. Infested shoots are very easy to detect by the color, the crook,
or the pitch. Pupation is in the shoot in May and June, with moths
starting to emerge in early or mid-June and continuing to mid-July.

The moths have reddish-brown fore wings marked with silver cross-
lines, dark brown hind wings. They are about ¾ inch across. Eggs
are laid near tips of twigs, on bark, or in needle sheaths. In 10 days
the larva starts boring through needle bases, with needles on terminal
shoots turning yellow; at the end of summer the larva moves over to
a bud and bores in for the winter.

Control. Infestations in small pines around the house are easily taken
care of by breaking off infested shoots in May before moths emerge,
making sure the brown caterpillar is inside the part broken off and
dropping everything into a paper bag for burning. When pines are too
large for this, or in nurseries or plantations, spray with DDT (2 pounds
50 per cent wettable powder per 100 gallons, 2 teaspoons per gallon)
to kill young larvae. Ideally this means 3 applications, at 2-week intervals, with the second application timed for 50 per cent of emergence,

late June in most areas. Formerly lead arsenate or derris with fish oil was recommended. Airplane spraying of older pines has not proved effective.

Grape Berry Moth (*Paralobesia viteana*)—Generally distributed east of the Rocky Mountains on wild and cultivated grapes, most injurious in the Northeast, common in home gardens. Grape berries are webbed together, turn dark purple, drop when about half size. A nearly ripe berry will have a hole and be attached by webbing to a leaf. The moth winters in cocoons, usually in fallen grape leaves, sometimes attached to loose bark scales. About flowering time the grayish-purple adult, ½ inch across the wings, emerges to lay flat, circular, cream-colored eggs on stems, flower clusters, newly forming berries. The larvae, greenish with brown heads, ⅓ to ½ inch long, web parts together as they feed, each worm destroying several berries. When full-grown, the larva cuts out a bit of leaf, folds it over, and constructs a cocoon within the fold. These remain on the leaves or fall to the ground. Moths of the second generation emerge in July; there may be 3 generations in the South. Cocoons of the second generation are formed on bits of leaves under the trellis.

Control. Spray with DDT (1½ pounds 50 per cent wettable powder to 100 gallons or 1½ tablespoons to 1 gallon of water) just before blossoming, and repeat 2 or 3 times at 10- to 20-day intervals. Methoxychlor is almost as effective as DDT. Rake and burn fallen leaves and debris around grapevines in fall or winter.

Grape Plume Moth (*Pterophorus periscelidactylus*)—Common on grapevines. Eggs winter in branch crotches on old canes; pale yellow-green larvae enter buds, then web together unfolding leaves. After the first molt caterpillars are fuzzy, covered with long yellow hairs. Pupation is in the webbed leaf. The moth is brown with divided wings. Use a dormant oil or lime-sulfur spray when buds start to swell.

Gypsy Moth (*Porthetria dispar*)—An expensive pest of shade, forest, and fruit trees in New England. In 1869 a scientist at Medford, Massachusetts, lost, due to a windstorm which broke open screened cages, some caterpillars he had imported for improving the breed of silkworms. About 10 years later caterpillars were numerous on trees in that vicinity and in 20 years trees in eastern Massachusetts were being defoliated. An appropriation was made for control, but in a year or two the legislature decided to "economize" and stopped the work. By 1905, when control measures were resumed, the gypsy moth covered 4000 square miles. In 1953, the gypsy moth defoliated a million and a half acres of trees in New England. An infestation that started in New Jersey in 1920 was eradicated within a few years, a small infestation in Ohio was promptly wiped out, and a larger one in Pennsylvania is almost subdued. Discovery in the spring of 1954 of a 10,000 acre infestation near Lansing, Michigan, brought prompt action by state and federal agencies.

A barrier zone, 30 miles wide, extending from Canada to Long Island along the Hudson Valley, is maintained to keep the gypsy moth east of the Hudson River. Cleanup operations and careful scouting keep the moth from crossing this zone and invading the rest of the country. Quarantine regulations provide for federal-state certification of plant, forest (including Christmas trees), and stone products, on which the gypsy moth can lay eggs, before shipment south or west of the barrier zone.

Gypsy moths are devastating to ornamental trees around the house and defoliate, sometimes kill, many hardwood forest trees. They are partial to apple, alder, basswood, gray and river birch, hawthorn, oak, poplar, and willow, but also feed on other birches, cherry, elm, black gum, hickory, hornbeam, larch, maple, sassafras. Older larvae eat beech and hemlock, cedar, pine, and spruce. The caterpillars are brown, hairy, 2 inches long, with 5 pairs of blue tubercles along the back followed by 6 pairs of red tubercles (Plate VI). They feed at night in June and July, stripping the trees, pupate inside a few threads spun on limb or tree trunk, and produce moths in 17 or 18 days. The brown, yellow-marked male flies freely; the heavy female does not use her wings with their wavy, dark markings. She lays large, oval egg clusters, covered with tan hairs, near the place of pupation, on a tree, stone, or any hard surface. There is 1 generation; the eggs hatch about the first of May. Distribution is by wind dispersal of young larvae, crawling of caterpillars, or moving of an automobile, railroad car, plant, or other object with attached egg cluster.

Control. DDT is very effective applied by airplane to forest areas, or by hydraulic sprayers or mist blowers to shade trees in residential areas, about the time the eggs hatch or when trees are coming into full leaf. Ground application requires 1 to 2 pounds actual DDT per acre (¼ to ½ pound per 100 gallons for hydraulic sprayers), but with airplanes only ½ to 1 pound actual DDT per acre is required. Lead arsenate is more expensive, requiring 5 to 10 pounds plus 1 pint fish oil per 100 gallons and about 30 pounds per acre, and is less effective. Ornamental trees can have a burlap band tied around the trunk and folded down at the middle. The larvae seek shelter during the day inside the fold and can be destroyed daily. Egg masses can be killed in winter by touching them with a brush wet with coal-tar creosote. Many parasites and predators have been imported to aid in control.

Hag Moth (*Phobetron pithecium*)—One of the slug caterpillars, more interesting than destructive. The larva is brown, about ¾ inch long, with 10 tapering, curved, plume-like processes extending from either side of the back like hanks of hair. It feeds on foliage of various trees and shrubs during the summer but not extensively. It has stinging hairs.

Hickory Tussock Moth (*Halisidota caryae*)—Hickory Tiger Moth, ranging from New England through North Carolina and west to Missouri, a general feeder on deciduous trees and shrubs but preferring walnut, butternut, apple, pear, and hickory. It may be abundant locally but seldom causes widespread defoliation. The moth has light brown fore wings with 3 irregular rows of transparent light spots and thin, pale yellow hind wings; expanse 2 inches. It appears in June to lay white eggs in patches of 100 or more on underside of leaves. The larvae pass through 8 or 9 instars and feed for 2 or 3 months before spinning cocoons among leaves on the ground. The full-grown caterpillar is 1½ inches long, covered with dense tufts of gray-white hairs and a row of black tufts along the back; it has a pair of black "pencils" of hairs on the first and seventh abdominal segments. Some parasites, an ichneumon wasp in particular, attack the caterpillars.

Hornet Moth (*Aegeria apiformis*)—Rather widely distributed in northern states; also in California. The moth resembles the giant hornet, with brown abdomen banded with yellow, transparent wings with brown borders. The larvae are borers in roots, trunks, and large limbs of poplar and willow, causing swellings, and sometimes death of young trees. They are stout, smooth, white with brown heads and rims around spiracles, and they make extensive burrows. They winter in cocoons in wood-borings at the base of trees and pupate in spring. It takes 2 years to complete the life cycle. Spraying trunks with DDT may help.

Imperial Moth (*Eacles imperialis*)—A large moth, wing expanse 4 to 6 inches, sulfur yellow, banded and speckled with purple brown. The caterpillar is 3 to 4 inches long, green with a brown head, and 6-spined yellow horns behind the head. It feeds on many forest and shade trees in eastern United States but is not an important defoliator. Control is seldom necessary.

Io Moth (*Automeris io*)—In eastern states and west to New Mexico, sometimes abundant locally on birch, blackberry, wild cherry, currant, black locust, poplars, willow, and other deciduous trees and shrubs. The female moth is purplish red with a large black eyespot on each hind wing; wing expanse 3 inches. The male is smaller; deep yellow. The caterpillar is pale green with a broad brown or reddish stripe, underscored with white, along each side of the body, which bears 6 rows of branching green spines tipped with black. The spines are irritating; some people may be poisoned by them.

64. Leopard moth.

Leopard Moth (*Zeuzera pyrina*)—A European species first noted in 1879 in a spider's web at Hoboken, New Jersey, now present from northern Massachusetts to Philadelphia. It is recorded on nearly 100 plants; favored are elm, maple, ash, beech, walnut, oak, chestnut, poplar, willow, lilac; apple, plum, pear, and other fruits. The moths are white with blue and black spots, the female 3 inches across the wings, the male 2 inches; they emerge from May to September. The female has a heavy body, is a feeble flier, but lays up to 800 salmon-colored eggs, singly or in small groups, in bark crevices. The young larvae hatch in 10 days and bore into heartwood or enter twigs at base of buds, causing wilting. They make irregular galleries in large limbs and the main trunk, feeding for about 2 years before pupation. The borers are pale yellow or pinkish spotted with brown or black tubercles of hairs. Small nursery trees and branches of larger trees die; small branches break and hang down; the bark is full of holes with protruding sawdust. Prune off and destroy infested branches; cut down heavily infested trees. With valuable trees, kill borers in place with a wire or with carbon bisulfide or other fumigant.

Luna Moth *(Actias luna)*—The lovely adult has delicate green wings expanding to 4 inches, a purple band on front edge of fore wings and around eyespots, hind wings extending into long, narrow swallowtails. The caterpillar is 3 inches long, green with 6 pink or green tubercles bearing yellow bristles on each segment, a blue-green head, and a yellow crossline at the joining of each segment. It feeds on hickory and walnut, sometimes on beech, birch, persimmon, sweet gum, willow, and other trees, but control measures are unnecessary.

Nantucket Pine Moth *(Rhyacionia frustrana)*—Pine Tip Moth, found from Massachusetts to Florida and west to Texas, injurious to almost all 2- and 3-needle pines. A variety of this species occurs in Minnesota, the Dakotas, Nebraska. There hibernation is in a cocoon in litter on the ground, but usually it winters inside the injured twig tip. There is 1 generation in Massachusetts, 2 around Delaware and Pennsylvania, 4 in Louisiana and Texas. In Delaware spring-brood moths start emerging the first of April and continue to early June; second-brood moths work from early July to early August. They are small, ½-inch wingspread, reddish brown with silver-gray markings; they lay yellow, flattened, circular eggs on needles, buds, or shoots. The larvae, yellow to pale brown, ⅜ inch long, mine in needles, then in buds, spinning a web around the needles, often covered with pitch, and then burrow in twigs of new growth to pupate. Young pines are seriously deformed and occasionally die. Loblolly pine is often injured.

Control. Cut off infested tips in late fall or winter (except in central states where larvae are not in the tips at that time). Spray with DDT as for European pine shoot moth, but start much earlier with an application at the end of April (in Delaware) and 2 more at 14-day intervals.

Oriental Fruit Moth *(Grapholitha molesta)*—Introduced from the Orient, prior to 1915, on nursery stock; established wherever peaches are grown in eastern states and now becoming important in the West. Most important on peaches, the fruit moth also attacks quince, apple, pear, apricot, plum, cherry, and Chinese hawthorn. First indication in spring is blackening and dying back of new growth. Fruit injury is similar to that of codling moth in apple, but because the worm enters through the stem there may be no external sign of injury until breakdown after picking reveals numerous feeding burrows.

Full-grown larvae, pinkish white with brown heads, ½ inch long, winter in cocoons on bark or in rubbish, weeds, or mummied fruit on ground; they pupate in late spring. Moths, gray with chocolate-brown markings on wings, only ½ inch across, lay flat white eggs on leaves or twigs shortly after peaches bloom. First-brood larvae attack growing tips, which die, and spin cocoons on bark. Larvae of later broods attack both shoots and fruit. There are 3 or 4 broods around New York, up to 7 further south.

Control. Until the advent of DDT not much could be done except the release of parasites; now spraying is the rule. To control first-brood larvae make 3 applications 10 to 12 days apart beginning at petal-fall or shuck-split stage of fruit development. For second and third broods spray 7 to 8 weeks and again 3 to 4 weeks before harvest. Use 2 pounds of 50 per cent DDT, or 1½ pounds 25 per cent EPN, or 2 pounds 15 per cent parathion per 100 gallons of water. Spray recommendations for home gardens are often aimed at the summer broods, with ½ cup of DDT in 5 gallons of water used with sulfur for brown rot control. Don't use the phosphate sprays for back-yard peaches; do get exact recommendations for timing of DDT sprays from your county agent.

65. Oriental fruit moth injury to peach, and detail of moth and larva.

Oriental Moth (*Cnidocampa flavescens*)—A Japanese insect found around Boston in 1906 and still confined to eastern Massachusetts. The larvae are sluglike, shaped like a dumbbell, with long spiny tubercles, ⅞ inch long, with yellow, blue, green, and purple markings. They feed preferably on Norway and sycamore maple, buckthorn, black birch, cherry, apple, pear, and plum, but may also eat other maples, oak, aspen, willow, honey locust, hickory, and hackberry. The moth has a wing expanse of 1¼ to 1½ inches, inner portions of wings yellow, outer portion reddish brown, with dark fringe. They appear in late June and July, lay oval eggs on underside of leaves. The larvae pupate in hard cocoons in limb crotches; there is 1 generation. Native and introduced parasites are holding the oriental moth in check. Young larvae can be killed with arsenate of lead.

Pale Tussock Moth (*Halisidota tesselaris*)—Throughout eastern United States, feeding on almost any deciduous tree. The adult has translucent pale green fore wings marked with darker bands, pale yellow hind wings, expanse 1½ to 2 inches. The 1¼-inch caterpillar is blackish, sparsely covered with yellow-buff hairs. It also has dense tufts of yellow-gray hairs, 3 pairs of black "pencils" of hairs, with a white pencil beneath each.

Pandora Moth (*Coloradia pandora*)—Important in western pine belts. Moths have brownish-gray fore wings with a spattering of white scales, black lines with a black spot; hind wings with pinkish hairs; expanse 3 to 4 inches. They lay flattened green eggs in clusters on bark of pine trees in spring. Caterpillars, appearing in August, are dark when young, brown to green with short spines, 2½ to 3 inches long when mature. The life cycle takes 2 years. Large areas of yellow and Jeffrey pines may be defoliated. There are many natural enemies including a wilt disease, ground squirrels and chipmunks. Indians have used the caterpillars for food, drying them, then making into a stew. Some tribes roast the pupae.

Pea Moth (*Laspeyresia nigricana*)—A serious pest in northern pea-canning areas, sometimes a garden problem. Present since 1900, it attacks all field and garden peas, sweet pea, and vetch. Growing peas have irregular cavities eaten out of the side; seeds are spoiled and pods are partly filled with pellets of excrement and caterpillar silk; they turn yellow, ripen prematurely. Inactive larvae winter in silk cocoons covered with soil particles just below the soil surface or in cracks and crevices around barns. They change to brownish pupae in late spring when peas bloom. Small brown moths, marked with black and white lines on fore wings, are active about pea plants in late afternoon, laying minute, flattened white eggs singly on pods, leaves, flowers, or stems, or on other nearby plants. On hatching, young larvae drill into pods. They are yellow white with dark spots, pale short hairs over body, dark areas at each end, ½ inch long. They eat their way out of pods and make cocoons in soil. Some transform to moths for a second generation, others remain in soil until the next spring.

Control with cultural measures, deep plowing in spring, early varieties, early planting to avoid most of the injury, burning all crop remains, disking soil after harvest.

Pine Tube Moth (*Argyrotaenia pinatubana*)—On white pine through eastern states, lodgepole pine and whitebark pine in the Rocky Mountain region. Moths have rust-red fore wings, with 2 oblique lines across each, silky gray hind wings, ½-inch wingspread. They emerge in late April and May and the second brood in July. Larvae are greenish yellow with a faint dark line down the back, ⅓ inch long. They make tubes by tying needles together side by side, squarely eating off the free end. The tubes stand erect and may be quite conspicuous; pupation is in the tubes. Control by removing and burning tubes in winter. Parasites are effective.

Pitch Twig Moth (*Petrova comstockiana*)—On hard pine from Massachusetts to Virginia, west to Minnesota. The moth is reddish brown mottled with gray, ⅝-inch wingspread; the larva is pale brown with dark brown head; ½ inch long. It infests small branches and twigs, leaving a thick mass of pitch at the entrance. Cut out such twigs.

Polyphemus Moth (*Antheraea polyphemus*)—One of the giant silkworms, feeding on oak, elm, sassafras, wild cherry, ash, sweet gum, maple, poplar, lilac, birch, and other trees, but rarely injurious. The moth has brownish-yellow wings crossed with a dusky band edged with pink, and a large eyespot on each hind wing. The caterpillar is 3 inches long, light green with an oblique yellow line on sides of each abdominal segment except first and last, 6 small golden tubercles on each segment with 1 to 3 bristles.

Promethea Moth (*Callosamia promethea*)—The most common of the giant silkworms, feeding on lilac, wild cherry, tuliptree, ash, sassafras, and other plants. The female has light reddish-brown wings, crossed near the middle with a white waxy line and an angular discal spot, spreading to 3 inches. Each fore wing also has an eyespot near the tip. The male has dark brown nearly black wings with light brown borders and a zigzag line. The caterpillars are 2 inches long, pale bluish green with rows of black, polished, warty tubercles, 2 larger coral-red pairs of tubercles on second and third thoracic segments and a yellow pair on the eighth abdominal segment. The cocoon is long, spindle-shaped, enclosed in a leaf.

Rusty Tussock Moth (*Oryia antiqua*)—A European species present in northern states, a pest of apple, quince, and other fruits, feeding also on beech, mountain-ash, birch, poplar, willow, and other trees. The male moth has rusty brown wings marked with gray lines, a white spot near the hind border of each wing; the female is gray and wingless. The caterpillar is dark gray, 1⅛ inches long, with a pair of black hair pencils from orange tubercles on the second abdominal segment, tufts of white or yellowish hairs on other segments, black head.

Satin Moth (*Stilpnotia salicis*)—First discovered in Massachusetts in 1920, now present in New England, New York near Albany, and in Oregon and Washington, defoliating poplars, feeding also on willow, sometimes on oak. Partly grown larvae winter in small webs in bark crevices, start feeding in late April or May. They are black with conspicuous irregular white blotches down the back and a transverse row of reddish-brown tubercles with tan hairs on each segment. They pupate in a cocoon in leaves or on twigs, and the satin-white moths, wing expanse 1½ to 2 inches, emerge in July. They lay eggs in white glistening clusters on trunk, branches, and leaves. The larvae appear in 2 weeks but grow slowly, finishing their development the next spring. Then they feed ravenously, sometimes causing death to defoliated trees, sometimes migrating to fences, walks, and buildings, and annoying people.

Control. State and federal quarantines are maintained to prevent introduction to uninfested areas; municipalities spray trees in spring with DDT or lead arsenate; several parasites have been introduced.

Sequoia Pitch Moth (*Vespamima sequoiae*)—Opaque, dirty-white larvae infest branches and trunks, mine the cambium layer of knobcone, lodgepole, Monterey and yellow pine, Douglas-fir, redwood, and other conifers in Montana, Washington, Oregon, and California. The moth looks like a yellow-jacket wasp, black with the last segment of the abdomen bordered with bright yellow. The larvae start working from wounds and a large mass of gummy pitch covers the point of entrance. They pupate in this mass and the pupa case is protruded so the moth does not touch the pitch on emergence. This species is common but not serious enough to call for control measures.

Snapdragon Plume Moth (*Platyptilia antirrhina*)—Small greenish larvae at first mine leaves, then feed openly on terminal leaves, bore inside developing flowers, seeds, and inside main stems. Mature caterpillars are green or purplish red. Naked pupae are suspended from any part of plants, giving rise to grayish-brown moths, ½-inch wingspread. Netted ovate eggs are laid singly anywhere on plants. There are 3 generations a year outdoors in California, more in greenhouses. Spray or dust with pyrethrum.

Snowberry Clearwing (*Hemaris diffinis*)—From New England to Georgia and the Great Plains on snowberry and bush honeysuckle. The hornworm larvae are green to brown or purplish, with dark spiracles, 1½ to 2 inches long. The sphinx moths have clear, transparent wings with dark brown margins, expanding 1½ to 2 inches, a black body marked with gold. There are 2 generations; hibernation is as pupae in soil. Hand-picking is usually sufficient control.

Spotted Tussock Moth (*Halisidota maculata*)—Common in the northeast, ranging through northern states to California, feeding on alder, apple, birch, boxelder, wild cherry, maple, oak, and willow, but not a serious defoliator. The moths are about 2 inches across, with dark yellow fore wings marked with bands and spots, plain, nearly transparent hind wings. Larvae are 1¼ inches long with tufts of yellow hairs in the middle of the body, black hairs at both ends, a line of black spots along the back, and a few long whitish pencils of hairs.

Spruce Epizeuxis (*Epizeuxis aemula*)—Common on ornamental spruce in the Northeast. Small brown larvae, with black tubercles and spiracles, web needles together in large masses and fill them with excrement. They feed on older needles. Moths, brownish gray, with wings crossed by narrow bands, emerge in June and July. Eggs hatch in late summer; partly grown larvae winter in webbed masses of dry needles.

Strawberry Crown Moth (*Ramosia bibionipennis*)—In various sections, most common in the Northwest. White to yellowish larvae, ½ to ¾ inch long, bore in the crown, as many as 50 borers sometimes working in a single plant. The foliage turns yellow, recent transplants die; older plants are much weakened. Raspberries and blackberries may be infested. The clear-wing moth resembles a yellow-jacket wasp. Nearly mature larvae winter in strawberry crowns, pupate in May; moths emerge in June and July, laying eggs on lower leaves; there is 1 generation. Control by sanitary measures; pull and burn infested plants in spring before moths emerge; top plants after harvest; cover bed with straw after topping to prevent egg-laying.

Sunflower Moth (*Homoeosoma electellum*)—Destructive to cultivated sunflowers. The moth is gray, lays eggs in florets; the larva is greenish yellow with 5 brown stripes down the back. The larvae feed on the head, in a mass of webbing and frass, and destroy the seeds; they pupate in the head. Dusting with 10 per cent DDT-40 per cent

MOTHS 313

sulfur or with 20 per cent toxaphene-40 per cent sulfur, applied when flowers first appear, has reduced injury.

Sycamore Tussock Moth (*Halisidota harrisii*)—Abundant on sycamore in the Northeast, but rarely calling for control measures. The yellow larva has white to yellow hairs and long orange hair pencils. The adult is like the pale tussock moth.

Western Tussock Moth (*Hemerocampa vetusta*)—California Tussock Moth, on Pacific coast from southern California to British Columbia. The female is gray, wingless; the male has brown wings with gray markings. Eggs are laid in felty gray masses on old cocoons or bark of host plants—apple, almond, apricot, blackberry, California Christmasberry (toyon), California coffeeberry, cherry, hawthorn, manzanita, oak, pear, plum, prune, walnut, willows. The caterpillars are gray with red, blue, and yellow spots, 4 white tufts of hairs in the middle of the body, 1 white and 1 black tuft at the end, and 2 long black tufts, looking like horns, at the head; ¾ to 1 inch long. They feed on leaves and young fruit. There is only 1 brood; eggs are laid on trees in late summer and fall, hatch when leaves unfold in spring.

Control. Remove egg masses in winter; jar caterpillars from trees and prevent return by banding as for cankerworms. Spray with oil to kill young larvae; protect young fruit with pyrethrum sprays. Sprays for other fruit pests usually keep tussock moths in check.

White-lined Sphinx (*Celerio lineata*)—Striped Morning Sphinx, common in the West, occurring throughout the country on apple, azalea, beet, collards, currant, elm, fuchsia, gooseberry, grape, melon, pear, plum, portulaca, prune, tomato, turnip, and other crops. The hornworm larva is serious on beets and tomatoes in Florida.

The moths resemble hummingbirds, with brown bodies marked with white and darker brown, fore wings with white-lined veins and a broad buff stripe; dark hind wings with a rosy band across the middle of each. They visit flowers at dusk. The larvae, 2½ to 3½ inches long, are usually green with yellow head and horn, with pale spots bordered with black, but some are black with orange head and horn, 3 yellow spots on the back. Pupation is in the soil, in shiny, dark brown chrysalids. There are 2 broods.

White-marked Tussock Moth (*Hemerocampa leucostigma*)—A native, common in the East, ranging west to Colorado. This is primarily a city pest, feeding on many deciduous shade trees—elm, linden, maple, horsechestnut, poplar, sycamore, buckeye, willow, and others—and on fruits—apple, pear, quince, plum—but not on evergreens. Foliage is skeletonized and fruits scarred by conspicuous hairy caterpillars, 1½ inches long, with red heads, 2 pencil-like tufts of long black hairs projecting like horns, with a third tuft at the rear; a black stripe down the middle of the back bordered with a wide yellow line, 4 white brushes or tussocks of hairs on the first segments of the abdomen.

The female moth is nearly wingless, gray, hairy; the male has brownish wings marked with gray, spreading to 1¼ inches, feathery antennae, legs tufted with white hairs. Eggs are laid in fall in conspicuous masses, about 1 inch long, of 50 or 100, covered with a white lathery substance, on trunk, branches, dead leaves, or on top of the cocoon from which the female emerged. Caterpillars feed in April to June, depending on location, pupate in cocoons on trunk and branches, and the moths emerge to lay eggs for a second generation which feeds in August and September. There are 3 generations in Washington, D.C., and further south.

Control. A great many parasites work on this insect, but unfortunately there are also a great number of hyperparasites living on the parasites. Birds eat young larvae. Tree experts climb trees to scrape off egg masses or daub them with creosote containing a little lampblack to mark those treated. Lead arsenate or DDT sprays for cankerworms or elm leaf beetles will also control tussock moths.

66. *Larva of white-marked tussock moth.*

White-pine Shoot Moth (*Eucosma gloriola*)—First seen in Connecticut in 1930, now spread to New York and Maine, attacking lateral shoots of white pine. The white caterpillar, ½ inch long, burrows in center of shoots, causing them to die back 6 to 8 inches. The small moth is coppery red with 2 shining gray bands on fore wings. Cut and burn infested tips as soon as noticed.

Yucca Moth (*Tegeticula yuccasella*)—A southwestern species responsible for the pollination of yucca plants. The female has specially modified mouth parts with which she scrapes together pollen from the stamens and carries it with her to another flower where she lays eggs through the wall of the ovary into the seed cavity.

Zimmerman Pine Moth (*Dioryctria zimmermani*)—On Austrian, pitch, red, Scotch, Swiss, white, and yellow pines over most of their range, reported on other conifers in the West. The moth is reddish gray marked with dark and light lines, 1 to 1½ inches across the wings. It lays eggs on bark, often near wounds, and the larvae, white to reddish yellow or green, ¾ inch long, bore into trunks and branches. Entire tops of trees may break off, or branch tips turn brown. Pitch tubes are formed at the base of injured parts. Prune out infested portions where possible.

NEMATODES

Nematodes are microscopic wormlike animals belonging to the phylum Nemathelminthes, also called nemas, eelworms, or roundworms. They live in moist soil, water, decaying organic matter, and tissues of other living organisms. Some are beneficial because, like the nematodes parasitic on Japanese beetles, they live on harmful insects. Some cause diseases of man or animals; others cause plant diseases. Until recently, nematodes to a gardener meant merely those causing root knot, but now we know there are many other nematodes responsible for plant diseases hitherto unexplained. Some of these are endoparasites, living inside the plants but not always causing knots or galls, and some are ectoparasites, feeding on plants from the outside.

Nematodes can move through the soil with a threshing motion but rarely travel more than 30 inches a year. Dissemination of eelworms to a greater distance involves movement of infested soil or plants, or irrigation, or surface water. Nematodes have a hollow spearlike organ, the buccal spear, with which they suck juices from living cells. In some species both males and females are wormlike; in others the female is pear-shaped, the male long and narrow. Control is difficult. It usually involves fumigation of fallow soil and we are still looking for safe ways to kill nemas around living plants. The species described here are some of those likely to cause trouble in home gardens; there are many others. They are particularly important in the South but by no means negligible in northern gardens.

Awl Nematode (*Dolichodorus* sp.)—An ectoparasite, feeding on root tips and causing severe stunting of many kinds of plants.

Bulb and Stem Nematodes (*Ditylenchus dipsaci* and other species)— Causing eelworm disease of narcissus, ring disease of hyacinth, onion bloat, stem disease of phlox, also found on grape-hyacinth, scilla, tulip, galtonia, garlic, shallot, campanula, sweet william, primrose and evening primrose, goldenrod, schizanthus, anemone, foxglove, orchids, and others.

If an infested narcissus bulb is cut across you can see brown rings contrasting with healthy tissue. Eggs, larvae, and adults are present in the brown tissue. Both males and females are wormlike, up to 1.8-mm. long. The larvae work out of the bulbs in creamy tufts through a break in the basal plate and scales and work through the soil to adjacent plants. Badly infested bulbs either do not grow in spring or fail to form flowers; leaves are twisted and have small yellowish swellings, "spikkels." The strain on hyacinths produces yellow flecks or blotches in the leaves, which are often twisted, short, split. On onions the inner bulb scales are enlarged, causing a split onion that seldom flowers, sometimes a rot at the base; seedlings are twisted, stunted, covered with yellow spots. On phlox, the nematodes enter through stomata of young shoots, working upward as stems develop. The plants take on all kinds of abnormal forms—threadlike, spindling, wrinkled, curled. Stems are swollen near the tip or bent sidewise; plants are stunted, fail to bloom, die prematurely. Some varieties are very susceptible; others remain quite free from trouble. Seed of phlox and other composites may be infested and the nemas disseminated by this means.

Control. Take up and burn infested phlox and similar plants. Put new plants in another location or fumigate soil. Commercial growers treat bulbs in hot water, held at 110°F. for 3 hours, with formalin added as a precaution against basal rot.

Chrysanthemum Nematode (*Aphelenchoides ritzema-bosi*)—Chrysanthemum Leaf Nematode, common and serious on this host in garden and greenhouse in most parts of the country. The nematodes swim in a film of water up the stems and from leaf to leaf, entering through stomates in wet weather. First symptoms are dark spots on underside of leaves, but by the fifth day after infestation discolored veins stand out sharply on upper leaf surface and the leaves turn brown or black in distinct wedges between the veins. Later the leaves dry, wither, and hang down along the stem, the plants appearing to suffer from drought.

Control. A good mulch helps to prevent upward movement of the nemas from the soil, and so does keeping the tops dry by avoiding overhead watering. Commercial growers spray foliage with parathion, 2 or 3 applications at 10- to 14-day intervals, using 2 level tablespoons of 15 per cent wettable powder to 1 gallon of water. Somewhat safer for home gardeners, but still to be used with great caution, is soil treatment with sodium selenate. Dissolve 1 ounce sodium selenate crystals in 1 gallon of water; label it "Stock Solution—POISON." To use, dilute 1 cup stock solution with water to make 1 gallon. Apply at rate of 1 pint to 1 square foot of bed or 1 pint per plant. After treatment, sprinkle area with water; keep well watered during dry spells. Repeat treatment in 3 to 4 weeks. Do NOT use on soil that may be planted to vegetables later; the toxin will be taken up by the plants and be poisonous to you when they are eaten. Don't make crown divisions of chrysanthemums. Start new plants from tip cuttings taken from long shoots on apparently healthy plants that have been protected from splashing.

67. Leaf nematode injury to chrysanthemum—usually a dark, sometimes a tan, wedge-shaped area on the leaf.

Citrus Nematode (*Tylenchulus semipenetrans*)—A root nematode not forming galls, attacking larger roots of citrus trees, reported also on olive, retarding growth of tops and producing yellow leaves. The males are long, cylindrical; the females broad, flask-shaped. All measures for the general health of trees, including use of bulky organic fertilizers, are helpful. Fallow soil can be fumigated with D-D mixture.

Dagger Nematodes (*Xiphinema* spp.)—Ectoparasites on root tips, causing stunting of various plants.

Fern Nematode (*Aphelenchoides olesistus*)—A foliar nematode similar to the one on chrysanthemums, recorded on ferns and many flowers, anemone, bouvardia, calceolaria, chrysanthemum, clematis, coleus, crassula, dianthus, doronicum, geranium, hydrangea, lily, peony, primrose, Saintpaulia, scabiosa, zinnia, and others. Ferns have dark brown to black areas on the fronds; in some species there are narrow dark bands from midrib to border. Greenhouse begonias may have brown spots with water-soaked margins, or entire leaves dark, plants stunted. The nemas are spread by syringing or careless watering. Easter lilies grown in the Pacific Northwest turn brown and die back, with leaves bronzy and undercurled.

Control. Removal of infested leaves and care in watering are important for greenhouse plants. Plants in small pots can be submerged in hot water: begonias 1 minute at 121°–120°F. or 3 minutes at 119°–117°; ferns 10 to 15 minutes at 110°F.; lily bulbs 1 hour at 111°F.

Golden Nematode of Potatoes (*Heterodera rostochiensis*)—A new and alarming importation, now held to a small potato area on Long Island, New York. Long thought to be limited to potatoes and tomatoes, it is now known to infest eggplant. Crops do not show much damage until heavy populations have been built up in the soil over a period of years; then there is midday wilting, stunting, poor root development, early death with up to 85 per cent reduction in potato yield. The eggs live in the soil in the form of cysts (dead bodies of females) each containing up to 500 eggs and barely visible to the naked eye. They remain viable in the cyst for at least 17 years. In spring when soil temperature is around 60°F. a chemical given off by potato or tomato roots stimulates hatching and the larvae leave the cyst and migrate to host plants, entering the roots. The females become stationary, swell to pear-shape, and break through the roots though remaining attached by a thin neck. The cylindrical males also work out of the roots, cluster around to mate with the females. The eggs are formed and the dead female becomes the cyst, first white, then gold, orange, finally brown. Cysts detached from the roots remain in the soil or may be spread in potato bags, crates, machinery, even in trouser cuffs of farm workers.

Control. A quarantine restricts marketing of potatoes, nursery stock, top soil, and root crops grown on infested land. Healthy potatoes are sold in paper bags to prevent infestation from secondhand burlap bags.

Lance Nematodes (*Hoplolaimus* spp.)—Another root nematode, responsible for poor corn, for a disease of pin oaks that resembles gas injury, and miscellaneous plant problems.

Meadow Nematodes (*Pratylenchus* spp.)—Widely distributed and important root nematodes, cause of decline of almond, apple, cherry, fig, peach, and walnut trees, decline or death of boxwood, brown root rot of tobacco and other plants. The males and females are both worm-like, live in the cortical tissue of roots, causing them to slough off, but they do not form galls. First symptoms are yellow, black, or brown lesions on fine feeder roots, followed by loss of most of the root system but often with a "witches' broom" of fine roots formed again near the surface. Boxwood symptoms include defoliation and sudden death of branches, discoloration of foliage ranging from dark bronze to orange, plants sickly, stunted.

Control. Soil can be fumigated before planting with D-D mixture or ethylene dibromide. Adequate fertilization and mulching help tree roots to grow faster than nematodes can destroy them. Parathion applied to the soil around boxwood has been rather effective. Home gardeners can help with extra watering and organic mulches to compensate for loss of roots. Propagate only from healthy plants, in clean sand.

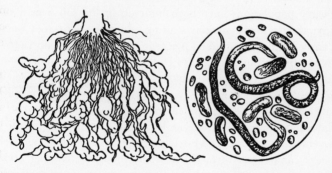

68. *Root-knot nematode, showing knots or galls on tomato roots, and nematodes as seen under the microscope.*

Root-knot Nematodes (*Meloidogyne* spp.)—The common root-knot disease, thought for many years to be due to a single nematode (*Heterodera marioni*), is now known to be caused by at least 5 species of Meloidogyne distinguished by the hosts they attack and their distribution, though there is overlapping of both. The northern root-knot nematode (*Meloidogyne hapla*) prevalent in North Carolina and northward has been found on tomatoes and gladiolus in Florida, on peanuts in Alabama. This species makes very small galls on roots with excessive proliferation. It does not attack watermelon, but the peanut nematode (*M. arenaria*) does. The other species do not attack peanut. The southern root-knot nematode (*M. incognita*) does not attack tomato, but its variety (*M. incognita acrita*) and the 3 other species do work on tomato. The situation is more than complicated with nearly 1400 plant species susceptible to some form of root knot. Grains and grasses are not susceptible.

Root-knot nematodes are favored by short, mild winters, long, hot summers, light sandy soils. Infected plants are stunted; they often wilt, turn yellow, and die. The roots have small or large swellings on galls, round or long and irregular, but always a part of the root and not detachable as are the desirable bacterial nodules. Larvae develop to maturity inside the root galls and mate there. The male is long, worm-like; the female is pear-shaped, white, glistening, can be just seen as a white dot with the unaided eye. It extrudes a sac of brownish eggs, about the size of dust particles. Observed just before hatching, under the microscope, the larvae can be seen coiled up inside the eggs. They move from the decaying knot and attack the same root at a new point or a new root, injecting a chemical that stimulates gall formation around the larvae. At 80°F. a generation takes only 25 days; at 67° it takes 87 days; below 55° activity ceases.

Control. The fumigants suited for home garden use contain dichloropropene, sold as D-D and Nemafume, or ethylene dibromide, sold as Dowfume W-40, Soilfume 60-40, Iscobrome 40, Bromofume 40. Ethylene dibromide is also sold in capsules, Soilfume Caps, each containing ½ cc. of the pure chemical. For best results the soil should be moderately loose, the temperature around 70° or above. The chemical is injected 6 inches into the soil at 1-foot intervals, or applied in furrows 1 foot apart, using 2.5 to 3 cc. of fumigant for each foot. This small amount can be applied by using a fruit jar with 2 small nail holes punched into the lid and practicing with water to find the size hole that will distribute ½ cup in 45 feet of row. Special applicators are also available. Wait 2 or 3 weeks after treatment before planting. Organic fertilizers encourage beneficial nematodes that feed on the others.

Spiral Nematodes (*Rotylenchus* spp.)—Injuring turf grasses and other plants.

Sting Nematode (*Belonolaimus gracilis*)—A major pest of strawberries, celery, sweet corn, and other winter-grown crops in Florida, destroying young roots and root tips. It can be controlled by fumigating soil with D-D or ethylene dibromide.

Strawberry Bud Nematode (*Aphelenchoides fragariae*)—Causing spring dwarf of strawberry, "cauliflower," a cold-weather disease from Cape Cod to Virginia. Leaves are small, narrow, twisted, glossy, blossom buds are killed; some plants die, others recover. Summer dwarf or crimp (due to *A. besseyi*) is a major strawberry disease in the Southeast. Infested plants in a garden should be rogued and burned. Buy certified new plants.

Stubby Root Nematode (*Trichoderus* spp.)—Another ectoparasite destroying root tips of various plants, resulting in a small, compact root system with short stubby branches. It occurs as far north as Maryland and Indiana but is most injurious in the Deep South, on sweet corn, tomatoes, lima beans, celery, chayotes. Fumigants are not very effective for this type. Spading the garden 2 or 3 weeks before planting and again just before planting is quite helpful. Keep out Bermuda grass, which harbors this nematode.

Stylet or Stunt Nematode (*Tylenchorhynchus* spp.)—A root nematode responsible, along with other nemas, for chlorotic patches and sometimes bare spots in lawns and golf courses in Rhode Island, capable of surviving in the North, perhaps cause of unexplained grass failures.

NEWTS AND SALAMANDERS

Newts and salamanders are tailed amphibians, looking something like lizards but with smooth instead of scaly skin. They are not garden pests but useful as destroyers of insects. Newts have flatter tails than salamanders and are more aquatic, living in the water during the breeding season. The crimson-spotted newt (*Triton viridescens*) common in northeastern states is about 3½ inches long, greenish brown above, with 2 rows of crimson dots, orange, spotted with black, below. The western species (*Triton torosus*) is larger, up to 6 inches.

Salamanders live in or near the water as larvae, breathing by means of gills, but as adults they are terrestrial, breathing through lungs, though usually living in moist places. True salamanders, of the genus *Salamandra*, are European, but there are several relatives in America called salamander. The tiger salamander (*Ambystoma tigrinum*) is black with yellow spots as an adult, gray or white, with branching gills, 7 inches long, in the larval state. It can continue reproducing as a larva without changing to the adult form if land conditions are unfavorable. The blotched salamander (*Ambystoma opacum*) likes dry and rocky country, the blue-spotted salamander (*Plethodon glutinosus*) prefers mountains, and the dusky salamander (*Desmognathus fuscus*) lives in fast-moving water.

I frequently get letters asking how to control the "lizards" found under damp stones in the garden. They are probably salamanders or newts and the answer is, "Leave them alone. They are not garden enemies and probably are helpful in eating insects."

ORTHEZIA

Greenhouse Orthezia (*Orthezia insignis*)—A close relative of scales and mealybugs, in the family Coccidae. It infests 125 or more varieties of greenhouse plants and is a garden pest in warm climates. Favored hosts are lantana, coleus, chrysanthemum, cacti, heliotrope, periwinkle, petunia, salvia, silver lace vine, verbena. It is called lantana bug for its predilection for that plant and has even been introduced in Hawaii as a beneficial insect to cope with *Lantana camea* which has become a weed there.

The dark green wingless nymphs are about the size of pinheads and are covered with rows of minute waxy plates. The mature female is pale brown or dark green with a conspicuous waxy fringe around the body and a long white fluted egg sac. The total length of adult and sac is only 1/3 inch. Plants become sickly and sometimes die from the constant sucking on leaves and stems.

Control measures are the same as for mealybugs: malathion or nicotine sulfate or oil sprays.

PLANTHOPPERS

Planthoppers are sucking insects of the family Fulgoridae. They have been called fulgorids, lightning leafhoppers, lanternflies, mealy flata. The tropical species have many grotesque forms but ours are very similar to leafhoppers, with the same jumping habit, but larger, and with the antennae arising below and behind the eyes and with few spurs on the hind tibiae.

Planthopper (*Ormenis pruinosa; O. septentrionalis*)—Mealy Flata, common through most of the United States east of the Great Plains on shrubs and woody vines, viburnum particularly, also boxwood, privet, mulberry, catalpa, Japanese cherry, hawthorn, honeysuckle, wild grape, even dahlia, salvia, and lilies. Tree trunks and branches are covered with white flocculent strands concealing the young greenish nymphs, which jump quickly when disturbed. *Ormenis pruinosa* as an adult is just over ¼ inch long, with purple or brownish wings entirely covered with a white powdery material. *O. septentrionalis* is a little larger, is pale bluish green, and is present a little later in the season, August and September. Eggs are laid in slits in bark of twigs and covered with a white waxy secretion. There is only 1 generation. Gardeners are always worried when they see the white cottony masses on stems, but there is seldom enough injury to call for control measures.

Corn Planthopper (*Pereginus maidis*)—Also called Corn Leafhopper, serious in Florida, reported from South Carolina, Texas, and other states. The adult is yellowish green, ⅙ inch long; it has clear wings longer than the body with dark markings near the tip, antennae with greatly thickened basal portion. Abundant in late August in Florida, the lanternflies collect in large numbers near buds or in axils of leaves; nearly every stalk of young corn may be killed before reaching tasseling stage. Control with sulfur or pyrethrum dust.

PSYLLIDS

Psyllids belong to the family Psyllidae (Chermidae) of the order Homoptera. They are related to aphids, often known as jumping plant lice, small sucking insects, usually under ¼ inch, with hind legs enlarged for jumping. Adults are very active, moving quickly when disturbed. Some species are serious pests; some are a nuisance because of copious honeydew and subsequent growth of disfiguring sooty mold.

Alder Psyllid (*Psylla floccosa*)—Common in the Northeast. The nymphs produce large amounts of wax and groups of the psyllids look like masses of cotton on stems.

Apple Sucker (*Psylla mali*)—An introduced species recently established in Canada. Eggs laid on apple twigs in fall hatch as buds open. When the psyllids become adults in June they often leave apples to feed on vegetables, returning in autumn for egg-laying. The feeding of the nymphs injures opening buds, destroys flower clusters, prevents setting of fruit. There is a great amount of honeydew.

Blackberry Psyllid (*Trioza tripunctata*)—A native on wild blackberry in the Northeast, infesting cultivated blackberries and other brambles. The adult is ⅙ inch long, yellow brown, each wing marked with 3 yellow-brown bands. It winters in protected places and soon after growth starts in spring lays eggs in hairs of leaf stems and tender shoots. Nymphs and adults puncture stems, curl leaves, produce stunting and almost gall-like distortion. There is 1 generation. Spray with nicotine sulfate (1½ teaspoons per gallon) and soap when you see the first psyllid or notice curling; repeat in 5 to 7 days.

Boxelder Psyllid (*Psylla negundinis*)—On boxelder, similar to alder psyllid. Use a delayed dormant spray, followed by nicotine sulfate, if necessary.

69. Boxwood leaves cupped by boxwood psyllid.

Boxwood Psyllid (*Psylla buxi*)—Confined to boxwood. Terminal leaves are cupped and young twig growth checked by a small, gray-green nymph covered with a white cottony or waxy material. The adult, a small green "fly" with transparent wings, appears in late May or June and lays eggs in the base of buds. First instar nymphs winter there and infest terminal leaves as they unfold in spring. Their feeding punctures cause the leaves to curl and form a cup concealing and protecting the nymphs. Lindane, 25 per cent emulsion, applied twice (May 14 and June 1 in Connecticut) or nicotine sulfate applied 3 times, either used at 1 teaspoon per gallon, has given good control of boxwood psyllids. A summer spray with nicotine for the adult state means fewer eggs laid and fewer nymphs to start work the next season.

Laurel Psyllid (*Trioza alacris*)—A pest of laurel or sweet bay in California, New Jersey, and other Atlantic states, also on cherry-laurel. Leaves curl and thicken, redden at margins, form galls; plants are unsightly, lose much of their foliage. Nymphs are pale yellow and orange, hidden by long white wax; adults are very small, $\frac{1}{12}$ inch long, greenish yellow to pale brown with light and dark spots. Eggs are white to yellow, covered with fine powdery wax, laid in March or April in New Jersey, adults having wintered on or in hosts. Spray with nicotine sulfate or lindane.

Pear Psylla (*Psylla pyricola*)—An important pest of pear in eastern states since it was first found in Connecticut in 1832 and serious in the Pacific Northwest since 1939. The copious honeydew secreted by pear psyllids covers foliage and fruit; sooty mold growing in this makes brown spots on the leaves, scars and blackens the fruit. There may be partial defoliation, loss of vigor; buds may not develop normally. Bartlett and d'Anjou pears are especially susceptible; quinces are occasionally infested. The adult is dark reddish brown, $\frac{1}{10}$ inch long, and looks like a miniature cicada (Plate XXII). It winters in bark crevices or under leaves on ground and starts in early spring to lay pear-shaped yellow eggs around buds. In 2 weeks these hatch into wingless nymphs, $\frac{1}{80}$ inch long, which broaden and darken through 5 molting periods, becoming adult in a month. There are 3 to 5 generations in a season, with summer eggs laid on leaves or petioles. Nymphs cluster at axils and on underside of leaves, secreting their abundant sticky honeydew.

Control. A dormant oil spray in early spring kills many adults and eggs, but summer sprays may be necessary by July. Parathion, 15 per cent wettable powder, at rate of $\frac{1}{2}$ pound per 100 gallons, has been used effectively in orchards, with 1 or 2 treatments sufficient. Toxaphene has been promising. Nicotine sulfate, or rotenone with summer oil, is fairly effective and safe for home gardeners. The New Jersey Experiment Station suggests $2\frac{1}{2}$ tablespoons of 40 per cent nicotine sulfate with 2 pounds of hydrated lime to 5 gallons of spray if psyllids appear after fruit is set.

Potato Psyllid (*Paratrioza cockerelli*)—Also Tomato Psyllid, present from the Great Plains west to the Pacific coast, causing a disease known as psyllid yellows. Adults are first green, then black with white margins, $\frac{1}{10}$ inch long. The females lay bright yellow oval eggs, each attached by a stalk to edges of underside of leaves, preferably when the temperature is around 80°F. They hatch in 4 to 15 days into flat, scalelike nymphs, first yellow or orange, then green with a fringe of hairs all around the body. During feeding they inject into the potato plant a substance that disturbs the proper relation between foliage and tubers. The effect on the potato or tomato varies somewhat with the number of insects present, 10 to 30 being required for full expression of the disease. Even when psyllid nymphs feed on only a few leaves, symptoms appear over the whole plant. Basal portions of leaflets turn yellow at margin and roll upward; terminal leaves have a reddish or purple cast; older leaves turn brown and die; stems do not elongate; nodes swell; axillary buds on potatoes develop into aerial tubers or short shoots with swollen bases and small distorted leaves. Feeding by adults does not produce such symptoms; the power is confined to nymphs.

The psyllid winters in southern Texas, New Mexico, and Arizona on wild plants, mostly matrimony vine (*Lycium*), and moves northward to potato and tomato fields in late spring, returning to the southern range in October or November. Other plants of the nightshade family, especially Chinese lantern and groundcherry, may be infested.

Control. Dusting with 5 per cent DDT or with sulfur or spraying with 2 pounds 50 per cent DDT in 100 gallons of water is effective if there is thorough coverage of underside of leaves. Eliminate weed hosts as far as possible and potatoes sprouting in cull piles. There are several useful parasites and predators.

Sumac Psyllids (*Calophya* spp.)—In the East *C. flavida* infests smooth sumac. The immature nymphs are dark gray or black with a narrow white fringe, found on the bark of terminal twigs in winter. *C. nigripennis* infests shining sumac; the adult has black, opaque wings. *C. californica* on sumac in southern California is black to brown in color.

Willow Psyllid (*Trioza maura*)—Common in Utah; has various predators.

REPTILES

Reptiles are generally useful members of the garden community. There are, of course, a few poisonous snakes and no one wants to harbor a rattlesnake even if it does eat mice and other rodents, but most snakes are harmless to man and helpful in getting rid of pests. Lizards are more than welcome garden additions, often kept in greenhouses for their insectivorous habits.

Reptiles (snakes, lizards, turtles) bridge the gap between amphibious animals (newts, salamanders, and toads), which live part of their lives in water, part on land, and mammals. Reptiles have lungs and breathe air throughout their lives and their young are born on land, but they

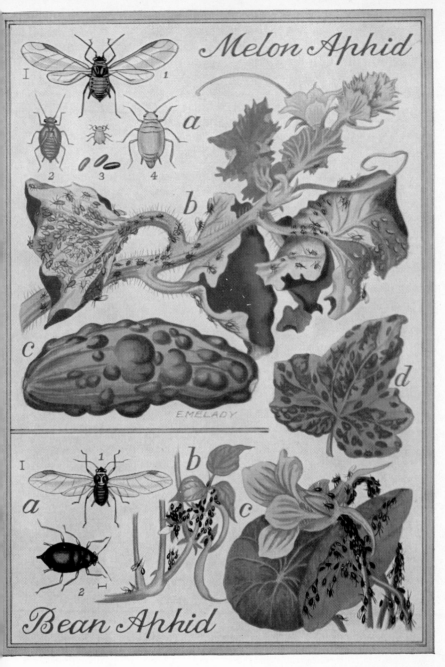

I MELON APHID: (a,1) winged female; (a,2) last nymphal stage; (a,3) eggs and young nymph; (a,4) wingless female or stem mother; (b) cantaloupe leaves starting to curl; (c) aphid-transmitted cucumber mosaic on fruit; (d) cucumber leaf mottled by mosaic. BEAN APHID: (a,1) winged female; (a,2) wingless female; (b) aphids on bean; (c) aphids clustering under nasturtium leaves.

II ROSY APPLE APHID: (a,1) first generation; (a,2) summer aphid; (a,3) eggs, much enlarged, and eggs hatching on apple bud; (a,4) fall aphid, winged female; (a,5) fall aphid, winged male; (a,6) egg-laying female; (a,7) apples distorted, leaves curled. POTATO APHID: (b) injured potato leaves. WOOLLY APPLE APHID: (c) woolly masses on twig, galls on roots. MELON APHID: (d) wingless form and curled leaves. EASTERN SPRUCE GALL APHID: (e) galls on Norway spruce. COOLEY SPRUCE GALL APHID: (f) terminal gall on blue spruce. SNOWBALL APHID: (g) viburnum foliage curled, distorted.

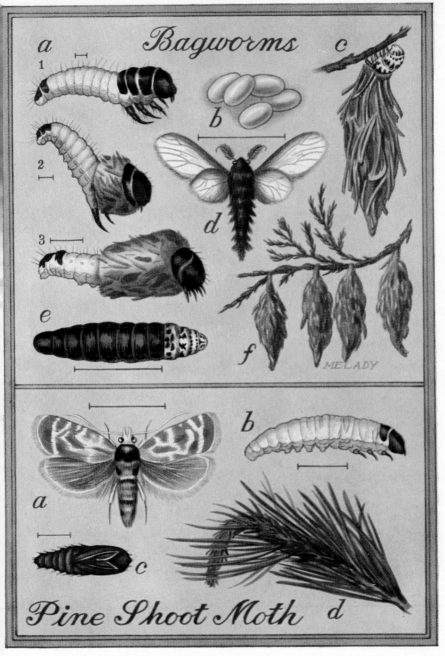

III BAGWORMS: (a,1,2,3) larva and stages in construction of bag; (b) eggs, highly magnified; (c) female in bag, actual size; (d) winged male moth; (e) wingless female removed from bag; (f) bags in winter. EUROPEAN PINE SHOOT MOTH: (a) moth; (b) larva removed from infested tip; (c) pupa; (d) pine shoot with typical crooking and discoloration.

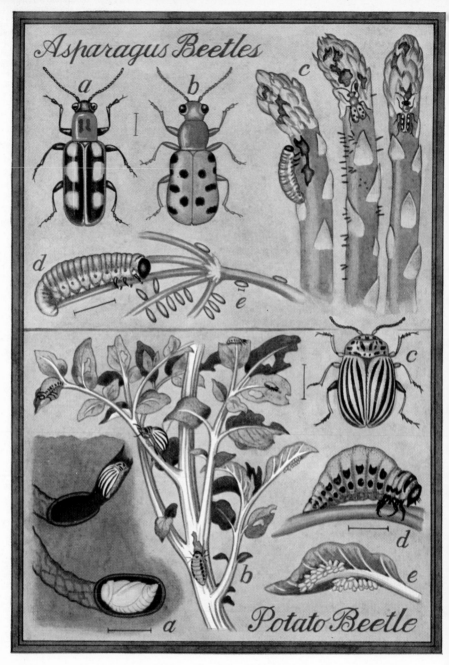

IV ASPARAGUS BEETLE: (a) adult; (c) typical injury to asparagus shoots by grubs and beetles; (d) grub and eggs. SPOTTED ASPARAGUS BEETLE: (b) adult. COLORADO POTATO BEETLE: (a) pupa in soil and adult emerging from soil; (b) portion of potato vine showing larvae, eggs, and beetles; (c) adult beetle; (d) humpbacked grub; (e) egg clusters on underside of potato leaf.

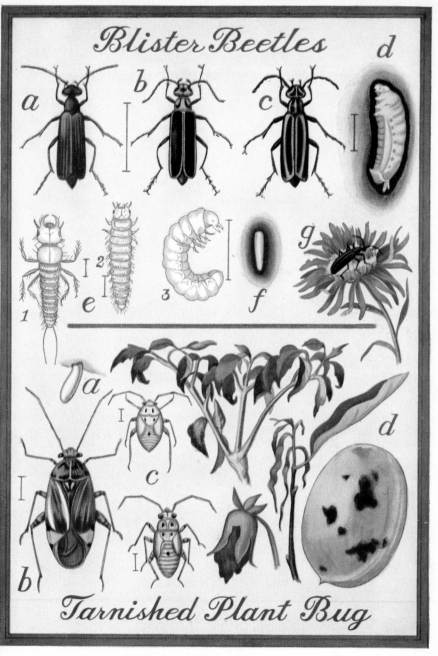

V CLEMATIS BLISTER BEETLE: (a) adult. MARGINED BLISTER
BEETLE: (b) adult. STRIPED BLISTER BEETLE: (c) adult; (d) pseudopupa
in soil; (e,1) triungulin or first larval stage; (e,2) second larval stage; (e,3) third
larval stage; (f) egg in soil, much enlarged; (g) adult feeding on aster. TARNISHED
PLANT BUG: (a) egg, enlarged, inserted in stem; (b) adult bug; (c) nymph in two
instars; (d) injury to fruit, bug, terminal shoot, leaves.

VI GYPSY MOTH: (a) large female moth; (b) small dark male moth; (c) pupa inside scanty thread cocoon; (d) pupa enlarged; (e) full-grown hairy caterpillar; (f) egg mass. ELM LEAF BEETLE: (a) adult; (b) pupa; (c) grub; (d) egg cluster on underside of leaf and single egg, much magnified; (e) elm leaves skeletonized by larvae and with holes eaten by adults.

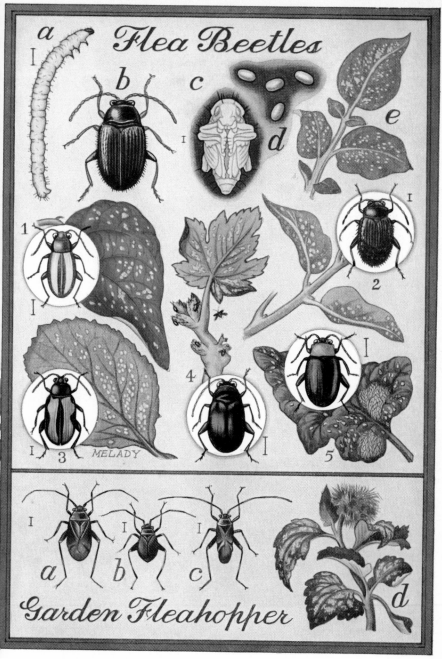

VII POTATO FLEA BEETLE: (a) grub; (b) adult; (c) pupa in soil; (d) eggs in soil; (e) "shot-hole" injury to potato leaf. PALE-STRIPED FLEA BEETLE: (1) adult and injury on bean. EGGPLANT FLEA BEETLE: (2) adult and riddled foliage. STRIPED FLEA BEETLE: (3) adult and injured cabbage leaf. GRAPE FLEA BEETLE: (4) adult and injury to grape leaf. SPINACH FLEA BEETLE: (5) adult, and spinach leaf skeletonized by grubs, riddled by beetles. GARDEN FLEAHOPPER: (a) long-winged female; (b) short-winged female; (c) male; (d) ageratum with foliage yellowed by loss of sap.

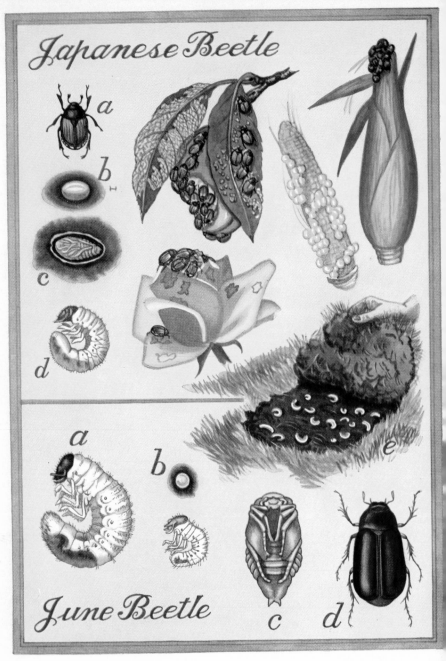

VIII JAPANESE BEETLE: (a) adult, with injury on peach, rose, corn; (b)
egg in soil, much enlarged; (c) pupa in soil; (d) grub; (e) turf damage from
grubs. JUNE BEETLE: (a) white grub actual size; (b) egg, enlarged, and young
larva; (c) pupa; (d) adult.

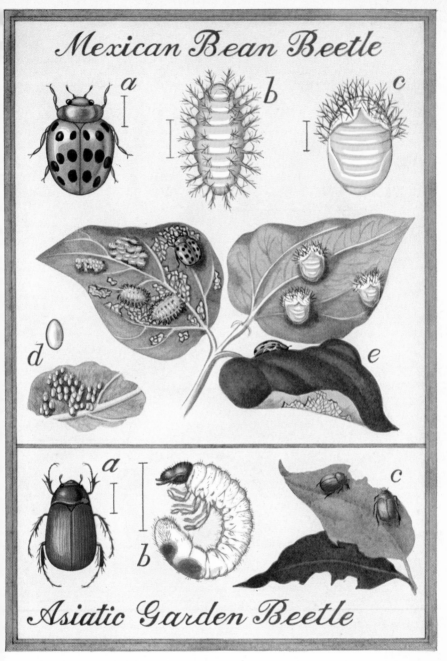

IX   MEXICAN BEAN BEETLE: (a) adult; (b) grub; (c) pupa with larval skin pushed back at one end; (d) egg cluster on back of leaf and single egg enlarged; (e) bean leaf showing beetle in all stages and feeding pattern. ASIATIC GARDEN BEETLE: (a) adult; (b) grub; (c) beetles, natural size, feeding on foliage.

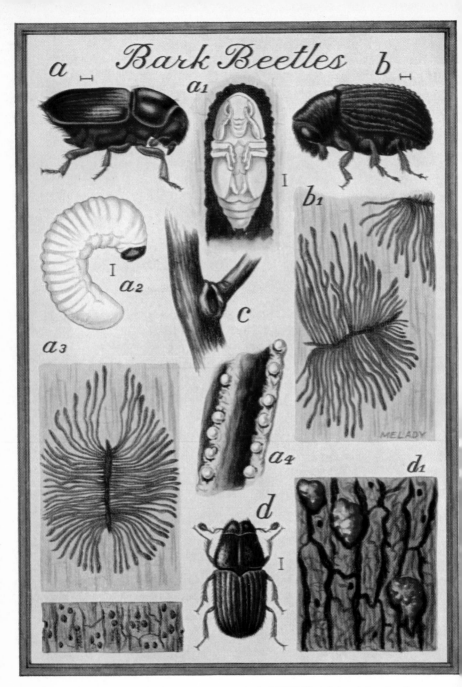

X SMALLER EUROPEAN ELM BARK BEETLE: (a) adult; (a,1) pupa; (a,2) grub; (a,3) characteristic pattern of galleries under bark and exit holes in bark; (a,4) eggs lining gallery, much enlarged; (c) feeding injury at crotch. NATIVE ELM BARK BEETLE: (b) adult; (b,1) galleries in transverse position. WESTERN PINE BEETLE: (d) adult; (d,1) pine bark with resin tubes around entrance holes and small exit holes.

Rose Chafer

Rose Snout Beetle

Willow Leaf Beetle

EVA MELADY

Tortoise Beetle

Green June Beetle

Rhinoceros Beetle

XI ROSE CHAFER: beetle feeding on rose. ROSE CURCULIO: (Rose Snout Beetle) on rosebuds. IMPORTED WILLOW LEAF BEETLE: willow leaves showing skeletonization by larvae, holes eaten by adults, and single beetle much enlarged. BLACK-LEGGED TORTOISE BEETLE: black-spined larva with excrement on back, adult feeding on leaf, natural size and enlarged. GREEN JUNE BEETLE: feeding on fruit and foliage. RHINOCEROS BEETLE.

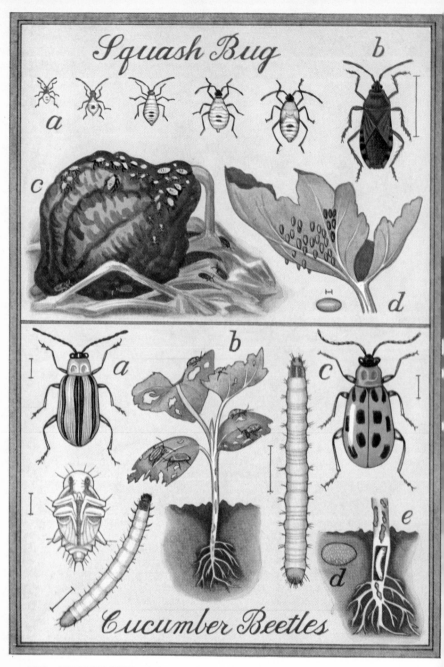

XII SQUASH BUG: (a) nymphs in successive instars; (b) adult; (c) nymphs feeding on squash; (d) eggs grouped on underside of leaf, and single egg, enlarged. STRIPED CUCUMBER BEETLE: (a) adult, pupa, and grub; (b) adults feeding on seedling. SPOTTED CUCUMBER BEETLE: (c) adult and rootworm larva; (d) egg in soil, enlarged; (e) larva in underground corn stem.

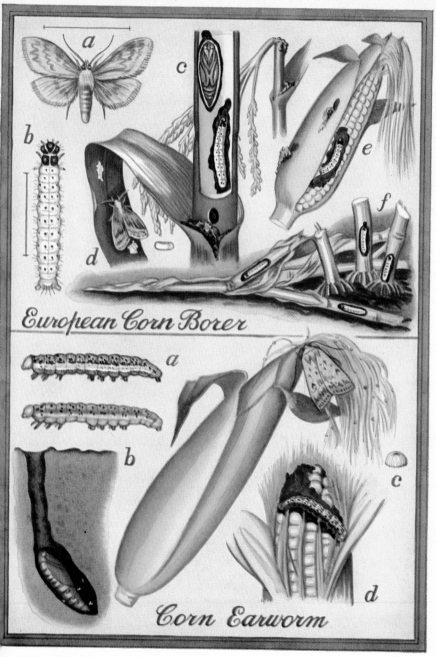

XIII EUROPEAN CORN BORER: (a) adult moth; (b) larva; (c) pupa and larva inside corn stem, frass protruding from hole; (d) moth laying eggs on corn leaf; (e) borer working in ear; (f) larvae overwintering in old corn stalks. CORN EARWORM: (a) larvae, brown or green striped caterpillars; (b) pupa in soil; (c) moth laying eggs on corn silk and single egg, much enlarged; (d) worm feeding in mass of frass at tip of ear.

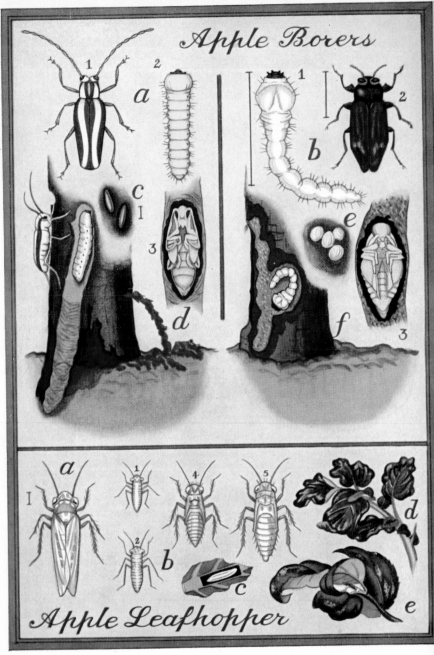

XIV ROUNDHEADED APPLE TREE BORER: (a,1) adult beetle; (a,2) roundheaded grub; (a,3) pupa in wood cell; (c) eggs; (d) section of tree trunk, showing borer at work, frass protruding. FLATHEADED APPLE TREE BORER: (b,1) larva with flat enlargement behind head, characteristic curved position; (b,2) beetle; (b,3) pupa in cell; (e) eggs; (f) larva in winter chamber in tree trunk. POTATO LEAFHOPPER (Apple Leafhopper): (a) adult; (b,1,2,4,5) nymphs in different instars; (c) egg in leaf vein.

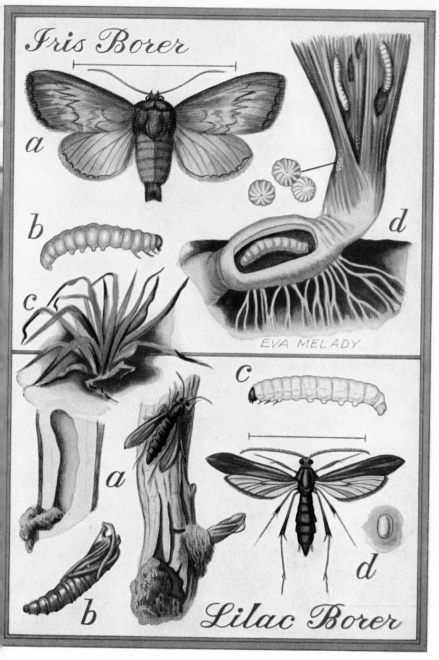

Iris Borer

EVA MELADY

Lilac Borer

XV IRIS BORER: (a) moth, somewhat enlarged; (b) borer, not quite full grown; (c) infested iris; (d) young borers on outside of leaves (usual position is inside fold), older borer in hollow rhizome, and eggs, enlarged. LILAC BORER: (a) lilac stems showing tunnel and protruding sawdust, moth and pupa case; (b) pupa; (c) borer; (d) adult moth and egg (enlarged).

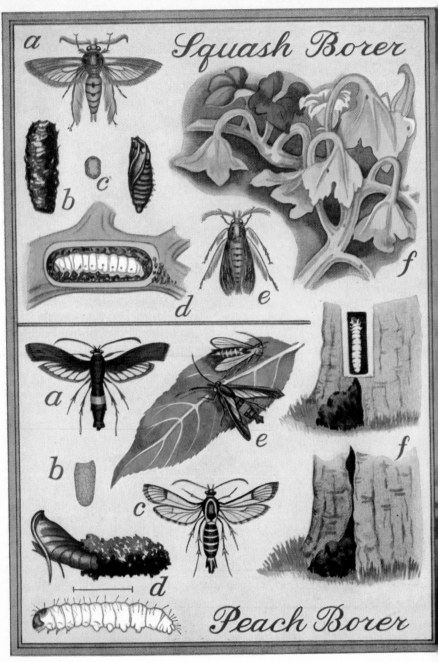

XVI SQUASH BORER: (a) female moth; (b) cocoon; (c) egg, enlarged, and pupa; (d) borer in stem; (e) male moth; (f) vine wilting from borer injury. PEACH TREE BORER: (a) female moth; (b) egg, enlarged; (c) male moth; (d) pupa protruding from cocoon, and borer; (e) adults on peach leaf; (f) section cut in tree trunk to show borer in position, jellylike frass at base.

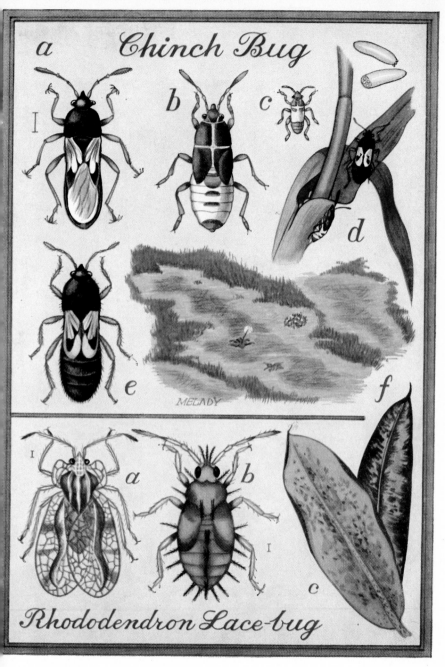

XVII CHINCH BUG: (a) long-winged adult; (b) fifth instar; (c) nymph, first instar. HAIRY CHINCH BUG: (d) eggs, much enlarged, and bugs in typical position behind boot of lower grass blade; (e) short-winged adult; (f) turf with brown areas killed by bugs and yellow margins where bugs are working. RHODO-DENDRON LACE BUG: (a) adult; (b) nymph in last stage of development; (c) rhododendron leaves showing browning of lower surface and loss of color on upper surface.

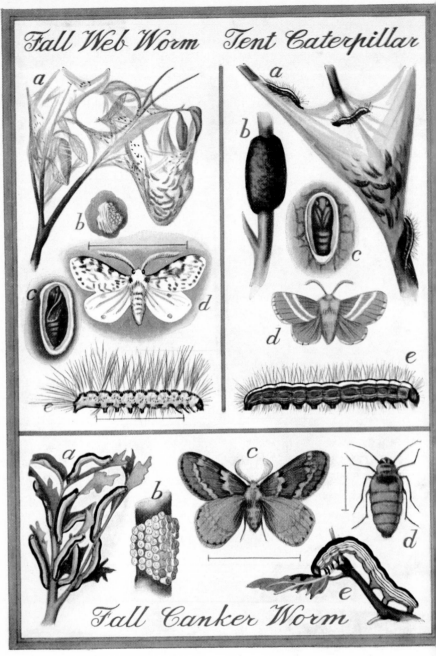

Fall Web Worm · Tent Caterpillar · Fall Canker Worm

XVIII FALL WEBWORM: (a) web or nest over end of branches; (b) egg mass covered with hairs on underside of leaf; (c) pupa in cocoon in soil; (d) adult moth; (e) full-grown hairy caterpillar. EASTERN TENT CATERPILLAR: (a) nest of caterpillars in tree crotch; (b) egg collar around twig; (c) pupa inside cocoon on bark; (d) adult moth; (e) full-grown caterpillar. FALL CANKER-WORM: (a) larvae ravaging foliage; (b) egg mass on twig; (c) male moth; (d) wingless female moth; (e) full-grown caterpillar with 3 prolegs.

XIX   TOBACCO HORNWORM, on Tomato: (a) adult moth, natural size; (b)
egg on leaflet and egg enlarged; (c) larva with "horn"; (d) pupa in soil. CELERY-
WORM: (a) chrysalid; (b) male butterfly, black swallowtail; (c) caterpillar on
celery; (d) front view showing forked horn.

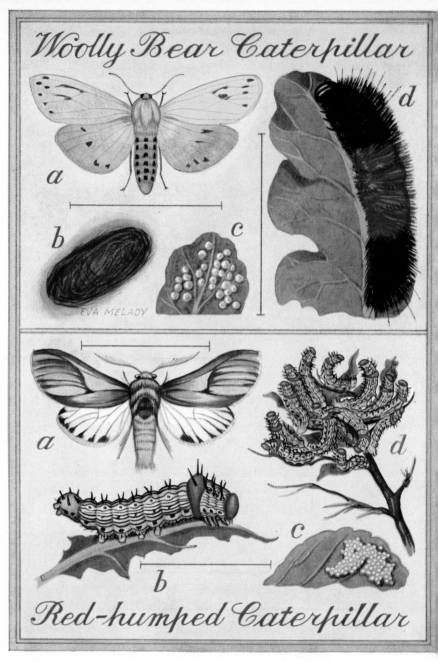

Woolly Bear Caterpillar

EVA MELADY

Red-humped Caterpillar

XX BANDED WOOLLYBEAR CATERPILLAR: (a) moth; (b) pupa in hairy cocoon; (c) eggs; (d) hairy caterpillar. RED-HUMPED CATERPILLAR: (a) moth; (b) larva with red head and hump; (c) eggs; (d) caterpillars in typical position.

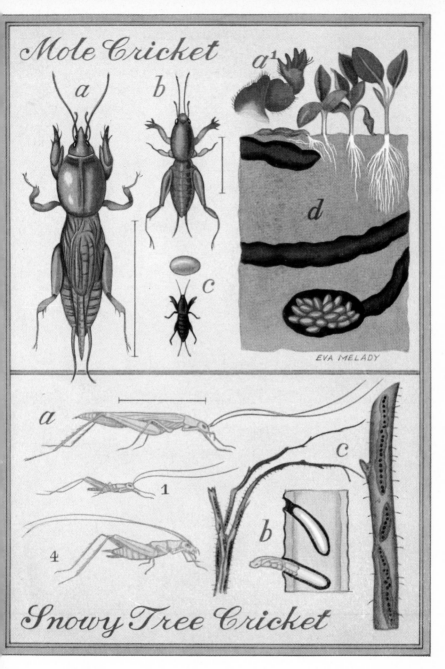

Mole Cricket

EVA MELADY

Snowy Tree Cricket

XXI NORTHERN MOLE CRICKET: (a) adult, slightly enlarged; (a,1) detail of front leg showing adaptation for digging; (b) nymph; (c) egg, magnified, and
first nymphal stage; (d) injury to seedlings from burrows, and eggs in soil pocket.
SNOWY TREE CRICKET: (a) adult; (a,1) first instar; (a,4) fourth instar,
nymphs with wing pads; (b) egg in position in wood and hatching nymph, much
enlarged; (c) egg punctures in a row along stem.

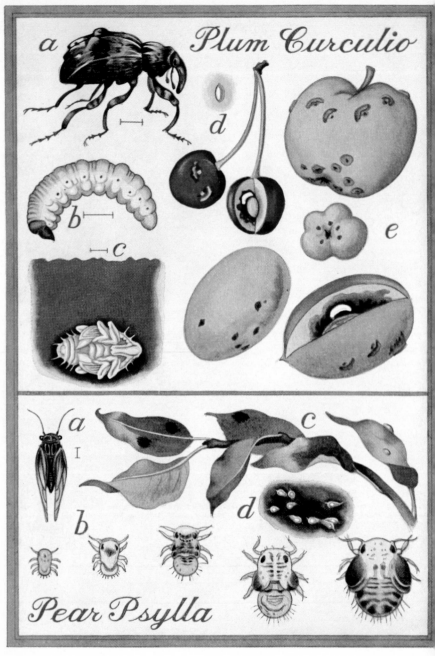

XXII PLUM CURCULIO: (a) adult snout beetle; (b) grub; (c) pupa in soil; (d) egg; (e) typical injury, crescent-shaped scar, on cherry, plum, and apple. PEAR PSYLLA: (a) adult; (b) nymph in different instars; (c) injury to pear leaves; (d) eggs attached to bark by one end.

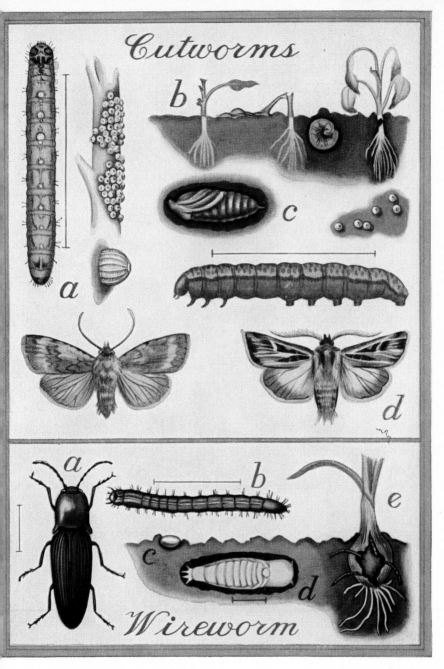

XXIII VARIEGATED CUTWORM: (a) larva, egg cluster, and single egg enlarged, and moth. DINGY CUTWORM: (b) seedlings cut off and cutworm in typical coiled position; (c) pupa in soil, eggs and larva. WIREWORM: (a) click beetle adult; (b) larva; (c) egg; (d) pupa in soil; (e) larvae feeding in bulb.

XXIV BEET LEAFHOPPER: (a) curly-top disease of beet, the virus transmitted by leafhopper, showing clearing of veins, wartlike protuberances, leaf rolling; (b) nymph in fifth instar; (c) adult; (d) eggs on leaf and young nymph; (e) diseased tomato leaf. SIX-SPOTTED LEAFHOPPER: (a) adult, showing 6 black spots; (b) yellows disease of lettuce, transmitted by leafhopper; (c) aster yellows.

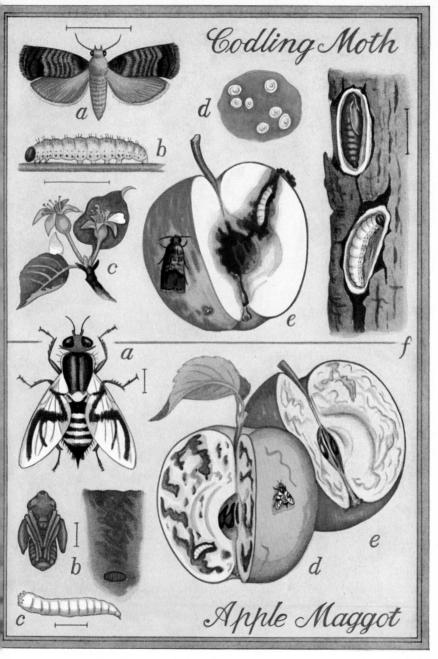

XXV CODLING MOTH: (a) adult; (b) larva or "worm"; (c) stage of fruit when first worms enter; (d) eggs, enlarged; (e) larva tunneling out, moth on surface of apple, and sting from second-brood larva entering fruit; (f) larva in winter position under bark scales and pupa formed in spring. APPLE MAGGOT: (a) adult fly; (b) pupa, enlarged, and puparium (containing pupa), natural size in soil; (c) maggot; (d,e) injury to fruit with maggot inside and fly puncturing skin to lay eggs.

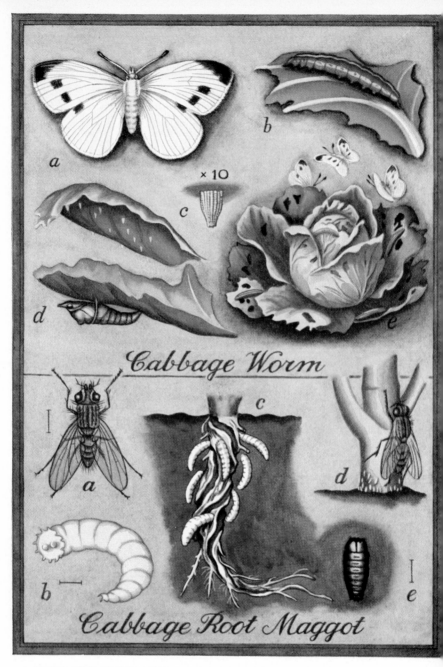

Cabbage Worm

Cabbage Root Maggot

XXVI IMPORTED CABBAGEWORM: (a) adult butterfly; (b) full-grown caterpillar; (c) egg, magnified 10 times; (d) chrysalid attached to leaf; (e) injury to cabbage head by larvae, adults laying eggs. CABBAGE MAGGOT: (a) adult fly; (b) legless maggot (much enlarged); (c) maggots working on roots; (d) fly laying eggs at base of stem; (e) puparium in soil.

XXVII TWO-SPOTTED MITE (Red Spider): (a) adult 8-legged mite, magnified 50 times; (b) young 6-legged larva or nymph; (c) egg enlarged and mites in web on underside of bean leaf; (d) typical mite injury to phlox, juniper, rose, bean, and violet. LONG-TAILED MEALYBUG (a). CITRUS MEALYBUG (b). COCONUT MEALYBUG (c). MEALYBUGS: (d) on begonia; (e) on fuchsia; (f) on coleus; (g) on palm.

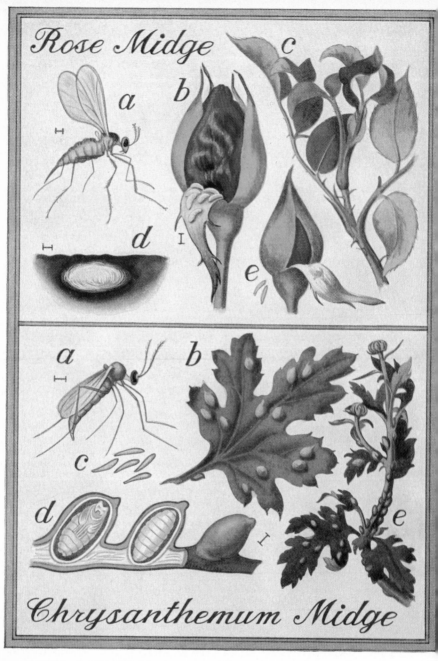

XXVIII ROSE MIDGE: (a) adult; (b) larvae on inside of sepal, injury to bud; (c) distortion of young shoot; (d) pupa in cocoon in soil, much enlarged; (e) egg mass on sepal and egg magnified. CHRYSANTHEMUM GALL MIDGE: (a) adult, much enlarged; (b) conical galls on leaf; (c) eggs; (d) stem cut to show pupa and maggot inside galls; (e) shoot with galls on stem and leaves.

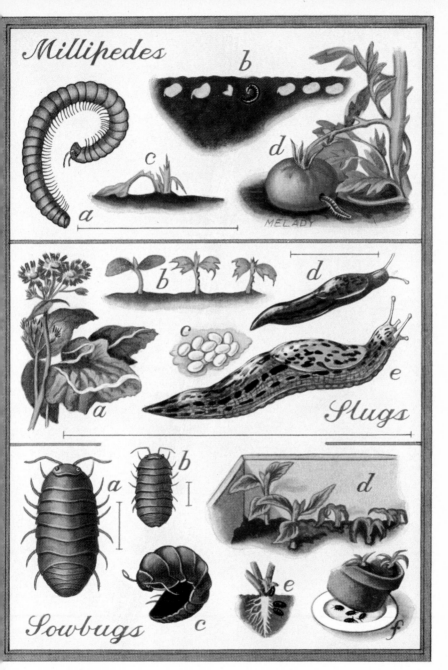

XXIX MILLIPEDES: (a) millipede enlarged to show 2 pairs of legs on each segment, typical coiled position; (b) seeds injured by millipedes; (c) injury to young seedling; (d) tomato attacked when resting on ground. SPOTTED GARDEN SLUG: (a) slimy trail on cineraria; (b) seedlings eaten; (c) egg cluster; (d) month-old slug; (e) mature slug with spots. SOWBUGS: (a) adult; (b) young sowbug; (c) form known as pillbug, which rolls into a ball; (d) infested seedlings; (e) sowbugs working at roots; (f) favorite hiding place under moist flowerpot.

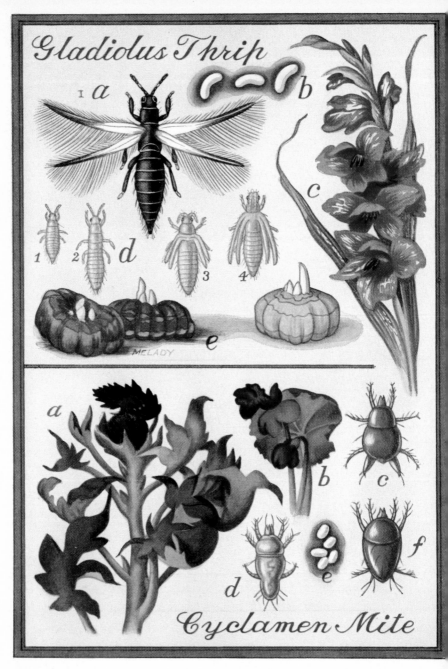

XXX GLADIOLUS THRIPS: (a) adult, showing fringed wings; (b) eggs, much enlarged; (c) typical injury to flowering spike and foliage; (d,1) first-stage larva; (d,2) second-stage larva; (d,3) third-stage (prepupa); (d,4) pupa with wing pads; (e) injured corms at left, healthy corm at right. CYCLAMEN MITE: (a) delphinium spike, with typical distortion; (b) injured cyclamen; (c) adult male, highly magnified; (d) young 6-legged larva; (e) eggs; (f) adult female.

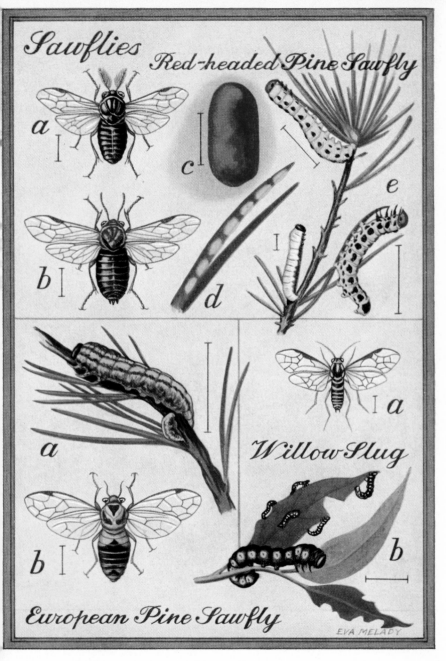

XXXI RED-HEADED PINE SAWFLY: (a) male adult; (b) female sawfly;
(c) pupa in papery cocoon on ground; (d) eggs in slits along needle; (e) young
and mature larvae feeding on pine. INTRODUCED PINE SAWFLY (labeled
European Pine Sawfly): (a) larva in typical position on twig; (b) adult. WILLOW
SAWFLY (Willow Slug): (a) adult; (b) larvae feeding on willow leaves.

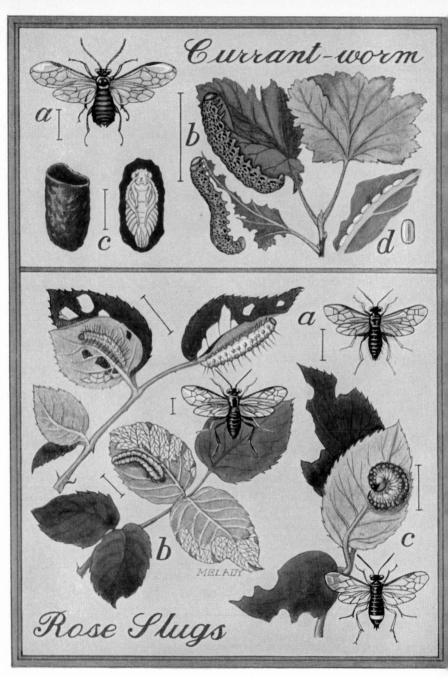

Currant-worm

Rose Slugs

MELADY

XXXII IMPORTED CURRANTWORM: (a) adult female sawfly; (b) larvae and feeding injury; (c) cocoon and pupa inside cocoon; (d) eggs along vein and single egg, enlarged. BRISTLY ROSE-SLUG: (a) adult sawfly and larvae feeding on leaf. ROSE-SLUG: (b) leaf showing typical skeletonizing but larva and adult enlarged. CURLED ROSE SAWFLY: (c) larva in coiled position, injured leaf, adult.

XXXIII JUNIPER SCALE: (a) round, white, female scale, much enlarged; (b) male scale, same enlargement; (c,d) scale on juniper twigs. PINE NEEDLE SCALE: (a) two forms of the female scale; (b) ridged male scale; (c) infested pine needles. EUONYMUS SCALE: (a) dark, oyster-shaped female; (b) narrow, white, ridged male; (c) infested euonymus; (d) on bittersweet.

XXXIV SAN JOSE SCALE: (a) round female scale; (b) oblong male scales; (c) young crawler; (d) adult winged male; (f) infested apple twig and fruit. SCURFY SCALE: (a) single female, much enlarged, and branch with male scales; (b) single male and branch with male scales; (e) female scale removed, showing eggs. OYSTERSHELL SCALE: (a) single female and branch with female scales; (c) young crawler; (d) adult male; (e) female turned over to show eggs under the shell. COTTONY MAPLE SCALE: (a) female with cottony egg mass and infested maple twig; (c) young crawler; (e) eggs.

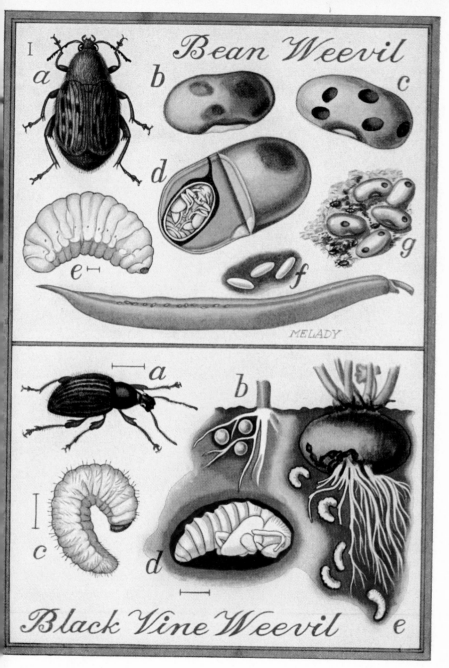

XXXV BEAN WEEVIL: (a) adult weevil; (b) bean with blemishes indicating weevils inside; (c) exit holes in seed; (d) pupa in position inside seed; (e) grub, much enlarged; (f) eggs, magnified and in position on bean pod; (g) remains of a weevil-infested bag of seeds. BLACK VINE WEEVIL: (a) adult; (b) eggs among roots in soil; (c) grub, enlarged; (d) pupa in earthen cell below soil surface; (e) grubs in soil, natural size, and injury to cyclamen corm.

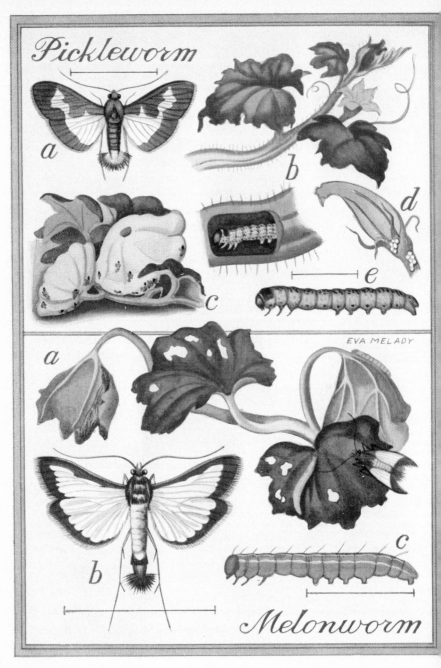

XXXVI PICKLEWORM: (a) moth with characteristic scaly brush at end of abdomen; (b) melon shoot showing feeding injury, and stem cut to show young larva; (c) squash with entrance holes; (d) eggs at base of bud; (e) full-grown larva. MELONWORM: (a) squash vine with feeding holes, pupa in folded leaf, moth; (b) adult moth; (c) full-grown larva.

are cold-blooded like amphibians, their temperature dependent on environment. They have scaly skins.

True lizards are usually found in southern gardens; the so-called lizards of the North are more often newts or salamanders. Most lizards have long tails and if they are caught they sometimes leave their tails behind in the hands of the enemy and grow new ones. The little garden lizard is a friendly creature, sunning itself on the front porch near the vines, every so often running out its forked tongue to collect an insect in an action incredibly fast.

I have had one complaint about turtles. A New Hampshire gardener who lives beside a lake tells me that when the turtles come on land to lay eggs they make a mess of her flower beds.

ROOTWORMS

Rootworms are larvae of beetles that work on roots of plants, sometimes on plants quite different from those injured by the adults. For instance, the clover rootworm is the grape colaspis; the southern corn rootworm is the spotted cucumber beetle. Both have been discussed under Beetles.

Cranberry Rootworm (*Rhabdopterus picipes*)—Important in the beetle stage on rhododendron, camellias, and other ornamentals, not too serious as a root pest of cranberry. It is found along the coast from New England to Florida and along the Gulf to the Mississippi River. The beetles are oval, ¼ x ⅛ inch, brown to black with a metallic luster. They hide in leaves or rubbish during the day, feed at night or on cloudy days on young foliage as it is opening, making characteristic right-angled holes or crescents. Dusting ornamentals with 5 per cent DDT, 5 per cent chlordane, 10 per cent toxaphene, or lead arsenate at time new growth starts, repeating in 10 to 14 days, has given fairly good control, but DDT injures many camellia varieties. Spraying plants and mulch with toxaphene, 1 ounce 40 per cent wettable powder to 2½ gallons of water, gave best control in Florida experiments. See also Rhabdopterus Beetles under Beetles.

Grape Rootworm (*Fidia viticida*)—Present in eastern states, except extreme North and far South, on grape and related wild plants. Small, curved, white, brown-headed grubs winter deep in soil, migrating near the surface in spring, changing to soft, white pupae in small cells. About 2 weeks after grapes bloom, brown, hairy, chunky beetles, ¼ inch long, feed on upper side of leaves, making conspicuous chains of small holes. They lay eggs in clusters on grape canes, often under loose bark. Young grubs drop to the ground, burrow in soil until they reach the roots; they cut off small feeding roots and gouge channels in larger roots until cold weather. Infested vines lack vigor, have little new growth, and yellow foliage.

Control. Spray with DDT for the beetle stage as soon as first leaf punctures are noticed, using 1½ tablespoons of 50 per cent wettable powder to a gallon of water, repeating in 10 days if necessary. The spray schedule for grape berry moth usually controls the rootworm.

Northern Corn Rootworm (*Diabrotica longicornis*)—Present from New York to Kansas, causing most injury in Upper Mississippi Valley. The larvae feed only on corn, the adults on many summer-flowering plants. Eggs laid on the ground in fall, around roots of corn, hatch rather late in spring. The larvae, threadlike, wrinkled white worms with brown heads, ½ inch long when grown, burrow through corn roots, making brown tunnels. They leave the roots in July and pupate in soil. Beetles, uniform yellow green, ⅙ to ¼ inch long, appear in late July and August, feed on corn silk and pollen of other plants, lay eggs in the cornfields, and die at first frost.

Control by rotating corn with another crop, or by dusting silks with DDT, or by applying lindane to the soil as a side dressing before cultivation.

Strawberry Rootworm (*Paria canella*)—Found over much of the United States on strawberry, raspberry, blackberry, grape, rose, peach, apple, walnut, butternut, wild crab, mountain ash, and several other hosts. Rose leaves, in greenhouses or outdoors, may be riddled with small shot-holes, bark of new shoots gnawed off, buds eaten out. Leaves of strawberries and other fruits may be destroyed. The beetles, very small, ⅛ inch long, shining dark brown, winter as adults and lay eggs on ground near plants in spring. The grubs, small, white, brown-spotted, feed on strawberry roots all spring, then pupate, with beetles feeding until frost. In greenhouses and warm climates there may be 2 or more generations.

Control. Treating the soil with chlordane before setting out plants is effective for the first year or two. Dusting with 5 per cent chlordane at time of first bloom gives partial control, as does dusting with a combination of sulfur, 85 parts, and lead arsenate, 15 parts. In greenhouses a parathion aerosol is effective.

Western Grape Rootworm (*Adoxus obscurus*)—Present on grape in California, with fireweed as the native host. The beetle is fat, nearly black, covered with short hairs. It eats chainlike strips in leaves and gouges into young berries. The white grubs eat smaller roots entirely, the bark of larger roots. Spray foliage with DDT or an arsenical or cryolite when beetles appear in spring.

SAWFLIES

Sawflies belong to the order Hymenoptera, along with bees and wasps. As members of that order, the adults have 2 pairs of transparent wings hooked together. As members of the suborder Symphyta (Chalastogastra) the females have an ovipositor (egg-laying apparatus) adapted for sawing or boring but not stinging. It consists of 2 short outer plates and 2 saw-toothed blades which move in opposite directions when the female is slitting a leaf before laying her egg. Almost all sawflies feed on plants in the larval stage. Larvae look like caterpillars, but they have more than 5 pairs of prolegs and they do not have crotchets. Most live exposed on foliage, singly or in groups, a few spin webs, some are leaf miners. The families given here include those of importance to gardeners.

Pamphiliidae. Web-spinning and leaf-rolling sawflies, small, stout-bodied.

Cimbicidae. Large robust sawflies with clubbed antennae, resembling bumblebees. The elm sawfly is the most common species.

Diprionidae. Medium-sized sawflies with 13 or more antennal segments, serrate in the female, comblike in the male. The larvae are very injurious to pine, spruce, and other crucifers.

Tenthredinidae. Typical sawflies, medium-sized to small, brightly colored, usually found on foliage or flowers. Larvae are highly destructive to trees and shrubs. The family includes birch and elm leaf miners, rose-slugs, pear-slugs, imported currantworm, larch sawfly.

Balsam Fir Sawfly (*Neodiprion abietis*)—From New England west to Minnesota and Missouri, defoliating balsam fir, feeding some on spruce. Larvae are green, striped with darker green and brown, with black head, ¾ inch long when grown. Adults emerge from late June to early September, cut slits singly in needles for the eggs, which hatch in late May or June. Larvae feed gregariously, then spin reddish-brown cocoons on twigs or in litter on ground. Spray for young larvae with DDT or lead arsenate.

Blackberry Sawfly (*Pamphilius dentatus*)—Occasionally blackberry leaves are rolled and webbed by bluish-green larvae, ¾ inch long, which feed inside the roll. Adults appear in May, lay oval white eggs end to end on larger veins; larvae feed until July, then enter the soil to remain until the next May. Spray with lead arsenate to prevent defoliation.

Black-headed Ash Sawfly (*Tethida cordigera*)—Distribution and habits like the brown-headed ash sawfly. The larva is whitish with a yellow tinge, with shiny black head, 3/4 inch long when grown.

Bristly Rose-slug (*Cladius isomerus*)—Found east of the Mississippi north of Richmond, Virginia, and in California, a very serious defoliator of wild and cultivated roses. Larvae are sluglike, greenish white, with long, rather stout bristles, 5/8 inch long. They first skeletonize the leaves by feeding from the undersurface, later eat holes clear through. Eggs are laid in slits in upper side of the midrib. There may be as many as 5 or 6 generations. Pupation for summer broods is in cocoons on leaves or twigs; overwintering cocoons are in the soil. Almost any stomach poison on the foliage *before* larvae start feeding and repeated at frequent intervals will control rose-slugs: DDT, methoxychlor, lead arsenate, and rotenone are effective.

Brown-headed Ash Sawfly (*Tomostethus multicinctus*)—A serious defoliator of red and white ash used as shade trees in eastern and central states. Adults emerge when leaf buds show green and lay eggs in developing leaflets. Yellow-white or greenish-white larvae, with brown heads, eat ravenously until late May or June, then construct cocoonlike cells in the soil where they stay until spring.

Butternut Woollyworm (*Blennocampa caryae*)—Found on butternut, hickory, and English walnut. The false caterpillars are covered with long white filaments, standing straight up, and when several of them feed side by side on the undersurface of leaves they seem to be covered with masses of white wool. Underneath the filaments the larvae are pea green, about an inch long, with 8 pairs of prolegs (abdominal legs). They eat from the side of the leaf inward, often leaving nothing but the midrib. They pupate near the surface of the ground. The adult is black with reddish thorax. The injury is ordinarily not enough to call for spraying.

Cherry Fruit Sawfly (*Hoplocampa cookei*)—A Pacific coast pest of cherry, plum, prune, sometimes peach and apricot. Adults have black bodies, yellow appendages, are 1/8 inch long. Larvae, white with brown heads, 1/4 inch long, work in partly developed fruits and feed on seeds, then leave through a hole in the side to pupate in a silken cocoon for winter. Fruits wither and drop. Spray with lead arsenate just before blossoms open.

Curled Rose Sawfly (*Allantus cinctus*)—Coiled Rose Worm, found from Maine to Virginia and west to Minnesota on wild and cultivated roses. It curls up like a cutworm, starts in by skeletonizing but ends by devouring entire leaflets except the largest veins. The larva is metallic green above, marked with white dots, grayish white underneath, yellow-brown head, ¾ inch long when grown. The larvae form cells in the pith of pruned ends of rose shoots and pupate there. There are 2 generations in the southern part of the range, 1 in New England. Eggs are laid in upper surface of leaflets. Spray or dust with any stomach poison.

Dusky Birch Sawfly (*Croesus latitarsus*)—Common in New England and Great Lakes states on gray birch, sometimes other birches. Larvae, yellow green with black markings, black heads, up to 1 inch long, feed in gangs all around the margins of leaves. Saplings may be defoliated. There are 2 overlapping generations, with larvae feeding from early June to late fall. Adults, blue black with white leg markings, appear in May and June, July to September. Spray young trees with DDT or lead arsenate.

70. Elm sawfly larvae—note how the rear end is secured to stem.

Elm Sawfly (*Cimbex americana*)—Giant American Sawfly, distributed through northern states to Colorado, with a related species on the Pacific coast. Adults are large, body nearly an inch long, steel blue and black, with 3 or 4 yellow spots on each side, long buff antennae with knobbed ends, smoky-brown transparent wings. The larva is pale yellow green with a black stripe down the back, black spiracles, 8 pairs of prolegs, 1¾ inches when grown. It rests in a coiled position, feeds with its rear end curled around a twig. Eggs are laid in leaf tissue in May, each egg showing as a blister on the underside of the leaf. Young larvae crawl out through a slit in the epidermis, feed for 6 to 8 weeks (from June to October), then spin brown, papery cocoons in soil litter, transforming to true pupae in spring or early summer. Elm and willow are their principal food plants, but alder, basswood, birch, maple, and poplar are sometimes eaten. Adults are sometimes injurious by gnawing bark of twigs.

Control. Spraying with lead arsenate or DDT for elm leaf beetles should also control sawflies. Several parasitic wasps and flies are on the job.

European Apple Sawfly (*Hoplocampa testudinea*)—First discovered on Long Island in 1939, now destructive to apples and crabapples in home gardens in southern Connecticut, southeastern New York. Adults, brown and yellow "flies," emerge from puparia in ground when trees bloom; eggs are inserted in calyx cups. Larvae, white with 7 prolegs, bore into the fruit, leaving a chocolate sawdust on the surface. One larva may damage several fruits. There is 1 generation. Two sprays of rotenone, one at petal fall and the second a week later, are suggested for home gardens. Chlordane and methoxychlor are possibilities; DDT has not been very effective.

71. Young larvae of European pine sawfly chewing off needles.

European Pine Sawfly (*Neodiprion sertifer*)—An introduced species first noted in New Jersey in 1925, exceedingly troublesome in home gardens in this state and in part of New York and Connecticut, found also in Ohio, Illinois, Michigan, and Canada. Favored food plants are are red, jack, Swiss mountain, mugho pines, which are seriously defoliated.

Eggs are laid in rows in slits in pine needles; just before hatching in late April or early May they look like pine leaf scales. The tiny young larvae, green with shiny black heads, join together in gangs, but they match the needles so well they are scarcely ever noticed until far too much damage has been done. They feed at first on sides of needles, causing a few tip needles to turn straw-colored and curl slightly, an excellent diagnostic sign. After the first molt, larvae eat entire needles, right down to the base. Several hundred may work together and after demolishing one twig move on to the next. When disturbed, they move in uncanny unison, elevating their rear ends. Feeding is confined to old needles; infested ornamental pines about the house will show, by the end of May, new green plumes waving at the end of long naked branches. After 4 or 5 weeks of feeding, the full-grown larva is grayish green with a light stripe down the back, 2 white lines bordering a broken stripe of intense green, ⅞ inch long.

Mature larvae drop or crawl to the ground to spin golden-brown cocoons in litter on top of the soil or in protected places on the trunk, sometimes in frass left by pine webworms. Pupae are formed in the cocoons in late summer, adults emerging in September and October to lay their eggs in the current year's growth of needles. They look like small bees or large, fuzzy flies; males are blackish with feathery antennae, females are yellow brown.

Control. One thorough spraying, at the time larvae are hatching, with DDT, 2 tablespoons 50 per cent wettable powder to a gallon of water, or with lead arsenate, will give control for the season. In most seasons this should be the end of April or first of May. A delay of a week or two may mean conspicuous defoliation, naked branches that the pine can never replace. Parasitic wasps have been liberated for pines on watersheds and recently a virus, disseminated both by airplane and ground equipment, has been quite effective in killing off the larvae.

European Spruce Sawfly (*Diprion hercyniae*)—This European species was first found on the American continent in 1922 near Ottawa but did not attract attention until 1930 when there was great damage on the Gaspé Peninsula. Since then it has spread at an alarming rate, and by 1937 was ranked as the worst enemy of northeastern spruce forests. In Maine it reached its high peak of population in 1939; since then it has declined in numbers due to rodents eating cocoons on the ground, insect predators and parasites, and a wilt disease. It is now present in all of New England, most of New York and New Jersey, feeding on white, red, black, and Norway spruces, occasionally others. Trees that are entirely defoliated usually die.

Eggs are laid singly on the needles, with young larvae beginning to feed at the tip. They are light green at first, later dark green with 5 narrow white stripes. They pupate in small brown cocoons beneath trees. The female sawfly is stout-bodied, black with yellow markings; males are rare; reproduction is usually without fertilization. There are 2 or 3 broods. Ornamentals can be sprayed with DDT or lead arsenate. In forest areas most reliance is placed on natural controls.

Goldenglow Sawfly (*Macrophya simillima*)—Light gray larvae, with a darker gray median stripe and a row of black spots, occasionally defoliate plants. They rest on leaves in a typical coiled position. There is 1 generation; adults appear in June. Spray with lead arsenate or DDT.

Hemlock Sawfly (*Neodiprion tsugae*)—A western species defoliating hemlock from Oregon northward. Larvae are green, striped when young, 1 inch long when grown. Cocoons are attached to needles or laid in debris on ground. There is 1 generation with larvae feeding in July and August. A number of parasites keep this sawfly in check.

Honeysuckle Sawfly (*Zaraea inflata*)—Climbing and bush honeysuckles may be stripped of leaves by dull gray, yellow-striped, black-dotted larvae about an inch long. They spin cocoons in the soil. Adults, emerging in spring, are large, with a black abdomen, yellow ring at the base, a line of silver hairs on each segment. Lead arsenate or DDT will protect the foliage.

Imported Currantworm (*Nematus ribesii*)—Arrived from Europe about 1857, now general over the United States. It is rare to find a garden with currants or gooseberries without this problem. Larvae or pupae winter in cocoons on the ground; black, yellow-marked adults appear in spring to lay white, flattened, shiny eggs on veins and midribs on underside of leaves. Larvae hatch about the time currants are in full leaf (around Memorial Day in New Jersey). They feed in from the leaf margins in groups, eventually devouring entire leaves. The worms are green with black heads and body spots (Plate XXXII). When disturbed they elevate front and rear ends of their bodies. After feeding for 2 or 3 weeks they pupate in the ground. Eggs for the second generation, which is less injurious, are laid in late June and July.

Control. Rotenone dust is satisfactory in home gardens, though lead arsenate can be used if worms are present before fruit is set. Pyrethrum sprays or dusts can be used.

Introduced Pine Sawfly (*Diprion simile*)—Commonly defoliating ornamental pines in the Northeast, first discovered in Connecticut in 1914. White pines and other 5-needled pines are preferred, but others may be eaten. Larvae are yellow green, with a double black stripe the entire length of the back, a broken yellow stripe on each side, and the sides mottled yellow and black; an inch long. Adults are black and yellow, wings spreading ¾ inch (Plate XXXI). Adults emerge from pupae on ground in April and May, lay eggs in slits in the edge of needles. There are 1 or 2 generations annually, with most of the larval feeding in May and June and August and September, on new growth as well as older needles. There may be complete defoliation and death of small pines.

Control. Rake up and burn debris under trees in autumn. Watch for first-brood larvae and spray with DDT or lead arsenate. Nicotine sulfate added at the rate of 1 teaspoon per gallon will kill all young sawflies hit with the spray.

Jack-pine Sawfly (*Neodiprion americanus banksianae*)—On ponderosa and lodgepole pines in Idaho, Montana, and the Great Lakes states.

Larch Sawfly (*Pristiphora erichsonii*)—A serious defoliator of larch, first recorded in Maine and Massachusetts in 1882, in Minnesota in 1909, though apparently present long before that. Outbreaks have been periodic, sometimes defoliating and killing large stands of forest trees or larches in home plantings for 2 or more years in succession. The wasplike, yellow and black adults, wings expanding ⅘ inch, lay eggs from late May to early July, in slits cut in young twigs, causing a twisting. The eggs hatch in about a week, and the larvae feed ravenously in groups of 40 to 50, working the lower branches first. They are dull gray green above, paler underneath, with black head and legs. There is 1 generation, sometimes a partial second. The larvae winter in tough, brown cocoons in duff on the ground.

Control. Birds and mice destroy cocoons; parasitic wasps and flies and a fungus attack larvae. Rake up debris from under ornamental larches in autumn. Spray with lead arsenate in June or July if necessary.

Loblolly Pine Sawfly (*Neodiprion americanum*)—In Atlantic states, defoliating loblolly pine in Virginia, sometimes feeding on shortleaf pine. The larvae, greenish white with a green line down the back, black spots along the side, reddish-brown head, ⅞ inch long, feed from late April to June on old needles. There is 1 generation.

Lodgepole Sawfly (*Neodiprion burkei*)—Distributed through Oregon, Idaho, Montana, Wyoming, defoliating and killing lodgepole pine. Larvae are green or grayish with lighter stripes, brown heads, 1 inch long. Street trees have been successfully protected with lead arsenate.

Monterey Pine Sawfly (*Itycorsia* sp.)—Attacking and killing only Monterey pine in its native habitat in California. Larvae, dark green or brown with black heads, web needles and excrement into a mass.

Mountain-ash Sawfly (*Pristiphora geniculata*)—More or less abundant in New England, New Jersey, and New York on mountain-ash. Winter is passed in cocoons on soil; adults, yellow with black spots, deposit eggs in slits near edges of leaves in late May. Larvae, green with black dots, work from early June to the middle of July. Often feeding shortly before Japanese beetles appear in New Jersey, their chewing is wrongly attributed to the beetles. They work mostly on the upper foliage, leaving nothing but larger veins and midribs. Occasionally there is a partial second generation. One thorough spraying with lead arsenate after the leaves are fully open will control these sawflies. If young larvae are already present when spraying is done add 1 teaspoon of nicotine sulfate per gallon.

Peach Sawfly (*Pamphilius persicus*)—One of the leaf-rolling species. Pale blue-green larvae sometimes eat foliage in June and July. They winter in cocoons in the soil, pupate in spring. Adults, black with yellow markings, emerge in late spring. They will ordinarily be controlled by sprays for other peach insects.

Pear-slug (*Caliroa cerasi*)—Cherry Slug, on pear, cherry, plum, throughout the country, occasionally on hawthorn, Juneberry, mountain-ash, quince. Larvae are dark green to orange, tadpole-shaped, covered with slime, ½ inch long, looking like small slugs. They skeletonize the leaves, eating everything but a network of veins. Black and yellow sawflies, slightly larger than houseflies, emerge from cocoons in the earth just after cherries or pears come into full leaf and lay their eggs in leaves. Larvae feed for 2 or 3 weeks from the upper leaf surface, drop to the ground and pupate, with adults coming out in July or August for a second brood, which may completely defoliate young trees.

Control. Lead arsenate at the rate of 2 pounds to 100 gallons readily controls the slug, or a dust of 1 pound of lead arsenate to 5 of hydrated lime, talc, or gypsum. For the second brood use nicotine sulfate with soap.

Pin-oak Sawfly (*Caliroa lineata*)—Noted seriously damaging pin oaks in New Jersey in 1946, with widespread infestation in the state the next two years, of less importance since then; reported also from North Carolina and parts of New York. The larvae are similar to pear-slugs, up to ½ inch long, yellowish green with black heads, skeletonizing leaves from the upper surface. Infestation starts at top of trees with the foliage in upper third of trees turning golden brown by late summer; most disfiguring to street trees and those in public parks. There are 2 or more broods. Spraying with lead arsenate or DDT is effective.

Plum Web-spinning Sawfly (*Neurotoma inconspicua*)—Serious in the Dakotas, present also in northeastern states, on plums and sand cherries. Webs, like those of the fall webworm, enclose ends of branches soon after plums come into full leaf. Smooth, grayish-yellow larvae, up to ¾ inch long, feed inside webs, sometimes defoliating branches. Black adults, with red legs, insert eggs in leaf midribs in early spring. Cut off webbed ends of branches; spray early with lead arsenate. There are several predators attacking larvae.

Poplar Leaf-folding Sawfly (*Nematus bozemani*)—Occurs in the prairies of Canada and south into the United States. Adults lay eggs May to July, injuring leaves so they fold over; injured portions turn black, making foliage unsightly. Larvae eat holes through leaves. When grown they drop to the ground with leaves and pupate inside the folds.

Poplar Sawfly (*Trichiocampus viminalis*)—A European species long present in northeastern and northern states, often destructive to ornamental Carolina or Lombardy poplars. The larvae are bright yellow with 2 rows of black spots on the back, 2 rows of smaller black spots near the spiracles, tufts of short white hairs over the body, black heads, ¾ inch long. They arrange themselves side by side on a leaf and eat ravenously; trees may be entirely defoliated. When grown, in 35 to 40 days, they make cocoons in bark crevices or under clods of earth. There may be 2 generations. Spray with lead arsenate when larvae are very young.

Raspberry Sawfly (*Monophadnoides geniculatus*)—Ranging through northern states but more common on the Pacific coast, on raspberry, loganberry, dewberry, and blackberry. Adults are black with yellow and reddish markings; larvae are pale green with white spiny tubercles. They feed on underside and on edges of leaves, sometimes stripping the plants. Spray with lead arsenate just before blossoming; use rotenone dust or spray after fruit is set.

Red-headed Pine Sawfly (*Neodiprion lecontei*)—Leconte's Sawfly, injurious to ornamental pines from Maine to Florida and west to Minnesota and Louisiana, on Virginia, jack, red, eastern white, Scotch, loblolly, lodgepole, mugho, longleaf, pitch, ponderosa, and Austrian pines, also American larch and deodar. This is the most widespread and destructive of our native pine sawflies. The larvae live in groups and devour the needles, often defoliating young pines, which either die or are spoiled for ornamental purposes. Young larvae are whitish with brown heads, later yellow with 6 rows of conspicuous black spots and a red head, an inch long. In many sections there are 2 overlapping broods, with larvae feeding from May until late fall. Prepupal larvae winter in tough, papery, capsule-shaped cocoons in duff or topsoil under trees. Eggs are laid in slits in needles. The larvae prefer old needles but will eat new growth toward the end of the season, including tender bark of young twigs.

Control. Spray thoroughly with lead arsenate or DDT when larvae are young.

72. Older larvae of red-headed pine sawfly, which have eaten off needles down to the base of the fascicles.

Rose-slug (*Endelomyia aethiops*)—Rose Sawfly, European Rose Slug, common on rose east of the Rocky Mountains. This is a yellow-green rather velvety slug, up to ½ inch long, appearing dark green from the food ingested. It eats the soft part of leaves, which, with nothing left but a network of veins and one epidermis, turn brown and crisp, making rose growers think they have "rust." When the leaves are only partly eaten they appear to have windows in them. When full grown the larva enters the soil, constructs a capsule-shaped cell, and stays quiet in this cavity until early spring when the adult lays eggs in pockets in leaf tissue (Plate XXXII). There is only 1 generation of this species; feeding in late summer is due to the bristly rose-slug.

Control measures are the same and it is important to have lead arsenate or other stomach poison on the foliage almost as soon as roses come into full leaf to prevent unsightly disfiguration.

Striped Alder Sawfly (*Hemichroa crocea*)—May defoliate various species of alder in northeastern and Great Lakes states, occasionally feeding on birch. Young larvae are pure white, later yellow with brown stripes, ⅘ inch long. They eat everything except midrib and larger veins. There are 2 generations.

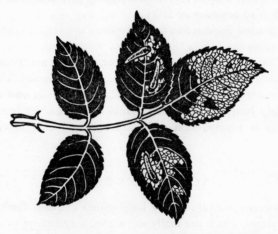

73. Larvae of the rose-slug skeletonizing leaf.

Violet Sawfly (*Ametastegia pallipes*)—Often a serious pest of violets and pansies in eastern states, outdoors and in greenhouses. Larvae are blue black or olive green, smooth, about ½ inch long, marked with white spots on back and sides. They work at night, first skeletonizing lower surface of leaves, later eating holes or feeding from leaf margins to entirely defoliate plants, most often in May and June. Pupation is in stalks of pithy plants; adults, black and yellow, emerge in 2 weeks to blister leaves with eggs inserted in lower side; foliage may wither. There may be several broods. Spray or dust with lead arsenate or rotenone.

White-pine Sawfly (*Neodiprion pinetum*)—Abbott's Pine Sawfly, on white pine, occasionally on pitch, shortleaf, red, and mugho pines in the Northeast. Larvae are similar to the red-headed sawfly except for their black heads; they are yellowish with only 4 rows of black dots.

Willow Sawfly (*Nematus ventralis*)—Yellow-spotted Willow Slug, widely distributed in eastern states on willow and poplar, often defoliating willows in ornamental plantings, very injurious to basket willows in the South. The small, dark brown to black sawfly, marked with yellow spots, lays eggs in leaves, producing blisters. The slugs are black with a greenish tinge and heart-shaped yellow spots along each side of the body. They feed close together in characteristic curved positions for about 3 weeks, then pupate on the ground for a second generation. There may be several overlapping generations in the South. Spray with lead arsenate or DDT.

Yellow-headed Spruce Sawfly (*Pikonema alaskensis*)—In the most northern states and New England, on white, red, black, Norway, Colorado blue, and Engelmann spruces. Larvae are yellow green, striped with gray green, and have chestnut-brown heads. They prefer new foliage until they are half grown. Eggs are laid in new needles in May or early June, with hatching in 6 to 8 days. Larvae feed 30 to 40 days. There is 1 generation with pupation in spring in cocoons in the soil.

SCALE INSECTS

Scale insects constitute a very large group of plant feeders. Along with mealybugs, which are really soft scales, they belong to the family Coccidae, order Homoptera. Armored scales are covered with a protective shell or scale of wax, usually hard and separate from the body, though made of wax secreted by the insect together with cast skins (exuviae) of the early stages. Females are wingless and are mostly responsible for plant injury. After a very brief 6-legged crawling stage they insert their threadlike mouth parts through the epidermis of a leaf, or bark of a stem, and start sucking sap. They molt twice, lose legs and antennae, and remain in the same spot the rest of their lives, laying eggs, in some cases giving birth to living young, under the shell. The males have an elongated body after the second molt and after a fourth molt have 1 pair of wings, legs, and antennae but no mouth parts. They look like small gnats but have a stylelike process at the end of the abdomen.

Soft scales or tortoise scales are not covered by a separate shell, but their chitinous bodies may be as hard as the shell on an armored scale. They also keep their small and poorly developed legs and can move, though so sluggishly they appear stationary.

Heavy scale infestations kill branches or entire trees or shrubs. Standard control for armored scales has been a dormant spray, oil or lime-sulfur, before growth starts in spring, but some scales can now be controlled in the crawling stage with malathion or, in a few cases, with DDT. White oil or summer oil sprays have been advised for unarmored scales prevalent in greenhouses and warm climates, but in recent years parathion has been rather extensively used by commercial growers with malathion recommended to home gardeners.

Araucaria Scale (*Eriococcus araucariae*)—Imported into California on Norfolk Island pine. Pure white, feltlike, oval sacs enclose bodies and eggs of females.

Artemisia Scale (*Eriococcus artemisiae*)—With conspicuous globular white sacs, crowded on twigs of artemisia.

Azalea Bark Scale (*Eriococcus azaleae*)—Azalea Mealybug, a native of Japan, common on outdoor azaleas in the South, occasional in the North. White cottony sacs, enclosing dark red females and their eggs, are present in forks of branches and over twigs, sometimes on main stems down to the ground. The males have a similar white covering but are smaller and more elongate. Foliage and twigs are often covered with black sooty mold growing in secreted honeydew. Azaleas appear yellow and unthrifty, sometimes die. Rhododendrons may be infested.

The winter is spent in the nymph stage, on the plant. There are 2 generations in the South, 1 in the North. In Alabama females mature very early in spring and start to lay eggs in March, with reddish-brown crawlers hatching in 3 weeks and maturing in about 100 days. The second brood appears in September. In Connecticut eggs start hatching about June 20 with the young migrants not maturing until the next spring.

Control. Nicotine sulfate and the phosphate sprays are effective, with relatively safe malathion nearly as good as the more dangerous parathion and TEPP. In Connecticut 1 treatment July 15 with malathion (2 to 3 teaspoons of 57 per cent emulsion per gallon, or 2 to 4 teaspoons of 50 per cent wettable powder, or 5 per cent dust) has been satisfactory. In the Deep South sprays are applied in May and late September. An oil spray has been standard (3 level tablespoons of Florida Volck or 4½ tablespoons of Nursery Volck plus 2 tablespoons of powdered derris and 1 teaspoon of nicotine sulfate per gallon), but malathion can be substituted.

Barberry Scale (*Lecaniodiaspis* sp.)—Convex, reddish-brown, soft scale, sometimes numerous. Spray with a 1 to 15 dilution of miscible oil when plants are dormant or with malathion for the crawling stage.

Barnacle Scale (*Ceroplastes cirripediformis*)—Found in California, Florida, Louisiana, and Mississippi. The female is reddish brown covered with white wax shading to gray or light brown. It attacks Australian pine, citrus, bignonia, eupatorium, guava, jasmine, Jerusalem thorn, lignum-vitae, myrtle, pear, poinsettia, quince, persimmon, tea.

Beech Scale (*Cryptococcus fagi*)—A European species first present in Nova Scotia, found in Massachusetts in 1929, and now present in most of New England and New York, infesting American and European beech. In Massachusetts eggs are laid from mid-June to late July, with hatching starting about August 1 and continuing into September. Young crawlers are abundant during this period. When the pale yellow nymph settles into a bark crevice it secretes cottony material which spreads out to cover several individuals. It becomes adult the next spring, nearly circular, $\frac{1}{50}$ to $\frac{1}{30}$ inch across, covered with white wax.

The feeding of the scale kills inner tissue of outer bark, but the most important injury comes from a fungus (*Nectria coccinea* var. *faginata*), which enters the tree through scale wounds. Foliage and twigs die, bark cracks, wood is infected. Apparently the fungus cannot enter until the scale has fed for a year, nor can it produce the disease without the scale.

Control. A thorough dormant spray with 5 gallons liquid lime-sulfur to 95 gallons of water or 20 pounds dry lime-sulfur to 100 gallons is very effective. Miscible oils would kill the scale but are often injurious to beech. Late summer spraying for crawlers with malathion or nicotine sulfate can supplement the dormant spray.

Black Araucaria Scale (*Chrysomphalus rossi*)—Almost black, much like the Florida red scale. This is a tropical species with a limited distribution on ornamentals in southern California—araucaria, rarely on redwood, sometimes on abutilon, artemisia, banksia, euonymus, hyssop, oleander, olive, orchids, palm, cycad.

Black Pine Leaf Scale (*Aspidiotus californicus*)—Distributed over most of North America, often associated with pine needle scale on pine, reported also on Douglas-fir, hemlock, and other crucifers. It may kill young pines. Mature scales are nearly circular, $\frac{1}{16}$ inch across, yellow brown to black. There are 1 to 3 generations with hibernation as half-grown scales. They can be controlled with lime-sulfur. Seedlings sometimes have to be dipped in 1 to 12 lime-sulfur before shipping.

Black Scale (*Saissetia oleae*)—An unarmored species, possibly the most important economically, present in all citrus-growing regions but not so important in the Gulf states as in California, where it causes an annual $2,000,000 loss. It is also a greenhouse pest in the North. Besides orange, grapefruit, and lemon, important food plants include almond, apple, apricot, avocado, beech, fig, grape, oleander, olive, plum, rose, and English walnut. Injury comes not only from extraction of sap but from the black sooty mold fungus which, growing in honeydew, covers all surfaces of foliage, cutting off light and reducing photosynthesis, coating fruit so it has to be washed.

Overwintering females become adult in spring. They are almost hemispherical, ⅕ inch across, dark brown to black, with a longitudinal ridge and 2 transverse elevations on the back forming the letter H; they deposit an average of 2000 eggs. These are white at first, later orange; they hatch in about 20 days. The young remain under the parent briefly but start crawling and feeding within 3 days, settling on leaves or new growth. They migrate to twigs and branches when partly grown and take 8 to 10 months to mature. There is usually 1 generation, sometimes 2 or a partial second. Males, thin, narrow, flat, semi-transparent, are rare; most reproduction is parthenogenetic.

In addition to the favored food plants listed, there are many ornamental hosts—aralia, artemisia, mountain-ash, asparagus fern, aster, banana, buckthorn, California mountain-holly, California nutmeg, camellia, deodar, chrysanthemum, citron, croton, eucalyptus, fuchsia, guava, holly, jasmine, Irish juniper, laurel, locust, honey locust, magnolia, maple, myrtle, orchids, palms, pear, phlox, pittosporum, pomegranate, poplar, privet, prune, Japanese quince, rose-of-Sharon, rhubarb, rubber plant, sumac, sycamore, tangerine, sago palm, strawberry tree, watermelon, and others.

Control. Originally the black scale was controlled on citrus trees by fumigation with hydrogen cyanide under fumigation tents, but in many areas of California the scale has developed a resistance to cyanide. Oil sprays (1½ to 2 per cent medium oil, or 1 per cent with rotenone) and parathion sprays and dusts are effective. Volck or other white oil can be used on ornamentals, or malathion. This scale is not so important as formerly; it is held in check with a wasp and other important parasites and beetle predators.

Black Thread Scale (*Ischnaspis longirostris*)—Sometimes a serious enemy of palms. The female is very narrow, threadlike, ¹⁄₁₆ inch long, dark brown to black. Its habit of attaching itself parallel to the ribs keeps it from being observed before palms are abundantly infested.

Boisduval's Scale (*Diaspis boisduvalli*)—On palms and orchids. The female is snow white to light yellow, $\frac{1}{25}$ to $\frac{2}{25}$ inch across. The male is white, narrow, with 3 ridges on the back. Spray with DDT, 1 tablespoon of 50 per cent wettable powder to a gallon of water or with DDT emulsion.

Cactus Scale (*Diaspis echinocacti*)—A common species in the Southwest and on house cacti. This is an armored scale; female gray, circular; male white, slender. The surface of many cacti may be completely encrusted. A white summer oil with nicotine sulfate is effective but must be used with caution on cacti. Some scales can be rubbed off with a stiff brush or a piece of wood. Use malathion for crawlers.

Calico Scale (*Lecanium cerasorum*)—Found in California, on cherry, elm, maple, pear, prune, Boston ivy, Virginia creeper, English walnut. The female, hemispherical, shiny, marked with yellowish areas on a brown background, winters on lower surfaces of larger branches, and the young move to smaller twigs and branches in spring. Control measures are seldom necessary.

California Red Scale (*Aonidiella aurantii*)—The most important citrus pest in California, also serious in Arizona and Texas, less damaging in more humid Gulf states. It probably came from Australia to southern California prior to 1875 on citrus nursery stock. Found in greenhouses in many parts of the country it occurs outdoors only in the South. Ordinarily a pest of citrus—citron, grapefruit, lemon, orange, tangerine—it also infests acacia, aloe, apple, aspidistra, avocado, breadfruit, banana, boxelder, boxwood, chinaberry, coconut, eucalyptus, euonymus, fig, fuchsia, grape, hibiscus, holly, Japanese yew, jasmine, mango, mulberry, oak, olive, palms, passion-flower, pistachio, privet, quince, rose, sago palm, sweet bay, tea, English walnut, willow, yucca. The scales attack leaves, twigs, or fruit, injecting a toxic substance into the tree. Leaves and fruit are spotted with yellow; sometimes the entire foliage turns yellow.

The mature female is pinhead size, $\frac{1}{12}$ inch across, armored, reddish brown, circular. Young scales are born alive; they stay under the parent shell for a few hours, crawl about for a day or two, then settle down and insert their sucking beaks at the places where they will spend the rest of their lives. Cottony secretions are molded into a caplike covering with a small nipple in the center. After the first molt, in 10 to 15 days, the cast skins (exuviae) are incorporated into the center of the cap, which is enlarged at the side. After a second molt and enlargement there is a gray margin extending beyond the body and the gray adult is fertilized by the small, yellow-winged male. She continues to give birth to 2 or 3 scales a day for 2 or 3 months. There may be 4 generations a year.

Control. Standard treatment has been hydrogen cyanide fumigation, preferably in winter, often preceded or followed by spraying with a medium oil, 2 per cent emulsion. Races of California red scale have developed, however, that are resistant to cyanide. DDT emulsion kills young crawlers and other early stages. Parathion is used successfully by many orchardists. Deciduous ornamentals can have a dormant oil spray from December to February (16 to 20 tablespoons to a gallon) and evergreens a summer oil emulsion (3 to 6 tablespoons per gallon) or malathion or nicotine sulfate can be used for crawlers. There are a number of parasites, some of which are produced in mass quantities for liberation. In some counties in California, separated from others by natural mountain barriers, local quarantines have kept infestations at a minimum.

Camellia Parlatoria (*Parlatoria camelliae*)—The most common scale on camellia on the Pacific coast, especially on plants under lath. It is very small, flat, oval, brownish; on both leaf surfaces. The female body under the shell is light purple. Parathion has been used effectively by commercial growers.

Camellia Scale (*Lepidosaphes camelliae*)—Not so important as the tea scale on camellia, present most often on cuttings and on young plants in greenhouses. The female shell is light to dark brown, oyster-shaped, $\frac{1}{10}$ inch long, covering a white to purplish body. The male shell is smaller and narrower. The female starts laying eggs 40 to 50 days after birth, with the life cycle completed in 60 to 70 days. Few crawlers are present during the winter months outdoors because the females do not reproduce then. Foliage is devitalized, drops prematurely, but is not discolored. The camellia scale can be controlled with oil or other sprays applied for tea scale. A parasitic wasp and lady beetles are helpful.

Camphor Scale (*Pseudaonidia duplex*)—First noted in New Orleans in 1920, now present in Alabama, Mississippi, Louisiana. This scale is circular, moderately convex, dark blackish brown with orange exuviae, about $\frac{1}{10}$ inch across. It feeds on nearly 200 plants, with preference for the camphor tree, Japanese persimmon, sweet olive, camellia,

Satsuma orange and other citrus, Japanese honeysuckle, fig, Confederate jasmine, glossy privet, rose, and is sometimes injurious to avocado, elm, grape, hackberry, and pecan. It is so injurious to camphor trees that just a few scales on a twig can cause defoliation and a tree can be killed within 6 months of attack. Ants apparently help to disseminate this scale. Spraying with a 2 per cent oil emulsion is effective.

Chaff Scale (*Parlatoria pergandii*)—A greenhouse pest, infesting some outdoor plants in California, more in Florida. Food plants include asparagus fern, araucaria, camellia, citrus, croton, camphor, cinnamon, cycad, euonymus, guava, jasmine, mango, magnolia, maple, orchids, palms, sweet olive, wandering Jew. The female is circular to elongate, smooth, semi-transparent, brownish gray with marginal yellow exuviae; found on bark or leaves.

Citricola Scale (*Coccus pseudomagnoliarum*)—A serious citrus pest in parts of California; found also on hackberry, pomegranate, English walnut, and elm. It resembles soft scale but is grayer, lays eggs instead of producing living young, has only 1 generation. It feeds on underside of leaves and on smaller twigs during the summer, migrating to branches in late winter or early spring. This scale has developed resistance to cyanide fumigation in southern California but may be controlled with light-medium oil sprays, DDT emulsion in late winter, or parathion.

Coconut Scale (*Aspidiotus destructor*)—On palms in Florida. It is very small, circular, thin, faint yellow but transparent, and may be abundant on foliage.

Cottony Bamboo Scale (*Antonia crawi*)—On bamboo in greenhouses, outdoors in warm climates. Oval, dark reddish-purple bodies are enclosed in thick white cottony sacs, often crowded at leaf axils. They may be quite injurious. Spray with malathion or other phosphate or with a summer oil such as Volck, at a 1 to 50 dilution, hosing off with water the next day.

Cottony-cushion Scale (*Icerya purchasi*)—An Australian scale introduced into California on acacia about 1868, soon threatening the entire citrus industry and now present throughout the South, and in greenhouses, on a long list of hosts. Food plants include acacia, almond, amaranthus, apple, apricot, boxwood, buckeye, California sage, castorbean, casuarina, cedar of Lebanon, chrysanthemum, citron, cypress, fig, geranium, grape, grapefruit, sweet gum, Guadalupe palm, hackberry, ironwood, Boston ivy, laurel, lemon, lime, locust, magnolia, maple, mistletoe, holly oak, white oak, orange, peach, pear, pecan, pepper, pine, pittosporum (very commonly infested), poinsettia, pomegranate, potato, quince, rose, sunflower, verbena, veronica, English walnut, willow. Trees may be completely covered with white cushions and sooty mold growing in the honeydew.

The insect itself is reddish brown, but the female attaches a large, compact, white, fluted mass, holding from 600 to 800 bright red eggs. This white egg mass sticks out at an angle from the twig and is very conspicuous. Hatching of eggs in the fluted ovisac occurs in a few days in summer, up to 2 months in winter. Young larvae are red with black legs, dark antennae, long hairs at the end of the body. Even after molting the scale keeps its legs and can move about until the egg sac is formed. The males are very tiny, with long white filaments. There are 3 or more generations.

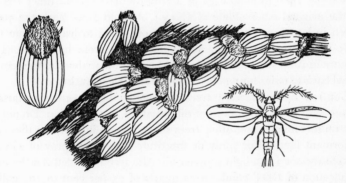

74. Cottony-cushion scale—females with fluted egg masses, and winged male.

Control. The spectacular control of cottony-cushion scale by Vedalia, the Australian lady beetle, marked the first successful subjugation of a pest by the introduction of a natural enemy. Vedalia still keeps this scale from obtaining economic importance on citrus, except where the biological balance has been disturbed by chemicals such as DDT which have more effect on the predators than on the scale. Where Vedalia is not present or is unable to act, spraying with parathion has been very effective and malathion can probably be substituted for ornamentals in home gardens. Oil sprays have been long recommended, but the results have not been too satisfactory.

Cottony Maple Scale (*Pulvinaria innumerabilis*)—A native species distributed through the country, most destructive in the North. With some preference to silver maple, it attacks almost all maples, boxelder, linden, black locust, red mulberry, white ash, and sometimes alder, apple, beech, blackberry, boxwood, buckeye, currant, dogwood, elm, euonymus, grape, gooseberry, hackberry, hawthorn, lilac, honey locust, mountain-ash, oak, osage-orange, peach, pear, plum, poplar, quince, rose, spirea, sumac, sycamore, viburnum, Virginia creeper, willow. This is a conspicuous scale covering trees with cottony masses on underside of twigs and branches. These may die and the foliage of the whole tree may turn a sickly yellow. The attack predisposes the tree to borer injury.

The scale winters as a small, brown, flattened female, ⅛ inch long, attached to bark. When sap flows in spring it starts growing rapidly, depositing 1500 to 3000 eggs in a cottony mass several times the size of the original scale (Plate XXXIV). Around New York the young hatch in late June or July, crawling from twigs to leaves where they suck sap along the midrib and veins and secrete honeydew. They mature in August and September and mate; the males die, the females crawl back to twigs for winter. There is only 1 generation.

Control. Spray infested trees thoroughly before growth starts in spring with a miscible dormant oil, usually 1 to 15 dilution. Do not use this on soft maples and other trees subject to oil injury. For these, use a dormant lime-sulfur spray or substitute a summer spray of nicotine sulfate and soap or a light summer oil. Also recommended is a thorough application of DDT emulsion (2 quarts of 25 per cent to 100 gallons of water) applied when young are hatching. Spraying a tree with water from the hose will wash off some honeydew and dislodge some scales. There are many natural parasites and predators which check outbreaks, but they cannot be relied on for controlling the scale every season.

Cottony Peach Scale (*Pulvinaria amygdali*)—Fruit Tree Pulvinaria. The scale is flat, oval, yellow or reddish, usually covered with white cottony wax, and with a compact white cottony egg sac. It feeds on leaves, bark, fruit of peach, prune, plum, apple in California and New Mexico.

Cottony Taxus Scale (*Pulvinaria floccifera*)—A tropical insect, a greenhouse pest of camellia, abutilon, and acalypha, reported injuring yew in Rhode Island in 1950 and in Connecticut in 1953. It winters as a small, light brown, flattened hemispherical scale, ⅛ inch long, and in spring produces a long, narrow, fluted cottony egg mass. Eggs hatch in June and infest underside of needles and sometimes twigs of previous year's growth. One or 2 egg masses may cover the underside of a needle and the scale may be abundant enough to coat branches, with serious injury to plants. In experiments in Connecticut, malathion emulsion, 3 teaspoons to a gallon, gave complete control applied in August. In Rhode Island DDT applied in late April was effective.

Cyanophyllum Scale (*Aspidiotus cyanophylli*)—On orchids, rubber plants, and other greenhouse plants. The scale is translucent, covered with a waxy secretion, becoming white and opaque after death.

Cypress Bark Scale (*Ehrhornia cupressi*)—Cottony Cypress Scale. Common on Monterey cypress, also attacking Guadalupe and Arizona cypress and incense cedar in California. Limbs turn yellow, then red or brown; trees look scraggy; some die, especially those in hedges. The scale has a pink body covered with loose white wax and is usually found in pits or cracks in bark. Spray with a miscible oil emulsion in August and again in late September, or try malathion.

Dictyospermum Scale (*Chrysomphalus dictyospermi*)—Spanish Red Scale, widely distributed in subtropics, reported as serious in Connecticut greenhouses on palms in 1905, found outdoors in California, Louisiana, Mississippi, and Florida. It is a rather important pest of avocado, a potential threat to citrus though not yet very injurious, fairly common on acacia, palms, latania, rose, reported on orchids. In Florida it is rather generally distributed on about 60 hosts besides citrus. The female is circular, $\frac{1}{16}$ to $\frac{1}{12}$ inch with dark brown armor. It deposits eggs; there are 3 or 4 generations in California, 5 or 6 in Florida. It can be controlled with malathion. Palms in greenhouses should be syringed forcefully and repeatedly with water. Ants, which carry around the young scales, should be eliminated.

Dogwood Scale (*Chionaspis corni*)—A northern species present from Massachusetts to Indiana and Kansas, looking much like scurfy scale on apple. It is occasionally so abundant on pagoda, silky, and red osier dogwood it turns the stems white. A dormant lime-sulfur spray is effective, but a miscible oil may be substituted, just before growth starts in spring. The scales are heavily parasitized.

Elm Scurfy Scale (*Chionaspis americana*)—Distributed from New England south to Florida and west to Oklahoma and Texas, more serious in the Middle West than in the East. Found most often on American elm, it may attack Camperdown and other elms, killing branches or young trees outright. It also attacks hackberry. The female, pear-shaped, convex, rather thick, $\frac{1}{12}$ to $\frac{1}{8}$ inch long, naturally white but grayish from bark fragments, is found only on bark. The male, white, very small and narrow, is found on both bark and leaves. Purple eggs winter under the female shell. There are 2 generations in the North, more in the South. It can be controlled with a dormant spray, 3 per cent lubricating oil emulsion or miscible oil at a 1 to 15 dilution, before growth starts in spring.

Euonymus Scale (*Unaspis euonymi*)—Doubtless known to everyone growing euonymus, though my personal observations lead me to believe it is not as prevalent in the Deep South and in California as in cooler climates. It is also common on bittersweet and pachysandra, is sometimes present on ivy and other ground covers growing near euonymus. Female scales look like dark brown oyster shells, $\frac{1}{16}$ inch long; males are almost needle-thin, pure white (Plate XXXIII). Stems and leaves are often entirely covered with white males, with a scattering of brown females. Leaves turn yellow, drop; vines die back. Climbing euonymus covering walls is more often infested than some of the upright forms; winged euonymus is usually free from scale. Eggs are laid under female shells and hatch in late spring, with pale yellow crawlers visible in late May or June. A second brood appears in late August and September.

Control. Use a dormant oil spray, same strength as for lilacs and other deciduous shrubs, before growth starts in spring. This may cause some defoliation of old foliage but new leaves will soon replace it. Elgetol may be used in place of a dormant oil but may stain walls, etc., temporarily yellow. DDT emulsion and malathion are both effective for crawlers. Use 2 teaspoons malathion (57 per cent emulsion) to a gallon of water and apply in June or early July and in early September. Watch for the crawlers to time the spray for your own locality. Apply with force to get as much coverage as possible on vines against a house or wall. Before spraying, cut off and burn vines so completely encrusted with scales they have little chance of recovery.

European Elm Scale (*Gossyparia spuria*)—A soft scale, first found at Rye, New York, in 1884, now spread across the country wherever American, European, slippery, cork, and other elms are found. It is particularly destructive to ornamental and street elms. Infested trees have yellowed foliage, usually shed prematurely; small branches die, then the larger branches, sometimes the whole tree. Copious honeydew drops to sidewalks and cars and keeps branches sooty black with mold. Nymphs winter in bark crevices and in very early spring the males form conspicuous white cocoons in which they transform to minute, reddish, winged or wingless "gnats." Females become adult early in May; they are oval, reddish brown, surrounded by a white fringe, ⅙ to ⅜ inch long. They deposit eggs under their bodies from late May through June, and these hatch within an hour into yellow crawlers which migrate to the leaves, feeding there until fall. Most migrate back to trunk or branches before leaves drop in autumn.

Control. Apply a dormant oil spray in spring just before buds break. A foliage spray with a summer oil or DDT a few weeks after eggs hatch is useful. Malathion is helpful. There are few natural enemies, so spraying must be relied on for control. A strong stream of water from the hose will wash off some scales.

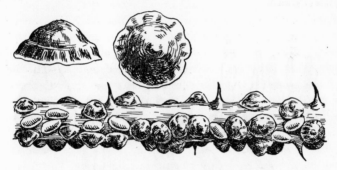

75. European fruit lecanium on blackberry cane.

European Fruit Lecanium (*Lecanium corni*)—Brown Apricot Scale, Brown Elm Scale, distributed through the country, quite injurious on the Pacific coast. Besides fruit trees—apricot, plum, prune, peach, cherry, apple, persimmon, quince—it may also infest arborvitae, alder, ash, basswood, beech, blackberry, black walnut, boxwood, boxelder, butternut, Catalina cherry, chinaberry, currant, elm, gooseberry, greasewood, grape, hawthorn, hackberry, hazelnut, hickory, locust, magnolia, maple, mulberry, oak, osage-orange, pecan, poplar, redbud, rose, sassafras, willow. The scale has various forms and may represent more than 1 species. Typically the female is large, ⅛ to 1/16 inch, hemispherical to oval and very convex, smooth shiny brown or reddish brown but sometimes covered with white powder. It winters on twigs and branches, laying eggs under the shell in spring, with hatching from May to July. The males are smaller, flatter, elongated, and almost transparent, with ridges down the back. The nymphs migrate to the leaves and are found mostly among the veins, but they return to the bark of twigs and branches for winter. There is 1 generation.

Control. Spray trees when dormant (December to February in California, perhaps March elsewhere) with a miscible oil emulsion or lime-sulfur, preferably the oil. The fruit lecanium is heavily parasitized, infected individuals turning black.

European Fruit Scale (*Aspidiotus ostreaeformis*)—Pear Tree Oyster Scale, on deciduous fruit and ornamental trees, willow and poplar.

European Peach Scale (*Lecanium persicae*)—Much like the fruit lecanium but longer, less convex, slightly larger. It is found on, but does not seriously injure, English ivy, ginkgo, gooseberry, grape, holly, Japanese quince, mulberry, nectarine, oleander, peach, pear, plum, rose, silver thorn.

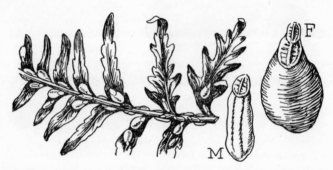

76. Fern scale, with detail of pear-shaped female, thin male.

Fern Scale (*Pinnaspis aspidistrae*)—Besides aspidistra and ferns in homes and greenhouses, this scale also infests acacia, banana, fig, mango, orange, orchids, palms, pepper-tree, and other plants in mild climates. This is an armored scale. The males are thin, white, conspicuous, the females ocher brown, oyster-shaped. Parathion has given good control in greenhouses; malathion may be satisfactory. An old recommendation for house plants was to spray with Lemon Oil, or to dip small potted ferns in a solution of nicotine sulfate and soap.

Fig Scale (*Lepidosaphes ficus*)—On figs in California, infesting fruit, leaves, wood up to 2 years old. It is similar to the purple scale but smaller, and may be controlled with a 4 per cent dormant oil spray, December to March, or a foliage spray of parathion or 2 per cent summer oil in May.

Fletcher Scale (*Lecanium fletcheri*)—Arborvitae Soft Scale, on arborvitae for many years, recently damaging yew, reported on pachysandra. Branches and underside of foliage may be covered with scales, with loss of color, vigor, premature defoliation, sooty mold growing in honeydew. Young scales are amber, mature females, dark brown, hemispherical. Immature scales winter on stems and underside of foliage; eggs are deposited under the female in late spring, with hatching in June. There is little summer development and most of the feeding and injury occur the next spring. Malathion, 2 to 3 teaspoons of 57 per cent emulsion per gallon, is effective if applied in August, or April to mid-May. Malathion dust, 5 per cent, can be substituted.

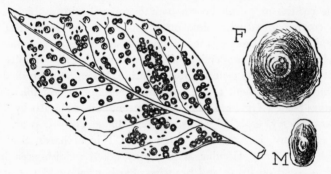

77. Florida red scale on underside of leaf with detail of male and female.

Florida Red Scale (*Chrysomphalus aonidum*)—An important citrus pest in Florida and other Gulf states, occurring on some nursery plants in California but not on citrus to any extent. It is fairly common on ivy and other house and greenhouse plants, and outdoors in mild climates infests aralia, araucaria, banana, begonia, camellia, camphor, coconut, eucalyptus, eugenia, fig, grape, guava, iris, English ivy, jasmine, mango, oleander, orchids, rubber plant, rose, sago palm, zamia. This is an armored scale, small, $\frac{1}{12}$ inch, circular, reddish brown to nearly black with a lighter central portion, often very numerous on leaves, either surface, and on fruit, but not infesting twigs. It deposits eggs which hatch in a few hours, and there can be 5 or more generations in greenhouses. This species does not produce noticeable honeydew.

Control. Parathion sprays are used successfully by Florida citrus growers and parathion or TEPP aerosols in greenhouses. Home gardens can have malathion or summer oils for the crawling stages. Keeping ivy and other house plants frequently bathed with water will reduce scale infestation.

Florida Wax Scale (*Ceroplastes floridensis*)—Found in Florida, Louisiana, Mississippi on fruits and ornamentals, including apple, avocado, andromeda, custard apple, anthurium, bay, blueberry, boxwood, cape jasmine, cherry-laurel, cinnamon, citrus, croton, cryptostegia, euonymus, fern, ficus, guava, lignum-vitae, ilex, India hawthorn, ixora, loquat, mango, magnolia, maple, mulberry, crapemyrtle, oleander, peach, pomegranate, pear, pine, pittosporum, plum, poinsettia, prickly ash, sapodilla, sea-grape, tea.

The reddish or purple-brown body is covered with a thick, white, waxy coating tinted with pink, often with some dark spots. Red eggs are laid under the body of the scale, which shrinks as they accumulate. Crawlers collect on underside of leaves along midribs; adults cling to twigs. There are 3 generations in Florida. It can be controlled with a summer oil emulsion, 1 to 2 per cent according to host tolerance.

Forbes Scale (*Aspidiotus forbesi*)—Present east of the Rocky Mountains on cherry, especially sour cherries, apple, apricot, pear, plum, quince, currant, increasing with use of DDT in orchards. Scales are grayish, thin, flaky, circular, with a tiny raised reddish area in the center, massed on trunk and branches. Partly grown scales winter on bark; young appear in May, born alive and produced from eggs. There are 1 to 3 generations. Dormant oil sprays may not give complete control. Spraying with parathion or malathion in the cover sprays has been effective, and in North Carolina, where Forbes scale is the chief apple scale at elevations below 3000 feet, a delayed dormant spray of 2 per cent superior oil has been satisfactory.

Frosted Scale (*Lecanium pruinosum*)—In California and Arizona, increasing as a walnut problem with DDT used for codling moth, and infesting about the same list of fruit and ornamental hosts as the European fruit lecanium. It is a large, convex brown scale, covered with a frosty wax. It has natural parasites, but if these are killed it can be controlled with a dormant parathion spray.

Gloomy Scale (*Chrysomphalus tenebricosus*)—Present from Washington, D.C., to Georgia and Texas, most injurious to soft maples, also on sugar maple, hackberry, elm, and boxelder. It is dark gray, circular, very convex, melting into the bark in color. It can be controlled with a dormant lime-sulfur spray.

Glover Scale (*Lepidosaphes gloverii*)—Found in southern states, often associated with purple scale and with a similar life history; more important in Florida than California. Food plants include cabbage palmetto, cherry, coconut, croton, laurel, mango, magnolia, palms. The female is long and narrow, straight or curved, yellow brown to dark brown.

Golden Oak Scale (*Asterolecanium variolosum*)—Pit-making Oak Scale, found wherever oaks are grown, often injurious to young ornamental trees and sometimes killing mature trees if they suffer from drought. The scale is circular, slightly convex, polished greenish gold, with a marginal fringe and minute glassy spines. It makes small pits in the bark and lies in these depressions, its feeding producing galls or swellings. It winters as a mature female and because of its waxy case is rather resistant to oil sprays. A summer oil spray with toxaphene has given good control in California.

Grape Scale (*Aspidiotus uvae*)—Generally distributed on grape, sometimes on peach, hickory, sycamore, resembling San Jose scale in size and habits. Shells are circular to elliptical, gray or yellow brown with a pale yellow spot and white nipple at one side of center; they are usually present on old canes under loose bark. There is 1 generation. Severe pruning may be sufficient; if not, apply a dormant spray of oil or lime-sulfur.

Greedy Scale (*Aspidiotus camelliae*)—A common armored scale, attacking ornamentals throughout the country, mostly in greenhouses, outdoors in warm climates. The female is quite convex, elliptical to round, small, gray, with yellow or dark brown exuviae near one edge. The scales are omnivorous feeders on bark, sometimes leaves and fruit, of acacia, almond, apple, avocado, bay, birch, cactus, camphor, chinaberry, camellia, ceanothus, cherry, cissus, cotoneaster, cottonwood, English holly, English ivy, English laurel, eucalyptus, euonymus, fig, fuchsia, genista, guava, sequoia, grape, heather, mountain-holly, honeysuckle, Japanese quince, California laurel, lavatera, locust, magnolia, maple, manzanita, mistletoe, myrtle, mulberry, olive, orange, Oregon grape, oak, palms, passion-flower, pear, pecan, pepper-tree, pittosporum, pomegranate, pyracantha, quince, redbud, rose, sage, sedum, strawberry tree, silver tree, strelitzia, silk oak, umbrella tree, English walnut, willow. Control with aerosols in greenhouses and by spraying with malathion or summer white oils in gardens.

Green Shield Scale (*Pulvinaria psidii*)—On ornamentals in Florida. A white cottony egg sac projects from a green shield. Food plants include avocado, Australian oak, bay, citrus, clerodendron, croton, cycad, cypress vine, fern, ficus, guava, gardenia, hibiscus, ixora, jasmine, apple, mango, palm, persimmon, rose, sapodilla, sea-grape, tea, wax myrtle, yellow alder.

Ground Pearls (*Margarodes* and *Eumargarodes* spp.)—Small, shining bodies with an iridescent luster, found loosely scattered in soil or on roots of plants. Those in the tropics have been used for adornment by the natives. Some species are becoming turf problems in the United States, being found damaging Bermuda, centipede, and St. Augustine grass in the Southeast. The only successful treatment seems to be ample water and fertilizer applied through the growing season.

78. Hemispherical scale on fern—note detail showing cushion shape and height.

Hemispherical Scale (*Saissetia hemisphaerica*)—A tropical species common in greenhouses and in gardens in mild climates. It is frequently present but not important on citrus and avocado, is quite conspicuous on ferns, palms, and other ornamentals, including aloe, ardisia, asparagus fern, banana, begonia, bignonia, bougainvillea, camellia, chrysanthemum, crapemyrtle, citron, croton, cycad, custard apple, apple, guava, mountain-holly, oleander, orchids, sago palm, sourberry, sumac, pepper-tree, zamia. The female is a smooth glossy brown, hemispherical with flared margins, about ⅛ inch in diameter. It secretes much honeydew, which attracts ants and is a medium for black sooty mold, making fern fronds an eyesore. Parathion kills some stages but not late immature scales. Nicotine sulfate and soap, or a summer oil and nicotine, or a thiocyanate spray, or malathion may be satisfactory, depending on host and circumstances.

Hemlock Scale (*Aspidiotus ithacae*)—A native American species, widely distributed, quite common in the West. Scales are circular, nearly black, in great numbers on underside of needles of hemlock, Douglas-fir, Monterey, yellow, knob-cone, and other pines. They sometimes kill young trees. Another species is causing trouble on hemlock in the East. Malathion has been effective.

Holly Scale (*Aspidiotus britannicus*)—On holly in Pacific coast states. The scales are circular, flat, $\frac{1}{16}$ inch across, on leaves, twigs, and berries. When numerous they weaken trees. Another holly scale (*Asterolecanium puteanum*) feeds on American holly and yaupon and bumelia from Delaware to Alabama. It makes shallow and deep pits in twigs.

Howard Scale (*Aspidiotus howardi*)—A Rocky Mountain species occurring mostly at high altitudes in Colorado and New Mexico. The female is circular, flat, pale gray with a reddish tinge; it causes pitting and a reddish stain on fruit. Pear is the preferred host, but it may feed on almond, apple, ash, peach, plum, prune, and other deciduous fruits and vegetables. Control is the same as for San Jose scale.

Italian Pear Scale (*Epidiaspis piricola*)—A California pest of pear, peach, plum, prune, apple, Persian walnut, and a very special pest of California Christmasberry (mountain-holly, toyon), which may be killed or disfigured. The female is dark red or purple, covered with a circular, dark gray, shiny shell with dark brown exuviae. The male is slender, white with yellow exuviae. Infestations of long duration cause deep depressions in limbs and may hasten death. Lichens usually cover the scales. Spray in winter with a heavy oil emulsion, drenching limbs and trunk, adding 1 ounce of caustic soda to each 2 gallons of spray to remove the lichens protecting the scales.

Japanese Scale (*Leucaspis japonica*)—A pest of privet and maple, established in New York and Connecticut. It looks like a narrow oyster shell, $\frac{1}{16}$ to $\frac{1}{12}$ inch long, dull grayish white, often thickly encrusting trunk and branches. A dormant miscible oil spray is satisfactory.

Juniper Scale (*Diaspis carueli*)—On juniper, sometimes arborvitae, incense cedar, and cypress used as ornamentals throughout the United States, not important in forest stands. Whenever shrubs around the house look dingy gray or yellowish and generally unthrifty, examine the needles closely for very small, $\frac{1}{20}$-inch, dirty-white, round scales with a yellow center. These are females; the male is even smaller, white, narrow with a ridge down the back. They winter as nearly grown scales and the young hatch in early June (Plate XXXIII).

Control. A dormant miscible oil spray, 1 to 25 dilution, is recommended for this scale, except on those junipers whose needles form a cup to hold the oil and so are subject to injury. I have had much better luck with lime-sulfur, 1 to 9 dilution, applied in early April before growth starts, but this cannot be used near painted surfaces. Malathion or nicotine sulfate and soap can be used for the crawling stage in June.

Latania Scale *(Aspidiotus lataniae)*—Widely distributed in greenhouses and warm climates on palms, orchids, canna, gladiolus, raspberry, rose, tamarisk, and other ornamentals, and a special pest of avocado in California. It is armored, gray, circular, $\frac{1}{16}$ to $\frac{1}{12}$ inch. It lays yellow eggs. Sulfur-yellow crawlers appear on branches, twigs, leaves, or fruit. Malathion is effective in control, and there are several introduced natural enemies.

Lecanium Scale *(Lecanium coryli)*—Tree Lecanium, a European species attacking a wide variety of woody plants. It is present along the Pacific coast on maples, horsechestnut, hawthorn, cherry, beech, lime, apple, pear, plum, alder, sometimes birch, poplar, willow, and elm. The female is hemispherical, mottled brown, rather large. Young insects crawl to the leaves in summer, return to twigs in fall.

Lesser Snow Scale *(Pinnaspis minor)*—A general pest of ornamentals in Florida. The female is pear-shaped, white, semi-transparent, sometimes speckled with brown from incorporation of bark fragments. The male is white, elongate. Food plants include avocado, abutilon, asparagus fern, albizzia, Australian silk oak, bignonia, boxwood, bryophyllum, cactus, caladium, camphor, cassava, cassia, castor-bean, century plant, chinaberry, citrus, croton, cycad, ficus, grape, hackberry, hibiscus, hollyhock, mango, mesembryanthemum, morning glory, mountain ebony, oleander, palm, paradise vine, parkinsonia, peppertree, pelargonium, pittosporum, royal poinciana, sapodilla, spider lily, sumac, sweetpotato, thunbergia, wisteria, woodbine.

Control with summer oil sprays or with malathion.

Magnolia Scale *(Neolecanium cornuparvum)*—A soft scale, probably a native, distributed through eastern states on various species of magnolia. It is the largest scale insect in the United States. The female is $\frac{1}{2}$ inch across, notably convex, covered with much white wax under which the body is shining brown with honeycomb pits and large glands. When scales are numerous the branches appear to be covered with white cotton, and when the scales are removed a scar is left on the bark. Trees may be severely injured and look sickly; leaves remain small. There is much honeydew to encourage sooty mold over leaves and branches. Young nymphs hibernate on newer wood, molt early in spring, again in June, and start secreting white wax. By August, they are producing living young. There is 1 generation in the North.

Control. A dormant oil spray gives excellent results. In summer the large scales can be scrubbed off with a stiff brush. A spray of summer oil and nicotine, or malathion, can be timed for crawlers in late summer.

Maple Phenacoccus (*Phenacoccus acericola*)—In northeastern states, mostly on sugar maple. It resembles cottony maple scale with its large white cottony masses, but these are always on the underside of leaves and not on the twigs. It is conspicuous but not very important.

Mexican Wax Scale (*Ceroplastes ceriferus*)—Japanese Wax Scale, on camellia, azalea, tea, other ornamental shrubs, quite damaging near Norfolk, Virginia. The female is circular, thick, very convex, with creamy white wax. The body of the male is dark brown or purple brown and looks like a globular berry when freed of wax.

Mining Scale (*Howardia biclavis*)—On many ornamental plants in warm climates, including hibiscus, Australian pine, oak, begonia, citrus, jasmine, ficus, poinsettia, pomegranate, privet, wisteria. The scale, circular, moderately convex, white or grayish, mines partly into bark and epidermis of leaves and twigs.

Oak Gall Scale (*Kermes pubescens*)—Kermes, distributed widely, along with similar species, on oak in northern United States; it is more conspicuous than injurious. The females, globular, mottled light brown, ⅛ inch across, look more like hard galls along the leaf veins and terminal twigs than scales. Leaves are sometimes distorted, puckered; growth checked. Winter is spent on bark, but in spring females migrate to leaves. The young are at first covered with a white pubescence.

Obscure Scale (*Chrysomphalus obscurus*)—On pecan, hickory, elm, hackberry, and oak, found from Massachusetts to Florida and Arkansas. It is a special pest of pecans from Alabama to Texas, may occur also on chestnut, chinquapin, dogwood, grape, plum, maple, willow, wild myrtle. The female is roughly circular, grayish, closely resembling tree bark. The male is half her size. On pecans the infestation starts on lower and inner tree parts and gradually spreads up and out, killing many smaller branches, reducing vigor, making the tree more susceptible to attacks of other insects. There is 1 generation a year, with crawlers moving in June, developing their scale until January.

Control. Spray very thoroughly with a dormant oil emulsion (2 per cent for weak trees, 3 per cent for vigorous) in January or February before buds begin to swell.

Oleander Scale (*Aspidiotus hederae*)—Ivy Scale, present throughout the warmer states and in houses and greenhouses in the North. As the names imply, it is especially serious on oleander and ivy, but it is an omnivorous feeder with a very long list of host plants including century plant, cycads, palms, olive, lemon, orange, also acacia, aloe, avocado, azalea, cactus, camellia, ferns, genista, magnolia, orchids, pepper-tree, poinsettia, redbud, rubber tree, yucca. The females are circular, somewhat flattened, pale yellow, sometimes with a purple tinge, $\frac{1}{10}$ inch across. The males are much smaller, pure white, numerous. Heavily infested plants lose their color and vigor, may die. Rhododendrons may be seriously injured.

Control. Prune out heavily encrusted branches. Spray for crawlers with malathion or white oil emulsion, or nicotine sulfate and soap. Parathion is satisfactory for commercial growers.

Olive Scale (*Parlatoria oleae*)—Olive Parlatoria, an introduced pest established at 3 widely scattered points, near Baltimore, Maryland, on privet, in California, and in Arizona. Since it was found in California in 1934 it has become a major agricultural pest, being reported on 211 plant species, including, besides olive, almond, apricot, apple, peach, pear, plum. For many years the insect stayed on a few plants on the university campus at Tucson, Arizona, but after a series of mild winters became epidemic on many new hosts, affecting twigs, leaves, fruit, of citrus and deciduous fruits, and infesting many ornamentals, including ash, Brazilian pepper, cotoneaster, elaeagnus, grape, English ivy, jasmine, Kentucky coffee tree, loquat, Chinese lilac, mulberry, oleander, palms, periwinkle, photinia, pomegranate, privet (California, Chinese, glossy, Japanese), pyracantha, rose, sage, trumpet vine, tung-oil, viburnum, Virginia creeper. The female shell is dirty gray, ovate, circular, very small; the insect itself is purplish brown. The scales overwinter as adult females with egg-laying starting in late March. Hatching on deciduous fruit trees is in April, on olives in May. There are 2 generations.

Control. The most effective spray for commerical growers seems to be parathion applied with oil. Malathion injures young olive fruit but can be used on ornamentals. Natural enemies are being introduced.

Oystershell Scale (*Lepidosaphes ulmi*)—Generally distributed on deciduous trees and shrubs, known to every home gardener and fruit grower. As the name implies, the scales look like miniature oysters encrusted over trunks, limbs, twigs, or on soft stems (Plate XXXIV). There are 3 color races of this scale with different life cycles. The gray race occurs on common lilac, beech, maple, willow, and other ornamentals. The scales are small, ⅛ inch long by ¹⁄₁₆ inch wide, broadened at the posterior end, usually curved, with many parallel cross ridges, acquiring a whitish bloom with age. There is only 1 brood, with crawlers appearing in June.

The brown race, the apple oystershell, is common on fruits, apple, apricot, pear, plum, quince, currant, fig, grape, raspberry, almond, and Persian walnut; it is also serious on dogwood, hybrid lilacs, boxwood, mountain-ash, horsechestnut. When old, the scales are very dark, almost black; there are 2 generations. The yellow-brown race has a yellow fringe on the rear portion, is common on birch and poplar, has a second brood in late July. Other plants that may be infested with oystershell scales are peonies, ailanthus, alder, aspen, basswood, bittersweet, boxelder, butternut, camellia, camphor, clematis, cotoneaster, elm, ginseng, hackberry, heather, holly, honeysuckle, Juneberry, locust, mountainholly, New Jersey tea, oak, orchid, pachysandra, sassafras, spirea, sycamore, tamarisk, tuliptree, viburnum, Virginia creeper, yucca.

The winter is passed as elliptical, nearly white eggs under female shells; they hatch late in spring, late May or June. The young crawlers, whitish with 6 barely visible legs, move about for a few hours, then insert their beaks into the bark and start the waxy scale covering. The brown and yellow-brown races mature about mid-July when the tiny yellowish 2-winged males mate with the females. As the female deposits her eggs under the shell her body gradually shrinks until death. With the brown and yellow-brown races the eggs hatch in 2 weeks; with the gray race, not until the next spring.

Control. Lilacs and other shrubs that almost always have some scale should have a dormant spray, a 1 to 15 dilution of miscible oil, just before buds break, usually late March. Remove heavily encrusted and weak branches before spraying. Malathion is probably the best spray for crawlers; DDT is effective but may lead to other problems. There are many natural enemies: birds, mites, parasitic wasps, and other insects.

Parlatoria Date Scale (*Parlatoria blanchardi*)—Date Palm Scale, a small gray and white scale, introduced from Egypt in 1890, a menace to the date industry of California and Arizona. An eradication campaign started in 1922, which included destroying some infested trees, pruning others and searing them with a gasoline torch, was successfully concluded in 1934.

Peony Scale (*Pseudaonidia paeoniae*)—Killing twigs and branches of azaleas and camellias in the South, sometimes present on ligustrum and other shrubs. The small, brown, convex shell is very inconspicuous, looking like a slight hump on the bark, until the scale is rubbed off, or dies and falls off, leaving a conspicuous white circle on the twig. Crawlers, purple in color, are present in May; there is only 1 brood. Sprays are ineffective unless timed for crawlers, usually late May. Parathion is good and used by some nurserymen. Volck, at a 1 to 60 dilution, or perhaps malathion, will be safer for home gardeners.

Pineapple Scale (*Diaspis bromeliae*)—A tropical pineapple pest, also present in greenhouses; it infests canna, hibiscus, English ivy, olive, palm, sago palm, and various tropical plants. It has a nearly round, thin, white or light gray shell over an orange-yellow body with purplish tints.

Pine Needle Scale (*Phenacaspis pinifoliae*)—A native, widely distributed, common in home plantings on nearly all species of pines and various spruces, occasional on hemlock, fir, incense cedar, most prevalent east of the Mississippi River. The female is pure white, widening toward the lower end, varying in shape according to the needle it is on, $\frac{1}{10}$ inch long. The male is white, with 4 parallel ridges, $\frac{1}{25}$ inch long. Pine branches infested with scale usually turn yellow. On small Austrian and mugho pines every leaf may be white with scales, the needles yellowing, the whole shrub unhealthy, or a single branch may be heavily infested and the rest free from scale (Plate XXXIII). Reddish eggs winter under the scales and start hatching in May, with a second brood appearing in late July.

Control. Spray with lime-sulfur, 1 to 9 dilution, or with a dormant oil, evergreen strength, before new growth starts, or spray with malathion for crawlers in late May. When a single branch is infested it can usually be pruned out without spoiling the shape too much. Lady beetles and some hymenopterous wasps share in control measures.

Pine Tortoise Scale (*Toumeyella numismaticum*)—On Scotch, Austrian, and jack pines in northern states. Another species (*T. pini*), infesting mugho, lodgepole, Scotch, and cluster pines, is reported in Connecticut, Pennsylvania, Michigan, and Florida. Females are reddish brown, oval, very convex. Heavily infested pines are coated with black sooty mold; there is heavy foliage drop; needles are shorter than normal; young trees may die.

Prescott Scale (*Matsuccocus vexillorum*)—Causing extensive killing of branches of ponderosa pine in the Southwest. The females settle on twigs, mainly at nodes, lay eggs, and cover them with fluffy white wax. Larvae feed beneath scales at base of needles and in cracks and crevices in twigs.

79. *Purple scale on citrus fruit, with detail of oyster-shaped male and female.*

Purple Scale (*Lepidosaphes beckii*)—The most important citrus pest in Florida and the Gulf states, outranked in California only by California red and black scales. It appeared in Florida in 1857 on lemons imported from Bermuda; it reached California in 1889 when 2 carloads of Florida orange trees were planted without previous disinfection. Besides citrus, purple scale infests allamanda, avocado, banksia, bergamot, Barbados cherry, croton, elaeagnus, eucalyptus, fig, magnolia, mistletoe, jessamine, oak, olive, orchid, passion-flower, pecan, sago palm, silver thorn, Spanish bayonet, and other plants.

This is an armored scale, the female shaped like an oyster shell, straight or curved, light to dark brown or purple, ⅛ inch long. The male is similar but smaller and narrower. Foliage turns yellow where scales have been feeding, may even turn brown and fall out; fruit is stunted, ripening delayed, color and flavor affected; feeding wounds afford entrance to disease fungi. The female deposits from 40 to 80 pearly eggs under her shell which hatch in 2 weeks to 2 months. The pale nymphs crawl for a short time, seek a shaded location on bark or fruit, insert their beaks, and settle down, secreting 2 long protective threads. The females molt twice at 3- to 4-week intervals, becoming thicker and purplish or reddish brown. The male molts 4 times, emerging in 2 months as a 2-winged insect. There are 3 generations. Some sprays, notably those containing copper and zinc, increase populations of purple scale on citrus.

Control. In Florida, summer sprays of 1.3 to 1.5 per cent oil are used to control purple scale, with parathion another possibility. In California either fumigation with hydrogen cyanide or summer oil sprays have been used.

Putnam Scale (*Aspidiotus ancylus*)—Similar to San Jose scale but not so serious, found over most of the United States. It is circular, dark gray to nearly black, with brick-red exuviae, just off center. Basswood and soft maples are quite susceptible to this scale; it is also found on apple, ash, beech, blueberry, bladdernut, cherry, chestnut, currant, cranberry, elm, gooseberry, hackberry, hawthorn, hickory, linden, locust, osage-orange, oak, peach, pecan, persimmon, pear, plum, quince, snowball, tuliptree, willow, walnut.

Red Date Scale (*Phoenicococcus marlatti*)—Common on date palm in California and Arizona but apparently not very injurious. The female is reddish purple, resting in, and somewhat enveloped by, cottony filaments. The male is wingless. Food plants are restricted to 3 species of Phoenix palms.

Red Pine Scale (*Matsucoccus resinosae*)—First discovered in Connecticut in 1946 and on Long Island in 1950, this scale has been killing red pine in parts of New York and Connecticut. There is first a slight yellowing of needles of current year's growth, then the foliage turns brick red and the tree dies. Larvae and adults are small, inconspicuous, yellow to brown, hidden in bark or beneath needle fascicles. There are 2 generations, with eggs laid in May and late August.

Rhodes Grass Scale (*Antonina graminis*)—Recently destructive to lawns and golf courses in Lower Rio Grande Valley, Texas. St. Augustine grass loses color and vigor. The scales are small, dark, covered with a white growth. They usually stay around nodes at base of grass blades; mature adults live on roots in winter. Crawlers are dark, lively, found on any part of grasses, and on any of 74 grass species. Parathion dust, 1 per cent, applied at rate of 50 pounds per acre, or a spray with ¼ pound actual parathion in 200 gallons per acre has been effective if repeated at 10-day intervals. Other materials have not given satisfactory control.

Rhododendron Scale (*Aspidiotus pseudospinosus*)—A small, circular, dirty-tan scale on rhododendron, covering stems and underside of leaves, with yellow spots appearing on upper leaf surfaces. This came into prominence in New Jersey following spraying of trees with DDT, although present before DDT came into use. A dormant oil spray is fairly effective. Use malathion for crawlers in June or July.

Rose Scale (*Aulacaspis rosae*)—Widely distributed wherever roses or bramble hosts are known. The round, flat white female shells, covering orange or pinkish bodies and red eggs, $\frac{1}{5}$ inch across, are very conspicuous on canes, which often appear as if whitewashed. The males are small, narrow, snow white. Blackberry, loganberry, raspberry, dewberry, thimbleberry, and related plants may be infested. Climbing roses and neglected hybrid perpetuals are more likely to be attacked than hybrid teas pruned low each spring, but with the modern moderate to high pruning of hybrid teas, scale becomes a problem here, too. In New York eggs hatch in late May or June with a second generation in August.

Control. If roses are sprayed with lime-sulfur at a 1 to 9 dilution directly after pruning in spring (if buds have not opened more than $\frac{1}{4}$ inch), rose scale is readily controlled. For climbers near painted surfaces, a dormant miscible oil will have to be substituted, but in my experience it is much less satisfactory. Before spraying, prune out canes too well supplied with scales. Treating with malathion in summer may eliminate some of the crawlers.

San Jose Scale (*Aspidiotus perniciosus*)—Probably from China, first discovered at San Jose, California, in 1880, now present in every state. It is particularly injurious to deciduous fruit trees, often causing death if left unchecked. Fruit hosts include apple, pear, quince, peach, plum, prune, apricot, nectarine, sweet cherry, blackberry, currant, gooseberry. Ash, mountain-ash, poplar, hawthorn, lilac, linden, elm, willow are also subject to injury. Other host plants include acacia, actinidia, akebia, alder, almond, arborvitae, beech, birch, false bittersweet, buttonbush, buckthorn, catalpa, ceanothus, chestnut, cotoneaster, dogwood, elder, eucalyptus, euonymus, fig, hackberry, hibiscus, honeysuckle, locust, loquat, maple, mulberry, pecan, orange, osage-orange, persimmon, photinia, privet, Japanese quince, rose, sassafras, shadbush, silver thorn, smokebush, snowball, snowberry, spirea, sour-gum, strawberry, sumac, Virginia creeper, English walnut, willow.

The female is yellowish, covered with a gray, circular, waxy scale, $\frac{1}{16}$ inch in diameter, elevated in the center into a nipple surrounded by a yellow ring. Young scales are small and nearly black. The male is oblong, oval, acquires 2 wings. Young scales winter on bark, becoming full grown when apples bloom. After mating, females give birth to living young, crawlers with 6 legs which move over the bark until they find a suitable place to insert their mouth parts. There are 2 to 6 generations a year, depending on location. The scale is spread by being carried on bodies of birds and larger insects, and through shipments of infested nursery stock. Bark on trees is often reddened around the scales, which may be so numerous they overlap, completely covering a branch. On fruit they form gray patches at blossom and stem ends; there is often a red, inflamed area around each scale.

Control. Lime-sulfur first came into use as a dormant spray for the control of San Jose scale and it may still be used in many places at a 1 to 9 dilution before buds break in spring. However, as early as 1914 the scale started to show some resistance to lime-sulfur and oil sprays have been used, sometimes combined with bordeaux mixture. When orchardists started using DDT for codling moth they noted a decrease in San Jose scale, enough so that dormant sprays could be omitted in some cases. A summer program of DDT and parathion is sometimes used commercially. But if DDT is not used in cover sprays, a dormant spray is practically obligatory. In the Northwest commercial growers may mix 3 per cent lime-sulfur with an oil emulsion containing 1 per cent actual oil.

Scurfy Scale (*Chionaspis furfura*)—A native pest of deciduous fruit and ornamental trees, widely distributed in the United States. The female is grayish white, rounded at one end so it is rather pear-shaped, ⅛ inch long; the male is smaller; snow white, narrow, with 3 longitudinal ridges (Plate XXXIV). Food plants include pear, apple, quince, cherry, gooseberry, currant, black raspberry, peach, and many shade trees, such as mountain-ash, white and prickly ash, aspen, black walnut, elm, hawthorn, hickory, horsechestnut, maple, willow. The scales are abundant on bark, giving it a scurfy appearance, infest foliage, and may spot fruit. Scurfy scale is most often present on shaded parts of trees in neglected orchards where foliage is too dense; it is not so important on trees receiving good care.

Reddish-purple eggs winter on bark under female shells, hatching in late spring, May or June, after trees are in full leaf. Purple crawlers move about for a few hours, then settle down on bark. There are 2 generations in the southern range, with eggs of the summer brood laid in July; overwintering eggs are laid in late August and September. There is only 1 brood in the North.

Control. A 3 per cent or 4 per cent dormant oil spray is usually effective. In some spray programs this is supplemented with DN compounds to kill the eggs. Sometimes it takes 2 applications of a dormant oil applied 2 weeks apart or 1 dormant oil spray and 2 parathion sprays for crawlers, to clean up a heavy infestation on apples.

Soft Azalea Scale (*Pulvinaria ericicola*)—Has prominent white egg sacs.

Soft Scale (*Coccus hesperidum*)—Soft Brown Scale, widely distributed in greenhouses and outdoors in warm climates on ornamentals and fruits. It is rather flat, soft, oval, yellowish green or greenish brown, often with a marbled or ridged effect, ⅛ inch long. It usually resembles the host plant in color and is unnoticed until the infestation is very large. Young are born alive, 1 or 2 daily for a month or two; they are sluggish, settling down near the parent, maturing in about 2 months. A large amount of honeydew is produced, resulting in much smutting of foliage. Plants are weakened, stunted. This is a rather common pest of gardenia, on foliage and tender branches, on fern, camellia, oleander.

Other host plants, indoors and out, include abutilon, aloe, apple, apricot, aralia, araucaria, ash, avocado, banana, bougainvillea, box-elder, bursera, cassia, citron, clematis, clerodendron, date palm, fig, grape, grapefruit, guava, hawthorn, hibiscus, holly, English ivy, jasmine, Kentia palm, laurel, California laurel, lemon, locust, madrona, magnolia, manzanita, maple, morning glory, mulberry, myrtle, orange, peach, pear, phlox, pittosporum, plum, poinsettia, poplar, prune, rose, sago palm, strawberry tree, water hyacinth, willow, and many others.

Control. There are a large number of parasites which do an excellent job of controlling soft scale, but many of these are killed when parathion is used on orchards and greenhouses, while the scale flourishes. Malathion does control soft scale effectively. Summer oil sprays are also satisfactory.

Spirea Scale (*Eriococcus borealis*)—Occasionally infesting spirea. It is a white mealy scale in forks of branches and resembles azalea bark scale.

Spruce Bud Scale (*Physokermes piceae*)—A special pest of Norway spruce, but present on other species, distributed from New England to Maryland and Minnesota. Mature scales are ⅛ inch across, round, gall-like, reddish brown with flecks of yellow, dusted with powdery wax, situated in clusters of 3 to 5 at base of branchlets, and so closely resembling spruce buds they are difficult to detect. Infestation is at tips of lower branches. Great quantities of honeydew attract bees and form a medium for black mold. Young insects are born in June or July, winter as partly grown scales. There is 1 generation. Use a dormant oil spray in spring before growth starts or a summer nicotine and oil spray when young are present.

Sycamore Scale (*Stomacoccus platani*)—Occurring naturally on native sycamore in California and now a serious pest of introduced oriental plane. The female is deep yellow, $\frac{1}{16}$ inch long. It winters on bark of trunk and branches, protected by loose cottony threads. Nymphs migrate to leaves and mature there, causing brown spots, sometimes distortion and defoliation, but they return to trunk and limbs for egg-laying. There are 3 generations, with young scales becoming active in late January, which is the best time for a spray. A light-medium oil, 1.5 per cent used with toxaphene, DDT, or benzene hexachloride seems to be more effective than the standard 3 per cent oil. Parathion is efficient and can be used in nurseries but is dangerous for street trees.

80. *Tea scale on camellia, showing brown females and nymphs covered with white cotton on underside of leaf and yellowing of upper leaf surface.*

Tea Scale (*Fiorinia theae*)—The most important camellia insect in the Deep South, not so serious in California; sometimes found on greenhouse camellias in the North. Although the scales are on underside of foliage, infested camellias can be told at a distance by yellowish blotches on upper leaf surface, generally unhealthy appearance of the whole plant, premature dropping of leaves. Bloom is decreased; cuttings may die before roots develop. The scale is as serious on Chinese holly as on camellias in some parts of the South (Texas especially), and may at times infest ferns, palms, orchids, figs, and a few other plants.

The female is at first thin, light yellow, later hard, brown, elongate-oval or boat-shaped, $\frac{1}{16}$ inch long, with the residue from the first molt attached at one end. Yellow eggs, 10 to 16, are held under the shell. The male is soft, white, narrow, with a ridge down the middle. Both scales are held in a conspicuous tangle of white cottony threads; often the entire undersurface of the leaf is white, dotted with small brown female shells. The eggs hatch in 7 to 21 days, depending on the weather. Flat yellow crawlers move to new growth, attach themselves after 2 or 3 days, secreting first a thin white covering, later the many white threads. The first molt is in 18 to 36 days, the second a week later; egg-laying starts 41 to 65 days after birth. There are many overlapping broods so that crawlers and young nymphs are present on foliage at any time between March and November in Alabama.

Control. Spray thoroughly in spring after blooming and when cold weather is past (around April 1) with a white oil emulsion such as Florida Volck, using 6 level tablespoons per gallon, hitting underside of leaves with great force. A second application may be required later in the spring or in September. Parathion is effective and safer than oil on the plants but so dangerous for the operator it should be left to nurserymen who understand necessary precautions. Malathion can be substituted by home gardeners.

Terrapin Scale (*Lecanium nigrofasciatum*)—Black-banded Scale, a native insect, widely distributed over eastern states. It is a branch and twig scale, attacking common fruit trees, many shade trees, and shrubs. A partial list of hosts includes maple, sycamore, boxelder, hawthorn as preferred food plants, with occasional infestation on ash, cottonwood, European plane, mulberry, linden, live oak, redbud, willow. The soft unarmored female is nearly hemispherical, $\frac{1}{8}$ inch in diameter, dark reddish brown, smooth, shining, with 10 or 12 dark bands radiating from the high center of the back to the fluted edges. Partly grown females winter on twigs, reach full size in June when they give birth to living young. Each nymph leaves the mother in a day or two, migrates to a leaf for 6 weeks, then moves back to a branch where it is fertilized by a minute winged male. When scales are numerous twigs are said to give off a putrid odor. The drain on the tree is serious; smaller branches die; foliage is thin; sooty mold grows in quantity in honeydew, covering trunk and branches and dropping to sidewalks.

Control. There are many predaceous and parasitic insect enemies. Lime-sulfur has little effect, but a dormant miscible oil, 1 to 16 dilution, applied as late in spring as possible before buds burst, is effective.

This cannot be used on some maples. For these try malathion or nicotine sulfate in summer for crawling stages.

Tessellated Scale (*Eucalymnatus tessellatus*)—A tropical tortoise species appearing in greenhouses on many kinds of palms, orchids, and other plants. It is like the soft scale but larger, darker brown, with the surface marked with pale lines to form a mosaic.

Tuliptree Scale (*Toumeyella liriodendri*)—Probably a native, noted as injurious in Michigan in 1870. It is distributed over the United States east of the Rocky Mountains, on tuliptrees for the most part, sometimes on magnolia and linden. One of the largest of the soft scales, the female is ⅓ inch across, very convex, hemispherical, a dark rich brown. Scales are usually crowded together and somewhat distorted along the twigs and branches. The winter is spent as small, partly grown nymphs, brown with lighter ridges, clinging tightly to twigs. They grow fast in spring and are producing young by August. There is 1 generation. Spray with a dormant oil emulsion in spring. During the season large scales can be scrubbed off twigs or small trees with a rag or brush and soapy water.

Walnut Scale (*Aspidiotus juglans-regiae*)—A European scale found on a wide variety of trees and shrubs, including English, Persian, and Japanese walnuts, apple, apricot, ash, boxelder, cherry, cherry-laurel, cottonwood, currant, dogwood, elm, grape, sweet gum, gordonia, haw, holly, hackberry, horsechestnut, linden, locust, maple, oak, peach, pear, plum, prune, rose. The female is mottled orange, covered with a flat, nearly circular, gray to reddish-brown shell, ⅛ inch in diameter. Spraying thoroughly with lime-sulfur, 1 to 8 dilution, just before buds expand in spring has been recommended in the past.

White Peach Scale (*Pseudaulacaspis pentagona*)—West Indian Peach Scale, present from Florida north to Maryland and occasionally farther up the coast. It is an armored scale occasionally attacking privet, flowering peach and cherry, lilac, catalpa, and various fruits, peach, plum, prune, cherry, pear, apricot, grape, persimmon, walnut. The female is ¹⁄₁₀ inch, light gray or dingy white, with yellow exuviae; the male is elongated, pure white. The scales are often clustered at base of branches, which die. There are several generations. A dormant spray of oil or lime-sulfur is usually recommended.

Willow Scurfy Scale (*Chionaspis salicis-nigrae*)—A common scale on willow in northern states, also infesting poplar, dogwood, shadbush, tuliptree, alder, ceanothus. The female is large, white, somewhat pear-shaped but broadest at the middle; the male is long, narrow, snow

white. Purple eggs winter under the female shell; there are 2 generations. Willow twigs and branches may be coated with scales. Both
branches and young trees may die. Spray with lime-sulfur at dormant
strength or with miscible oils just before buds break.

Yellow Scale (*Aonidiella citrina*)—Almost identical with California
Red Scale except for yellow color and the fact that it is found only
on foliage and smaller twigs.

Zamia Scale (*Diaspis zamiae*)—Reddish with a prominent convex
shield which is waxy with marked radial stripes.

SLUGS AND SNAILS

Slugs and snails are not insects but mollusks, belonging, along with
oysters, clams, and other shellfish, to the large animal phylum Mollusca, characterized by individuals which have soft, unsegmented
bodies, usually protected with a hard calcareous shell. A slug is merely
a snail without a shell, or with a shell reduced and located internally
(Plate XXIX). Snails have 2 pairs of tentacles or feelers, a large pair
above, bearing eyes at the tips, and a smaller pair below used for
smelling. The mouth is in the center of the head, below the lower pair
of tentacles and below that is the opening of a large mucous or slime
gland. The soft visceral hump contains most of the internal organs.
Over this is formed the shell, secreted by the mantle which forms a
fold where the shell joins the body or "foot" of the snail. On the right
side, under the edge of the mantle, is the breathing pore with the anus
immediately back of that. The foot contains mucous glands and muscles
by which the animal crawls. When disturbed it may withdraw entirely
into the shell. It can even become dormant under unfavorable conditions, sealing the opening of the shell with a mucous sheet, the opercu-
lum, which soon hardens to a leathery texture. Snails have been known
to remain dormant as long as 4 years.

Slugs are much like snails in structure but they lack the visceral
hump and shell. The mantle is a smooth area in the anterior fourth
or third of the back. Slugs range in length from ¼ inch to 8 or 10
inches, in color from whitish yellow to black, usually mottled. Without
the protection of a shell they need damp places and are usually found
in the daytime under decaying boards and logs or any debris around
the garden. They feed at night by rasping holes, their mouths being
equipped with a horny file, the radula. Although 32 species of slugs

and several hundred species of snails have been recorded in this country only a few are of economic importance.

Banded Wood Snail (*Cepaea nemoralis*)—In flower gardens in parts of the South. The shell is conspicuous, light yellow with longitudinal chocolate-brown striping, 1 inch across.

Brown Garden Snail (*Helix aspersa*)—European Brown Snail, distributed over the world, known in California since 1850, where it is thought to have been deliberately "planted" for food purposes from stock brought from France. It is now very numerous in citrus orchards, eating holes out of leaves, making pits or scars on fruit, covering tree trunks with shells. It is a menace to avocados, feeding on foliage, blossoms, and young fruits, which are scarred. It is likewise destructive to many grasses, vegetables, flowers, shrubs, and trees. Most serious on the Pacific coast, it does occur in many parts of the South.

Full-grown shells have 4½ to 5 whorls, are 1¼ to 1½ inches in diameter. They are grayish yellow with brown applied in 5 bands. The mouth is surrounded by fleshy lips, but inside there is a chitinous jaw to cut or scrape off food. White spherical eggs are laid in a nest in the soil. Young snails have only 1 whorl; they take 2 years to reach maturity.

Control. Hand-pick snails; surround trees with a barrier of lime on the soil which acts as an irritant and keeps snails from walking through it. Scatter bran mash baits, slightly moistened, under citrus, avocado, and other infested trees, about 1 pound per tree, or 1 pound per 1000 square feet, in the garden. Commercial baits containing metaldehyde mixed with either calcium arsenate or sodium fluosilicate are available. Some can be purchased in convenient pellet form. All are poisonous to children, pets, birds.

Gray Field Slug (*Deroceras laevis*)—Also known as Fern Snail, dark gray or buff to black, ½ to 1 inch long. It is common in lawns and fields and sometimes in greenhouses. There it hides in soil during the day but at night eats parenchyma tissue from the underside of fern leaves. Spray underside of fronds with nicotine sulfate and soap early in the morning; remove slugs by hand.

Gray Garden Slug (*Deroceras reticulatum*)—True Garden Slug. Very common, small, averaging ¾ inch, never over 1½ inches, hiding in small cracks and crevices. The color varies from white to pale yellow, lavender, purple, or nearly black with brown specks and mottlings.

Greenhouse Slug (*Milax gagates*)—Widely distributed, very destructive. It is uniform black to dark gray with a longitudinal ridge down the body and a diamond-shaped mark in the center, 1½ to 3 inches long. It shows some preference for coleus, cineraria, geranium, marigold, and snapdragon. A 15 per cent metaldehyde dust is available for floricultural crops.

Greenhouse Snails (*Oxychilus* spp.)—Four species of snails are common in greenhouses and cellars throughout the United States. The shell is a uniform gray or brown, with a very flat coil, ½ inch in diameter.

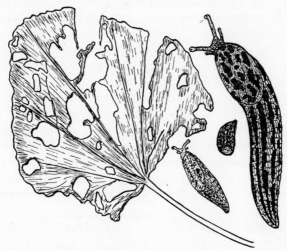

81. Slug injury to hollyhock.

Spotted Garden Slug (*Limax maximus*)—Giant Slug, ranging from 1½ to 7 inches, averaging 3 or 5 inches. The smaller slugs are often a uniform dark gray or black, the larger are yellow gray or brown mottled with black, usually with 3 rows of black spots extending from the mantle to the rear end of the body; the mantle is yellowish with black spots. The eggs are oval, translucent light yellow with a tough elastic outer membrane. They are laid in masses of 25 or more, held together with a mucilaginous substance, under boards, or trash, flowerpots, in compost piles, under stones or in other damp places, any time from spring to fall outdoors, in greenhouses also in winter. The eggs hatch in about 28 days at room temperature, sooner at high temperatures. The young slug is dull white, less than ½ inch long, thin; it darkens and develops slowly. In a month it is an inch long, dark brown, with spots beginning to show. It usually takes more than a year to develop full size.

Working mostly at night these slugs extend their slimy length over leaves eating out large ragged holes, and leave behind a viscous trail of slime. Slugs are among the earliest pests to start chewing in gardens and they keep on until late in the autumn. Hollyhock leaves almost always show slug holes in early spring, as do primroses, iris, saxifrage, violets, and many other plants with foliage close to the ground. Slugs also like to hide in cabbage and lettuce heads.

Control. Cleaning up the garden to get rid of hiding places is always effective. Removing old iris leaves after first frost not only outwits borers, it makes slugs homeless. Shingles in the garden will trap slugs, ready for mass execution. They hate to crawl through anything dusty or scratchy, so a circle of lime or cinders or even sharp sand around plants is a deterrent. Chlordane dust helps some. Spraying or dusting plants with lead arsenate prevents chewing by slugs. Practically all slug baits have a base of metaldehyde. It can be prepared at home (1 ounce of metaldehyde mixed with either 2 ounces of calcium arsenate or 1 ounce sodium fluosilicate and added to 2 pounds wheat bran or corn meal), but it is easier to purchase baits already prepared. For the safety of children, pets, and birds, it is wiser to place the bait, about a tablespoon every few feet near plants attacked, under jar covers, bits of board, half a tin can, or similar cover.

Subulina Snail (*Subulina octona*)—A small species found in greenhouses and readily transported on plants; it is gray with an elongate, pointed shell.

Tawny Garden Slug (*Limax flavus*)—Somewhat smaller than the spotted garden slug, seldom up to 4 inches, and with a more uniform tawny or yellowish color with faint lighter spots. It has a yellow mantle and bluish tentacles.

White Garden Snail (*Theba pisana*)—One of the species used as food in Europe. It has a white shell with irregular darker mottlings, a little smaller than the brown snail. It became established in California in 1914 as an important pest of citrus, but infestations have been eradicated as they appeared in various counties by quarantines and inspection, hand-picking in residential areas, cutting and burning infested wild vegetation, flaming of rocks and soil, and use of calcium arsenate-bran bait.

SOWBUGS AND PILLBUGS

The words sowbug and pillbug are used rather interchangeably for soil pests in the class Crustacea, which includes all arthropods having 2 pairs of antennae and at least 5 pairs of legs. Sowbugs are related to crayfish. They have flat, oval, gray to brown segmented bodies, about ½ inch long, and 7 pairs of legs (Plate XXIX). One species, the common pillbug (*Armadillidium vulgare*), also called roly-poly, has a habit of rolling into a ball like an armadillo, which it resembles in miniature. The dooryard sowbug (*Porcellio laevis*) does not roll up when disturbed. The female sowbug has a ventral pouch known as a marsupium. The eggs are laid in it and held for about 2 months, and then the young, 25 to 75 in a brood, stay in the pouch for some time longer. Young sowbugs are similar to adults; they take a year to mature.

Sowbugs and pillbugs breathe by means of gills and prefer damp, protected places. They are found as scavengers on rotting plant parts, under flowerpots or decayed boards, or in manure, and they may be quite injurious to seedlings, eating roots, girdling the young stems. They are mostly greenhouse problems, though commonly present in garden soil, but occasionally they damage tender growth of field or garden crops.

Control. A poison bait of 1 part Paris green to 9 of sugar has long been recommended for greenhouses, and a dust of 2 parts calcium arsenate mixed with 5 parts white flour, spread thinly over 1000 square feet, has been used in gardens. This has been largely replaced by dusting with 5 per cent DDT, or 2 per cent lindane or chlordane.

SPANWORMS

Spanworms are caterpillars with the looper or measuring-worm habit, and some have already been discussed under Caterpillars.

Bruce Spanworm (*Operophtera bruceata*)—In northern states on sugar maple, poplar, birch, with serious outbreaks reported in Vermont and Wisconsin. The larva is bright green with 3 narrow yellowish-white stripes, ¾ inch long. The male moth is gray with flecks of brown, 1⅛ inch wing expanse; the female is brownish gray, wingless. They lay eggs in November in bark crevices and these hatch in early spring. There is 1 generation.

Currant Spanworm (*Itame ribearia*)—Present in various parts of

the East and in Colorado, feeding on currants and gooseberries, sometimes blueberries. The worms are light yellow with many prominent
black dots, just over an inch long. Like other loopers they drop down
on a silken thread when disturbed. Sometimes they are numerous
enough to defoliate bushes. The moths have slender bodies with broad
yellow wings marked with black. Eggs are laid in stems in summer,
hatching the next spring when leaves are out. Use rotenone sprays or
dusts.

Elm Spanworm (*Ennomos subsignarius*)—The Snow-white Linden
Moth, found from New England to Georgia and west to Colorado.
Before 1880 this species was very abundant around New York and
Philadelphia; about 1910 it was numerous in forest areas in the
Catskills; there was a major outbreak in Massachusetts in 1914 and
one in Connecticut in 1938. It is a particular pest in cities and in
outbreak years it defoliates maple, beech, linden, elm, horsechestnut,
yellow birch, and other trees, but there are long periods between epidemics. The worm is about 1½ inches long, brownish black, with head
and anal segments bright red. The moth is frail, pure white, wings
expanding 1¼ to 1½ inches. Eggs are laid about midsummer, in groups
on branches, and do not hatch until the next spring. Larvae begin at
once to devour foliage, grow rapidly, and pupate in a loose cocoon
in a crumpled leaf. When moths appear in late July they migrate
long distances, appearing in cities like a summer snowstorm.

Control. The English sparrow is credited with doing a grand job of
ridding cities of this pest, helped along by at least 2 insect parasites.
In years of peak infestation trees should be sprayed with lead arsenate
as they come into full leaf.

SPITTLEBUGS

Spittlebugs are sucking insects of the order Homoptera, family Cer-
copidae. They are not true bugs but rather closely related to leafhoppers and are sometimes called froghoppers. The adults are drab
brown, gray or black, sometimes marked with yellow, and they look
rather like short robust leafhoppers. Antennae and 2 ocelli are situated between the eyes. Hind tibiae are smooth with only 1 or 2 heavy
spines on their outer sides and clusters of small ones at the extremities.
They hop away but do not fly very much. They insert eggs in plant
stems or between stem and leaf sheath in grasses.

The remarkable thing about spittlebugs is the frothy mass (children call it frog spit) enveloping the nymphs. This spittle is a combination of a fluid voided from the anus and a mucilaginous substance excreted by glands on the seventh and eighth abdominal segments, mixed with air drawn in between a pair of plates under the abdomen and forced out under pressure, like a bellows, to make uniform bubbles of the liquid secretion. The tail going regularly up and down operates the bellows and keeps the bubbles coming. As soon as the first bubbles are formed the nymph reaches back with its legs and hooks on to the globules, dragging them forward to its head. The greenish nymph is soon hidden under a mound of snow-white foam, protected from sun and preying insects. Many spittlebugs are relatively harmless, but several are economically injurious to plants.

Dogwood Spittlebug (*Clastoptera proteus*)—Blueberry Spittlebug, causing frothy masses on twigs.

Meadow Spittlebug (*Philaenus leucophthalmus*)—The most important species, damaging alfalfa and other forage crops, strawberries, chrysanthemums, stocks, and various other flowers in greenhouses and gardens. Strawberry fruit is distorted, small, and the plant greatly weakened; chrysanthemums may be seriously stunted. Rotenone was formerly used on edible plants and is still good but requires rather frequent application. Methoxychlor, 5 per cent dust, is nearly as safe and has a much longer residual effect; it should not be used within 2 weeks of harvest. Methoxychlor is also used on forage crops for hay, but lindane and DDT can be used on ornamentals. Heptachlor, toxaphene, and dieldrin are promising.

Pecan Spittlebug (*Clastoptera achatina*)—Crop reduction by killing of terminal shoots which would have produced bud-bearing wood. There are 2 broods in Illinois, appearing in May and July. Dieldrin, lindane, and benzene hexachloride are all effective.

Pine Spittlebug (*Aphrophora parallela*)—A native pest of pine from New England to Arkansas, most injurious on Scotch pine but also infesting white, pitch, red, jack, and Virginia pines, and Norway spruce. Eggs are laid at base of terminal buds in July and August, hatch in May, and the young feed on twigs, which are covered with spittle. The insects continually eject undigested sap, like light rain, and branches are covered with a black sooty mold. Scotch pine may die within 2 or 3 years. Standard control has been to spray with pyrethrum extract in June, but lindane, chlordane, or some other organic chemical would probably be more effective.

Saratoga Spittlebug (*Aphrophora saratogensis*)—From New England to Florida, and west to the Great Lakes states, seriously damaging jack and red pine. The nymphs live on sweet fern and other plants, below the surface of the litter in forests, just above the root collar. Adults migrate to pine in late June and July, where they feed until October, extracting large quantities of sap.

SPRINGTAILS

Springtails belong to the insect order Collembola, a group of small insects, less than 1/5 inch long, without wings, and with almost no metamorphosis. They have chewing or piercing mouth parts and short antennae with few segments. They can jump incredible distances by means of a forked appendage, the furcula, which is folded forward under the abdomen when at rest. Under the first abdominal segment there is a short tubelike structure believed to have a respiratory function. There are more than 2000 species distributed from the Arctic to the Antarctic in damp places, and about 70 attack seeds and seedlings, mushrooms, sugar cane, and invade houses. Of these, only 1 is usually considered in garden literature. Some species congregate on the surface of snow and are called "snowfleas"; others live on surface of ponds or on sea beaches; others are in leaf mold or decaying material. In fact, springtails are around us most of the time, but they are so small we seldom notice them.

82. Garden springtail.

Garden Springtail (*Bourletiella hortensis*)—A dark, active species found most often on young plants in seedbeds and outdoor gardens. They have a soft, round body, black to dark purple with yellow spots, and a distinct head; they are very small, 1/25 inch long. They jump quickly by means of the tail-like appendage. They chew holes in thin leaves like spinach, and make pits in cotyledon leaves of beans and cucumbers, and may damage any small plant close to the ground. Malathion dust has given good control. Chlordane and aldrin have been reported satisfactory in some instances, unsatisfactory in others. TEPP is fairly effective. Lindane has been used on ornamentals in some greenhouses.

TERMITES

Termites are not ants, though they are often called "white ants." They are not even in the order Hymenoptera but in the Isoptera (meaning equal wings) and they have long, narrow membranous wings superimposed flat over the back when at rest. The best way to tell termites from ants is to look at the "waist." Ants are deeply constricted while termites have a broad joining between thorax and abdomen. They have chewing mouth parts, but a gradual metamorphosis. They live in galleries in wood or in the ground, except when the winged forms are swarming.

Termites are social insects like ants and have a well-developed caste system with: 1, primary reproductive members, kings and queens—sexual forms with wings which escape from an old colony to found a new one, losing their wings after migrating; 2, secondary reproductive members—mature males and females without wings but with wing buds, which take charge in case the king and queen are killed; 3, ergatoid kings and queens—sexually mature but lacking wings entirely; 4, workers, blind, pale, wingless—non-reproductive, constituting the main population for the colony; 5, soldiers—wingless insects with enlarged heads and mouth parts.

The food of termites is wood or cellulose in some form and they have protozoa in their intestines to enable them to digest this cellulose. Some species live in dry wood above ground, but the species most important to the householder and gardener are the soil-inhabiting forms—particularly the eastern subterranean termite (*Reticulitermes flaviceps*) and the western subterranean termite (*R. hesperus*). These work on wood on or in the ground or build covered runways to reach wood above the ground. They are not new pests, as some termite-control operators advertise; they have been found in fossils and probably were on this continent before man. Their periods of abundance seem to be in waves, however, with some years when damage to buildings is abnormally high.

Subterranean termites sometimes injure living trees and shrubs, being more harmful in warm climates. In Florida they eat away the bark in the collar around newly planted orange trees, sometimes injure apple, peach, pear, cherry, plum, apricot, lemon, guava, pecan, walnut. The injury is usually worse in recently cleared woodland containing old decaying stumps, or in land rich in humus. Fruits which drop and lie on the ground may be invaded. In cities, roots and heartwood of shade trees are entered; seedlings are injured in nurseries.

Flowering plants, mostly those with woody stems, can be infested in gardens or greenhouses, the termites starting on decaying wooden stakes or labels or wooden benches in contact with moist earth. Chrys-anthemums are rather commonly injured and heliotrope, begonia, geranium, poinsettia, cosmos, jasmine, pansy, oleander, and others have been injured on occasion. Termites reach potted plants through the hole in the bottom of the pot. In southern states field and truck crops may be injured—corn, cotton, sugar cane, rice, grasses, white and sweetpotatoes, artichoke, bean, beet, cabbage, carrot, cranberry, peanut, rhubarb, squash, turnip, cantaloupe, and other melons. In California the desert damp-wood termite (*Kalotermes simplicicornis*) sometimes severely injures roots of young citrus trees, while the dry-wood termite feeds on dead wood above ground.

83. Termites: winged sexual form and nymph; and wood tunneled by termites. Note thick "waist" compared to true ant.

Control. Use resistant wood for garden posts and stakes—redwood is excellent for grape stakes and fence posts—or use wood treated with creosote, zinc chloride, or mercuric chloride. Tree surgery and cleaning up old grapevines and other woody debris around the garden reduce the termite menace. Paint pruning scars with a mixture of 1 part creosote to 3 parts coal tar after shellac has been applied to protect living tissue at edges of the bark. Avoid use of manure while termites are in the soil.

Subterranean termites can be killed in soil around trees by applying carbon bisulfide or carbon tetrachloride emulsion. Poke small holes around plants 12 inches apart and pour in about 1 teaspoon in each; more can be used in fallow soil. DDT, chlordane, lindane, or lead arsenate worked into soil around living trees and shrubs will deter termites. Sap pine stakes can be used to trap them, then pulled up, and the insects killed with boiling water. When swarming indicates the position of a colony, drench the spot with kerosene. In new greenhouses proper construction makes termites unnecessary. Benches in older houses can be cleaned up with kerosene emulsion.

THRIPS

Thrips belong to the insect order Thysanoptera, the name meaning bristle or fringe wings. They are very small, slender insects, about as wide as a fine needle, only just visible to the naked eye. The 2 pairs of long narrow wings, with few or no veins, are edged with long hairs like stiff fringe. The mouth parts are fitted for piercing and rasping; antennae are usually short, 6- to 10-segmented; tarsi (feet) have 1 or 2 segments and end in a bladderlike vesicle instead of claws. Thrips often scar fruit and foliage with their scraping mouth parts and are commonly found on flowers. Some are predaceous on mites and small insects, some eat fungi and decayed vegetable matter, most are very injurious. There are 2 suborders and most of the plant pests belong to the one, Terebrantia, distinguished by having a sawlike ovipositor, and to only a few families in this group.

Aeolothripidae. Broad-winged or banded thrips. Adults are dark, have broad wings with a few veins, banded or mottled.

Thripidae. Common thrips, including most of the injurious plant feeders in the genera *Thrips, Taeniothrips, Heliothrips, Hercothrips, Scirtothrips,* and *Frankliniella.* The wings are narrow and pointed; antennae 6- to 9-segmented.

Phloeothripidae. Larger than other thrips and without an ovipositor, the last abdominal segment being tubular; mostly dark colored. Most species feed on spores or are predaceous, but *Liothrips* is a plant pest.

Banded Greenhouse Thrips (*Hercinothrips femoralis*)—A pest in greenhouses, and of sugar beets, cacti, and date palm outdoors in California and Arizona. The thrips is dark brown or black, with head, prothorax, and end of abdomen reddish yellow, fore wings dusty with white areas. It can moderately or heavily infest alstroemeria, amaryllis, agapanthus, aralia, buddleia, yellow calla, chrysanthemum, dracaena, rubber plant, gardenia, gerbera, gladiolus, hydrangea, hymenocallis, nerine, sprekelia, sweet pea, snapdragon, screw-pine, and other greenhouse plants, including young sweetpotatoes and tomatoes. Control is the same as for the greenhouse thrips.

Bean Thrips (*Hercothrips fasciatus*)—Widely distributed, a general feeder on legumes, truck, field, and forage crops, grasses, deciduous and citrus trees, a special pest of beans, avocado, olive, pear, and orange. Nymphs are reddish yellow, adults gray black with black and white wings. They feed in colonies, making foliage of beans, peas, and other crops bleached or silvered, wilted, covered with black bits of excrement. Eliminate weeds around the garden, especially prickly lettuce and sow thistle. Spray or dust with DDT, except on edible plant parts.

Blueberry Thrips (*Frankliniella vaccinii*)—A pest of blueberries in Maine and part of New York. Adults appear when first blueberry leaves separate in the buds, causing a tight curling, reddening, and malformation of leaves. The female is light brown with gray head, legs, wings, and first antennal segments. Recommended procedure has been a quick burning over of blueberry fields.

Camphor Thrips (*Liothrips floridensis*)—Very injurious to camphor trees in the Gulf states. The adult is black, $\frac{1}{50}$ inch long; the young are straw-colored, changing to orange red at the second molt. They feed on buds and tender tips, causing dieback, and on branches, causing blackening, cracking of bark, deformation of limbs. Breeding is nearly continuous. Injury is worse on nursery trees, or on older trees which have been trimmed and cut back. Apply shellac to pruning cuts. Trees have been sprayed with lime-sulfur, 1 to 100 dilution plus fish-oil soap and nicotine, but DDT is probably better.

Chrysanthemum Thrips (*Thrips nigropilosus*)—Often serious on greenhouse chrysanthemums, sometimes outdoors. Young leaves are flecked whitish from loss of sap and often have a gummy residue. The shoots die back if thrips are numerous. DDT or lindane sprays or dusts are effective outdoors, and DDT and other aerosols in greenhouses.

Citrus Thrips (*Scirtothrips citri*)—Important in the Southwest on sweet and mandarin oranges, lemon, lime, grapefruit, pomelo, kumquat, sometimes infesting pomegranate, grape, pepper-tree, umbrella tree, apricot, rarely on walnut, olive, willow, almond. The injury is a very definite ring scar around the fruit at the blossom end, withering and curling of leaves, blossom drop before fruit is set. The adults, very small, $\frac{1}{50}$ inch long, orange yellow with black eyes, hibernate in trees or weeds, lay whitish eggs on young trees in April and throughout the summer; there are 6 to 10 broods a year.

Control. DDT sprays and DDT-sulfur dust have been effective but have caused increase in cottony-cushion scale and in some orchards the thrips have become resistant to DDT. Dieldrin prevents scarred fruit and does not kill beneficial insects. Finely ground sulfur dust in 2 or 3 applications will control this thrips.

Composite Thrips (*Microcephalothrips abdominalis*)—Frequently found on zinnias, marigolds, calendulas, and other flowers, but of minor importance. The entire life cycle is passed in the flower heads. Adults are very small, dark brown; greatest abundance is in autumn when there may be injury to flower seeds.

Dracaena Thrips (*Heliothrips dracaenae*)—Dusky yellow with abdomen shaded with brown, with netted head, thorax, and wings. It is present in California on dracaena, rubber tree, Kentia palm, sago palm, and century plant.

Florida Flower Thrips (*Frankliniella bispinosa*)—A southern pest of roses, the white-blossomed Spanish needle, and other flowers, of strawberry blossoms, which either drop off or turn into brown, hard berries, of citrus bloom. They are found in tomato blossoms but are only occasionally damaging to these. The adult has an orange head and thorax, lemon-yellow abdomen, which is often curled over the back when disturbed. The larvae are similar but paler in color, lack wings.

84. Rosebud blasted by thrips, and opening flower with petal edges browned.

Flower Thrips (*Frankliniella tritici*)—Wheat Thrips, present in nearly every state but primarily an eastern species. It is an omnivorous feeder on grasses, weeds, flowers, field, forage, and truck crops, fruit and shade trees, berries, vines, but with preference for grasses, legumes, roses, and peonies. Young thrips are lemon yellow, adults amber or brownish yellow with an orange thorax, $\frac{1}{20}$ inch long. They injure only the flowers, not foliage, and come to roses and other ornamentals from flowers on trees, grasses, weeds, etc., nearby.

Rosebuds turn brown and either ball, petals staying stuck together, or open part way to crippled, distorted blossoms with brown edges on the petals. The thrips can be seen inside the petals, usually near the base. They prefer light-colored blossoms and are most injurious with the June bloom. The life cycle may be completed in 2 weeks and there can be many generations, but there is comparatively little injury on the fall display of roses. Daylilies and peonies are often markedly injured by flower thrips and they are common on Japanese iris, though seldom so harmful on this host.

Control. This is an exceedingly difficult insect to control because thrips are continuously arriving on rosebuds from nearby weed, tree, and grass flowers. The old tartar emetic and brown sugar concoction was given up in favor of DDT, but that has not been too efficient. Lindane is temporarily effective but frequent applications have to be made. There is a small aerosol bomb containing lindane for use on garden roses, and frequent spot treatment of buds helps a little. Some find a malathion spray useful. Dieldrin is promising. Infested buds and all blooms as they start to fade should be cut off and destroyed to reduce the thrips population.

Gladiolus Thrips (*Taeniothrips simplex*)—All too universally present in gardens. A relatively new insect, noticed first in 1929 in Ohio and Canada and rapidly distributed through the country. Of chief importance on gladiolus, it is also a pest of iris—Spanish, Japanese, German, and bulbous—and is known to feed and breed on amaryllis, narcissus, freesia, aster, delphinium, hollyhock (Plate XXX).

Although one of the larger species of thrips, the adult is $\frac{1}{16}$ inch or less in length, black or brownish black with a creamy white band across the base of the wings. Females insert kidney-shaped eggs in growing plant tissues. First-stage larvae, white with red eyes, hatch in about a week, changing soon to pale yellow second-stage larvae. The next, prepupa, stage is orange; the true pupal stage is light yellow with white antennae, wing pads, and legs, red eyes; the dark adult appears in about 3 days. The complete life cycle takes 2 to 4 weeks, depending on the temperature, the effective range being from 50° to 90°F. There are several generations in the garden, and breeding may continue on corms in storage. Thrips are killed by low temperatures and do not winter in the ground except in warm climates.

Injury on gladiolus is a silvery appearance of the foliage, due to the many small areas where cell sap has been lost, followed by browning and dying of leaves. Flowers are deformed, with whitish flecks or streaks, spikes may not open. Corms in storage become sticky, corky, russeted, and fail to germinate when planted or produce poor or no flowers.

Control. Until DDT came to the rescue many gardeners had almost given up growing gladiolus; now thrips can be readily controlled. Starting when leaves are about 6 inches high, spray every 7 to 10 days with DDT (2 tablespoons 50 per cent wettable powder to a gallon of water) or apply 5 per cent DDT until flowering. If the thrips in your garden seem to be getting resistant to DDT there are several other effective new materials—toxaphene, 20 per cent dust, chlordane, 5 per cent dust, or lindane or dieldrin. All of these may injure flowers in cool weather and treatment should cease when spikes begin to show color. Malathion can probably be used safely even on plants in bloom. After harvest and curing, put corms in a paper bag, add a little DDT 5 per cent dust, and shake until they are evenly coated, then store as usual. This has largely replaced the older treatment with naphthalene flakes. Infested corms that have not been treated over the winter can be soaked for 3 hours in Lysol, 1½ tablespoons to 1 gallon of water, just before planting.

Grape Thrips (*Drepanothrips reuteri*)—A pest of grapes in California. It looks like the flower thrips and causes burning and curling of young leaves, scarring of berries. Spray or dust with DDT.

Grass Thrips (*Anaphothrips obscurus*)—Sometimes abundant on grains and grasses, occasionally on corn, destroying softer parts of foliage, flowers, and developing kernels. Destroy old stems and litter where insects hibernate.

Greenhouse Thrips (*Heliothrips haemorrhoidalis*)—Practically world-wide, present outdoors in California, Florida, Georgia, and similar warm climates, and in greenhouses nearly everywhere. Infested garden plants include avocado, on which this is a major pest, citrus, grape, mango, sapote, cherimoya, guava, and other subtropical fruits and many ornamentals, including arbutus, azalea, carissa, croton, cypress, eucalyptus, eugenia, hibbertia, laurestinus, mandevilla, mesembryanthemum, myrtle, rhodendron, rose, statice, toyon, viburnum. In greenhouses there may be serious injury to amaryllis, begonia, chrysanthemum, citrus plants, croton, cyclamen, dahlia, ferns, fuchsia, gloxinia, nasturtium, orchids, palm, rubber plant, and others.

The greenhouse thrips is distinguished by a deep network of lines over head and central portion of the body, which is blackish brown, with the posterior end lighter; $\frac{1}{24}$ inch long, legs yellow, wings slightly clouded but without bands, antennae slender and needlelike at tip. Feeding is almost entirely on foliage and fruits, often in concentrated colonies on inner parts of trees and shrubs, with all stages present at the same time. Eggs are inserted just under the epidermis of leaves or fruit, producing egg blisters. Plants look silvery or bleached, leaves papery, wilting, dying, sometimes dropping off. Foliage and fruit are spotted with reddish-black dots of excrement.

Control. Avocados can be sprayed with DDT with a miticide added to take care of the increase in mites. Dieldrin is coming into use as a 1 per cent dust where residue is not a problem. Malathion and lindane are used as sprays or dusts and, in commercial greenhouses, parathion as a spray or aerosol.

Hollyhock Thrips (*Liothrips varicornis*)—Apparently limited to a semi-arid climate; found in California principally on hollyhock. It resembles the toyon thrips; larvae are brilliant red and black, adults all black. Colonies feed in depressions in leaves, stems, and roots. Water the soil around base of infested plants heavily; destroy all old stalks and volunteer plants during fall and winter.

Iris Thrips (*Bregmatothrips iridis*)—Often abundantly infesting Japanese iris. Larvae, first white, later yellow, rasp folds of inner leaves, causing russeting, blackening, stunting; tops die and turn brown. DDT should control this pest.

Lily Bulb Thrips (*Liothrips vaneecki*)—Confined to lily and orchids; known in New York, North Carolina, California, Oregon, and Washington. This species, shiny black, $\frac{1}{16}$ inch long, with salmon-pink and black larvae and pupae, spends its entire life on bulbs, feeding on epidermis of outer scales near base. Injured areas tend to turn rusty brown and be sunken or flabby, but there is no great damage.

Madrona Thrips (*Thrips madroni*)—In Oregon and California on ceanothus, madrona, azalea, elderberry, rhododendron. It is pale yellow to dark brown.

Onion Thrips (*Thrips tabaci*)—Probably the most widely distributed thrips in the world, found in all onion-growing sections, attacking nearly all garden plants, many field crops, and weeds. Many hosts are incidental with little breeding upon them, but aside from onions some of the more important vegetable hosts are: bean, beet, carrot, cabbage, cauliflower, celery, cucumber, melons, peas, squash, tomato, and turnip. Injury to onions shows first as whitish blotches, then blasting and distortion of leaf tips, followed by withering, browning, and falling over on the ground. The bulbs are distorted, undersized. Thrips congregate in great numbers between leaf sheaths and stem, and carry over on bulbs in storage. Peas, cucumbers, and melons have crinkled, curled, dwarfed foliage.

Roses and carnations have petals spotted and streaked. Other ornamentals infested by onion thrips include asparagus fern, campanula, chrysanthemum, dahlia, gaillardia, gloxinia, mignonette, Jerusalem-cherry, sweet pea. Onion thrips transmit the spotted wilt virus to tomatoes and many flowers.

It is variable in color, ranging from pale yellow to dark brown, $\frac{1}{25}$ inch long. Wings are a uniform dusky gray without bands; larvae are creamy white; pupation is in soil. Eggs are laid in surface tissue and hatch in about 5 days in summer. The first molt of the larvae is on plants, the second in the soil. A generation is completed in a little over 2 weeks and in mild climates like California continues through the year. Winter hosts are weeds and bulbs in storage.

Control. DDT dust, 5 or 10 per cent, sometimes combined with sulfur, has been giving fairly satisfactory control of onion thrips, but some of the newer hydrocarbons may be more effective. Dieldrin, $2\frac{1}{2}$ per cent dust, has a long residual action, giving commercial control on onions at 21-day intervals; $1\frac{1}{2}$ per cent dust is satisfactory at shorter intervals. Heptachlor, 5 per cent dust, has been highly effective in tests, with $2\frac{1}{2}$ per cent aldrin and 20 per cent toxaphene also giving commercial control.

Pear Thrips (*Taeniothrips inconsequens*)—An imported species, first noted in California in 1904, now present in Washington and Oregon and in New York, Pennsylvania, and Maryland. Prune is injured even more than pear. Other hosts include apple, apricot, cherry, grape, peach, plum, poplar, maple, California laurel, madrona, willow, and weeds and grasses around orchards. The adult pear thrips is uniformly dark brown, slender, bluntly pointed at each end, $\frac{1}{25}$ inch long, with grayish wings lighter at the base. It emerges from the ground in spring and feeds in developing buds, causing a bleeding and gumming of pear buds, blackening of prune buds, deformed leaves and blossoms and crop reduction. After feeding 3 weeks eggs are laid in stems of fruit and foliage. White larvae appear in 2 weeks and feed under husks of young fruit causing scarring and distortion. After 3 more weeks they drop to the ground, burrow into the soil, and construct cells several inches to 3 feet below the surface, where they remain until the next spring.

Control. Spray trees thoroughly after buds begin to show green with DDT, at rate of 2 pounds 50 per cent wettable powder per 100 gallons of water.

Privet Thrips (*Dendrothrips ornatus*)—An eastern species very injurious to privet in some seasons, turning hedges uniformly gray and dusty looking. The leaves may be somewhat puckered. The larvae are yellow, spindle-shaped, as many as 20 to 25 on the underside of a single small leaf. The adults are dark brown to black with a bright red band. They can be killed with DDT, but this will encourage privet mites. Two treatments with nicotine sulfate and soap or a rotenone-pyrethrum spray at 10- to 14-day intervals will control this species without increasing mites.

Tobacco Thrips (*Frankliniella fusca*)—On tobacco, cotton, and other plants, a vector of the spotted wilt virus. Nymphs are yellow, adults brown.

Toyon Thrips (*Rhyncothrips ilex*)—On California Christmasberry. The adult, black, glossy, with silvery-white wings, hibernates in curled leaves, mates in early spring, feeds on new unfolding leaves, and lays yellow waxy eggs loosely on them. The larvae, pale yellow, later reddish, feed with adults on new growth, causing it to be distorted, curled, sometimes killed. When mature, larvae drop to the ground to pupate, rest while the toyon is in bloom, then the new adults feed on the second rush of new growth. Natural spread is slow; most dissemination is on nursery stock. Pick off and destroy curled leaves in fall and winter. Spray for active stages with DDT, nicotine sulfate and soap, or pyrethrum.

Western Flower Thrips (*Frankliniella moultoni* and *F. occidentalis*) —On practically all types of plants. They vary in color from lemon yellow to dusky yellow brown, winter on weeds, and feed in tree blossoms in spring, causing scarring and distortion of fruits. They are more injurious to apricot, peach, plum, and nectarine blossoms in southern California than farther north, where the blooming season is over before populations build up. They injure grapes in season, beans as they come through the ground. They injure cucurbit vines suffering from lack of water, cause blossom drop of peas, tomatoes, melons, sometimes strawberries. Blooms of roses, carnations, sweet peas, and gladiolus are streaked. This thrips spreads spotted-wilt disease that infects tomatoes and many other vegetables and ornamentals on the West coast.

Eggs are laid in tender stems, buds, flowers, and hatch in 5 to 15 days. Larvae feed on succulent portions for 7 to 12 days, molt once on the host, drop to the ground, pupate, molt once during this resting stage, and, in cool climates, hibernate in protected spots. Peak of infestation is in late spring. Adults can be carried long distances by wind, but migrations are usually local. See Flower Thrips for control.

TOADS

Toads, family Bufonidae, are tailless amphibians which commonly live on land, although their eggs are laid in water. They have stout, puffy bodies and warty skin, but the skin is not scaly like that of reptiles (snakes and lizards). They take about 5 years to mature and are very definitely garden friends, eating countless numbers of insects, snails, slugs, and worms. It has been estimated that a toad can devour in 24 hours insects equal to 4 times the capacity of its stomach. Because they are cold-blooded they may, like fish, succumb to rotenone and some other chemicals, so let the toads hop out of the way before spraying or dusting. They do not cause warts!

TREEHOPPERS

Treehoppers are sucking insects in the order Homoptera. They are closely related to leafhoppers but belong to the family Membracidae, which is characterized by having a pronotum (taking the place of the thorax in other insects) greatly enlarged and grotesquely developed into horns, knobs, and other peculiar shapes. Treehoppers have been called the brownies of the insect world. They injure trees and shrubs by their egg-laying, and the nymphs feed on weeds, grasses, corn, and legumes.

Buffalo Treehopper (*Stictocephala bubalus*)—Serious in the Middle West, often damaging in the East to apple, pear, peach, quince, cherry, and other fruits, and to rose, elm, locust, cottonwood, and other ornamentals. The injury comes from the wounds made by the female in oviposition. These are double rows of curved slits inside which 6 to 12 elongated yellowish eggs are embedded in the inner bark. Infested trees look rough, scaly, or cracked and seldom make vigorous growth. The fungi causing rose cankers and other diseases gain entrance through the slits.

Eggs winter in the wood; they hatch in late spring into pale green spiny nymphs which drop from the tree and feed on sap of various weeds and grasses until mid-July or August when they become adult. Viewed from above they are triangles, light green, blunt at the head end with a short horn at each upper corner, pointed at the rear, ¼ inch long. The female has a knifelike ovipositor to cut slits in twigs for her August egg-laying.

Control. Until recently, spraying has not helped much; most reliance has been placed in weed removal around orchards and avoiding such cover crops as alfalfa and sweet clover, although dormant oil spraying has destroyed some eggs. DDT has been reported effective in some experiments, not in others. In Connecticut parathion has given successful control (at rate of 1 pound 15 per cent to 100 gallons) applied to trees and ground covers in June before egg-laying.

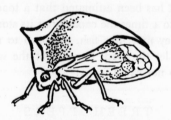

85. Buffalo treehopper, side view.

Three-cornered Alfalfa Hopper (*Spissistilus festinus*)—A western alfalfa pest, also a nuisance in Florida on beans, cowpeas, tomato, watermelon, with adults common on hickory, oak, black locust, viburnum. It is yellow green with the outline of a triangle when viewed from above. DDT combined with lindane has been helpful in some instances.

Two-marked Treehopper (*Enchenopa binotata*)—Frequently found on butternut, sometimes on locust, bittersweet, sycamore, hickory, willow, wild grape, redbud, and hoptree. This small treehopper looks much like a bird in side view, with a high curved horn projecting forward from the thorax. It is dusky brown with 2 lemon-yellow spots on the back. The female lays eggs in butternut buds and in twigs just below the buds. These are uncovered, but she also lays eggs in bark of locust and other trees and these she covers with a frothy, waxy material in corrugated layers. Eggs are laid in August and September and hatch the following May into small, white, powdery nymphs which mature in late June and July into very active adults. Butternut buds are often destroyed by the egg-laying and leaves punctured. Grape stems and bittersweet vines may be noticeably punctured. There is no very satisfactory control. Some nymphs can be killed with nicotine sulfate in late May.

WALKINGSTICKS

Walkingsticks belong to the grasshopper order, Orthoptera, and to the family Phasmatidae, a remarkable group of insects which so closely resemble their environment, twig or leaf, they go unnoticed until they move. Many species are tropical. Those in this country, except for one in Florida, are wingless. They are very long and thin, with the thorax about half the body length; they have long legs and antennae. The legs are all alike, the fore legs not being modified for grasping as in the mantids, with which they might be confused. They have the power of partially replacing a lost leg at another molt. They have biting mouth parts and feed on foliage.

Walkingstick (*Diapheromera femorata*)—Northern Walkingstick, the common species from New England to the Rocky Mountains. It prefers black oak and wild cherry but feeds also on hickory, locust, and other trees, even on roses and various shrubs. Young walkingsticks are pale green, changing to dark green, gray, or brown as they mature. The female is stouter and longer than the male, up to 3 inches. They are adult after 4 or 5 molts, mate in August, and drop bean-shaped black eggs promiscuously on the ground from the trees. They remain in the litter until the next May, or even the following May. The nymphs feed on tree foliage rather ravenously, and shade trees and other ornamentals can be sprayed with lead arsenate.

WASPS

Most wasps are not garden pests. The few harmful species are many, many times outweighed by the parasitic wasps which do so much to keep insects within bounds. Like bees and sawflies, wasps belong to the order Hymenoptera, characterized by 2 pairs of membranous wings hooked together. The abdomen is joined to the thorax by a slender waist; the mouth parts are adapted for chewing and lapping; there is complete metamorphosis. The female has a definite ovipositor and in some species this is used as a stinger, but there are other species which do not sting man. There are about 90,000 species in the world in a great many families. Only a few families of importance to gardeners are listed here.

86. *Tomato hornworm parasitized by braconid wasp. The white egglike objects are cocoons.*

Agaontidae. Fig wasps, imported to pollinate the Smyrna fig, which bears only female flowers. They develop in galled, infertile flowers on anther-bearing caprifig and take the pollen to the Smyrna.

Braconidae. Braconid wasps, small with a short abdomen, important parasites of aphids (note the many dead aphids with a round hole in the back), of larvae and pupae of moths and butterflies and some beetles. Some pupate in cocoons on the outside of the body of the host. Tomato hornworms and catalpa sphinx caterpillars are often covered with white oval objects that look like eggs but are cocoons of braconid wasps.

Chalcididae. Chalcid wasps, minute or very small, short-bodied, with head as wide as or wider than the thorax, black or brown, wings almost veinless, legs short with hind femora much enlarged. All are parasites, chiefly on larvae of beetles, moths, butterflies, and flies, but some are hyperparasites living on other beneficial insects and in that way become harmful.

Chrysididae. Cuckoo or jewel wasps, brilliant blue, green, red, or purple, with body sculptured, seldom over ½ inch. They are external parasites of other bees and wasps, lay eggs in other nests.

Cynipidae. Gall wasps, very small, responsible for most of the galls on leaves and twigs of oaks and other plants. There are many species and the galls may be numerous and unsightly, but the hosts are never killed and seldom even weakened.

Ichneumonidae. Ichneumon wasps, a large family of slender insects with elongate abdomens (sometimes sickle-shaped), often with an ovipositor longer than the body but not used for stinging man. One species has a body 1½ inches long and a 3-inch hairlike ovipositor which penetrates bark of trees to parasitize horntails. The various members of this family are important natural controls of harmful beetles, caterpillars, and sawflies.

Scelionidae. Egg parasites, useful in controlling Mormon crickets and grasshoppers, but sometimes killing mantids, lacewings, and other beneficial insects.

Sphecidae. Solitary wasps, tunneling in soil or wood, stocking their larders with spiders, grasshoppers, caterpillars, aphids, bugs, and flies. This group includes the mud-daubers and the giant cicada-killer.

Tiphiidae. Tiphiid wasps, mostly fair-sized, black, somewhat hairy, parasites on grubs of scarabaeid beetles. One species was introduced to control Japanese beetles and has been quite a help.

Torymidae. Very small, metallic green parasites, mostly on insects living inside plant tissues, galls, or seeds.

Trichogrammatidae. Very minute parasites inside eggs of other insects, important in the control of various caterpillars.

Vespidae. Social wasps, the hornets, yellow jackets, etc., making nests of paper from wood fiber, and solitary potter wasps. Most are beneficial, feeding their young on injurious caterpillars, acting as pollinators, but the giant hornet is a real garden pest.

Cicada-killer (*Sphecius speciosus*)—Digger Wasp. A very large wasp, up to 1½ inches long, black with the abdomen banded with yellow, and a wickedly long curved ovipositor or stinger. Appearing in mid- and late summer this wasp makes a mess of lawns, tunneling far underground and marking the openings to its burrows with little mounds of earth. It also damages paths, banks, and terraces. I have seen it abundant enough to lift and crack concrete sidewalks with its tunnels and mounds, to say nothing of scaring to death all the passers-by. After making her burrow, the wasp goes to look for a cicada in a tree. She

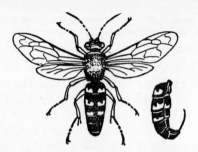

87. *Cicada-killer, or digger wasp, with side view of abdomen showing ovipositor, "stinger."*

darts at it and they both fall to the ground. The wasp stings the cicada to paralyze it and then, straddling her bulky prey, she crawls up a tree to a good launching point to take flight toward her burrow. If she does not make it the first time, she tries another tree and a second glide. Arriving at the opening, she drags in the cicada, stores it in a cell, and lays an egg between its legs. Each cell is provided with 1 or 2 cicadas, sealed off before the next cell is filled. The egg hatches in 2 or 3 days and the larva feeds on the cicada contents for about 2 weeks, then makes a cocoon of silk, and rests in it until the next summer, when it pupates and produces the adult.

Control. I used to whack these creatures with a kind of giant fly swatter made of heavy wire mesh on a stick and I used to squirt carbon bisulfide into the holes. Dusting 5 per cent chlordane into and around the openings is easier and probably more effective.

Giant Hornet (*Vespa crabro* var. *germana*)—European Hornet, Vespa Hornet. It is the largest hornet in this country, 1 inch long, dark reddish brown with orange markings on the abdomen, resembling the cicada-killer but stouter and more hairy, and without such a terrifying ovipositor. It is a special pest of lilacs near New York City, tearing the bark from twigs and branches and girdling them. This looks like the work of a squirrel; it seems impossible that an insect could inflict that much damage. It may also injure boxwood, birch, willow, poplar, and other trees and shrubs, and is found from Massachusetts to North Carolina, mostly along the seaboard but also in Ohio and Pennsylvania. The injury is in late August and September. The wasps use the bark for their nests in hollow trees or suspended from the roof inside barns and other buildings or from the eaves of houses.

88. Giant hornet, natural size and slightly enlarged, tearing bark from lilac stem for nest.

Control. Some recommend trying to find the nest and puffing in calcium cyanide dust but I never have time for that. I have had good success spraying trunks and branches of lilacs with a very heavy dose of rotenone or, more recently, DDT at 2 tablespoons of the 50 per cent powder per gallon. You have to work quickly at first sign of hornets at work. They can tear off a lot of bark in a short time.

WEBWORMS

Webworms are caterpillars that feed protected by webs. Some, like the tent caterpillar, have been treated elsewhere; those commonly known as webworms are discussed here.

Ailanthus Webworm (*Atteva aurea*)—From New York to Illinois and southward, more common in southern states. Tree-of-heaven is the preferred host. The adult moths have bright orange fore wings, marked with 4 crossbands of yellow spots on a dark blue ground, expanding to 1 inch, and dusky, nearly transparent hind wings. The caterpillars, olive brown with fine white lines, feed gregariously in fine webs in August and September, with moths appearing in September and October. Control measures are seldom used, but either lead arsenate or DDT should be effective for young larvae.

Alfalfa Webworm (*Loxostege commixtalis*)—Larvae are greenish-yellow caterpillars with a light stripe down the back; adults are buff-colored moths, irregularly marked with light and dark gray, with a row of spots on underside of hind wings, spreading to 1 or 1¼ inches. Food plants and control are the same as for the beet webworm.

Barberry Webworm (*Omphalocera dentosa*)—Black, white-spotted caterpillars, 1½ inches long, web twigs together and devour leaves of common and Japanese barberry in late summer and fall. The ugly, frass-filled masses remain over ends of shoots during the winter. Spray in summer with lead arsenate or DDT.

Beet Webworm (*Loxostege sticticalis*)—Present from the Mississippi Valley west to the Continental Divide. Along with the alfalfa webworm, this small webbing caterpillar is a general and destructive feeder on cabbage, beet, sugar beet, bean, pea, potato, spinach, cucurbits, and other vegetables, alfalfa and field crops. The larvae work like armyworms, cleaning up one field, then moving en masse to the next. They are yellow or green to nearly black, with a black stripe down the middle of the back and 3 small black dots bearing bristles at the end of each segment. As they skeletonize and devour leaves they make a tube, several inches long, to a hiding place under a clod of earth or other protected spot where they retreat when disturbed. They pupate 2 to 3 weeks in a cell an inch or two underground. The night-flying moth is smoky brown with straw-colored spots and lines and a continuous dark line near the margin of the hind wings. White to yellow or green oval eggs are laid on underside of leaves. There may be 3 partial generations.

Control. Spray or dust with DDT or DDD, changing to rotenone when edible plant parts are formed.

Cabbage Webworm (*Hellula rogatalis*)—An imported species distributed through the states. The caterpillars, grayish yellow with purple stripes, ½ inch long, feed under webbing on inner leaves, hearts, stalks of cabbage, cauliflower, kale, sometimes on beets, collards, horseradish, radish. The moths are grayish, mottled with brown. Use DDT very early, before worms are protected by their webs.

Corn Root Webworm (*Crambus caliginosellus*)—One of the sod webworms. The caterpillar is whitish, just over ½ inch long; the snout moth is straw-colored with indistinct markings. When one stirs them up walking over grass they move in jerky flights and rest with wings so tightly folded around their bodies they look like tubes. Eggs are laid in summer; young larvae feed a little, then hibernate in nests in grass and sodland, becoming active in spring. They destroy roots and work from the crown into cornstalks, injuring developing leaves like budworms, and often chew stalks at the surface of the ground like cutworms. Full grown in July and August, they pupate underground in a silken cocoon. Do not plant corn in land recently taken over from sod. If young corn shows injury, dig it up and plant a substitute crop.

Cotoneaster Webworm (*Cremona cotoneaster*)—First noted in Oregon in 1929, present also in Washington. Yellow larvae, turning dark when grown, make silken tubes from a larger silken refuge at the base of branch junctions. They skeletonize leaves and make unsightly webs. They winter in the refuge, pupate there in spring, produce grayish-black, night-active moths. Small plants die, others are weakened. Use DDT or lead arsenate or rotenone spray or dust.

Fall Webworm (*Hyphantria cunea*)—Widely distributed, feeding on at least 120 varieties of fruit, shade, and woodland trees. Popular hosts are apple, cherry, peach, pecan, English walnut, black walnut, ash, boxelder, birch, chokecherry, elm, hickory, linden, poplar, sycamore, white oak, willow. Roses and other shrubs are sometimes webbed. The webworm acts much like the tent caterpillar but makes its nest over the ends of branches rather than at tree crotches.

Cocoons enclosing brown pupae winter under trash on the ground or under bark. Satiny white moths, often marked with brown spots, wings spreading 1½ to 1¾ inches, emerge over a long period in spring. They lay greenish eggs in masses of 200 to 500, often covered with a woolly layer of scales. The caterpillars are pale green or yellow with a dark stripe down the back and a yellow stripe along each side. The body is covered with very long silky gray hairs arising from black and yellow tubercles. When full grown, about an inch long after 4 to 6 weeks of feeding, they crawl down the trees to form cocoons. There are 2 broods in Middle Atlantic states, the first feeding in late May and June, the second and more destructive from July through September. The larvae spin a layer of silk over the surface of a leaf as soon as they start feeding, eventually webbing together the ends of several branches. The nests are always most unsightly and one or more branches may be defoliated but seldom the whole tree.

Control. Summer sprays for codling moth will prevent damage by webworms on apples. Ornamentals can be sprayed with DDT or lead arsenate. It is often possible to cut off webbed ends of branches and to burn the nests without resorting to spraying if this is done as soon as webs are first seen. There are several natural enemies, egg parasites and others.

Garden Webworm (*Loxostege similalis*)—A native, found over most of the country but more of a pest in the Middle West and Southwest. It is much like the alfalfa and beet webworms, attacking alfalfa, clover, and field crops, but also working on garden vegetables such as beans, soybeans, cowpeas, beets, and on strawberries, scarlet verbena, and castor bean. The hairy caterpillars are greenish with dark spots, a little over an inch long. They spin webs wherever they go and make silken tubes for shelter on the ground. The moth is buff-colored with grayish markings, an inch across the wings. There are up to 5 generations in Texas, 2 or 3 in the North.

Control. Dust vegetables near harvest with pyrethrum or rotenone, others with DDT or toxaphene.

Juniper Webworm (*Dichomeris marginella*)—A European species first recorded in 1910, now present from Maine to North Carolina and west to Missouri, also in California on common and Irish juniper and red-cedar. The winter is passed as partly grown larvae in silken cases in webbed foliage. They are light brown with a reddish-brown stripe down the back, 2 wider dark brown stripes along the side, with short white hairs over the body, ½ inch long. They feed again in spring, pupate in May. The moths, emerging in June and early July, have brown fore wings with white margins, fringed gray hind wings, wingspread only ⅗ inch. They lay eggs in leaf axils of new terminal growth, and the caterpillars web the needles together with silk. The webs enclose a good bit of frass and the needles turn brown and die. Sometimes the whole top of a small juniper is webbed and massed together.

Control. Spray with lead arsenate or DDT in midsummer to kill young caterpillars. Cut out webbed masses where possible. In spring a nicotine or pyrethrum spray applied with enough force to break the webs is helpful.

Mimosa Webworm (*Homadaula albizziae*)—Discovered on mimosa in Washington, D.C., in 1940 and now a serious pest of both mimosa and honey locust from Delaware through North Carolina, reported also from Georgia. The moths, gray with a silver luster, stippled with black spots, ½-inch wingspread, appear in June and lay eggs on mimosa flowers as well as foliage. The larvae, dark brown sometimes diffused with rose or pink, just over ½ inch long, feed first gregariously in a web spun over flowers and leaves, later singly on tender terminal leaves and on green pods of both hosts. The foliage is usually skeletonized, eaten from the underside with the upper epidermis left intact. Leaves die, turn dull gray on mimosa, brown as if fire-scorched on honey locust. In midsummer larvae descend to the ground on silken threads and spin cocoons in cracks in bark, or in the ground cover. There are 2 generations and a partial third. The webbing is most conspicuous in August from the second brood.

Control. Lead arsenate and DDT are both effective. In Maryland DDT at the rate of 2 pounds 50 per cent powder to 100 gallons of water has given satisfactory control applied about June 15 and August 20.

Parsnip Webworm (*Depressaria heracliana*)—Present on parsnip, celery, and related weeds in northern states east of the Mississippi River. Flower heads are webbed together and eaten by small yellow, green, or grayish caterpillars with small black spots and short hairs. They interfere with seed production and may mine in stems. The moth is gray, winters under loose bark, lays eggs in spring on developing flowers. Caterpillars pupate in mines in stems, moths coming out in late summer. Cut and burn infested flower heads. Spray or dust with DDT, calcium arsenate, or pyrethrum.

Pine False Webworm (*Acantholyda erythrocephala*)—A sawfly found in parts of Connecticut, New York, New Jersey, and Pennsylvania on red and white pines, sometimes other species. The larvae are greenish gray striped with purplish red, up to 4/5 inch long. Adults emerge from earthen cells from mid-April to early May and lay eggs on needles. These hatch the last 3 weeks in May and the young larvae feed gregariously in a loose webbing, cutting off the needles and pulling them into the web. There can be extensive defoliation. Older larvae make silken tubes along the twigs, then drop to the ground in late June. There is only 1 generation. Spray with DDT or lead arsenate in May before needles are webbed.

Pine Webworm (*Tetralopha robustella*)—Pine Pyralid, a native present from New England to Florida and west to Wisconsin on pitch, red, white, jack, and loblolly pines, injurious to seedlings or small trees, not to larger trees. The moths, with purple-black fore wings with a transverse gray band, smoky black hind wings, spreading to 1 inch, emerge from June to August. The larvae, yellow brown with 2 dark stripes along each side, 3/4 inch long when grown, work near the ends of terminal twigs, producing quantities of brown frass in silken webs. When mature they go into the ground and spin flimsy cocoons for the winter. Either lead arsenate or DDT is effective if applied before webbing starts.

Sod Webworms (*Crambus* spp.)—Lawn Moths, small millers that fly up when you walk across the grass. There are many species damaging lawns in different parts of the country, but they are more abundant in warm climates. They usually injure blue or bent grass. In California *Crambus bonifatellus* prefers moist lowlands, *C. sperryellus* drier locations. The former is a slender, gray, black-spotted larva with a brown head; the moth is creamy buff with small white, brown, or black spots. The latter is a light gray larva, with dark spots on head and body; the moth is golden with fore wings streaked with silver. The bluegrass webworm (*C. teterellus*) is more at home in Kentucky and other parts of the Southeast. It is often accompanied by the striped sod webworm and the leather-colored sod webworm. The predominant species in the East is *C. vulgivagellus,* the vagabond crambus or black-headed sod webworm, normally a grass feeder, sometimes attacking corn.

The moths all have snouts, made of labial palps, and they fly slowly over grass at dusk, in a zigzag fashion, dropping eggs anywhere. Young larvae skeletonize grass blades; older caterpillars cut them off completely. They make silken tubes between the grass stems, shelters camouflaged with bits of grass and bright green excrement. Pupation is in silken cocoons just below surface of the ground. There may be several overlapping generations.

Control. Dichlorethyl ether has been used on lawns for temporary control, but chlordane (1¼ pounds of 5 per cent dust or 2½ ounces in a spray, per 1000 square feet) or DDT (2½ pounds 5 per cent dust or 4 ounces wettable powder) gives a longer residual action.

Spotted Beet Webworm (*Hymenia perspectalis*)—The larva is green with purple dots on its head; the moth is cinnamon brown with narrow white bands on the fore wings. Eggs are laid on leaves of beet and amaranth. Use pyrethrum-sulfur dust if the foliage is to be used for greens, otherwise DDT.

WEEVILS

Weevils are really beetles, of the order Coleoptera, with the head more or less prolonged into a beak or snout, with mouth parts at the end. Most species are in the family Curculionidae and are injurious plant feeders. Weevils infesting fruits and nuts are often called curculios and have been treated under that heading.

Adaleres Weevil (*Adaleres humeralis*)—Light to dark brown beetles with grayish mottling, punctate wing covers, feeding on foliage and terminal buds of avocado.

Apple Flea Weevil (*Rhynchaenus pallicornis*)—Found from Missouri and Illinois east to New York, but more destructive in the western portion of this range, on apple, haw, winged elm, hazelnut, quince, wild crab, and blackberry. The adults, very small black snout beetles,

$\frac{1}{10}$ inch long, winter in trash or grass under apple trees. In spring they puncture newly opening leaves and buds, lay eggs along midribs. The grubs mine between upper and lower leaf surfaces, pupate in a cell inside the leaf, emerge as beetles in late May and June. They feed for 2 weeks on foliage, riddling the leaves with tiny shot holes, then go into hibernation. Two sprays of DDT or cryolite, applied at the pre-pink stage and 1 week later, give effective control.

Arborvitae Weevil (*Phyllobius intrusus*)—A Japanese species found in Rhode Island in 1947, now present in Connecticut and Massachusetts. The adult, covered with greenish scales and fine short hairs, emerges from the soil in early May and is around until July, laying eggs around roots, which hatch in 13 to 17 days. The larvae, white to light pink with brown heads, feed on roots of arborvitae, retinospora, juniper. They pupate in early spring, 10 inches deep in the soil, and the adults feed in the daytime on the top thirds of plants, eating tiny, cup-shaped areas from new terminal leaves. Adults can be killed by spraying with DDT or lindane.

Asiatic Oak Weevil (*Cyrtepistomus castaneus*)—A new and serious pest of oak and chestnut, first found in New Jersey in 1933, now known also in Delaware, Maryland, New York, Pennsylvania, Virginia, and West Virginia. There is a one-year cycle with larvae apparently feeding and wintering on roots. They pupate in June with adults emerging in great numbers about a week later. The weevils, black to dark reddish brown, with metallic green scales, start feeding on sapling oaks and chestnuts, eating everything but mid-veins of leaves, but by August they move to larger trees and may also invade hickory, hazelnut, beech, dogwood, raspberry, and some other trees and shrubs. They enter houses in the fall.

Bean Weevil (*Acanthoscelides obtectus*)—Probably a native American although found around the world. Beans stored for seed or food are almost certain to be devoured by weevils unless precautions are taken. This seed weevil is a small snout beetle, $\frac{1}{8}$ inch long, olive brown mottled with darker brown and gray, with reddish legs and antennae. Escaping from stored beans to the garden, it lays eggs in holes chewed along the seam of the bean pod. Small, hairy, white grubs, produced in 3 to 30 days, enter and feed in young seed (Plate XXXV). If the storage room is warm there may be many generations during the winter, the grubs pupating in cells inside the beans, the weevils eating their way out through the seed coat, leaving conspicuous round holes.

Control. Never plant seed known to be infested. After harvest weevils can be killed and increase prevented by mixing each 2 pounds of seed with 1 pound of hydrated lime or rotenone or pyrethrum dust (of course, wash off thoroughly before using for food). Other methods include fumigation with carbon bisulfide, or killing weevils with dry heat, 135°F. for 3 or 4 hours, or suspending seeds in a bag in water and heating to 140°F. Dusting with derris or DDT in the field soon after beans start to bloom helps to control the weevil.

Black Elm Bark Weevil (*Magdalis barbita*)—A small, jet-black beetle with a prominent snout, found from New York to South Dakota and south to Georgia. The beetles emerge from branches of unhealthy elms in May or June and lay eggs in bark. Grubs burrow to the inner bark and sapwood, making longitudinal galleries 1½ inches long. Maintain tree vigor by fertilizing; water during droughts.

Black Vine Weevil (*Brachyrhinus sulcatus*)—Cyclamen Grub, a European species now widely distributed here. It is a serious pest of yew, Taxus, of rhododendron, azalea, retinospora, and some other broad- and narrow-leaved evergreens and is a greenhouse menace. Nearly 80 hosts have been listed including ampelopsis, begonia, blackberry, cranberry, cyclamen, gloxinia, geranium, gardenia, maidenhair fern, primrose, raspberry, spirea, strawberry (though not as injurious as the strawberry root weevil), wisteria.

The adult is a small weevil, ⅜ inch long, with a short snout, black or brownish with fine yellow hairs, and a sort of corrugated effect down its hard, wingless body (Plate XXXV). Larvae are small, whitish, curved grubs which remain in soil feeding on small roots, often destroying them completely. Hibernation is usually as partly grown larvae, sometimes as adults in soil. After feeding on roots during April and May larvae turn into soft white pupae, emerging as weevils in June. They hide in the soil during the day, feed on foliage at night. They feed for a month or more before laying eggs in cracks and crevices in the soil and in trash around plants. The young grubs, hatching in 10 days, feed on fine hair roots and on bark around the crown, but their heaviest damage is the next spring.

Specimens of yew newly transplanted from nursery to garden are particularly subject to grub injury. Small roots are eaten off, larger roots girdled. If certain plants in a yew hedge do not start into new growth at the normal time in spring, if tops turn yellow, then brown, the black vine weevil is probably to blame. Feeding by the adult is from the tip of the needle or along the side. On rhododendrons large irregular holes are eaten in from leaf margins at night. In greenhouses grubs continue to feed during the winter months, causing stunting, death, of cyclamen, primrose, and other plants. Adults appear earlier in spring than out-of-doors and lay eggs over a longer period.

Control. Watch newly transplanted evergreens closely; grubs or adults may enter gardens in soil around balled plants. The wingless adults do not migrate far, but they can crawl to established shrubs nearby. The adults are easier to kill than the grubs. Spray plants, foliage, and soil, in late June, with chlordane (1 pint 76 per cent emulsion to 100 gallons or 1 teaspoon to a gallon) or use 5 per cent chlordane dust (5 pounds to 1000 square feet); or spray with 25 per cent heptachlor emulsion; or 23 per cent aldrin emulsion; or 50 per cent malathion (1 pint to 100 gallons or 1 teaspoon per gallon); or use dieldrin (1 pound to 100 gallons). It is important to get the chemical on the soil as well as on the foliage. The use of baits, sodium fluosilicate or apple pomace, has been largely replaced by more efficient sprays.

Boll Weevil (*Anthonomus grandis*)—Cotton Boll Weevil, the most notoriously evil insect in the world, yet with such a beneficial influence on methods of agriculture in one section of the country it has had a monument erected to it! As home gardeners you are not directly concerned with controlling the boll weevil, but as citizens you are profoundly affected by it. It has been estimated that every person in the United States pays ten dollars a year more for cotton goods because of the boll weevil. Its arrival in Texas from Mexico in 1892 closed down cotton gin and oil mills, caused banks to fail, depreciated land values, made wealthy growers into paupers. It still costs us an enormous amount each year. Cotton farmers spend about $75,000,000 annually just for insecticides to beat the weevil and yet losses average nearly $230,000,000 a year.

If, when the boll weevil was first noted, a barrier zone, an area about 50 miles wide where no cotton was grown, had been instituted, the weevil might have been kept in bounds, just as the gypsy moth has been confined to New England. But at that time it did not seem possible to live in Texas without growing cotton and, rather than take away the source of livelihood from families in such a barrier zone the Texas legislature turned thumbs down on that proposal and let the boll weevil go its destructive way.

The weevil is small, ¼ inch long, hard-shelled, yellow, gray, or brown, nearly black with age, covered with grayish fuzz, with a long, slender snout. It lays an egg in 100 to 400 cotton buds or squares and there may be 8 to 10 generations a year. It also feeds on okra, holly-hock, and hibiscus, plants related to cotton.

When the boll-weevil devastation was at its height, cotton farmers learned to do two things. One was ordinary sanitation, clearing the fields and burning old stalks just as is recommended for nearly every pest in this manual. The other was diversification of crops. They grew corn, hay, potatoes, sugar cane, and especially peanuts and hogs. One county in Alabama cleared $5,000,000 on its first peanut crop. And so, at Enterprise, Alabama, the citizens of Coffee County erected a fountain in honor of the boll weevil, and put on it this inscription, which I once made a special trip to read:

> IN PROFOUND APPRECIATION
> OF THE BOLL WEEVIL
> AND WHAT IT HAS DONE
> AS THE HERALD OF PROSPERITY
> THIS MONUMENT WAS ERECTED
> BY THE CITIZENS OF
> ENTERPRISE, COFFEE COUNTY, ALABAMA.

Broadbean Weevil (*Bruchus rufimanus*)—Confined to the West coast, attacking broadbeans first, then peas and vetches. It is slightly smaller than the pea weevil and has several individuals in a seed instead of one, but resembles it otherwise.

Cabbage Seedpod Weevil (*Ceutorhynchus assimilis*)—In the Pacific Northwest and California, damaging seeds of crucifers—cabbage, turnip, radish, mustard. Adults are black to gray, ⅛ inch long; they lay eggs in seed pods after making punctures with their snouts. The larvae, small, white, legless, feed on seed embryos for about 3 weeks. Dusting with lindane or parathion has given commercial control.

Carrot Weevil (*Listronotus oregonensis*)—A pest of carrot, parsley, celery, feeding also on parsnip, dill, and related wild weeds, from New England to Georgia and west to Colorado. The beetles, dark brown, ¼ inch long, hibernate in grass and debris, lay eggs in May in cavities in leaf stalks. White, legless, curved, brown-headed grubs, up to ⅓ inch long, burrow down into the upper part of the carrot root or into celery hearts. The zigzag feeding destroys much tissue. Mature in about 2 weeks, the grubs leave the roots and pupate in soil. Beetles appear in July to lay eggs for a second brood which is injurious in August. There may be a partial third brood.

Control. Rotation of crops has been standard treatment. The New

Jersey Experiment Station recommends poison bait (1 part of Paris green or calcium arsenate to 20 dried apple pomace moistened with water) applied 3 times at 2-week intervals, starting in late April.

Cattleya Weevil (*Cholus cattleyae*)—Adults, just under ½ inch long, with white marks on their backs, feed on pseudobulbs and puncture leaves. Larvae also feed on leaves and stems and afford entrance to decay organisms. Hand-pick and spray with DDT.

Citrus Root Weevil (*Pachnaeus litus*)—Found in southern Florida on citrus, beans, strawberry, avocado, tobacco. Eggs are laid on leaves, larvae drop to the ground and feed on roots. Cryolite and parathion reduce populations to some extent but not entirely.

Clover Leaf Weevil (*Hypera punctata*)—Chiefly damaging alfalfa and clovers, but with adults feeding on many flowers. They are dark brown with black flecks on the back, paler brown underneath, with a robust snout. They can be controlled on ornamentals with DDT.

Cocklebur Weevil (*Rhodobaenus tredecimpunctatus*)—Cocklebur Billbug, common on sunflower, evening primrose, and similar plants, sometimes a pest of dahlia and chrysanthemum. The adult is reddish with 13 black spots and a long curved snout, about ⅓ inch long. It winters in trash, lays eggs on tender stalks in May or June; larvae hollow out the stalk near the base, pupate in August. Hand-pick the weevils; spray with DDT. Plant dahlias late to avoid injury.

Cowpea Weevil (*Callosobruchus maculatus*)—Present in southern states and California, where there may be 6 to 9 generations a year. Yellowish grubs, ¼ inch long, feed inside seeds in growing cowpea pods. Adults, bronze-black, hump-backed snout beetles, ⅕ inch long, feed on plants and lay eggs in holes eaten through pods.

Deodar Weevil (*Pissodes nemorensis*)—A native snout beetle present from southern New Jersey to Missouri and throughout the South, injurious to deodar, Lebanon and Atlas cedars, and feeding on weakened pines. The adult, brownish, with irregular mottlings of brown and white scales, gnaws through the bark with its slender beak and feeds on the cambium, often girdling a leader or side branch. It lays eggs in small holes in the bark; the grubs, white with brown heads, ⅓ inch long, burrow in wood and kill leaders and terminal twigs which start to die in January. Small trees may be killed. The grubs pupate in March, and the beetles feed in April, then disappear in the surface litter to rest until fall. Spray with DDT; feed the trees as necessary; water during drought periods.

Engelmann Spruce Weevil (*Pissodes engelmanni*)—Injuring terminals of Engelmann spruce in the West, similar to Sitka-spruce weevil.

Filbert Weevil (*Curculio uniformus*)—Infesting filbert nuts in New Mexico, Arizona, California, Oregon, Washington, and Utah. Cleaning up and destroying dropped nuts is quite effective in control.

Hollyhock Weevil (*Apion longirostre*)—A European species widely distributed in the United States, apparently confined to hollyhock. Adults are black, covered with gray hairs, with a long snout. They make small round holes in leaves and lay eggs in flower buds. Small, white, legless larvae eat the seed embryo and pupate in its place, adults emerging in August. Spray or dust hollyhocks before pods are formed with lindane; cut and burn stalks with infested seed pods.

89. *Imported long-horned weevil, showing characteristic long antennae and foliage injury.*

Imported Long-horned Weevil (*Calomycterus setarius*)—Another Japanese pest, first noted at Yonkers, New York, in 1929, a pest in Connecticut since 1932, reported also from Illinois, Iowa, Maryland, Massachusetts, New Jersey, Pennsylvania, Rhode Island, and Vermont. It is a general feeder, consuming foliage and blossoms of grasses, legumes, flowering garden plants, vegetables, field crops, ornamental shrubs, house plants, vines. It also wanders into houses, crawls over walls and ceilings, gets into food.

Adults, black but appearing gray from their gray scales, 3/8 inch long, with prominent long antennae (the long horns), emerge in late June and are abundant in July and August. They eat irregular areas in from the margins of leaves. Eggs are laid in sod and grubs are in the soil until the next June. Adults are wingless and natural spread is slow, but the weevils readily get around by crawling on people and into vehicles. Cryolite has given some control; chlordane would be more effective.

Iris Weevil (*Mononychus vulpeculus*)—Breeds commonly in seed pods of blue flag iris, sometimes punctures ovaries of Japanese and European iris, causing rough, corky scars. Fat grubs feed on the seeds, pupate within the pods. Adults, black, covered below with yellow and white scales, ⅕ inch long, emerge when pods burst open. Unless seeds are being saved for breeding, destroy all flower heads as they fade. If seeds are needed, cover blossoms with cheesecloth bags or dust with DDT.

Japanese Weevil (*Pseudocneorhinus bifasciatus*)—Found at scattered locations in Connecticut, New York, New Jersey, Pennsylvania, and District of Columbia, feeding heavily on California privet, sometimes on Japanese barberry, lilac, rose, mimosa, rhododendron, azalea and other shrubs, veronica, geranium, lily-of-the-valley. I have met it only once in the New Jersey gardens I doctor, but the weevils then were present by the hundreds, cutting broad rounded sections from the margins of leaves, giving a crenulated appearance. The adults were dark with broad abdomen, rather short snout. I had little luck trying to control it with lead arsenate and I have since learned that chlordane would have been more effective.

Large Chestnut Weevil (*Curculio proboscideus*)—A limiting factor in growing Asiatic chestnuts to replace our lost American species. DDT sprays are quite effective in control.

Lily-of-the-Valley Weevil (*Hormorus undulatus*)—Notches leaves in from the margin in curious fashion. The injury is common but appears after blooming so that control measures are seldom tried.

Monterey Pine Weevil (*Pissodes radiatae*)—Infesting Monterey and other pines on the Pacific coast. It mines the stems, tops, and bases of young pines above and below ground.

New York Weevil (*Ithycerus noveboracensis*)—Sometimes injurious to apple trees and young pears near woodlands and on oak, hickory, beech in the Northeast. Large snout beetles, ¾ inch long, gray, spotted with black, prune off twigs and eat into buds. Control measures are seldom used, but the beetles can be jarred from young fruit and shade trees and destroyed.

Orchid Weevil (*Diorymerellus laevimargo*)—Dendrobium Weevil, on various species of cattleya and dendrobium. The beetles, ⅛ inch long, shiny black with striated (grooved) wing covers, feed on tender leaves or flower petals, and lay eggs in root tips, especially in the cattleyas. Small, legless, curved larvae feed on new roots, hollow out old roots, cause tips to blacken. DDT kills the adults as they emerge.

Pales Weevil (*Hylobius pales*)—A native, found from Maine to Florida, west to Minnesota, favoring white pine, often on red, sometimes on Scotch, loblolly, shortleaf pines, American larch, Norway spruce, and other conifers. The adult is reddish brown to black, speckled with gray or yellow scales, black head and thorax, 1/3 inch long. The larva is white with a light brown head, 1/2 inch long. The weevils feed, mostly at night, on bark of seedlings, girdling young trees near ground level and killing many; they also feed on twigs of older trees. They hibernate as adults, lay eggs in fresh-cut logs or stumps in May. Grubs burrow beneath bark, grow slowly, pupate under the bark in September. Most damage comes from the young adults after emergence, before winter hibernation.

Control. Spray ornamental pines with DDT or lead arsenate, making sure the base of the trunk is thoroughly covered.

Pea Weevil (*Bruchus pisorum*)—A seed weevil, present throughout the country. The beetles are short, chunky, 1/5 inch long, brown, flecked with white, black, and gray patches. The larva is white with a small brown head. The female lays her eggs on the outside of a pea pod; the larva bores through the wall of the pod and into one of the young peas, growing inside for 5 or 6 weeks, consuming the contents. It pupates inside the pea and the adult emerges in 1 to 3 weeks. Several larvae may enter a pea, but only 1 survives; there is no continuous breeding in storage as with bean weevils. The weevils may remain in stored seed a year or two before emerging, but usually they come out soon after pupation and hibernate in any protected place.

Control. In home gardens dusting with rotenone or DDT weekly from the time peas start to blossom until they go out of bloom will give nearly weevil-free peas. Destroy vines immediately after harvest. Many birds feed on pea weevils.

Pecan Weevil (*Curculio caryae*)—Hickory Nut Weevil, found wherever pecans or hickories grow, sometimes causing loss of 80 per cent of the pecan crop. The dark brown adults, 3/8 inch long, attack newly formed pecans, causing them to shrivel and drop. Early-maturing varieties, such as Stuart, Schley, Mahan, and Moneymaker, are most commonly infested. The female has a beak longer than its body (that of the male is slightly shorter) and with it she punctures the nuts and places eggs, usually 3 to a nut, in the kernel as soon as the water stage is passed. Larvae emerge from nuts in late fall, go down 3 to 9 inches deep in the soil, stay there 1 to 2 years, then pupate in September or October, transforming to the adult in 3 weeks. They remain in the soil until the next July or August, when they come out to feed on nuts. Thus the life cycle takes 2 or 3 years.

Control. DDT is very effective. Spray susceptible varieties with 6 pounds of 50 per cent wettable powder to 100 gallons of water, making the first application in late July or early August (when at least 6 weevils can be jarred from a tree onto a sheet spread below) and the second 10 to 14 days later. Toxaphene is also effective and does not increase mites as rapidly as DDT. Use 6 pounds of 40 per cent wettable powder to 100 gallons. With only a few trees, weevils can be greatly reduced by jarring the trees with a pole and collecting the beetles on sheets underneath and destroying by dropping into kerosene. Clean up all dropped nuts.

Pepper Weevil (*Anthonomus eugenii*)—A Mexican insect now important in California, Arizona, New Mexico, Texas, Georgia, and Florida. Small white grubs feed inside buds of bell, sweet, and chili peppers, causing buds and most of pods to drop off. Adults are reddish brown to black with a brassy luster; they have curved beaks, are ⅛ inch long. There are several generations a year. Dusting with 5 per cent DDT every 7 to 10 days until pods mature is effective. Cryolite is also used but may be somewhat injurious in Florida's climate. In Texas 20 per cent toxaphene dust is satisfactory.

Red Elm Bark Weevil (*Magdalis armicollis*)—A reddish snout beetle infesting weakened elms. Keep trees fed and watered; remove dying or injured limbs.

Sitka-spruce Weevil (*Pissodes sitchensis*)—Important in the Pacific Northwest, killing or injuring terminal shoots of young trees, causing a crook in the trunk and/or a forked, worthless tree. The weevil is so prevalent in much of Oregon and Washington Sitka spruce is no longer planted. Adults are light to dark brown, oval, 3/16 inch long, with a prominent curved beak. They lay eggs in cavities in bark of last year's terminals. The larvae work down the stem pupating in wood or pith. DDT should prevent egg-laying on small ornamental trees.

Small Chestnut Weevil (*Curculio auriger*)—More abundant than the large chestnut weevil, often destroying 90 per cent of the nuts in Asiatic chestnut stands. Three properly timed DDT sprays reduce the weevils considerably.

Strawberry Root Weevil (*Brachyrhinus ovatus*)—Present throughout the northern United States, a special pest of strawberries and conifers, hemlock, arborvitae, Japanese yew (*Taxus cuspidata*), some spruce, junipers, also on raspberry, blackberry, cranberry, grasses, cucurbits, crucifers, deciduous trees and shrubs. It is much like the black vine weevil in looks and habit. The beetles are nearly black, striated, ¼ inch long, with short, blunt snouts; the larvae are white, legless, curved. Strawberries are stunted, leaves bunched together, darkened, with fine roots and crowns eaten. Root feeding by grubs often kills small hemlocks, but needle feeding by adults is negligible. Arborvitae roots are not often seriously injured, but terminal twigs are girdled by adults and tender new foliage is eaten. The weevils start emerging from the soil in early June, feeding for 10 to 14 days before laying eggs through the summer. Eggs hatch in 7 to 10 days. Larvae feed on roots until cold weather when they move down 6 to 14 inches, working up and feeding again in spring. Some winter as adults in trash.

The same chemicals are used for the strawberry root weevil as for the black vine weevil but applied 2 to 3 weeks earlier. Spray foliage and soil with dieldrin, heptachlor, or chlordane. For strawberries a poison bait of apple pomace and sodium fluosilicate (sold as Go West) is helpful, a tablespoon around each plant.

Strawberry Weevil (*Anthonomus signatus*)—An eastern pest of strawberry, raspberry, dewberry; also found on wild blackberry and cinquefoil. The dark, reddish-brown, very small snout beetle winters under trash, is active early in spring when strawberries are coming into bloom. The female punctures buds with her long beak, inserts an egg, then crawls down and girdles the stem of the flower bud, causing it to wilt. The grubs feed in the buds for about 4 weeks, pupate, and adults emerge just before midsummer. Dust with lindane about 10 days before blossoms open. Lead or calcium arsenate dust or cryolite with sulfur is also recommended. No poisons should be used within 3 weeks of ripening.

Sweetpotato Weevil (*Cylas formicarius elegantulus*)—Sweetpotato Root Borer, confined to the Gulf states, feeding on sweetpotato, morning glory, and other plants of the same family. The beetles are ¼ inch long, slender, with head, wing covers, and abdomen blue, red thorax and legs, a long, straight black beak. It attacks potatoes in the field, entering near the stem, and breeds in stored roots, which are honeycombed by fat, legless white grubs.

Control. Sort out infested potatoes at harvest and destroy; clean up and burn all old vines; destroy volunteer sweetpotatoes and related weeds. Plants can be dipped before setting in DDT, 4 tablespoons 50 per cent wettable powder per gallon of water, or in lindane or aldrin emulsion, or in lead arsenate, 1½ ounces to a gallon, followed by spraying plants in the field. Endrin is effective.

Vegetable Weevil (*Listroderes costirostris obliquus*)—A beetle from Brazil, first reported in Mississippi in 1922, now spread through the Gulf states and along the coast in California. The weevils are buff-colored with a lighter V-shaped marking on the wing covers, ⅜ inch long. They have well-developed wings but seldom fly. They go into a summer resting period in late April or early May under trash or loose bark on trees, remaining inactive until early fall when the parthenogenetic females crawl to vegetable crops to feed and lay eggs, continuing through the winter, except in coldest weather. One weevil lays from 300 to 1500 eggs. The larvae are greenish, sluglike, ½ inch long. They feed voraciously on plants at night, along with adults. They attack beet, cabbage, carrot, cauliflower, lettuce, mustard, onion, potato, radish, spinach, Swiss chard, tomato, turnip, feeding first in the crown, then defoliating whole plants, leaving only stem and midribs.

Control. Dust with 10 per cent DDT or cryolite, but not within a month of harvest. Use rotenone or activated pyrethrum dust for edible plant parts or scatter apple pomace-sodium fluosilicate poison bait. Rotate crops and cultivate thoroughly to destroy pupae in soil; keep down weeds, rubbish, along fence rows.

White-pine Weevil (*Pissodes strobi*)—The most serious pest on white pine in the East, a constant threat in home plantings, plantations, and forests, sometimes injuring Norway spruce, Scotch, pitch, and jack pines, and other pine and spruce species. You can tell the injury at a distance, for the terminal leader is brown in sharp contrast to the rest of the tree. When the yellow, footless grubs, ⅓ inch long, mine in the bark and sapwood of the terminal shoot they girdle it; when it dies, a lateral branch turns up and tries to replace the leader. Sometimes 2 laterals grow up and the tree is forked. Sometimes the tree is killed back beyond the leader.

Adults are reddish to dark brown, somewhat mottled with brown and white scales, with a white spot on lower third of each wing cover, a long curved snout, ¼ inch long. Adults hibernate under cover on ground, feed in May, lay 2 or 3 pearly eggs in cavities dug in bark of leaders. Egg-laying continues through June. The grubs hatch in 6 to 10 days and feed on the inner bark as they girdle the shoot. They pupate in small, oval chambers in the wood and beetles emerge from late June to early September. There is only 1 generation. Wilting and drooping of terminal twigs in spring is the first sign of larval activity.

Control. Infested shoots must be cut off and burned as soon as noticed, making sure the cut is made below all grubs. Tie a lateral to a stake to replace the leader and cut off the others. To protect shoots from infestation spray in early spring, when buds are swelling, with 3 per cent DDT emulsion or with lead arsenate.

Willow Flea Weevil (*Rhynchaenus rufipes*)—A small native snout beetle found from Maine to Iowa and in Oregon and California, Colorado, and New Mexico on willow, Lombardy poplar, aspen, sometimes red birch. The grubs, dirty white, $\frac{1}{12}$ inch long, widest at the thorax, mine in leaves, mostly willow, sometimes poplar. The adult is a tiny, jet-black beetle, elliptical, covered with short gray hairs, with reddish-yellow antennae and legs. Weevils hibernate under loose bark or trash on ground, feed in May on opening buds and new leaves, eating circular holes, sometimes killing back twigs. They lay eggs in June, in pits on underside of leaves; larvae pupate in mined leaves; beetles emerge in August.

Control. Spraying with nicotine sulfate plus fish-oil soap has been recommended in the past. DDT, chlordane, or lindane would probably be more effective.

Yucca Weevil (*Scyphophorus yuccae*)—The adult, black with deeply grooved wing covers, feeds on sap of living yucca in southern California; the larvae breed in bases of green flower stalks and hearts of the same plants.

WHITEFLIES

Whiteflies are minute sucking insects belonging to the family Aleyrodidae (meaning like flour) of the order Homoptera. The adults have 2 pairs of broadly rounded wings covered with snow-white waxy powder; they look like tiny white moths. Whiteflies are often present in great numbers on the underside of leaves but are rarely noticed unless the plant is disturbed, when they fly out in clouds. They are primarily tropical insects but are abundant in greenhouses and house plants and are common on some garden plants in the summer in the North, most of the year in the South.

The life history is much the same for all species of whiteflies. Oval eggs, $\frac{1}{100}$ inch long, are attached to underside of leaves by short stalks. They hatch in 4 to 12 days into active, pale yellow, 6-legged crawlers. The crawlers, usually called larvae, sometimes nymphs, move about for a short time, avoiding strong light, then insert their beaks and start sucking sap. At the first molt they lose their legs and antennae and look like very small, very flat, oval scales, often with a marginal fringe of white waxy filaments, sometimes covered with rods or plates of wax. They secrete copious honeydew through a special opening on the upper surface of the body. After a second molt, the insect becomes a pupa, larger and more distinctly segmented, and then the 4-winged adult leaves the pupal skin by a T-shaped opening in the back.

For many years summer oil sprays were used for the control of whiteflies; now more reliance is placed on parathion (for commercial growers) or malathion (for back-yard gardeners) and sometimes DDT with oil.

Avocado Whitefly (*Trialeurodes floridensis*)—A pest of avocado in Florida, also occurring on papaya, banana, guava, anona, citrus. The adult is pale yellow with white wings; the larva has a white marginal fringe and remains fixed to the foliage over winter. Adults appear in early March to lay white eggs in circles in leaves. There are 3 generations and a partial fourth. For control see Citrus Whitefly.

Azalea Whitefly (*Aleyrodes azaleae*)—Widespread, almost always present on evergreen varieties of azalea with sticky bud scales and tomentose (hairy) leaves like those of the white *Indica alba*. The eggs are pale yellow, pupae greenish white, oval, present in great numbers on underside of foliage. The leaves lose color from sucking of plant juices and are often covered with black sooty mold growing in the honeydew. Spraying in spring with Volck or similar summer oil, at a 1 to 60 dilution, before flies emerge in spring has been standard control. This is in late February in the South, April in New Jersey. I have had quite good results by spraying with TEPP during the season, and malathion is now suggested.

Citrus Whitefly (*Dialeurodes citri*)—The most important economic species of whitefly, a native of Asia introduced in Florida prior to 1885, when it was found on oranges. It appeared in California in 1907 and at later dates, but infestations have been fairly well eradicated so it remains for the most part a pest in the Gulf states, where it is the most important citrus enemy or ranks after purple scale. It injures through the consumption of sap and by the honeydew which encourages sooty mold all over fruit and foliage. It breeds in large numbers on chinaberry trees. Besides these, and citrus, preferred food plants are umbrella trees, cape jasmine (gardenia), privets, Japanese and wild persimmons, lilac, coffee, prickly ash. Occasionally infested shrubs or vines include allamanda, banana, cerasius, camellia, choisya, cherry-laurel, green ash, jessamine, pear, pomegranate, smilax, viburnum, wild olive, ailanthus, water oak, osage-orange, palmetto.

Small yellow eggs, looking like dust, hatch in 10 to 12 days, those from unfertilized females turning into males. The larvae are thin, translucent, scalelike; they lose legs and antennae after the first molt, about 7 days after hatching. The second molt is in 5 or 6 days, the third after 10 to 12 days, after which the insect assumes the pupa or resting state, taking much less food, becoming thicker, the outline of the adult taking form, and finally the winged whitefly emerging through a T-shaped opening in the pupal skin. There are usually 3 generations in Florida, the spring brood of adults at its maximum in late March, the summer brood in June, and the fall—largest—brood in late August and early September.

Control. Oil emulsion sprays (such as Florida Volck) control whiteflies fairly well if applied to kill larvae before they change to adults. Two sprays in Florida, May and September, are suggested, but for citrus the spray schedule should be directed toward all pests; it varies in different states and even in different sections of Florida. Apply to your county agent or state experiment station for specific help. Many commercial growers have been using parathion, one spray at postbloom, the other between June and September, with 1 to 2 pounds of 15 per cent wettable powder plus 5 to 10 pounds wettable sulfur to 100 gallons of water. Sometimes it is advisable to cut down chinaberry trees to reduce infestations. Red and yellow fungi grow on whiteflies but are not now considered as useful in control as formerly.

Cloudy-winged Whitefly (*Dialeurodes citrifolii*)—Similar to the citrus whitefly, chiefly a Florida pest, not found in California. Aside

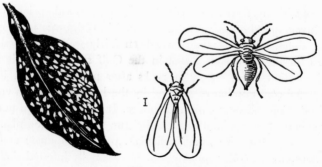

90. Citrus whitefly.

from citrus, special hosts are yam vines and a species of ficus. The eggs are black, covered with a network of ridges, often laid on watersprouts; the adults have a dusky area in each wing. Maximum spring flight is in early April; summer, in early July; fall, late October. Remove and destroy watersprouts when most eggs are present—May, August, September, or January. Spray as for citrus whitefly, or, if the cloudy-winged is the only species, about 3 weeks later.

Crown Whitefly (*Aleyrodes coronatus*)—Abundant on live, valley, and tan oaks, Christmasberry, manzanita, wild coffeeberry throughout California. The pupa case is dark surrounded with flat, white, waxy plates that give the appearance of a crown. Adults have pale yellow-white wings.

Fern Whitefly (*Aleyrodes nephrolepidis*)—Found on various ferns in homes and greenhouses. Pupa case of bright yellow, without covering.

Glacial Whitefly (*Trialeurodes glacialis*)—On bush fruits, blackberry, boysenberry, loganberry, raspberry, and on bean, columbine, wild clematis, coffeeberry, ninebark, sage, snowberry, tan oak in California. The young are yellow with a crystalline fringe, the adults pure white.

Grape Whitefly (*Trialeurodes vittatus*)—On leaves of European grape in California, but normally breeding on chaparral. The young appear in great numbers on underside of leaves, causing smutting of fruit and foliage with mold fungi. The pupa is dark brown with a white marginal fringe.

Greenhouse Whitefly (*Trialeurodes vaporariorum*)—The most common species in greenhouses and gardens. It does not live over winter outdoors in the North and gets to the garden with greenhouse-grown seedlings of tomatoes and other plants. In my own garden practice I always expect to find whiteflies on ageratum, eggplant, gourds, heliotrope, in dense quantities on underside of squash foliage, on tomatoes. In other sections they are also pests of aster, avocado, barberry, bean, begonia, bignonia, blackberry, calceolaria, calendula, chrysanthemum, cineraria, coleus, coffeeberry, cucumber, fern, fuchsia, geranium, grape, hibiscus, honey locust, black locust, honeysuckle, Jerusalem-cherry, lantana, lettuce, loganberry, lupine, mallow, morning glory, muskmelon, pea, pepper, potato, primrose, redbud, rose, sage, soybean, strawberry, watermelon. Infested plants lack vigor, turn yellow, sometimes wilt and die; leaves are sooted with black mold in the South, not so much outdoors in New Jersey.

The eggs are elongated, pale yellowish green; the young are oval, thin, flat, pale green, semi-transparent with white waxy threads radiating from their bodies. The larval stages last about a month; under greenhouse conditions there are several overlapping generations. Both male and female adults as well as larvae suck sap from undersurface of leaves.

Control. In greenhouses parathion or dithione aerosols kill adults with several applications, but sprays are required for the larvae, or fumigation with hydrogen cyanide. A spray of DDT combined with summer oil is often recommended for fuchsias, chrysanthemums and other greenhouse plants, malathion for some garden plants. For vegetables nearing harvest, spray with rotenone or nicotine sulfate and soap. For house plants try aerosol bombs containing rotenone and pyrethrum.

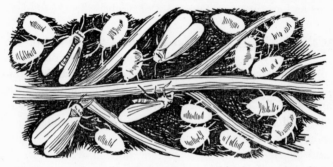

91. Nymphs and adults of greenhouse whitefly, much enlarged, on underside of leaf.

Inconspicuous Whitefly (*Aleyrodes inconspicua*)—Present along the West coast on California laurel, Christmasberry, clematis, coffeeberry, maple, manzanita, live and tan oaks, Oregon grape (mahonia). It is also reported from Florida. The pupa is pale or dark yellow with only a narrow fringe. The wings are dusky brown.

Iridiscent Whitefly (*Aleyrodes iridescens*)—On California laurel, Christmasberry, coffeeberry, manzanita, madrona, redberry, white sage. Larvae are dark, iridescent, with starlike whorls on the surface and a fringe of white filaments. Adults are pale yellow with pure white wings.

Iris Whitefly (*Aleyrodes spiraeoides*)—Often destructive to iris in California, feeding also on aster, fuchsia, morning glory, honeysuckle, ninebark. The pupa is pale yellow without waxy secretion or fringe. Adults have yellow bodies, dusky spots on wings.

Kellogg's Whitefly (*Aleyrodes kelloggi*)—Often present in numbers on leaves of Catalina cherry, growing wild or used as an ornamental. The pupa is pale yellow, resting on dense white rods and covered with wide white wax ribbons, so it looks like a minute flower.

Mulberry Whitefly (*Tetraleurodes mori*)—An eastern species that survives outdoors. Popular host plants include mulberry, dogwood, azalea, hackberry, holly, mountain-laurel, linden, maple, sycamore. The larvae are elliptical, $\frac{1}{35}$ inch long, jet-black, edged with a white fringe of waxy filaments. Adults are around from June to September, increasing in numbers late in the season. Apparently there is no great injury to host plants.

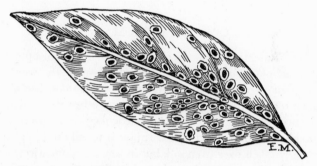

92. Nymphs of mulberry whitefly, black with white fringe.

Pruinose Whitefly (*Aleyrodes pruinosa*)—Often present in enormous quantities on undersurface of Christmasberry (toyon) leaves, causing serious smutting in central and southern California. Pupa is yellow to dark brown with a frosty white covering. Adults have yellow bodies with brown markings, 2 dusky spots on each fore wing.

Rhododendron Whitefly (*Dialeurodes chittendeni*)—Yellowish mottling on upper side of leaves together with rolling of margins is caused by flat, oval, greenish, almost transparent larvae. There is much honeydew accompanied by sooty mold. Only rhododendrons with smooth underleaf surfaces are infested. In the Pacific Northwest spraying with a 2 per cent white oil emulsion in fall before frost has been effective. In Rhode Island spraying twice in June with DDT has been satisfactory, with lindane and nicotine sulfate giving almost as good control.

Strawberry Whitefly (*Trialeurodes packardi*)—A not too important pest of strawberries.

Sweetpotato Whitefly (*Bemisia inconspicua*)—Destructive to sweet-potatoes in Florida, especially late-planted vines. Larvae are $\frac{1}{12}$ inch long, flat, thin, nearly round, very inconspicuous on underside of leaves. Their honeydew encourages black mold. Spraying with pyrethrum right after eggs hatch is useful.

Woolly Whitefly (*Aleurothrixus floccosus*)—Probably native to Florida on sea grape, later infesting citrus. The pupa is covered with white woolly filaments of wax, which give the common name. Eggs are brown, curved, laid in circles as the female revolves around her inserted beak. The first larval stage is green, others brown with a wide fringe of white wax. Adults are yellowish, do not fly much. There are 4 broods. Control as for the citrus whitefly.

WIREWORMS

Wireworms are the larvae of click beetles, order Coleoptera. They occur throughout North America and over most of the world as destructive pests of corn, small grains, grasses, potatoes, beets, carrots, and other root crops. They may also injure other vegetables, beans, peas, lettuce, radish, and onions in particular; and flowers such as asters, dahlia, gladiolus, and phlox. Injury is usually most extensive in land recently taken over from sod, but in some sections wireworms are numerous in soil continuously under cultivation. They eat seed, resulting in almost total loss of a planting of corn or peas; they feed on underground stems, causing death of seedlings; they eat the small roots of larger plants; they burrow into potatoes, carrots, beets, or bulbs. They are entirely soil pests, working on underground plant parts.

The larvae are smooth wiry worms, first white with dark jaws, but after feeding and molting several times they are hard, jointed, and shiny, dark yellow to brown, with the last segment of the body pronged or forked, $\frac{1}{4}$ to $\frac{3}{4}$ inch long (Plate XXIII). Adults are hard-shelled, tapering beetles, gray brown to black, with the joint in front of the wing covers loose and flexible. When they are placed or fall on their backs they right themselves with a sharp click.

The adults winter in soil cells, emerge in spring when soil temperature warms up, and crawl over the surface or make short flights to lay their eggs, in damp soil 1 to 6 inches deep. The larvae feed little and do not cause much injury until their second season. They sometimes change to soft white pupae in a year, but more often 2 or 3 years, sometimes 5 or 6 years, pass before they make a small cell 3 to 8 inches below soil surface and pupate. The pupa changes to the adult in 3 weeks but the latter does not emerge until spring. Due to overlapping of generations, wireworms of all sizes and ages are present in the soil at the same time. A few representative species are described here, followed by general control measures.

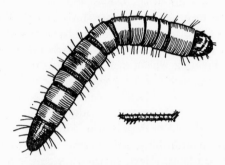

93. Wireworm, larva of a click beetle.

Columbia Basin Wireworm (*Limonius subauratus*)—A robust, slate-gray to nearly black beetle, larva pale yellow, somewhat flattened. It is a root pest of potato, corn, grains, with the adults feeding on buds and petals of wild rose and apple. It is particularly injurious in Washington, Oregon, and Idaho, also present in California, Arizona, New Mexico, and eastern states.

Eastern Field Wireworm (*Limonius agonus*)—Probably the most common eastern species, found even on land which has been under cultivation for many years. It is a serious pest in the tobacco areas along the Connecticut River and in upstate New York, attacking potatoes, beets, carrots, radishes, onions; most injurious in early spring.

Great Basin Wireworm (*Ctenicera pruinia noxia*)—Found in dry areas east of the Cascades in Washington, Oregon, Idaho. The beetle is black, slender, the larva yellow.

Gulf Wireworm (*Conoderus amplicollis*)—A most important subterranean pest of sweetpotatoes in Gulf states, its punctures followed by rots. Treating soil with lindane, benzene hexachloride, aldrin, or dieldrin 2 weeks prior to setting slips has given good control with no off-flavor in the potatoes. It is also important on Irish potatoes.

Oregon Wireworm (*Melanotus oregonensis*)—Common on the West coast.

Pacific Coast Wireworm (*Limonius canus*)—It infests bulbs along with other root crops. Wedgewood iris bulbs have been protected with benzene hexachloride or dieldrin included with thiram in a 10-minute pre-planting dip.

Plains False Wireworm (*Eleodes opaca*)—Found between the Mississippi River and the Pacific coast; preferring wheat but also attacking grasses, oats, corn, sugar beets, beans, and other garden crops. The beetle is black, with a flat back, sparsely clothed with white hairs. It cannot fly and when disturbed elevates the hind part of its body, keeping its head on the ground. The larvae are brown or yellow, prominently jointed. Treating wheat seed with a mixture of benzene hexachloride and phenyl mercury has given increased yields.

Sugar-beet Wireworm (*Limonius californicus*)—Common in California and north to Washington. The adult is a small, elongate click beetle, ⅜ inch long, light or dark brown, with coarse punctures on the back. The larvae, typical shiny, yellow-brown hard worms, feed mostly on roots of young plants, asters, chrysanthemums, and other flowers, as well as sugar beets, beans, corn, etc.

Tobacco Wireworm (*Conoderus vespertinus*)—Spotted Click Beetle, common in cornfields as well as a tobacco pest. The larva is hard, thick, ½ inch long, more destructive in dry than wet soils.

Western Field Wireworm (*Limonius infuscatus*)—Associated with the sugar-beet wireworm on the West coast, particularly injurious to potatoes in sandy river-bottom land.

Wheat Wireworm (*Agriotes mancus*)—Pest of potato, corn, wheat, and a wide variety of plants across the country.

WIREWORM CONTROL

There have been rapid advances in the control of wireworms in the past decade. The soil can be fumigated, treated with insecticides, or seeds and bulbs can be treated before planting. Fumigation gives immediate control, killing the wireworms present, but has no long residual action. Treatment is for fallow soil only and planting should be delayed at least 2 weeks after treatment. Punch holes in the soil 1 foot apart and at least 6 inches deep and pour in ½ to 1 teaspoon of a 10 per cent solution of ethylene dibromide or 1 to 2 teaspoons D-D mixture and close the holes with soil. Special applicators are available for large plots. Both fumigants are poisonous to man; do not breathe the vapors; wash off immediately any liquid spilled on the skin. Ethylene dibromide is combustible.

Soil insecticides are easier to apply than fumigants and have a long-lasting effect, though the initial kill may be slow.

DDT is applied at the rate of 10 pounds actual DDT per acre. For small plots use ½ to 1 pound of 5 per cent dust and mix it with the soil 6 to 9 inches deep. One treatment should last several years. Do not treat again until small wireworms appear. Chlordane is also effective. Use at half the rate of DDT.

Lindane and benzene hexachloride are very toxic to wireworms but may affect the flavor of certain root crops. Use 1 to 5 ounces of 1 per cent lindane dust to 100 square feet.

Chlordane and heptachlor, applied at 10 pounds per acre, 1 to 3 months in advance of planting, have given good control of wireworms in irrigated land for 3 years. Dieldrin at only 2 pounds per acre has controlled wireworms for 3 years.

In experiments on corn, seed treatments with aldrin, dieldrin, and heptachlor were more effective than with lindane. Soil treatment with heptachlor, however, was more effective than seed treatment.

Chapter VI

HOST PLANTS AND THEIR PESTS

In this section there are sorted out under their different host plants (the plants they live or feed on) the 1100 or so garden pests that are described in Chapter V. It is by no means a complete check list. Most plants have many more possible insect enemies than could be included between the covers of one book. But even in this abbreviated form, some of the lists, particularly those given for fruit and shade trees, are appallingly long. This is partly because trees attract a great many insects, some of which are only occasional visitors of no serious consequence; partly because these hosts are more important economically and so more work has been done on their insects; and partly because the lists, in attempting to represent all parts of the country, contain more pests than would ever be present in one section. Black Scale and Cottony-cushion Scale, for example, mean nothing to the New Englander with a maple tree. The Californian, however, has his warm-climate scales and the New Englander's Cottony Maple Scale, to boot, though he does not have the eastern Maple Phenacoccus.

The pests are listed under each host alphabetically according to the groups under which they are described in the pest section, Chapter V, also in alphabetical order. The group name, **Aphid, Beetle, Borer, Bug, Caterpillar,** and so on, is given in boldface. For instance, under ABUTILON we have **Beetle,** Fuller Rose, which means that you find BEETLES in Chapter V and then run down **Fuller Rose Beetle** just as if you were using a dictionary. So far as possible the common name given is the one presently approved by the Committee on Common Names of the Entomological Society of America. Other names frequently used as common names are given with the descriptions of the pests and in the Index. See pages 53, 54 for further help in finding the particular pest that is worrying you at the moment.

Although a brief comment is given in this section to designate some of the more important pests, in every case you should check back to Chapter V for a more complete description, life history, and treatment. Always read the introduction to each group of pests as well as the text on a particular species. If typical life histories and general control measures are given for the group as a whole the details are not repeated under every species.

ABUTILON (Flowering Maple)
Beetle, Fuller Rose (feeds from leaf margins).
Moth, Abutilon (looper caterpillar chews foliage).
Nematode, Root-knot (galls on roots).
Scale, Black Araucaria; Lesser Snow (white); Soft (brown).
Weevil, Imported Long-horned (feeds from edge of leaf).
Whitefly, Greenhouse (minute white flies on underside of leaves).

ACACIA (Wattle)
Beetle, Fuller Rose (feeds at night, notching edge of leaves).
Caterpillar, Omnivorous Looper; Orange Tortrix.
Mealybug, Ground (white powdery bugs on roots).
Scale, California Red (round, reddish); Cottony-cushion (white, fluted); Greedy (small, gray); Oleander (pale yellow); San Jose (small, gray, nippled).

ACANTHOPANAX (Five-leaf Aralia)
Bug, Four-lined Plant (dark depressed spots in terminal leaves).

ACONITE (Monkshood)
Bug, Four-lined Plant (dark, depressed spots in leaves).
Leaf Miner, Larkspur (tan blotches on foliage).
Mite, Cyclamen (leaves, buds deformed).

AFRICAN VIOLET (*Saintpaulia*)
Mealybug, Citrus (white cottony masses at leaf axils).
Mite, Broad (leaves glassy); Cyclamen (leaves deformed, stems twisted).
Nematode, Fern (brown areas in leaves); Root-knot (knots in roots).

AGERATUM (Floss Flower)

Budworm, Tobacco (feeds on buds).

Earworm, Corn (may eat buds or foliage).

Leaf Tier, Celery (feeds inside rolled leaves).

Mite, Cyclamen (leaves, flowers deformed); Two-spotted (leaves pale, webbed).

Whitefly, Greenhouse (common in late summer; leaves stippled white).

AILANTHUS (Tree-of-Heaven)

Borer, Brown Wood (brown beetle, yellow larva; bores winding galleries).

Moth, Cynthia (large green caterpillar). **Scale,** Oystershell.

Webworm, Ailanthus (brown caterpillars in fine webs).

AKEBIA

Scale, San Jose (small, round, grayish).

ALDER (*Alnus*)

Aphid, Hop; Woolly Alder (common, goes over to maple).

Beetle, Alder Bark (western bark miner); Alder Flea (steel blue, may defoliate).

Borer, California Prionus; Pacific Flatheaded; Poplar and Willow.

Bug, Alder Lace. **Casebearer,** Birch.

Caterpillar, Pacific Tent; Omnivorous Looper. **Leaf Miner,** Alder.

Leaf Skeletonizer, Birch.

Scale, Lecanium (brown, convex); Oystershell; San Jose; Willow (white).

ALLAMANDA

Scale, Purple (oyster-shaped, brown or purple). **Whitefly,** Citrus.

ALMOND (*Prunus*)

Aphid, Waterlily (winter host for).

Beetle, Western Striped Cucumber; Tobacco Flea.

Borer, California Prionus; Peach Twig; Shot-hole; Western Peach.

Casebearer, California.

Caterpillar, California Tent; Omnivorous Looper; Red-humped.

Leafhopper, Plum (transmits yellows).

Mite, Clover; European Red; Two-spotted (foliage discolored, may drop).

Moth, Western Tussock.
Scale, Black; Cottony-cushion; Greedy; Howard; Olive Parlatoria; Oystershell; San Jose.
Thrips, Citrus.

ALOE
Scale, California Red; Hemispherical; Oleander (pale yellow); Soft (brown).

ALSTROEMERIA
Thrips, Banded Greenhouse.

ALYSSUM, SWEET (*Lobularia*)
Caterpillar, Imported Cabbageworm.
Leafhopper, Six-spotted (transmits aster yellows).
Moth, Diamondback (green caterpillar).

AMARYLLIS
Beetle, Black Blister.   **Caterpillar,** Convict (black with white bands).
Cutworm, Climbing.
Fly, Lesser Bulb; Narcissus Bulb (bulbs rotting, maggot inside).
Mealybug, Citrus.
Mite, Bulb (in rotting bulbs); Two-spotted (on foliage).
Nematode, Bulb (dark rings in bulb).
Thrips, Gladiolus (foliage and flowers streaked); Banded Greenhouse; Greenhouse.

ANCHUSA (Bugloss)
Leafhopper, Six-spotted (transmits aster yellows).

ANDROMEDA (*Pieris*)
Bug, Japanese Lace (leaves stippled white or gray).
Mite, Two-spotted (leaves yellow).
Scale, Florida Wax (white, waxy, tinged with pink).

ANEMONE (Windflower)
Aphid, Crescent-marked Lily; other species.
Beetle, Black Blister (devours flowers, foliage, of Japanese anemone).
Cutworms.   Leaf Tier, Celery (webs foliage).
Nematode, Fern (dark blotches on leaves); Bulb and Stem.

ANTHURIUM
Scale, Florida Wax.

APPLE (*Pyrus*)

Aphid, Apple; Apple Grain; Clover; Cowpea; Hop; Mealy Plum; Potato; Woolly Apple.

Beetle, Apple Flea; Bumble Flower; Cherry Leaf; Fig; Fuller Rose; Grape Colaspis; Grape Flea; Green June; Japanese; Potato Flea; Rose Chafer; Rose Leaf; Imbricated Snout; Strawberry Leaf; Western Striped Cucumber.

Borer, Broad-necked Root; Flatheaded Apple; Pacific Flatheaded; Pear; Pigeon Tremex; Roundheaded Apple; Shot-hole; Western Peach.

Bud Moth, Eye-spotted.

Bug, Apple Red; Apple Lace; Boxelder; Green Stink; Lygus; Tarnished Plant; Willow Lace.

Casebearer, California; Cigar; Pistol.

Caterpillar, California Tent; Coast Tent; Eastern Tent; Forest Tent; Lesser Appleworm; Linden Looper; Orange Tortrix; Palmerworm; Saddled Prominent; Yellow-necked.

Cicada, Periodical.   **Curculio,** Apple; Plum.

Fly, Fruit, Mexican.   **Fruitworm,** Green.

Leafhopper, Apple; Grape; Rose; Three-banded; White Apple.

Leaf Miner, Apple Leaf Trumpet; Unspotted Tentiform.

Leaf Roller, Fruit Tree; Oblique-banded; Red-banded.

Leaf Skeletonizer, Apple and Thorn.

Maggot, Apple (common cause of wormy apples).

Mealybug, Citrophilus; Comstock; Grape; Taxus.

Mite, Clover; European Red (foliage sickly, drops); Pear Leaf Blister; Two-spotted.

Moth, Apple Fruit; Brown-tail; Codling (most important apple pest, fruit wormy, deformed); Gypsy; Oriental Fruit; Rusty Tussock; Western Tussock; White-lined Sphinx.

Psyllid, Apple Sucker.

Sawfly, European Apple.

Scale, Black; California Red; Cottony-cushion; Cottony Maple; European Fruit Lecanium; Florida Wax; Forbes; Greedy; Green Shield; Hemispherical; Howard; Italian Pear; Lecanium; Olive Parlatoria; Putnam; Soft; Walnut.

Termites, Subterranean.

Weevil, Apple Flea; New York. **Wireworms.**

SPRAYING STAGES
OF AN APPLE TREE

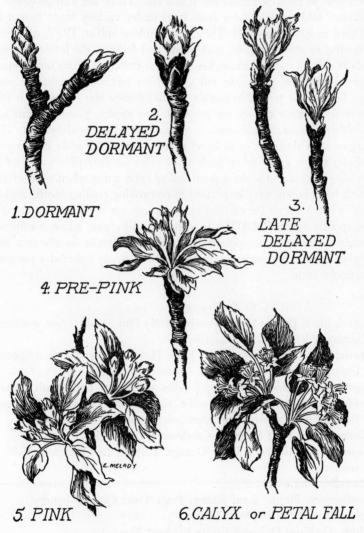

1. DORMANT

2. DELAYED DORMANT

3. LATE DELAYED DORMANT

4. PRE-PINK

E. MELADY

5. PINK

6. CALYX or PETAL FALL

94. Spraying stages of an apple tree.

The production of perfect apples means a lot of work, following a spray schedule tailored for the pests and diseases prevalent in your own state. Nearly every state experiment station provides fruit spray schedules for farmers and others for use in home gardens. These are revised each year as new chemicals are tested out. There are also all-purpose mixtures sold especially for fruit trees under various trade names to be used as sprays or dusts. They may combine sulfur, DDT, and lead arsenate; or methoxychlor, malathion, and ferbam, the latter a fungicide to control apple scab; or various other materials. Your own county agent is the best person to tell you which mixture is right for your own home fruit trees. No matter which mixture you choose, it is still necessary to time the sprays properly. For apples, 5 applications are considered about the minimum to get anywhere near healthy fruit. This may mean a dormant or delayed dormant spray for scale insects and aphids; a pink spray when buds show color for caterpillars and other chewing insects and scab; a petal-fall or calyx spray when most of the petals have fallen, very important in controlling codling moth; and at least 2 cover sprays for codling moth. A summer spray may be needed for apple maggot. If DDT is used in the all-purpose spray, a miticide should be included or applied separately. For details on selection and application of chemicals obtain Home Fruit Spray Schedules for your particular state.

APRICOT (*Prunus*)

Aphid, Black Peach; Green Peach; Mealy Plum (splits, smudges fruit, stunts tree); Thistle; Waterlily.

Beetle, Fig; Fuller Rose; Green June; Plum Gouger; Western Spotted Cucumber (eats holes in fruit, spreads brown rot).

Borer, Branch and Twig (small holes at base of buds, fruit spurs); Flatheaded Apple Tree; Pacific Flatheaded; Pacific Peach Tree; Peach Tree; Peach Twig; Shot-hole; Western Peach Tree.

Cankerworm, Fall; Spring. **Casebearer,** California.

Caterpillar, California Tent; Orange Tortrix; Red-humped; Yellow-necked.

Curculio, Plum.

Leafhopper, Plum. **Leaf Roller,** Fruit Tree; Oblique-banded.

Mite, Clover; Pacific; Willamette.

Moth, Codling; Oriental Fruit; Western Tussock.

Sawfly, Cherry Fruit.

Scale, Black; Cottony-cushion; European Fruit Lecanium; Forbes; Italian Pear; Olive Parlatoria; Oystershell; Soft; Walnut; White Peach.
Termites.

ARABIS (Rockcress)
Aphid, Crescent-marked Lily (yellow and black).

ARALIA
Aphid, Ivy.
Caterpillar, Imported Cabbageworm; Omnivorous Looper.
Leaf Miner, Serpentine.
Scale, Black; Florida Red (circular, brownish red); Soft (brown).
Thrips, Banded Greenhouse.

ARAUCARIA (Monkey-puzzle Tree and Norfolk Island Pine)
Mealybug, Citrus; Golden (covered with yellow wax); Cypress.
Scale, Araucaria (white); Black Araucaria; Chaff; Florida Red; Soft.

ARBORVITAE (*Thuja occidentalis*)
Aphid, Arborvitae (brown with white bloom).
Bagworm (small bags hanging on twigs).
Beetle, Northern Cedar Bark (twigs wilt, hang down).
Borer, Cedar Tree (brown beetle, may girdle trees).
Caterpillar, Hemlock Looper.
Leaf Miner (tips of twigs light-colored).
Mite, Spruce Spider (common, serious, shrubs turn brown); Two-spotted.
Scale, European Fruit Lecanium; Fletcher; Juniper; San Jose.

ARDISIA
Scale, Hemispherical (large, brown, convex).

ARTEMISIA
Aphid, Artemisia.
Midge, Artemisia Gall. **Mealybug,** Yucca.
Scale, Artemisia (large white sacs); Black.
Many other insects occur on artemisia, especially in California.

ARTICHOKE, GLOBE (*Cynara scolymus*)

Aphid, Oleaster-thistle (pale yellow to green); Bean (black).
Earworm, Corn.
Moth, Artichoke Plume (yellow caterpillar feeds in stems, heads).
Slug, Gray Garden; Greenhouse.

ASH (*Fraxinus*)

Bug, Ash Plant (serious on West coast); Ash Lace (tingid).
Borer, Ash (found in Midwest); Brown Wood; California Prionus; Carpenterworm (very large tunnels); Flatheaded Apple Tree; Lilac (common, tunnels in wood, scar tissue on trunk); Pacific Flatheaded.
Cankerworm, Fall.
Caterpillar, California Tent; Great Basin Tent; Hickory Horned Devil.
Cricket, Snowy Tree (may injure bark in egg-laying).
Gall, Ash Flower (on staminate flowers of white ash).
Leaf Miner, Lilac (blotches in leaves).
Leaf Roller, Fruit Tree; Oblique-banded (caterpillars in rolled leaves).
Moth, Brown-tail; Polyphemus; Promethea (large green caterpillars).
Sawfly, Brown-headed Ash (may occasionally defoliate).
Scale, European Fruit Lecanium; Howard; Oystershell (often injurious); Putnam; San Jose; Soft; Terrapin.
Webworm, Fall.   **Whitefly,** Citrus.

ASPARAGUS

Aphid, Bean; Melon; Crescent-marked Lily; Potato.
Beetle, Asparagus (feeds on shoots, foliage); Japanese (on foliage); Spotted Asparagus; Spotted Cucumber.
Bug, Garden Fleahopper; Harlequin; Say Stink.
Caterpillar, Orange Tortrix; Yellow Woollybear.
Centipede, Garden (important in California, injures shoots in ground).
Cutworms.   Leaf Miner, Asparagus (maggots sometimes girdle stems).
Mite, Bulb (may injure underground stems).

ASPARAGUS FERN (Smilax)

Beetle, Asparagus; Spotted Asparagus.
Bug, Garden Fleahopper (produces yellow spots on foliage).
Cutworm, Variegated (climbs plants, clips stems).
Mite, Two-spotted (mealy webs, loss of color).
Scale, Black; Chaff; Hemispherical; Lesser Snow.

Thrips, Onion (silvering, curling of leaves; brown, corky spots).

ASPEN (See Poplar)

ASPIDISTRA
Scale, California Red; Fern (white, conspicuous); Florida Red (round, dark).

ASTER, CHINA (*Callistephus chinensis*)
Aphid, Corn Root (grayish-white, powdery lice at root); Green Peach; Leaf-curling Plum; Potato; Sugar-beet Root; Western Aster Root.
Beetle, Ash-gray Blister; Asiatic Garden; Black Blister (common on flowers); June (grubs injure roots); Margined Blister; Potato Flea; Spotted Cucumber.
Borer, European Corn; Stalk.
Bug, Chrysanthemum Lace; Four-lined Plant; Tarnished Plant (blackens new tips).
Butterfly, Checker Spot. **Centipede,** Garden. **Cutworms.**
Leafhopper, Six-spotted (transmits yellows virus, causing stunted, deformed plants); Red-banded.
Leaf Miner, Wild Parsnip.
Leaf Roller, Oblique-banded. **Leaf Tier,** Celery.
Mealybug, Yucca. **Mites. Nematode,** Root-knot.
Scale, Black (not common).
Thrips, Banded Greenhouse; Gladiolus. **Wireworms.**

ASTER, HARDY (Michaelmas Daisy)
Aphid, Aster (green, clustered thick on flower stems).

ASTILBE (incorrectly called Spirea)
Beetle, Japanese (descends on flowers and foliage in hordes).

AUCUBA (Japanese Laurel)
Aphid, Aucuba (greenish).
Scale, California Red (yellow strain, making wounds for leaf-spot fungi).

AUSTRALIAN PINE (*Casuarina*)
Scale, Barnacle; Cottony-cushion; Mining (grayish, mines partly into bark).

AUSTRALIAN SILK OAK (*Grevillea*)

Caterpillar, Omnivorous Looper.
Mealybug, Citrophilus (white, with long filaments); Grape.
Mite, Avocado Red.
Scale, Greedy (gray, convex); Lesser Snow (white).

AVOCADO

Ant, Argentine; Fire. **Aphid,** Melon; Spirea.
Beetle, Ambrosia; Banded Flea; Darkling Ground; Fuller Rose; June (on young trees).
Borer, Branch and Twig; Shot-hole. **Bug,** False Chinch; Harlequin.
Caterpillar, Avocado (Amorbia, skeletonizes leaves, scars fruit); Omnivorous Looper; Orange Tortrix.
Cricket, Snowy Tree. **Cutworm,** Variegated (on young trees).
Mealybugs, Citrus; Long-tailed (on scions of newly grafted trees).
Mite, Avocado Brown; Avocado Red; Broad; Pallid; Platani; Six-spotted.
Scale, Black; California Red; Camphor, Dictyospermum; European Fruit Lecanium; Florida Wax; Greedy; Green Shield; Hemispherical; Latania (gray to yellow, serious pest); Oleander; Purple; Soft.
Snail, Brown Garden.
Thrips, Bean; Greenhouse (important, fruit scarred, leaves brown).
Whitefly, Avocado; Greenhouse.

AZALEA (*Rhododendron*)

Beetle, Asiatic Garden; Fuller Rose.
Borer, Azalea Stem (yellow grub in twigs); Rhododendron (in wood near base).
Bug, Azalea Lace (most common and serious pest); Rhododendron.
Caterpillar, Azalea. **Leaf Miner,** Azalea (rolls leaves).
Mealybug, Citrophilus; Striped.
Mite, Cyclamen; Privet; Southern Red (causes foliage drop); Two-spotted.
Moth, Azalea Sphinx; White-lined Sphinx.
Scale, Azalea Bark (white cotton, black mold on twigs); Oleander; Peony (serious in South, brown humps, white circles on branches); Soft Azalea (resembles bark scale).
Thrips, Greenhouse (leaves pale, covered with black dots); Madrona.
Weevil, Black Vine (grubs injure roots, beetles notch leaves at night, girdle stem); Strawberry Root.

Whitefly, Azalea; Mulberry; Rhododendron.

Spraying to control azalea lace bugs is almost always necessary. Bark and peony scales, thrips, and mites are more of a problem in warm climates.

BALSAM, GARDEN (*Impatiens*)

Aphid, Impatiens; other species.
Beetle, Spotted Cucumber (eats holes in blossoms).
Bug, Tarnished Plant (blackens new shoots).
Nematode, Root-knot (galls on roots).

BALSAM FIR (see Fir)

BAMBOO (*Bambusa*)

Aphids, Bamboo (yellow with black markings).
Scale, Cottony Bamboo (White sacs at leaf axils).

BANANA (*Musa*)

Mealybug, Long-tailed; Pineapple; Yucca. **Nematode,** Root-knot.
Scale, Black; California Red; Florida Red; Hemispherical; Soft.
Whitefly, Citrus.

BANKSIA (Australian Honeysuckle)

Scale, Black Araucaria; Purple.

BARBERRY (*Berberis*)

Aphid, Barberry (small, yellow green, on new shoots).
Beetle, Asiatic Garden. **Mites. Moth,** Eight-spotted Forester.
Scale, Barberry (convex, reddish brown, soft).
Webworm, Barberry (webs over twigs). **Whitefly,** Greenhouse.

BASSWOOD (see Linden)

BAY, SWEET or LAUREL (*Laurus*)

Bud Moth, Eye-spotted (brownish worm).
Psyllid, Laurel (black, scalelike, with white fringe).
Scale, Black; California Red; Cottony-cushion; Dictyospermum; Florida Red; Glover (brown, narrow); Greedy (small, gray, convex); Green Shield; Soft.

BAYBERRY (*Myrica*)

Caterpillar, Red-humped (has bright red head and hump, chews foliage).

BEAN, LIMA BEAN (*Phaseolus*)

Aphid, Bean (small, black); Cowpea; Melon; Potato; Turnip.

Armyworm, Fall; Yellow-striped.

Beetle, Banded Cucumber; Bean Leaf; Blister; Fuller Rose; Grape Colaspis; June; Mexican Bean (yellow with black spots, the worst bean pest); Pale-striped Flea; Potato Flea; Spotted Cucumber; Striped Cucumber; Western Striped Cucumber; White-fringed.

Borer, European Corn; Lesser Cornstalk.

Bug, Garden Fleahopper; Green Stink; Harlequin; Leaf-footed; Lygus; Pumpkin; Tarnished Plant.

Caterpillar, Alfalfa; Gallworm; Green Cloverworm; Salt-marsh; Yellow Woollybear.

Cricket, Field. **Curculio,** Cowpea. **Cutworms.**

Earworm, Corn (feeds on pods). **Leafhopper,** Beet; Potato.

Leaf Miner, Serpentine.

Leaf Roller, Bean; Oblique-banded. **Leaf Tier,** Celery.

Maggot, Seed-corn (tunnels in sprouting seeds).

Mealybug, Grape.

Mite, Two-spotted (foliage mealy, yellow); Pacific.

Nematode, Root-knot.

Thrips, Bean (leaves silvered); Onion; Western Flower.

Weevil, Bean (grubs in stored beans).

Whitefly, Glacial; Greenhouse.

The Mexican bean beetle is the most common bean problem in home gardens.

BEECH (*Fagus*)

Aphid, Beech Blight (white, woolly); Hickory (large, gray); Woolly Beech (fluffy white masses on underside of leaves of purple or copper beech).

Borer, Brown Wood; Flatheaded Apple Tree; Pacific Flatheaded; Pigeon Tremex.

Cankerworm, Fall; Spring.

Caterpillar, Eastern Tent; Hemlock Looper; Saddled Prominent; Walnut; Yellow-necked.

Leaf Cutter, Maple. **Leafhopper,** Grape.

Moth, Gypsy; Imperial; Io; Leopard; Luna; Rusty Tussock.

Scale, Beech (circular, pale yellow with wax, associated with Nectria disease); Black; Cottony-cushion; European Fruit Lecanium; Oystershell; Putnam; San Jose.

BEET (*Beta*)

Aphid, Bean; Green Peach; Melon; Sugar-beet Root.

Armyworm, Beet; Yellow-striped.

Beetle, Asiatic Garden; Blister; Carrot (works on root); Pale-striped Flea; Potato Flea (minute, black, makes pinholes in leaves); Spinach Carrion; Spotted Cucumber; Western Striped Cucumber.

Bug, Harlequin; Tarnished Plant.

Caterpillar, Cabbage Looper. **Cutworms.**

Leafhopper, Beet (important as vector of curly-top disease).

Leaf Miner, Serpentine; Spinach (common, tan blotches in leaves).

Leaf Tier, Celery. **Maggot,** Seed-corn. **Moth,** White-lined Sphinx.

Springtail, Garden (occasional injury to seedlings).

Webworm, Alfalfa; Beet; Cabbage; Spotted Beet.

Weevil, Vegetable (injurious in Gulf states).

Wireworm, Eastern Field; Plains False; Sugar-beet.

BEGONIA

Aphid, Melon. **Beetle,** Fuller Rose (may eat leaf margins at night).

Caterpillar, Orange Tortrix (rolls leaves).

Mealybug, Citrus (common, white cotton at leaf axils); Long-tailed.

Mite, Broad (leaves glassy); Cyclamen (plants stunted); Two-spotted.

Nematode, Fern (brown blotches in leaves); Root-knot.

Scale, Florida Red; Mining.

Thrips, Banded Greenhouse; Greenhouse (leaves silvered with rust spots).

Weevil, Black Vine (grubs destroy roots).

Whitefly, Greenhouse (very common).

Do not use nicotine sulfate to control sucking insects after plants are in bloom.

BERGAMOT (*Monarda*)

Scale, Purple.

BIGNONIA (Trumpet Flower)

Mealybug, Citrus. **Nematode,** Root-knot.

Scale, Barnacle (brownish with white wax); Hemispherical (brown, convex); Lesser Snow (white).

Whitefly, Greenhouse.

BIRCH (*Betula*)

Aphid, Common Birch, European Birch. **Beetle,** Japanese; June.

Borer, Bronze Birch (kills from top down); Poplar and Willow.

Cankerworms, Fall; Spring.

Caterpillar, Eastern Tent; Forest Tent; Hemlock Looper; Red-humped; Saddled Prominent; Variable Oak-leaf; Yellow-necked.

Gall, Witch Hazel Cone.

Leaf Miner, Birch (prevalent, important, nearly half of each leaf turns brown).

Leaf Roller, Oblique-banded. **Leaf Skeletonizer,** Birch.

Moth, Cecropia; Gypsy; Leopard; Imperial; Io; Luna; Polyphemus; Rusty Tussock.

Sawfly, Dusky Birch.

Scale, Oystershell; Lecanium; San Jose; Terrapin.

Webworm, Fall. **Weevil,** Willow Flea.

BITTERSWEET (*Celastrus*)

Aphid, Bean (black, common); Spirea (green).

Scale, Euonymus (almost always encrusting canes, covering leaves); Oystershell; San Jose.

Treehopper, Two-marked (small, birdlike).

BLACKBERRY (*Rubus*)

Beetle, Fuller Rose; Green June; Imbricated Snout; Japanese (injurious to fruit and foliage); Rose Chafer; White-fringed.

Borer, Currant; Raspberry Cane; Raspberry Root; Red-necked Cane; Pacific Flatheaded.

Bug, Negro (southern, bad taste in berries).

Caterpillar, Red-humped; Saddled Prominent; Yellow-necked.

Cricket, Black-horned Tree (eats buds, flowers); Snowy Tree.

Gall, Blackberry Knot. **Leafhopper,** Grape; Rose.

Leaf Miner, Blackberry (blotch mines at leaf margins).

Leaf Roller, Oblique-banded; Fruit Tree; Strawberry Leaf.

Maggot, Raspberry Cane (tips wilt). **Mealybug,** Citrophilus.

Mite, Redberry (in West) ; Pacific; Two-spotted.
Moth, Strawberry Crown; Western Tussock.
Psyllid, Blackberry (occasional distortion, stunting).
Rootworm, Strawberry.
Sawfly, Blackberry (leaves eaten by blue-green larvae) ; Raspberry.
Scale, Rose (white, common) ; Cottony Maple; European Fruit Lecanium (brown, convex) ; San Jose.
Weevil, Black Vine; Apple Flea; Strawberry; Strawberry Root.
Whitefly, Glacial; Greenhouse.

BLUEBERRY (*Vaccinium*)

Beetle, Blueberry Flea (grubs feed on buds) ; Green June.
Borer, Azalea Stem; Blueberry Crown Girdler.
Caterpillar, Forest Tent. **Curculio,** Plum.
Fruitworm, Cherry, Cranberry (wormy berries).
Gall, Blueberry Stem (hard, brown on twigs).
Leafhopper (vector of stunt disease).
Maggot, Blueberry (common cause of worms in berries).
Scale, Oystershell; Florida Wax; Putnam. **Spanworm,** Currant.
Thrips, Blueberry (curls, deforms buds and leaves).
Webworm, Fall. **Weevil,** Cranberry.

BOTTLEBRUSH (*Callistemon*)

Mealybug, Citrus.

BOUGAINVILLEA

Scale, Soft.

BOUVARDIA

Mealybug, Citrus.
Nematode, Fern (blotches in leaves; flower cluster deformed).

BOXELDER (*Acer negundo*)

Aphid, Boxelder (green, hairy, with conspicuous honeydew).
Bagworm. Beetle, Sweetpotato Flea.
Borer, Flatheaded Apple Tree; Pacific Flatheaded.
Bug, Boxelder (red and black, feeds on foliage, flowers, fruit) ; Green Stink.
Caterpillar, Forest Tent; Green-striped Mapleworm.
Leaf Roller, Fruit Tree; Oblique-banded. **Moth,** Spotted Tussock.

Scale, California Red; Cottony Maple; European Fruit Lecanium; Oystershell; Soft; Walnut.
Webworm, Fall.

BOXWOOD (*Buxus*)

Leaf Miner, Boxwood (common; injurious; blisters in leaves).
Mealybug, Comstock; Ground.
Mite, Boxwood (leaves grayish); Two-spotted. **Planthoppers.**
Psyllid, Boxwood (terminal leaves curled into cups).
Scale, California Red; Cottony-cushion; Cottony Maple; Lesser Snow; Oystershell (dark, oyster-shaped shells on twigs).
Wasp, Giant Hornet (tears bark).

BOYSENBERRY (*Rubus*)

Whitefly, Glacial.
Also, many of the pests listed under Blackberry, Raspberry.

BREADFRUIT (*Artocarpus*)

Scale, California Red.

BROADBEAN (*Vicia faba*)

Weevil, Broadbean.

BROCCOLI (*Brassica oleracea*)

Aphid, Cabbage (common, grayish lice on leaves, flower head); Turnip.
Beetle, Potato Flea (shot-holes in leaves).
Caterpillars, Cabbage Looper; Imported Cabbageworm (green).
Maggot, Cabbage (seedlings wilt; very common).
See Cabbage for many other pests.

BROOM (*Genista*)

Aphid, Bean (black).
Scale, Greedy (gray, convex); Oleander (round, flat, yellow).

BROWALLIA

Aphid, Western Aster Root (white, at roots).
Leafhopper, Six-spotted (transmits aster yellows).

BRUSSELS SPROUTS
Most of the pests listed under Cabbage attack this host, with Cabbage Aphid, Cabbage Maggot, Imported Cabbageworm, Flea Beetles, and Harlequin Bug rather important.

BRYOPHYLLUM
Scale, Lesser Snow (white, pear-shaped).

BUCKEYE (see Horsechestnut)

BUCKTHORN (*Rhamnus*)
Aphid, Buckthorn; Melon.
Moth, Oriental (varicolored caterpillar, near Boston).
Scale, Black; San Jose.

BUDDLEIA (Butterfly Bush)
Beetle, Japanese. Butterfly, Checker Spot.
Nematode, Root-knot. Thrips, Banded Greenhouse.

BURSERA (Gumbo-limbo)
Scale, Soft.

BUTTERFLY WEED (*Asclepias*)
Aphid, Melon; Oleander (black and yellow).
Beetle, Argus Tortoise.
Butterfly, Monarch (greenish caterpillar with dark bands).
Leaf Miner, Serpentine (winding tunnels in leaves).
Scale, San Jose. Thrips, Western Flower.

BUTTERNUT (*Juglans*)
Beetle, June. Borer, Painted Hickory.
Caterpillar, Hickory Horned Devil; Walnut; Yellow Woollybear.
Curculio, Butternut (beetles puncture twigs; grubs in nuts).
Moth, Hickory Tussock; Imperial; Luna.
Rootworm, Strawberry (beetle makes minute holes in foliage).
Sawfly, Butternut Woollyworm (leaves eaten by hairy larvae).
Scale, Oystershell; Walnut (round, gray).
See also Hickory for other pests possible on Butternut.

BUTTONBUSH (*Cephalanthus*)
Scale, San Jose.

CABBAGE (*Brassica oleracea*)
Aphid, Cabbage (gray lice numerous on underside of leaves); Turnip.
Armyworm, Fall.
Beetle, Argus Tortoise; Black Blister; Imbricated Snout; Potato Flea;
   Red Turnip; Rose Chafer; Sinuate-striped Flea; Spotted Cucumber;
   Western Black Flea; Western Striped Flea; White-fringed.
Bug, Green Stink; Harlequin (red and black, southern); Squash.
Caterpillar, Cabbage Looper; Cross-striped Cabbageworm; Imported
   Cabbageworm; Southern Cabbageworm; Yellow Woollybear.
Curculio, Cabbage (ash-gray weevil). **Cutworms.**
Earworm, Corn. **Leaf Tier,** Celery.
Maggot, Cabbage (seedlings wilt; common); Seed-corn.
Moth, Diamondback (green caterpillar). **Nematode,** Root-knot.
Slugs (several species make holes in leaves, enter heads).
Thrips, Onion. **Webworm,** Beet, Cabbage.

CACTUS
Aphid, Tulip Bulb (on roots). **Gall,** Cactus Fruit.
Mealybug, Citrus; Long-tailed (white, woolly); Root (may kill
   plants).
Mite, Two-spotted, other species (plants gray or yellow with webs).
Orthezia, Greenhouse (dark with white wax).
Scale, Cactus (female gray, male white); Greedy (gray, convex);
   Lesser Snow (white); Oleander (pale yellow).
   Use sprays on cacti with some caution. A pointed stick or stiff brush
will help to remove scales and mealybugs. For root mealybugs wash off
all soil and repot.

CALCEOLARIA (Slipperwort)
Aphid, Green Peach; Crescent-marked Lily; other species.
Nematode, Fern (brown areas in leaves). **Whitefly,** Greenhouse.

CALENDULA
Aphid, Bean (black, common); Western Aster Root; Green Peach;
   Crescent-marked Lily.
Beetle, Black Blister; Flea; Spotted Cucumber.
Borer, Stalk. **Bug,** Tarnished Plant. **Butterfly,** Painted Lady.

Caterpillar, Cabbage Looper; Yellow Woollybear.
Leafhopper, Red-banded; Six-spotted (transmits aster yellows).
Mites. Nematode, Root-knot.
Thrips, Composite (in flower head). Whitefly, Greenhouse.

CALIFORNIA CHRISTMASBERRY,
TOYON (*Photinia arbutifolia*)

Bug, Toyon Lace (leaves lose color, have brown flecks; common).
Caterpillar, California Tent; Omnivorous Looper.
Moth, Western Tussock.
Scale, Black; European Fruit Lecanium; Italian Pear (shiny, dark gray, sunken in bark, associated with lichens); Oystershell; San Jose.
Thrips, Greenhouse; Toyon.
Whitefly, Crown; Inconspicuous; Iridescent; Pruinose.

CALIFORNIA COFFEEBERRY (*Rhamnus californica*)

Borer, Pacific Flatheaded.
Caterpillar, California Tent. Moth, Western Tussock.
Whitefly, Glacial; Greenhouse; Inconspicuous; Iridescent.

CALIFORNIA LAUREL (*Umbellularia californica*)

Aphid, Crescent-marked Lily (yellow and black).
Caterpillar, Omnivorous Looper (yellow, green, or pinkish, striped).
Scale, Soft. Thrips, Onion; Pear.
Whitefly, Inconspicuous; Iridescent.

CALLA LILY (*Zantedeschia*)

Caterpillar, Yellow Woollybear. Mealybug, Grape; Long-tailed.
Mite, Bulb. Thrips, Banded Greenhouse; Greenhouse.

CAMELLIA

Aphid, Black Citrus (curls new leaves); Melon; Green Peach; Ornate.
Beetle, Fuller Rose; Rhabdopterus; Flea; Grape Colaspis.
Caterpillar, Omnivorous Looper; Orange Tortrix; Western Parsley.
Curculio, Cambium. Leaf Roller, Fruit Tree. Leaf Tier, Celery.
Mealybug, Citrus; Long-tailed.
Mite, Camellia Rust (rusty foliage); Southern Red (leaves speckled).
Nematode, Root-knot (rare, camellia is quite resistant).

Scale, Black; California Red; Camellia (brown, leaves may drop, important in Southeast); Camellia Parlatoria (brown, flat, oval, most important on Pacific coast); Chaff; Cottony Taxus; Degenerate; Florida Red (round, dark, important in Gulf states); Florida Wax; Glover; Greedy; Hemispherical; Latania; Mexican Wax; Oleander; Olive Parlatoria; Oystershell; Peony (white circles on branches, sometimes serious); Soft; Tea (the worst pest in Gulf states, white filaments on underside of leaves; upper surface yellow).

Weevil, Black Vine; Strawberry Root. **Whitefly,** Greenhouse.

DDT should not be used on camellias; it injures certain varieties. An oil spray, spring and fall, for scale insects has been standard. Many commercial growers now use parathion with home gardeners trying malathion.

CAMPANULA (Bluebell)

Aphid, Foxglove. **Slugs. Thrips,** Onion.

CAMPHOR-TREE (*Cinnamomum camphora*)

Mite, Avocado Red (leaves turn reddish); Platani; Southern Red.

Scale, Camphor (convex, dark brown, may cause death); Chaff; Florida Red; Florida Wax; Greedy; Oystershell.

Thrips, Camphor (most injurious; buds, branches die; bark cracks).

CANDYTUFT (*Iberis*)

Moth, Diamondback (greenish caterpillar).

CANNA

Beetle, Fuller Rose; Goldsmith; Japanese (common on flowers); Spotted Cucumber.

Caterpillar, Saddleback; Yellow Woollybear. **Earworm,** Corn.

Leaf Roller, Larger Canna (green caterpillar rolls leaves); Lesser Canna.

Leaf Tier, Celery.

Scale, Latania (small, gray, convex); Pineapple (white and gray).

CANTALOUPE (see Melon)

CAPE JASMINE (see Gardenia)

CAPE MARIGOLD, AFRICAN DAISY
(*Dimorphotheca*)
Leafhopper, Six-spotted (transmits aster yellows).

CARAWAY (*Carum*)
Caterpillar, Celeryworm (green, black-banded).

CARDINAL FLOWER (*Lobelia cardinalis*)
Bug, Negro (red to black, southern). **Leaf Roller,** Red-banded.
Nematode, Root-knot. **Wireworms.**

CARNATION (*Dianthus caryophyllus*)
Aphid, Green Peach. **Beetle,** Fuller Rose.
Caterpillar, Cabbage Looper. **Cutworm,** Spotted (climbs stems).
Leaf Roller, Oblique-banded. **Leaf Tier,** Celery.
Mealybug, Grape.
Mite, Two-spotted (leaves pale, dusty, with webs, plants stunted).
Nematode, Root-knot. **Thrips,** Onion (leaves silvered).

CAROB, ST. JOHN'S BREAD (*Ceratonia siliqua*)
Borer, Carpenterworm (large caterpillar in wood).
Mealybug, Long-tailed. **Scale,** Oleander (pale yellow).

CARROT (*Daucus carota*)
Ants, Pavement.
Aphid, Bean; Corn Root (white, powdery at roots); Green Peach; Leaf-curling Plum.
Beetle, Asiatic Garden; Black Blister and other species; Carrot; Potato Flea; Pale-striped Flea.
Caterpillar, Celeryworm (green, black-banded); Yellow Woollybear.
Fly, Carrot Rust (rusty tunnels in roots; serious in some sections).
Leafhopper, Six-spotted (transmits aster yellows).
Millipedes. Thrips, Onion. **Webworm,** Alfalfa; Beet.
Weevil, Carrot (tunnels in roots); Vegetable (feeds on foliage at night).
Wireworm, Western Field and other species.

CASSAVA
Mite, Two-spotted. **Scale,** Lesser Snow.

CASSIA
Bug, Eggplant Lace (brown and yellow).
Nematode, Root-knot.   **Scale.** Lesser Snow; Soft.

CASTOR-BEAN (*Ricinus*)
Armyworm, Southern (may defoliate and kill southern plants).
Earworm, Corn.   **Leafhopper,** Potato.   **Leaf Miner,** Serpentine.
Mite, Two-spotted.   **Scale,** Cottony-cushion; Lesser Snow.

CATALINA CHERRY (*Prunus lyoni*)
Borer, Pacific Flatheaded.   **Scale,** European Fruit Lecanium.
Whitefly, Kellogg's (looks like small white flower).

CATALPA
Aphid, Melon.   **Bug,** Green Stink.
Mealybug, Comstock (white fluffs in bark crevices; often serious).
Midge, Catalpa (small brown spots in leaves).
Moth, Catalpa Sphinx (large dark caterpillar, causes defoliation).
Nematode, Root-knot.   **Scale,** San Jose; White Peach.

CATNIP (*Nepeta*)
Leafhopper, Grape.   **Webworm,** Small Beet.

CAT-TAIL (*Typha*)
Aphid, Mealy Plum; Melon; Waterlily.
Borer, Potato Tuberworm.   **Grasshoppers.**   **Mites.**

CAULIFLOWER (*Brassica oleracea*)
Aphid, Cabbage; Turnip.
Beetle, Striped Flea; Western Striped Flea; Western Black Flea.
Bug, Harlequin; Tarnished Plant.
Caterpillar, Cabbage Looper; Imported Cabbageworm; Yellow
   Woollybear.
Curculio, Cabbage (weevil attacking seedlings).
Leaf Tier, Celery.   **Moth,** Diamondback.
Maggot, Cabbage (seedlings wilt).
Springtail, Garden (on seedlings).   **Thrips,** Onion.
Webworm, Cabbage.   **Weevil,** Vegetable.
   See Cabbage for other possible pests.

CEANOTHUS

Aphid, Ceanothus (red brown to black); Crescent-marked Lily.
Borer, Pacific Flatheaded.
Bug, Ceanothus Lace (black and brown, prevalent; leaves whitened).
Caterpillar, California Tent; Great Basin Tent.
Mealybug, Yucca (cottony sacs of axils).
Scale, Greedy (gray, convex); San Jose; Willow.
Thrips, Madrona.

CEDAR, DEODAR (*Cedrus deodara*)

Scale, Black (dark brown to black, hemispherical).
Weevil, Deodar (grubs burrow in wood, kill leaders).

CEDAR, INCENSE (*Libocedrus*)

Beetle, Cypress Bark.   **Mealybug,** Cypress.
Scale, Cypress (covered with white wax); Juniper (small, round);
Pine Needle (white, oval); Putnam (dark gray).

CEDAR, RED (see Juniper)

CEDAR, WHITE (*Chamaecyparis*)

Bagworm.   Moth, Imperial.   **Scale,** Juniper.

CELERY (*Apium*)

Aphid, Green Peach.   **Armyworm,** Southern.
Beetle, Carrot; Potato Flea.
Borer, European Corn (sometimes in stalks).
Bug, Negro; Tarnished Plant (causes "black joint" on stems); Garden
Fleahopper.
Caterpillar, Cabbage Looper; Celery Looper; Celeryworm (green with
black bands); Yellow Woollybear.
Fly, Carrot Rust (plants wilt, outer leaves turn yellow).
Leafhopper, Beet (transmits curly top); Six-spotted (transmits yel-
lows).
Leaf Roller, Oblique-banded.
Leaf Tier, Celery (major pest, webbing foliage, mining in hearts).
Mites, Two-spotted; other species (mealy webs).
Nematode, Bulb and Stem.   **Thrips,** Onion (foliage silvered).
Webworm, Parsnip.   **Weevil,** Carrot.

CENTURY PLANT (*Agave*)

Borer, Stalk.   **Moth,** Yucca.

Scale, California Red; Lesser Snow; Oleander (yellow).

Weevil, Yucca (black billbug).

CHERRY (*Prunus*)

Aphid, Black Cherry (prevalent on young shoots, curls leaves); **Green** Peach; Hop.

Beetle, Cherry Leaf; Imbricated Snout; Japanese; Plum Gouger; Rose Chafer.

Borer, Brown Wood; California Prionus; Flatheaded Apple Tree; Lesser Peach Tree; Peach Tree; Shot-hole.

Bud Moth, Eye-spotted.   **Bug,** Boxelder; Green Stink; Harlequin.

Cankerworm, Fall, Spring.   **Casebearer,** California; Cherry; Cigar.

Caterpillar, California Tent; Coast Tent; Eastern Tent (nests prevalent on cherry); Forest Tent; Omnivorous Looper; Red-humped; Saddleback; Saddled Prominent; Yellow-necked; Yellow Woollybear.

Curculio, Cherry; Plum (wormy cherries).

Fly, Black Cherry Fruit; Cherry Fruit (maggots in fruit).

Leaf Crumpler.   Leaf Miner, Unspotted Tentiform.

Leaf Roller, Fruit Tree; Oblique-banded; Red-banded.

Maggot, Apple.   **Mealybug,** Citrophilus.

Mite, Clover; Pacific; Willamette.

Moth, Brown-tail; Codling; Oriental Fruit; Western Tussock.

Sawfly, Cherry Fruit; Pear-slug.

Scale, Calico; European Fruit Lecanium; Florida Wax; Forbes; Glover; Greedy; Lecanium; Oystershell; Putnam; Terrapin; Walnut; White Peach.

Termites, Subterranean.   **Thrips,** Onion, Pear.

Treehopper, Buffalo (curved slits in bark).   **Whitefly,** Citrus.

A cherry spray schedule is made up chiefly to control aphids, scales, plum curculio, fruit flies, the brown rot fungus, and some leaf spots. See remarks under Apple about Home Fruit Spray Schedules.

CHERRY, ORIENTAL FLOWERING
(*Prunus*)

Aphid, Waterlily (when tree is near ponds).

Beetle, Japanese.   **Cankerworms.   Planthoppers.**

CHERRY, SAND (*Prunus pumila*)

Bug, Green Stink. **Sawfly,** Plum Web-spinning. **Scale,** San Jose.
Thrips, Greenhouse.

CHERRY-LAUREL (*Prunus laurocerasus*)

Whitefly, Citrus.

CHESTNUT (*Castanea*)

Although the American chestnut was practically exterminated by
blight, Asiatic chestnuts are being grown, hybrids are being produced,
and there is still the native chinquapin in the South.

Aphid, Hickory (large, gray).

Beetle, Japanese (very fond of chestnut foliage).

Borer, Broad-necked Root; Brown Wood; Chestnut Timberworm;
Dogwood; Flatheaded Apple Tree; Oak Sapling; Oak Timberworm;
Twig Pruner; Two-lined Chestnut.

Cankerworms.

Caterpillar, California Oakworm; Omnivorous Looper.

Moth, Brown-tail; Gypsy; Imperial; Leopard; Luna.

Scale, European Fruit Lecanium; Obscure; Oystershell; Putnam; San
Jose; Terrapin.

Webworm, Fall.

Weevil, Asiatic Oak; Large Chestnut; Small Chestnut (prevalent in
Asiatic chestnuts).

CHINABERRY (*Melia azedarach*)

Mite, Pacific (yellowing foliage).

Scale, California Red; Greedy; Lesser Snow.

Whitefly, Citrus (breeds profusely on this tree).

CHINESE LANTERN (*Physalis*)

Beetle, Tortoise, several species (very convex, yellow); Striped Cucumber (devours foliage, transmits mosaic).

Weevil, Imported Long-horned.

CHIONODOXA (Glory-of-the-Snow)

Nematode, Bulb and Stem.

CHOISYA (Mexican-Orange)

Mealybug, Citrophilus; Grape. **Whitefly,** Citrus.

CHOKEBERRY (*Aronia*)
Borer, Roundheaded Apple Tree.

CHRYSANTHEMUM
Aphid, Chrysanthemum; Foxglove; Green Peach; Leaf-curling Plum; Melon; Myrtle; Thistle.

Beetle, Asiatic Garden; Blister; Fuller Rose; Goldsmith; Rose Chafer; Spotted Cucumber.

Borer, European Corn; Stalk.

Bug, Chrysanthemum Lace; Four-lined Plant (round, tan, depressed spots in leaves); Harlequin; Lygus; Tarnished Plant.

Butterfly, Checker Spot.

Caterpillar, Yellow Woollybear; Zebra. **Cutworm,** Variegated.

Leafhopper, Six-spotted.

Leaf Miner, Chrysanthemum. **Leaf Tier,** Celery.

Mealybug, Citrus; Ground; Greenhouse; Mexican (serious in greenhouses).

Midge, Chrysanthemum Gall (conical galls in stem, leaf, bud).

Mite, Broad; Cyclamen; Two-spotted.

Nematode, Chrysanthemum (brown wedges in leaves; serious); Root-knot.

Scale, Black; Cottony-cushion; Hemispherical.

Slugs. Spittlebugs. Termites.

Thrips, Banded Greenhouse; Chrysanthemum; Greenhouse (leaves silvered).

Weevil, Imported Long-horned. **Whitefly,** Greenhouse.

The chrysanthemum or leaf nematode often causes progressive dying of leaves up the stem. Start with cuttings from healthy tips. Spray for aphids through the season.

CINERARIA
Aphid, Green Peach; Leaf-curling Plum; Melon; Potato.

Caterpillar, Cabbage Looper; Orange Tortrix. **Cutworms.**

Leafhopper, Six-spotted. **Leaf Tier,** Celery (feeds in webs).

Mealybug, Citrus; Long-tailed. **Mite,** Two-spotted.

Slug, Spotted Garden; Greenhouse. **Whitefly,** Greenhouse.

CINQUEFOIL (*Potentilla*)
Aphid, Rose (small, green). **Weevil,** Strawberry.

CISSUS (Kangaroo Vine)

Aphid, Grapevine (black). **Beetle,** Fuller Rose.

CITRUS FRUITS (including Calamondin, Citron, Grapefruit, Kumquat, Lemon, Orange, Tangerine)

Ant, Argentine (disseminates scales, mealybugs, aphids); Fire.

Aphid, Black Citrus; Cowpea; Melon; Potato; Spirea.

Beetle, Fuller Rose; Tobacco Flea.

Borer, Branch and Twig; California Prionus.

Bug, Cotton Stainer; Green Stink; Harlequin; Leaf-footed; Southern Green Stink; Western Leaf-footed.

Caterpillar, Omnivorous Looper; Orange Tortrix (bores in rind of fruit).

Mealybug, Citrus; Citrophilus; Grape; Long-tailed.

Mite, Citrus Red (purple mite in Florida, leaves grayish); Citrus Rust (fruit rusty, dry, rough); Six-spotted.

Scale, Black; California Red; Chaff; Citricola; Cottony-cushion; Florida Red; Florida Wax; Greedy; Green Shield; Hemispherical; Lesser Snow; Mining; Oleander; Purple (major pest); Putnam; San Jose; Soft.

Thrips, Citrus (scars fruit); Flower; Greenhouse.

Weevil, Citrus Root.

Whitefly, Citrus (trees devitalized, covered with sooty mold); Cloudy-winged; Woolly.

It is impossible to suggest a citrus spray schedule that would be generally applicable. The citrus whitefly so troublesome in Florida is not a problem in California. Conditions vary even within a state and a grower has to have a program marked out for his own location. For the homeowner, using citrus trees as ornamentals, a cleanup spray in May or June with a summer oil is perhaps most important. Malathion will also aid in control of scales and whiteflies.

CLARKIA

Leafhopper, Six-spotted (transmits aster yellows).

CLEMATIS

Beetle, Black Blister (may devour flowers and foliage).

Borer, Clematis (works in roots).

Caterpillar, Omnivorous Looper.

Mite, Two-spotted, probably other species (webby, yellow foliage).

Nematode, Root-knot (sometimes kills vines).
Scale, Oystershell; Soft. **Whitefly,** Glacial; Inconspicuous.

CLERODENDRON
Scale, Green Shield; Soft.

COCKSCOMB (*Celosia*)
Mite, Two-spotted; other species (mealy webs; serious in hot weather).

COCONUT PALM (see Palms)

COFFEE (*Coffea*)
Mealybug, Citrus. **Orthezia,** Greenhouse.
Scale, Black; Camellia; Tessellated (dark brown, soft).
Whitefly, Citrus.

COLEUS
Caterpillar, Yellow Woollybear.
Mealybug, Citrus; Long-tailed (white cottony masses at leaf axils).
Mite, Two-spotted; other species.
Nematode, Fern (brown areas in leaves); Root-knot (galls on roots).
Orthezia, Greenhouse (dark scale with white wax).
Slug, Greenhouse; Spotted Garden.
Weevil, Imported Long-horned (grayish snout beetle).
Whitefly, Greenhouse (hordes of tiny white "moths" underneath
  leaves).

COLLARDS (*Brassica*)
Aphid, Cabbage; Turnip (grayish lice, common).
Beetle, White-fringed. **Bug,** Harlequin; Southern Squash.
Caterpillar, Cabbage Looper; Imported Cabbageworm.
Moth, Diamondback; White-lined Sphinx.
Webworm, Cabbage.
  See also Cabbage for other pests.

COLUMBINE (*Aquilegia*)
Aphid, Columbine (cream-colored, abundant); Foxglove; Crescent-
  marked Lily; Melon; Spirea.
Beetle, Asiatic Garden.
Borer, Columbine (salmon caterpillar in crown); Stalk.

Budworm, Rose. **Bug,** Red-and-Black Stink.
Butterfly, Columbine Skipper. **Curculio,** Cambium.
Leaf Miner, Columbine (white winding tunnels in leaves); Wild Parsnip.
Mealybug, Citrophilus, Grape. **Mites. Moth,** White-lined Sphinx.
Weevil, Imported Long-horned. **Whitefly,** Glacial.

CORAL BELLS (*Heuchera*)

Mealybugs (occasional). **Nematode,** Fern (brown blotches in leaves).
Weevil, Strawberry Root (grubs at roots destroy plant).

CORN (*Zea mays*)

Aphid, Corn Leaf; Corn Root (woolly white lice at roots, distributed by ants); Potato; Rusty Plum.
Armyworm, Fall; True.
Beetle, Argus Tortoise; Asiatic Garden; Bean Leaf; Blister; Bumble Flower; Carrot; Corn; Corn Billbug; Corn Flea; Corn Sap; Desert Corn Flea; Green June; Imbricated Snout; June; Pale-striped Flea; Potato Flea; Rose Chafer; Seed-corn; Spotted Cucumber (southern corn rootworm); Striped Cucumber; Sweetpotato Flea; Western Striped; White-fringed.
Borer, European Corn (cream-colored caterpillars at base of ears and in stalks); Elder; Lesser Cornstalk; Southern Cornstalk; Southwestern Cornstalk; Stalk (dark, striped caterpillar).
Bug, Chinch (important in Middle West); Green Stink; Harlequin.
Caterpillar, Range; Yellow Woollybear. **Cutworm,** Bronzed.
Earworm, Corn (dark caterpillars at tips of ears; very common).
Grasshoppers. Leaf Miner, Corn Blotch.
Maggot, Seed-corn (injures germinating seeds).
Millipedes. Mites. Rootworm, Northern Corn.
Thrips, Grass. **Webworm,** Corn Root; Sod.
Wireworm, Plains False; Wheat; other species.

The two most important pests are the European corn borer, with control started when plants are young, and the corn earworm, treated just after silking.

CORNFLOWER, BACHELORS-BUT-TON (*Centaurea*)

Aphid, Western Aster Root; other species.
Borer, Stalk. **Leafhopper,** Six-spotted.

COSMOS

Aphid, Western Aster Root (white at roots); Bean (black); Potato (pink and green).

Beetle, Asiatic Garden; Japanese; Spotted Cucumber (feeds on flowers).

Borer, European Corn (cream-colored); Stalk (dark).

Bug, Four-lined Plant; Tarnished Plant.

Leafhopper, Six-spotted (transmits aster yellows).

Mite, Two-spotted (plants yellow or gray, mealy).

Termites, Subterranean.

COTONEASTER

Borer, Sinuate Pear.

Bug, Hawthorn Lace (leaves stippled gray, rusty flecks underneath).

Mite, Pear Leaf Blister (small, reddish-brown blisters); Platani.

Scale, Greedy; Olive Parlatoria; Oystershell; San Jose.

Webworm, Cotoneaster (webbing ends of branches).

COTTONWOOD (see Poplar)

COWPEA (*Vigna sinensis*)

Aphid, Bean (black, common); Cowpea. **Armyworm,** Fall.

Beetle, Bean Leaf; Blister; Grape Colaspis; Mexican Bean; White-fringed.

Borer, Lesser Cornstalk.

Bug, Garden Fleahopper; Green Stink; Harlequin; Leaf-footed; Pumpkin.

Caterpillar, Velvetbean; Green Cloverworm.

Cricket, Camel.

Curculio, Clover Root; Cowpea. **Cutworms.**

Leaf Miner, Serpentine.

Webworm, Garden. **Weevil,** Cowpea. **Wireworms.**

CRABAPPLE, ORNAMENTAL (*Pyrus*)

Aphid, Apple.

Borer, Flatheaded Apple Tree; Roundheaded Apple Tree.

Bug, Alder Lace. **Curculio,** Apple. **Leaf Crumpler.**

Maggot, Apple. **Moth,** Codling. **Rootworm,** Strawberry.

Scale, San Jose. **Weevil,** Apple Flea.

See Apple for other possible pests.

CRANBERRY (*Vaccinium*)

Caterpillar, Blackheaded Fireworm; Yellowheaded Fireworm (berries webbed).
Fruitworm, Cranberry.
Leafhopper, Blunt-nosed Cranberry (vector of false-blossom disease).
Moth, Gypsy. **Rootworm,** Cranberry.
Scale, Oystershell; Putnam. **Weevil,** Black Vine; Strawberry Root.

CRAPEMYRTLE (*Lagerstroemia*)

Aphid, Crapemyrtle (profuse honeydew with sooty mold).
Scale, Florida Wax.

CRASSULA

Mealybug, Citrus (white, woolly bodies congested on stems).
Mite, Cyclamen (plants deformed).

CRESS, GARDEN (*Lepidium*)

Leaf Miner, Serpentine. **Maggot,** Cabbage.

CROCUS

Aphid, Green Peach. **Mite,** Bulb.

CROTALARIA

Mite, Two-spotted, probably other species (leaves dusty).

CROTON

Mealybug, Citrus; Long-tailed.
Scale, Black; Chaff; Florida Wax; Glover; Green Shield; Hemispherical; Lesser Snow; Purple.
Thrips, Greenhouse.

CUCUMBER (*Cucumis sativus*)

Aphid, Melon (carries bacteria causing wilt).
Armyworm, Fall.
Beetle, Banded Cucumber; Imbricated Snout; Potato Flea; Spotted Cucumber (green with 12 black spots); Striped Cucumber (yellowish with 3 black stripes); Western Spotted; Western Striped.
Bug, Garden Fleahopper; Squash.
Caterpillar, Melonworm; Pickleworm (small, greenish, in blossom, fruit).

Centipede, Garden. Cutworms.

Leafhopper, Beet (transmits curly top). Leaf Tier, Celery.

Mite, Two-spotted. Nematode, Root-knot.

Thrips, Onion; Western Flower. Whitefly, Greenhouse.

Start plants under Hotkaps, later changing to cheesecloth or wire screening to give protection from all pests to young vines. Start dusting or spraying when they get too big for covering.

CURRANT (*Ribes*)
(Including Flowering Currant)

Aphid, Currant (leaves crinkled, cupped down, green lice in pockets); Chrysanthemum.

Beetle, Fuller Rose.

Borer, Currant (canes die back); Flatheaded Apple Tree; Pacific Flatheaded.

Caterpillar, California Tent; Western Tent; Yellow Woollybear.

Fly, Currant Fruit (maggots in fruit). Fruitworm, Gooseberry.

Leafhopper, Grape. Leaf Roller, Fruit Tree; Oblique-banded.

Mealybug, Ground. Mite, Currant Bud; Two-spotted.

Moth, White-lined Sphinx.

Sawfly, Imported Currantworm (green, black-spotted larvae devour leaves).

Scale, Cottony Maple; European Fruit Lecanium; Forbes; Putnam; San Jose; Walnut.

Spanworm, Currant (looper caterpillar).

Cut out canes with borers. Spray for aphids and sawfly larvae.

CUSTARD-APPLE (*Anona reticulata*)

Scale, Florida Wax; Hemispherical.

CYCAD, SAGO PALM (*Cycas*)

Mealybug, Long-tailed.

Scale, Black; California Red; Chaff; Florida Red; Green Shield; Hemispherical (brown, convex, common); Oleander (yellow); Pineapple; Purple; Soft.

Thrips, Dracaena.

CYCLAMEN

Aphid, Crescent-marked Lily; Melon.

Mite, Cyclamen (plants deformed, stunted, buds black); Broad.

Nematode, Root-knot. **Thrips,** Greenhouse.
Weevil, Black Vine (grubs on roots may kill plants).
Use new insecticides cautiously on cyclamen; some may be phytotoxic. Rotenone is relatively safe.

CYPRESS (*Cupressus*)

Aphid, Cypress (large, green); Arborvitae (brown).
Mealybug, Cypress (white, common).
Mite, Date; Platani; Southern Red.
Moth, Cypress Tip; Cypress Webber; Imperial; White-marked Tussock.
Scale, Cottony-cushion; Cypress Bark (serious on Monterey cypress; foliage turns yellow); Juniper.

CYPRESS, BALD (*Taxodium*)

Moth, Cypress (caterpillar feeds on foliage).

DAHLIA

Aphid, Bean (black, rather common); Green Peach; Leaf-curling Plum.
Beetle, Asiatic Garden; Carrot; Grape Colaspis; Japanese; Spotted Cucumber (eats petals); Western Spotted Cucumber.
Borer, Burdock; European Corn (a major pest); Stalk.
Bug, Four-lined Plant; Tarnished Plant (buds and new growth blackened).
Caterpillar, Yellow Woollybear.
Leafhopper, Potato (prevalent, serious; leaves curl, brown at the edges; plants are stunted).
Leaf Tier, Celery.
Mite, Cyclamen; Two-spotted (mealy webs).
Thrips, Flower; Greenhouse; Onion (transmits spotted-wilt virus).
Wasp, Giant Hornet (may tear stalks).
Weevil, Cocklebur. **Wireworms.**

DAISY, OXEYE (*Chrysanthemum leucanthemum*)

Bug, Daisy Plant (punctures leaves, flower buds, not described in Chapter V).
Caterpillar, Omnivorous Looper.
Leaf Miner, Chrysanthemum. **Leaf Tier,** Celery.
Mealybug, Ground (works at roots).

DAISY, SHASTA (*Chrysanthemum maximum*)

Aphid, Myrtle (green, not described in Chapter V).
Beetle, Spotted Cucumber (very common on flowers).
Bug, Daisy Plant; Four-lined Plant (small, depressed circles in leaves).
Butterfly, Checker Spot.
Leaf Miner, Chrysanthemum (irregular light mines in leaves).

DAPHNE

Aphids, several species. **Mealybug,** Citrus.
Scale, Gray Citrus; Greedy; Yellow; other species.

DATE (*Phoenix dactylifera*)

Bug, Western Leaf-footed (large, with leaflike legs).
Mealybug, Grape. **Mite,** Date (webs leaves together, scars fruit).
Scale, Parlatoria Date (small, gray and white, presumably eradicated).
Thrips, Banded Greenhouse.

DATURA (Angels Trumpet)

Leafhopper, Beet. **Mite,** Tomato Russet. **Psyllid,** Tomato.

DAYLILY (*Hemerocallis*)

Thrips, Flower; other species (blossoms streaked, foliage silvery).
Weevil, Imported Long-horned.

DELPHINIUM (Larkspur)

Aphid, Goldenglow (red on underside of cupped-down leaves); Green
  Peach; Crescent-marked Lily.
Beetle, Asiatic Garden; Japanese (not so prevalent on this host).
Borer, Burdock; Stalk. **Budworm,** Rose.
Bug, Four-lined Plant (occasional). **Cutworms.**
Leaf Miner, Larkspur (tan blotches in leaves).
Millipedes.
Mite, Cyclamen (the most important pest, plants stunted, leaves de-
  formed, flower buds black); Broad (leaves glassy); Two-spotted.
Nematode, Root-knot; Bulb and Stem.
Slugs. Sowbugs. Thrips, Gladiolus.

DEUTZIA

Aphid, Bean; Currant (leaves crinkled); Melon.

Beetle, Fuller Rose (leaves eaten in from margins).
Leaf Miner, Lilac (tan blotches in leaves).
Nematode, Root-knot (may be serious in South).

DEWBERRY (*Rubus*)

Borer, Red-necked Cane.   **Gall,** Blackberry Knot.
Leafhopper, Grape.   **Leaf Roller,** Oblique-banded; Strawberry.
Maggot, Raspberry Cane.   **Sawfly,** Raspberry.   **Weevil,** Strawberry.
   See also Blackberry and Raspberry for other pests.

DILL (*Anethum graveolens*)

Caterpillar, Celeryworm.   **Weevil,** Carrot.

DOGWOOD (*Cornus*)

Aphid, Melon.   **Beetle,** Pitted Ambrosia.
Borer, Azalea Stem; Dogwood (kills branches); Dogwood Cambium;
   Dogwood Twig; Flatheaded Apple Tree (injures young trees);
   Pecan.
Caterpillar, Red-humped.
Cicada, Periodical (injures twigs by egg-laying).
Gall, Dogwood Club (swelling in twigs).
Leafhoppers (occasionally foliage is sucked almost white).
Leaf Miner, Locust.   **Leaf Roller,** Oblique-banded.
Scale, Dogwood; Cottony Maple; Obscure; Oystershell; San Jose.
Whitefly, Mulberry (round, black, with white fringe).

DORONICUM

Aphid, Crescent-marked Lily (black and yellow).
Nematode, Fern (transparent to dark spots in leaves).

DOUGLAS-FIR (*Pseudotsuga*)

Aphid, Cooley Spruce Gall (alternate host for); Monterey Pine.
Beetle, Douglas-fir; Douglas-fir Engraver.
Borer, Cedar Tree (may girdle and kill); Fir Flatheaded.
Budworm, Spruce (webs needles).
Butterfly, Pine (green, white-striped caterpillar may defoliate).
Moth, Sequoia Pitch; Zimmerman Pine.
Scale, Hemlock; Pine Needle.   **Weevil,** Strawberry Root.

DRACAENA
Thrips, Dracaena.

DUTCHMANS-PIPE, PIPEVINE
(*Aristolochia durior*)
Butterfly, Pipevine Swallowtail (brown caterpillar eats leaves).

ECHEVIERIA
Nematode, Root-knot.   **Weevil,** Black Vine.

EGGPLANT (*Solanum*)
Aphid, Green Peach; Melon; Potato.
Beetle, Asiatic Garden; Blister; Colorado Potato (yellow with black stripes); Eggplant Flea (tiny shot-holes in leaves); Pale-striped Flea; Potato Flea (injurious to seedlings); Spotted Cucumber; Tobacco Flea.
Borer, Potato Tuberworm.
Bug, Cotton Stainer; Eggplant Lace; Garden Fleahopper; Harlequin; One-spot Stink; Pumpkin; Southern Green Stink.
Caterpillar, Yellow Woollybear.   **Cutworms.   Hornworm,** Tobacco.
Leafhopper, Potato.   **Leaf Miner,** Eggplant.
Maggot, Pepper (occasional, worms in fruit).
Mite, Two-spotted; other species.   **Nematode,** Root-knot.
Whitefly, Greenhouse (common on garden plants started in greenhouse).
See Potato for other possible pests.

ELAEAGNUS (Russian Olive)
Aphid, Oleaster-thistle (yellow and green).
Scale, Olive Parlatoria; Purple.

ELDER (*Sambucus*)
Aphids.   Beetle, Potato Flea; Rose Chafer.
Borer, Elder; Elder Shoot; Currant.   **Bug,** Green Stink.
Caterpillar, Omnivorous Looper.   **Cricket,** Black-horned Tree.
Mealybug, Grape.   **Scale,** San Jose.   **Thrips,** Madrona.

ELM (*Ulmus*)
Aphid, Elm Cockscomb Gall; Elm Leaf; Woolly Apple; Woolly Elm.
Beetle, Elm Leaf (usually the most important pest; leaves are skeleton-

ized, trees defoliated, weakened); Carrot; Grape Flea; Larger Elm; Japanese (may chew leaves to lace); Native Elm Bark; Red Elm Bark; Rose Chafer (important in some sections); Smaller European Elm Bark (transmits Dutch elm disease).

Borer, Azalea Stem; Brown Wood; Carpenterworm; Elm; Flatheaded Apple Tree (injurious to new transplants); Oak Timberworm; Pacific Flatheaded; Pigeon Tremex; Twig Girdler; Twig Pruner.

Bug, Alder Lace; Elm Lace.

Butterfly, Mourning-cloak (spiny caterpillar).

Cankerworm, Fall; Spring (important, may defoliate some years).

Casebearer, Elm.

Caterpillar, Eastern Tent; Hemlock Looper; Omnivorous Looper; Linden Looper.

Cricket, Black-horned Tree.

Leafhopper, Elm (vector of phloem necrosis); Virginia-creeper.

Leaf Miner, Elm; Locust.   **Leaf Roller,** Fruit Tree.

Mite, Avocado Red; European Red; Two-spotted; other species.

Moth, Brown-tail; Cecropia; Gypsy; Io; Leopard (borer); Polyphemus; White-lined Sphinx; White-marked Tussock.

Nematode, Root-knot.

Sawfly, Elm.

Scale, Calico, Camphor, Citricola; Cottony Maple; Elm Scurfy (important); European Elm (leaves yellow, drop early, much honeydew); European Fruit Lecanium; Oystershell; Putnam; Scurfy.

Spanworm, Elm.

Weevil, Apple Flea; Black Elm Bark.   **Webworm,** Fall.

DDT is very effective against bark beetles and elm leaf beetles but increases mites, Putnam scale, and elm leaf aphids.

ENDIVE (*Cichorium*)

Aphid, Bean (black); Pea (large green).   **Nematode,** Root-knot.

ERIGERON (Fleabane)

Aphid, Western Aster Root; Leaf-curling Plum.

ERIOPHYLLUM

Mealybug, Yucca.

ERYTHRONIUM

Aphid, Green Peach.

EUCALYPTUS

Aphid, Cowpea.

Borer, California Prionus; Pacific Flatheaded.

Caterpillar, Omnivorous Looper; Orange Tortrix; California Oakworm.

Mealybug, Long-tailed.

Mite, Avocado Red; Platani; Southern Red.

Scale, Black; California Red; Florida Red; Greedy; Oleander; Purple; San Jose.

EUGENIA

Mealybug, Citrophilus. **Scale,** Florida Red.

EUONYMUS

Aphid, Bean; Green Peach; Ivy. **Leaf Miner,** Lilac (infrequent).

Scale, California Red; Chaff; Cottony Maple; Dictyospermum; Euonymus (males thin, white, conspicuous; females brown; very common and injurious); Florida Red; Florida Wax; Greedy.

Thrips, Greenhouse.

Euonymus scale is the chief problem.

EUPATORIUM (Mistflower)

Aphid, Goldenglow (red, common on stems); Leaf-curling Plum.

Leaf Miner, Chrysanthemum (white serpentine mines in leaves).

Scale, Barnacle.

FERNS

Aphid, Fern (black); Lantana.

Beetle, Japanese (feeds on some types).

Caterpillar, Florida Fern (feeds at night); Orange Tortrix (rolls leaves); Yellow Woollybear.

Crickets. Cutworms. Grasshoppers.

Mealybug, Citrus; Long-tailed. **Moth,** Fern.

Nematode, Fern (black or brown bands across leaves).

Scale, Fern (white); Florida Wax; Green Shield; Hemispherical (brown); Oleander (flat, yellow, common); Soft (brown, prevalent); Tea (white filaments).

Snail, Fern (eats parenchyma tissue from lower leaf surface).

Thrips, Greenhouse; Onion.

Weevil, Black Vine (grubs work at roots). **Whitefly,** Fern; Citrus.

Use insecticides on ferns with caution; some are injured by certain chemicals.

FIG, CREEPING (*Ficus pumila*)

Scale, Chaff; Florida Wax; Green Shield; Lesser Snow; Mining.
Whitefly, Citrus.

FIG, TREE (*Ficus carica*)

Beetle, Fig; Green June.
Borer, Branch and Twig (black and brown beetle bores in twigs).
Mealybug, Citrophilus; Long-tailed (prevalent).
Mite, Pacific. **Nematode,** Root-knot (rather common).
Scale, Black; California Red; Camphor; Cottony-cushion; Fig (oyster-shaped, purple or brown); Florida Red; Greedy; Mining; Oyster-shell; San Jose; Soft; Tea.

FIR (*Abies*)

Aphid, Balsam Twig (white, cottony on needles).
Bagworm. Borer, Flatheaded Fir.
Budworm, Spruce (leaves webbed together).
Caterpillar, Hemlock Looper (green with black spots).
Mite, Spruce Spider (needles cobwebby). **Moth,** Spotted Tussock.
Sawfly, Balsam Fir (green worm).
Scale, Oystershell; Pine Needle.

FORGET-ME-NOT (*Myosotis*)

Aphid, Forget-Me-Not (not described in Chapter V); Green Peach.
Beetle, Potato Flea (small, black, very common; pinholes in leaves).
Butterfly, Painted Beauty (purple, yellow, and green caterpillars).
Leaf Tier, Celery.

FORSYTHIA

Bug, Four-lined Plant (occasional, tan circles in leaves).
Forsythia is usually free from insect pests.

FOXGLOVE (*Digitalis*)

Aphid, Foxglove; Crescent-marked Lily.
Beetle, Asiatic Garden; Japanese; Rose Chafer.
Mealybug, Citrophilus.
Nematode, Bulb and Stem (angular spots in leaves; infrequent).
Thrips.

FREESIA

Aphid, Crescent-marked Lily.   **Mite,** Bulb (in rotting bulbs).
Nematode, Root-knot.   **Thrips,** Gladiolus.

FUCHSIA

Aphid, Crescent-marked Lily; Ornate; Potato.
Beetle, Fuller Rose; Strawberry Flea.
Mealybug, Citrus; Long-tailed.
Mite, Privet (pits underside of leaves); Broad; Cyclamen; Two-spotted.
Moth, White-lined Sphinx.
Nematode, Root-knot (often serious in potted plants).
Scale, Black; California Red; Greedy.
Thrips, Greenhouse (leaves have "pepper-and-salt" effect).
Whitefly, Greenhouse (prevalent, injurious); Iris.

GAILLARDIA

Aphids.   Beetle, Asiatic Garden; Japanese.
Borer, Stalk.   **Bug,** Four-lined Plant (tan spots in leaves).
Leafhopper, Six-spotted (transmits aster yellows).
Mites.   Thrips, Flower; Onion.   **Wireworms.**

GALTONIA

Fly, Narcissus Bulb.

GARDENIA (Cape Jasmine)

Beetle, Fuller Rose (notches leaves at night).
Mealybug, Citrus (common); Long-tailed.   **Mites.**
Nematode, Root-knot (galls on roots, leaves may be discolored).
Orthezia, Greenhouse.
Scale, Florida Wax; Green Shield; Soft.
Thrips, Banded Greenhouse; Flower.
Whitefly, Citrus (very common, accompanied by sooty mold).

GARLIC (*Allium sativa*)

Nematode, Bulb and Stem.

GERANIUM (*Pelargonium*)

Aphid, Geranium; Green Peach; other species.
Beetle, Fuller Rose.   **Cankerworm,** Fall.

Caterpillar, Cabbage Looper; Omnivorous Looper; Orange Tortrix.
Earthworm, Corn.
Leaf Roller, Oblique-banded. **Leaf Tier,** Celery.
Mealybug, Citrus; Mexican.
Mite, Broad; Cyclamen (young leaves curl); Two-spotted.
Scale, Cottony-cushion; Lesser Snow.
Slug, Greenhouse; Spotted Garden. **Termites.**
Webworm, Tobacco. **Weevil,** Black Vine; Imported Long-horned.
Whitefly, Greenhouse (almost inevitable on greenhouse geraniums).

GERBERA
Mite, Broad; Cyclamen.

GINKGO
Caterpillar, Omnivorous Looper. **Mealybug,** Grape. **Scale,** Peach.

GINSENG
Scale, Oystershell.

GLADIOLUS
Aphid, Potato; Melon; Tulip Bulb (in corms).
Beetle, Asiatic Garden; Blister; Flea; June.
Borer, Stalk. **Bug,** Tarnished Plant.
Caterpillar, Zebra. **Cutworms. Earworm,** Corn.
Leafhopper, Red-banded. **Maggot,** Seed-corn.
Mealybug, Grape (on corms). **Mite,** Bulb (in corms); Two-spotted.
Scale, Latania.
Thrips, Gladiolus (universal pest, leaves and flowers streaked); Banded
   Greenhouse; Greenhouse; Western Flower.
Weevil, Imported Long-horned. **Wireworms.**

GLOBE THISTLE (*Echinops*)
Aphid, Green Peach (leaves curl down).
Bug, Four-lined Plant (small, round, tan spots in leaves).

GLOXINIA
Aphid, Green Peach; Crescent-marked Lily.
Thrips, Greenhouse; Onion. **Weevil,** Black Vine.

GOLDEN-CHAIN (*Laburnum*)

Aphid, Bean; Cowpea (infests ends of branches).   **Mealybug,** Grape.

GOLDENGLOW (*Rudbeckia*)

Aphid, Goldenglow (common, bright red on stems).
Beetle, Asiatic Garden; Fuller Rose.   **Borer,** Burdock; Stalk.
Bug, Tarnished Plant; Four-lined Plant.
Sawfly, Goldenglow (gray worm with dark spots; may defoliate).

GOLDENROD (*Solidago*)

Bug, Chrysanthemum Lace.   **Caterpillar,** Orange Tortrix.

GOOSEBERRY (*Ribes*)

Aphid, Currant (crinkled leaves); Gooseberry.
Beetle, Imbricated Snout.
Borer, Currant; Pacific Flatheaded.   **Bug,** Four-lined Plant.
Caterpillar, Yellow Woollybear.
Fly, Currant Fruit.   **Fruitworm,** Gooseberry.
Leaf Roller, Fruit Tree; Oblique-banded.
Mealybug, Grape.   **Moth,** White-lined Sphinx.
Sawfly, Imported Currantworm (green, black-spotted larvae).
Scale, Cottony Maple; European Fruit Lecanium; Oystershell; Peach;
    Putnam; San Jose; Scurfy.
Spanworm, Currant.

GOURDS (*Cucurbita*)

Aphid, Melon.   **Beetle,** Spotted Cucumber; Striped Cucumber.
Borer, Squash Vine.   **Bug,** Squash.
Whitefly, Greenhouse (often abundant on underside of leaves).

GRAPE (*Vitis*)

Aphid, Grape Phylloxera; Grapevine.   **Armyworms.**
Beetle, Bumble Flower; Darkling; Fig; Grape Bud; Grape Colaspis;
    Grape Flea; Green June; Japanese (prevalent on foliage, eats every-
    thing but veins); Rose Chafer; Rose Leaf; Spotted Grapevine; Steel-
    blue Flea.
Borer, Branch and Twig; Broad-necked Root; Grape Root.
Bug, Boxelder; Harlequin.
Caterpillar, Yellow Woollybear.   **Cricket,** Black-horned Tree.
Curculio, Grape.   **Cutworm,** Climbing (various species injure buds).

Earworm, Corn. **Gall,** Grapevine Tomato; others.

Leaf Folder, Grape. **Leafhopper,** Grape; Three-banded; Virginia-creeper.

Leaf Skeletonizer, Grape; Western Grape.

Mealybug, Grape; Ground; Long-tailed. **Midge,** Grape Blossom.

Moth, Achemon Sphinx; Eight-spotted Forester; Grape Berry (wormy berries, clusters webbed together); Grape Plume; White-lined Sphinx.

Rootworm, Grape (chains of holes in leaves); Strawberry; Western Grape.

Scale, Black; California Red; Camphor; Cottony-cushion; Cottony Maple; European Fruit Lecanium; Florida Red; Grape (round, gray, on old canes); Greedy; Lesser Snow; Obscure; Olive Parlatoria; Oystershell; Peach; Walnut; White Peach.

Thrips, Citrus; Grape; Pear; Western Flower.

Whitefly, Grape; Greenhouse; Woolly.

Most spray schedules are aimed primarily at the control of the grape berry moth.

GRAPEFRUIT (see Citrus Fruits)

GRASS (see Lawn Grasses)

GROUNDCHERRY (*Physalis*)

Aphid, Potato (pink or green).

Beetle, Potato Flea; Tobacco Flea (tiny holes in leaves).

Budworm, Tobacco. **Hornworm,** Tobacco; Tomato.

GUAVA (*Psidium*)

Fly, Mexican Fruit (in Texas). **Mealybug,** Long-tailed.

Scale, Barnacle; Black; Chaff; Florida Red; Florida Wax; Greedy; Green Shield; Hemispherical; Soft.

Termites, Subterranean.

GYPSOPHILA (Babysbreath)

Leafhopper, Six-spotted.

HACKBERRY (*Celtis*)

Borer, Painted Hickory; Twig Pruner.

Butterfly, Mourning-cloak. **Caterpillar,** Puss.

Gall, Hackberry Nipple; others. **Moth,** Oriental.
Scale, Camphor; Citricola; Cottony-cushion; Cottony Maple; Lesser Snow; Oystershell; Putnam; San Jose.
Spittlebug, Blueberry. **Whitefly,** Mulberry.

HAWTHORN (*Crataegus*)

Aphid, Apple; Apple Grain; Hawthorn; Rosy Apple (curls young leaves) ; Woolly Apple; Woolly Hawthorn (white masses on branches, twigs).
Beetle, Larger Elm Leaf; Japanese.
Borer, Flatheaded Apple Tree; Roundheaded Apple Tree; Pear; Shot-hole.
Cankerworm, Fall; Spring.
Caterpillar, Eastern Tent (common) ; Forest Tent; Red-humped; Variable Oak Leaf; Walnut.
Leaf Roller, Oblique-banded. **Leaf Skeletonizer,** Apple and Thorn.
Mite, Two-spotted. **Moth,** Gypsy; Western Tussock.
Planthopper (white, fluffy on stems). **Sawfly,** Pear-slug.
Scale, Barnacle; Cottony Maple; European Fruit Lecanium; Florida Wax; Lecanium; Putnam; Scurfy; Soft; San Jose.

HAZELNUT, FILBERT (*Corylus*)

Aphids. Bug, Alder Lace.
Caterpillar, California Tent; Filbertworm; Yellow-necked.
Leaf Roller, Oblique-banded. **Mite,** Filbert Bud (big-bud).
Scale, European Fruit Lecanium; Oystershell.
Weevil, Apple Flea; Filbert.

HEATH (*Erica*)

Scale, Greedy; Oleander; Oystershell.

HEATHER (*Calluna*)

Beetle, Japanese. **Mite,** Two-spotted. **Scale,** Oystershell.

HELENIUM (Sneezeweed)

Beetle, Helenium Snout.

HELIOPSIS

Bug, Four-lined Plant.

HELIOTROPE (*Heliotropium*)

Aphid, Green Peach; Crescent-marked Lily; other species.
Leaf Tier, Celery. **Mealybug,** Citrus; Citrophilus.
Mite, Two-spotted. **Orthezia,** Greenhouse. **Termites.**
Whitefly, Greenhouse (common, even in outdoor gardens).

HEMLOCK (*Tsuga*)

Bagworm. Borer, Fir Flatheaded; Hemlock (destructive).
Budworm, Spruce. **Caterpillar,** Hemlock Looper.
Leaf Miner, Spruce Needle.
Mite, Spruce Spider (important, needles turn nearly white); Two-spotted.
Moth, Gypsy. **Sawfly,** Hemlock.
Scale, Hemlock (gray, circular); Pine Needle (white).

HIBISCUS (Rose-mallow)

Aphid, Melon.
Beetle, Japanese (numerous on flowers); Fuller Rose.
Earworm, Corn. **Moth,** Abutilon (green caterpillar).
Scale, California Red; Green Shield; Lesser Snow; Mining; Pineapple; San Jose.
Whitefly, Greenhouse.

HICKORY (*Carya*)

Aphid, Hickory (very large, gray and black).
Beetle, Hickory Bark; Hickory Saperda; June.
Borer, Brown Wood; Flatheaded Apple Tree; Pecan Carpenterworm; Twig Pruner.
Caterpillar, Hickory Horned Devil; Red-humped; Walnut; Yellow-necked.
Cicada, Periodical. **Curculio,** Hickory Nut.
Moth, Hickory Tussock; Imperial; Io; Luna; Oriental.
Sawfly, Butternut Woollyworm.
Scale, Grape; Obscure; Putnam. **Treehopper,** Two-marked.
Walkingstick. Webworm, Fall. **Weevil,** New York, Pecan.

HOLLY (*Ilex*)

Beetle, Black Blister; Japanese; Potato Flea. **Bud Moth,** Holly.
Leaf Miner, European Holly (blotch mines, very common); American (serpentine mines).

Mealybug, Comstock. **Mite,** Southern Red (leaves turn grayish).
Moth, Gypsy.
Scale, Black; California Red; Greedy; Holly; Oleander; Oystershell;
Peach; Soft; Tea (white filaments, common on Chinese holly in the
South).
Whitefly, Citrus; Mulberry.

HOLLYHOCK (*Althea rosea*)

Aphid, Bean; Potato.
Beetle, Japanese (prevalent on flowers); Rose Chafer; Spotted Cu-
cumber.
Borer, Burdock; European Corn; Stalk.
Bug, Tarnished Plant. **Butterfly,** Painted Beauty; Painted Lady.
Caterpillar, Yellow Woollybear.
Leaf Roller, Red-banded. **Leaf Skeletonizer,** Cotton Leaf Perforator.
Mealybug, Mexican. **Mite,** Two-spotted; other species (leaves yel-
low; dusty or webby).
Moth, Abutilon (green caterpillar). **Nematode,** Root-knot.
Slugs (large holes in leaves, very common).
Thrips, Gladiolus; Hollyhock. **Weevil,** Hollyhock.

HONEY LOCUST (*Gleditsia*)

Caterpillar, Walnut.
Moth, Oriental. **Scale,** Black; Cottony Maple.
Webworm, Mimosa (very injurious). **Whitefly,** Greenhouse.

HONEYSUCKLE (*Lonicera*)

Aphid, Honeysuckle; other species.
Beetle, Flea. **Bug,** Four-lined Plant.
Caterpillar, Omnivorous Looper. **Katydids.**
Leaf Roller, Oblique-banded; Red-banded; European Honeysuckle.
Mealybug, Long-tailed.
Moth, Snowberry Clearwing; White-lined Sphinx.
Sawfly, Honeysuckle. **Scale,** Greedy; Oystershell; San Jose.
Webworm, Fall. **Whitefly,** Greenhouse; Iris.

HORNBEAM (*Carpinus*)

Scale, Maple Phenacoccus.

HORSECHESTNUT, BUCKEYE (*Aesculus*)

Bagworm.
Beetle, Japanese (very destructive, leaves like lace); Potato Flea.
Borer, Flatheaded Apple Tree. **Caterpillar,** Omnivorous Looper.
Leaf Roller, Oblique-banded. **Mealybug,** Comstock; Grape.
Moth, White-marked Tussock (black caterpillar with white tufts;
common).
Scale, Cottony Maple; Maple Phenacoccus; Oystershell; Putnam;
Scurfy; Walnut.
Spanworm, Elm.

HORSERADISH (*Armoracia*)

Beetle, Horseradish Flea; Western Black Flea. **Bug,** Harlequin.
Caterpillar, Cabbage Looper; Imported Cabbageworm.
Moth, Diamondback. **Webworm,** Cabbage.

HYACINTH (*Hyacinthus*)

Caterpillar, Yellow Woollybear.
Fly, Lesser Bulb; Narcissus Bulb (large maggot in rotting bulb).
Mite, Bulb (white, in rotting bulbs).
Nematode, Bulb (dark rings in bulb).

HYDRANGEA

Aphid, Crescent-marked Lily; Melon.
Beetle, Rose Chafer. **Bug,** Tarnished Plant.
Leaf Tier, Hydrangea (leaves tied around flower bud).
Mite, Two-spotted. **Thrips,** Banded.

HYMENOCALLIS (Spider Lily)

Caterpillar, Convict. **Scale,** Lesser Snow.
Thrips, Banded Greenhouse.

HYSSOP

Scale, Black Araucaria.

IMPATIENS (see Balsam, Garden)

IRIS

Aphid, Green Peach; Crescent-marked Lily; Potato; Tulip Bulb (white,
cottony, on bulbs or rhizomes).

Beetle, Rose Chafer; June.

Borer, Burdock; Iris (chief pest, producing ragged leaves; hollow rhizomes); Stalk.

Bud Moth, Verbena (green caterpillars on seed pod).

Caterpillar, Zebra.   **Fly,** Lesser Bulb.   **Mites.**

Nematode, Bulb.   **Slug,** Spotted Garden; other species.

Thrips, Florida Flower; Gladiolus; Iris (prevalent on Japanese iris).

Weevil, Iris (on seed pods).

IRONWOOD (*Ostrya*)

Aphid, Melon.   **Scale,** Cottony-cushion.

IVY, BOSTON (*Parthenocissus tricuspidata*)

Beetle, Japanese (serious).

Leafhopper, Grape; Virginia-creeper (foliage white in late summer).

Mite, Cyclamen.   **Moth,** Eight-spotted Forester.

Scale, Calico; Cottony-cushion.   **Weevil,** Imported Long-horned.

IVY, ENGLISH (*Hedera helix*)

Aphid, Bean; Green Peach; Ivy.   **Beetle,** Blister.

Caterpillar, Cabbage Looper; Omnivorous Looper; Puss.

Hornworms.   Leafhoppers.   Leaf Tier, Celery.

Mealybug, Citrus; Grape; Mexican.

Mite, Two-spotted; other species (very common on ivies in the house, leaves grayish, mealy).

Moth, Eight-spotted Forester.

Scale, Dictyospermum; Florida Red (round, reddish brown); Greedy; Oleander (yellow, flat); Olive Parlatoria; Peach; Pineapple; Soft.

Whitefly, Citrus.

IVY, GERMAN (*Senecio*)

Aphid, Melon.

IXORA

Scale, Florida Wax; Green Shield.

JACARANDA

Orthezia, Greenhouse.

JAPANESE QUINCE (*Chaenomeles*)
Aphid, Melon. **Beetle,** Japanese. **Bug,** Hawthorn Lace.
Mealybug, Grape. **Scale,** Black; Peach; San Jose; Scurfy.

JASMINE, JESSAMINE (*Jasminum*)
Scale, Barnacle; Black; California Red; Camphor; Chaff; Florida Red; Green Shield; Mining; Purple; Olive Parlatoria; Soft.
Whitefly, Citrus.

JERUSALEM-CHERRY (*Solanum pseudocapsicum*)
Aphid, Potato. **Caterpillar,** Orange Tortrix (rolls leaves).
Thrips, Flower; Onion. **Whitefly,** Greenhouse.

JOBS-TEARS (*Coix lacryma-jobi*)
Caterpillar, Orange Tortrix.

JUDAS TREE (see Redbud)

JUNIPER (*Juniperus*)
Aphid, Red-cedar.
Bagworm (bags on twigs, common). **Beetle,** Red-cedar Bark.
Mealybug, Taxus (occasional).
Mite, Spruce Spider (foliage webby, gray, unhealthy); Two-spotted.
Moth, Imperial.
Scale, Juniper (small, round, white, foliage yellow; common).
Webworm, Juniper. **Weevil,** Deodar; Strawberry Root.
Use oil sprays cautiously on junipers with cupped needles that will hold the oil. Lime-sulfur is preferable as a dormant spray for scale.

KALE (*Brassica*)
Aphid, Cabbage; Turnip.
Caterpillar, Cabbage Looper; Imported Cabbageworm.
Leaf Tier, Celery. **Moth,** Diamondback. **Webworm,** Cabbage.
See Cabbage for other pests.

KALMIA (see Mountain-laurel)

KERRIA
Beetle, Japanese (prevalent).

KOHLRABI

Aphid, Cabbage; Turnip. **Bug,** Harlequin.
Caterpillar, Cabbage Looper; Imported Cabbageworm.
See Cabbage for other pests.

KUDZU-VINE (*Pueraria*)

Beetle, Japanese. **Caterpillar,** Velvetbean.

KUMQUAT (see Citrus)

LANTANA

Aphid, Lantana (dark with white fringe).
Caterpillar, Orange Tortrix. **Leaf Tier,** Celery.
Mealybug, Citrus; Mexican; Yucca. **Mite,** Broad; Cyclamen.
Nematode, Fern (dark blotches in leaves). **Orthezia,** Greenhouse.
Whitefly, Greenhouse (common).

LARCH (*Larix*)

Aphid, Woolly Larch. **Bagworm** (may defoliate).
Beetle, Eastern Larch; Douglas-fir; Douglas-fir Engraver; Japanese.
Borer, Fir Flatheaded. **Budworm,** Spruce.
Casebearer, Larch (leaves mined, used as cases).
Moth, Gypsy; White-marked Tussock.
Sawfly, Larch (green larvae may strip trees). **Weevil,** Pales.

LARKSPUR, ANNUAL (*Delphinium*)

Aphid, Goldenglow (red, common in flower buds).
Borer, Stalk. **Leaf Miner,** Larkspur.
Mealybug, Ground. **Mite,** Cyclamen.

LAUREL (see Bay, Sweet; California Laurel; Cherry-Laurel; Mountain-Laurel)

LAURESTINUS (*Viburnum tinus*)

Thrips, Greenhouse.

LAVATERA (Tree-mallow)

Scale, Greedy.

LAVENDER (*Lavandula*)
Bug, Four-lined Plant (depressed round spots in leaves).
Caterpillar, Orange Tortrix; Yellow Woollybear.

LAWN GRASSES
Ant, Argentine; Cornfield; Pavement; other species (mounds in lawns).
Armyworms.
Beetle, Asiatic Garden; European Chafer; Japanese; June; Northern Masked Chafer; Oriental; Rose Chafer (all have grubs at grass roots).
Bug, Chinch; Hairy Chinch (lawns turn brown in patches; serious).
Crayfish (mounds near water, in the South).
Crickets, Northern Mole; Southern Mole. Cutworms.
Earthworm, Oriental. Grasshoppers. Mite, Clover. Moles.
Slugs. Wasp, Cicada-killer (holes, mounds in lawn).
Webworm, Sod (several species, resemble cutworms, have silk nests).
Wireworms.

LEMON (see Citrus)

LETTUCE (*Lactuca*)
Aphid, Goldenglow; Green Peach; Turnip.
Beetle, Pale-striped Flea; Potato Flea.
Bug, Harlequin; Garden Fleahopper; Pitted Lygaeid (southern, resembles chinch bug, not described in Chapter V); Tarnished Plant.
Caterpillar, Cabbage Looper; Celery Looper; Imported Cabbageworm.
Centipede, Garden. Cutworms. Earworm, Corn.
Leafhopper, Potato; Six-spotted (transmits yellows).
Leaf Tier, Celery. Millipedes. Whitefly, Greenhouse.

LIGNUM-VITAE (*Guaiacum*)
Scale, Barnacle; Florida Red.

LIGUSTRUM (see Privet)

LILAC (*Syringa*)
Aphid, Melon.
Beetle, Rhinoceros (occasionally feeds on roots, kills bushes).
Borer, Lilac (common, holes in trunk, protruding sawdust).

Caterpillar, Hickory Horned Devil.
Leaf Miner, Lilac (tan to brown blotches in leaves).
Leaf Roller, Oblique-banded.
Moth, Cynthia; Leopard; Polyphemus; Promethea.
Scale, Cottony Maple; Euonymus; Olive Parlatoria; Oystershell (may completely encrust and kill branches); San Jose; Scurfy; White Peach.
Wasp, Giant Hornet (tears off bark around branches).
Whitefly, Citrus.

LILY (*Lilium*)

Aphid, Crescent-marked Lily; Green Peach; Foxglove; Melon (dark green to brown, transmits mosaic); Purple-spotted Lily.
Beetle, Fuller Rose. **Borer,** Stalk. **Caterpillar,** Yellow Woollybear.
Fly, Narcissus Bulb (large white maggot).
Mite, Bulb (small, white, in rotting bulbs). **Thrips,** Lily.

LILY-OF-THE-VALLEY (*Convallaria*)

Nematode, Root-knot.
Weevil, Lily-of-the-Valley (curious notches in leaves).

LIME (see Citrus)

LINDEN, LIMETREE, BASSWOOD (*Tilia*)

Aphid, Linden (yellow and black, often abundant).
Bagworm. Beetle, Japanese (serious); Linden Leaf.
Borer, Flatheaded Apple Tree; Brown Wood; Linden.
Bug, Walnut Lace; Green Stink.
Cankerworms. Caterpillar, Variable Oak Leaf; Linden Looper.
Leaf Miner, Basswood. **Leaf Roller,** Basswood; Oblique-banded.
Mealybug, Taxus.
Moth, Cynthia; Cecropia; Gypsy; White-marked Tussock.
Sawfly, Elm.
Scale, Cottony Maple; European Fruit Lecanium; Oystershell; Putnam; San Jose; Terrapin; Tuliptree; Walnut; Willow.
Spanworm, Elm (snow-white linden moth).
Whitefly, Mulberry (dark with white fringe).

LOBELIA
Bug, Negro. Leafhopper, Six-spotted.
Leaf Tier, Celery. Nematode, Root-knot.

LOCUST (*Robinia*)
Bagworm. Beetle, Sweetpotato Leaf.
Borer, Brown Wood; Carpenterworm; Locust (serious, young trees killed); Locust Twig; Painted Hickory; Twig Pruner.
Butterfly, Silver-spotted Skipper.
Caterpillar, Red-humped; Velvetbean.
Leaf Miner, Locust (foliage looks brown, "blighted"; very common).
Leaf Roller, Fruit Tree.
Scale, Black; Cottony-cushion; Cottony Maple; Oystershell; Putnam; San Jose; Soft; Walnut.
Walkingstick.

LOGANBERRY (*Rubus*)
Beetle, Fuller Rose. Cricket, Snowy Tree; Black-horned Tree.
Fruitworm, Raspberry.
Leaf Roller, Fruit Tree; Oblique-banded. Maggot, Raspberry Cane.
Sawfly, Raspberry. Scale, Rose.
Weevil, Strawberry Root. Whitefly, Glacial; Greenhouse.
See Raspberry for other pests.

LONDON PLANE (see Sycamore)

LOQUAT (*Eriobotrya*)
Aphid, Apple; Melon.
Beetle, Flea; Western Striped Cucumber; Western Spotted Cucumber.
Borer, Pacific Flatheaded; Shot-hole. Bug, Harlequin; Squash.
Mite, Southern Red; Platani. Moth, Codling.
Nematode, Root-knot.
Scale, Olive Parlatoria; Florida Wax; San Jose.

LOVE-LIES-BLEEDING (*Amaranthus*)
Beetle, Carrot (on roots). Bug, Harlequin. Scale, Cottony-cushion.

LUPINE (*Lupinus*)
Aphid, Lupine (green with white wax; abundant).
Bug, Four-lined Plant. Butterfly, Painted Lady.
Weevil, Lupine (eats half moons out of leaves).

MADRONA, STRAWBERRY TREE
(*Arbutus*)
Borer, California Prionus.   **Caterpillar,** California Tent.
Scale, Black; Greedy; Soft.   **Thrips,** Madrona; Pear.
Whitefly, Iridescent.

MAGNOLIA
Caterpillar, Omnivorous Looper.   **Mealybug,** Comstock.
Scale, Black; Chaff; Cottony-cushion; European Fruit Lecanium;
   Florida Wax; Glover; Greedy; Magnolia (soft, brown, convex);
   Oleander; Purple; Soft; Tuliptree.
Whitefly, Citrus.

MAHONIA (Oregon Grape, Grape Holly)
Aphid, Barberry.   **Scale,** Greedy.   **Whitefly,** Inconspicuous.

MANGEL (*Beta vulgaris*)
Leaf Miner, Spinach.
See also Beet.

MANGO (*Mangifera indica*)
Fly, Mexican Fruit (in Texas).
Mealybug, Long-tailed.   **Mite,** Avocado Red.
Scale, California Red; Chaff; Florida Red; Florida Wax; Glover;
   Green Shield; Lesser Snow.
Thrips, Greenhouse.

MANZANITA (*Arctostaphylos*)
Aphid, Manzanita Leaf-gall.   **Moth,** Western Tussock.
Scale, Greedy; Soft.   **Whitefly,** Crown; Inconspicuous; Iridescent.

MAPLE (*Acer*)
Aphid, European Birch; Norway Maple (the most annoying of all
   maple pests because of its honeydew); Painted-maple; Sycamore;
   Woolly Alder.
Borer, Brown Wood; Carpenterworm; Flatheaded Apple Tree; Gall-
   making Maple; Maple Callus; Maple Petiole; Pacific Flatheaded;
   Pigeon Tremex; Sugar-maple (serious); Twig Pruner.
Bug, Boxelder; Green Stink.   **Cankerworm,** Fall; Spring.

Caterpillar, Eastern Tent; Forest Tent; Green-striped Mapleworm; Hemlock Looper; Omnivorous Looper; Saddled Prominent.

Cricket, Black-horned Tree.

Gall, Maple Bladder; Maple Gouty Vein; Maple Leaf; Maple Spindle (not described in Chapter V).

Leaf Cutter, Maple.   **Leafhopper,** Grape; Norway-maple.

Leaf Skeletonizer, Maple Trumpet.   **Mealybug,** Comstock; Taxus.

Moth, Brown-tail; Cecropia; Io; Leopard (borer); Oriental; Pale Tussock; Polyphemus; White-marked Tussock.

Sawfly, Elm.

Scale, Black; Calico; Cottony-cushion; Cottony Maple (widespread); Chaff; Florida Wax; Gloomy; Greedy; Japanese; Lecanium; Maple Phenacoccus; Obscure; Oystershell; Terrapin; Walnut.

Spanworm, Elm.   **Thrips,** Bean.

Whitefly, Mulberry; Inconspicuous.

Maples seldom have as many pests as this long list indicates, though aphids are a common nuisance. Use oil sprays with caution on maples, not at all on sugar and some other varieties. Japanese maples are sensitive to DDT and several other chemicals. Nicotine sulfate can be used safely for aphids.

MARGUERITE (*Chrysanthemum frutescens*)

Aphid, Leaf-curling Plum.   **Leaf Miner,** Chrysanthemum (Marguerite fly).

Mealybug, Ground.   **Mite,** Broad; Cyclamen.

MARIGOLD (*Tagetes*)

Beetle, Blister; Japanese (prevalent on African, seldom on French, marigolds).

Borer, Stalk.   **Bug,** Garden Fleahopper; Tarnished Plant.

Caterpillar, Yellow Woollybear.   **Cutworms.**

Leaf Tier, Celery.   **Leafhopper,** Potato; Six-spotted.

Mite, Broad (in greenhouses); Cyclamen; Two-spotted.

Slug, Spotted Garden; Greenhouse.

MATRIMONY VINE (*Lycium chinense*)

Aphid, Crescent-marked Lily; other species.

Borer, Potato Tuberworm.

Gall, Leaf Blister (not described in Chapter V).

MELON, CANTALOUPE (*Cucumis melo*)

Aphid, Melon (green to brown or black; transmits mosaic, curls leaves).

Beetle, Fig; Imbricated Snout; Pale-striped Flea; Potato Flea; Spotted Cucumber; Squash; Striped Cucumber; Striped Blister; Western Striped Cucumber.

Borer, Squash (vines wilt).

Bug, Squash (large, brown, shield-shaped).

Caterpillar, Melonworm; Pickleworm; Yellow Woollybear.

Leafhopper, Beet (transmits curly top).

Millipedes (get in fruit on ground).

Mite, Two-spotted; other species (foliage turns yellow).

Nematode, Root-knot.

Thrips, Onion; Western Flower. **Whitefly,** Greenhouse.

Start melons like cucumbers under protective Hotkaps or screens. Do not use sulfur on melons except on special varieties that are not sensitive to it.

MESEMBRYANTHEMUM (Ice-plant)

Mealybug, Yucca. **Scale,** Lesser Snow.

MIGNONETTE (*Reseda*)

Beetle, Potato Flea (small holes in foliage).

Caterpillar, Cabbage Looper; Imported Cabbageworm.

Earworm, Corn. **Leafhopper,** Six-spotted.

Mite, Two-spotted. **Thrips,** Onion.

MIMOSA (*Albizzia*)

Scale, Lesser Snow.

Webworm, Mimosa (very injurious; common).

MINT (*Mentha*)

Beetle, Mint Flea; June.

Bug, Four-lined Plant (common, dark spots in young leaves).

Cutworms. Grasshoppers. Millipedes.

MISTLETOE

Scale, Cottony-cushion; Greedy; Purple.

MOCK-ORANGE (*Philadelphus*)

Aphid, Bean; Green Peach. **Leaf Miner** (undetermined).

MONKEYFLOWER (*Mimulus*)
Butterfly, Checker Spot. **Mealybug,** Yucca.
Mite, Two-spotted. **Thrips.**

MOONFLOWER (*Calonyction*)
Beetle, Argus Tortoise (holes in leaves).
Mealybug, Citrus, Long-tailed. **Nematode,** Fern.
Orthezia, Greenhouse. **Thrips.**

MORNING GLORY (*Convolvulus*)
Aphid, Melon; Myrtle (not described in Chapter V).
Beetle, Asiatic Garden; Argus Tortoise; Golden Tortoise; Mottled
    Tortoise; Spotted Cucumber; Sweetpotato Flea.
Bug, Four-lined Plant; Garden Fleahopper.
Caterpillar, Yellow Woollybear. **Earworm,** Corn.
Leaf Cutter, Morning-glory. **Leaf Miner,** Morning-glory.
Scale, Lesser Snow; Soft.
Weevil, Sweetpotato. **Whitefly,** Greenhouse; Inconspicuous.

MOUNTAIN-ASH (*Sorbus*)
Aphid, Rosy Apple; Woolly Apple.
Beetle, Japanese (feeds voraciously on foliage).
Borer, Apple Bark; Flatheaded Apple Tree; Lilac; Pacific Flatheaded;
    Roundheaded Apple Tree; Shot-hole; Sinuate Pear.
Mite, Pear Leaf Blister. **Moth,** Rusty Tussock.
Rootworm, Strawberry.
Sawfly, Mountain-ash (eats all leaves except veins, especially in upper
    part of tree); Pear-slug.
Scale, Black; Cottony Maple; Oystershell; San Jose; Scurfy.

MOUNTAIN EBONY (*Bauhinia*)
Scale, Lesser Snow.

MOUNTAIN-LAUREL (*Kalmia*)
Beetle, Strawberry Flea. **Borer,** Azalea Stem; Rhododendron.
Bug, Rhododendron Lace (leaves stippled gray).
Whitefly, Mulberry (dark with white fringe).

MOUNTAIN MAHOGANY (*Cercocarpus*)
Borer, Pacific Flatheaded; other borers.

MUEHLENBECKIA
Scale, Florida Wax.

MULBERRY (*Morus*)
Borer, Painted Hickory. **Mealybug,** Comstock.
Mite, Two-spotted. **Nematode,** Root-knot. **Planthopper.**
Scale, California Red; Cottony Maple; Florida Wax; Greedy; Olive
Parlatoria; Peach; San Jose; Soft.
Whitefly, Mulberry (dark with white fringe).

MUSTARD (*Brassica*)
Aphid, Turnip.
Beetle, Black Blister; Western Black Flea; Western Striped Flea.
Bug, Green Stink; Harlequin.
Caterpillar, Cabbage Looper; Imported Cabbageworm.
Curculio, Cabbage. **Maggot,** Cabbage.
Mealybug, Citrophilus. **Moth,** Diamondback. **Weevil,** Vegetable.
See Cabbage for other pests.

MYRTLE (*Myrtus*)
Aphid, Crescent-marked Lily; Myrtle (not described in Chapter V).
Mealybug, Citrus.
Scale, Black; Barnacle; Greedy; Green Shield; Oystershell; Rose; Soft.

MYRTLE, PERIWINKLE (*Vinca*)
Aphid, Green Peach; Melon; Potato; other species.
Beetle, Fuller Rose.
Leafhopper, Six-spotted. **Scale,** Olive Parlatoria.

NARCISSUS (Daffodil)
Aphid, Tulip Bulb. **Caterpillar,** Convict.
Fly, Lesser Bulb; Narcissus Bulb (large maggot in rotting bulb).
Mealybug, Solanum. **Millipedes.**
Mite, Bulb; Bulb Scale; Two-spotted.
Nematode, Bulb (dark rings in bulbs). **Thrips,** Flower; Gladiolus.

NASTURTIUM (*Tropaeolum*)
Aphid, Bean (black, almost inevitable); Green Peach; Crescent-
marked Lily.
Beetle, Flea. **Bug,** Tarnished Plant.

Caterpillar, Cabbage Looper; Imported Cabbageworm.
Earworm, Corn. **Leaf Miner,** Serpentine. **Leaf Tier,** Celery.
Mite, Two-spotted. **Thrips,** Greenhouse.

NECTARINE (see Peach)

NELUMBO (Lotus)
Aphid, Melon; Waterlily.

NEMESIA
Aphid, Melon.

NERINE
Thrips, Banded Greenhouse.

NEW JERSEY TEA (*Ceanothus americanus*)
Scale, Oystershell.

NICOTIANA (Flowering Tobacco)
Beetle, Colorado Potato; Potato Flea; Tobacco Flea.
Cutworms. Hornworms.

NINEBARK (*Physocarpus*)
Borer, Dogwood. **Whitefly,** Glacial; Iris.

OAK (*Quercus*)
Beetle, Carrot; Fuller Rose; Japanese; June.
Borer, Broad-necked Root; California Prionus; Carpenterworm; Flat-
    headed Apple Tree; Live-oak Root; Oak Sapling; Oak Timber-
    worm; Pacific Flatheaded; Pecan Carpenterworm; Pigeon Tremex;
    Tiger Hickory; Twig Pruner; Two-lined Chestnut.
Bug, Oak Lace (common; leaves whitened in summer).
Cankerworm, Fall, Spring (may defoliate in peak years).
Caterpillar, California Oakworm; California Tent; Eastern Tent;
    Forest Tent; Green-striped Mapleworm; Oak Looper; Orange-
    striped Oakworm; Orange Tortrix; Saddleback; Spiny Oakworm;
    Saddled Prominent; Variable Oak Leaf; Walnut; Yellow-necked.
Cicada, Periodical (twigs hang down, brown).
Galls (many, common, not serious).
Leaf Miner, Gregarious Oak Leaf; Solitary Oak Leaf.

Leaf Roller, Fruit Tree; Oak Leaf; Oblique-banded.
Mite, Avocado Red; Oak; Platani; Southern Red.
Moth, Brown-tail, Buck; Cecropia; Gypsy (favors oak); Imperial;
Io; Leopard; Luna; Oriental; Polyphemus; Satin; Spotted Tussock;
Western Tussock.
Sawfly, Pin-oak (leaves skeletonized).
Scale, California Red; Cottony-cushion; Cottony Maple; Golden Oak;
Greedy; Lecanium; Oak Gall; Obscure; Oystershell; Purple; Put-
nam.
Walkingstick. Weevil, Asiatic Oak. **Whitefly,** Citrus; Crown; Gla-
cial; Inconspicuous.

Oaks often require a dormant spray for scale insects and very
frequently a foliage spray for cankerworms, which takes care of other
caterpillars at the same time.

OKRA (*Hibiscus esculentus*)

Aphid, Melon.
Beetle, Flea; Grape Colaspis; Japanese; Striped Cucumber.
Bug, Green Stink; Southern Green Stink; Harlequin; Pumpkin.
Cutworms. Earworm, Corn.
Mite, Two-spotted. **Moth,** Abutilon (okra caterpillar).
Nematode, Root-knot. **Whiteflies.**

OLEANDER (*Nerium*)

Aphid, Bean (black); Green Peach; Oleander (yellow and black).
Mealybug, Citrus; Long-tailed.
Scale, Black; Florida Red; Florida Wax; Hemispherical; Lesser Snow;
Oleander (yellow); Olive Parlatoria; Peach; Soft.
Termites, Subterranean.

OLIVE (*Olea*)

Beetle, Olive Bark. **Borer,** Branch and Twig.
Caterpillar, Omnivorous Looper.
Scale, Black; California Red; Greedy; Oleander; Olive; Pineapple;
Purple.
Thrips, Bean; Citrus.

ONION (*Allium*)

Armyworm, Fall. **Beetle,** Blister; Imbricated Snout.
Cutworms. Fly, Lesser Bulb.

Maggot, Onion (may kill seedlings); Seed-corn.
Mite, Bulb; Two-spotted. **Nematode,** Bulb.
Thrips, Onion (leaves silvery, streaked, and distorted).
Weevil, Vegetable. **Wireworms.**

ORANGE (see Citrus)

ORCHIDS

Aphid, Lantana; Crescent-marked Lily.
Borer, Dendrobium. **Bug,** Orchid Plant.
Fly, Orchid (maggots in brown buds; small black fly).
Mealybug, Citrus. **Midge,** Cattleya. **Mite,** Two-spotted.
Nematode, Fern (brown blotches in leaves).
Scale, Black; Boisduval's; Chaff; Cyanophyllum; Florida Red; Hemispherical; Latania; Oleander; Oystershell; Purple; Tea; Tessellated.
Slugs. Snails. Thrips, Greenhouse; other species.
Weevil, Cattleya; Orchid.
    DDT is used for most orchid pests.

OSAGE-ORANGE (*Maclura*)

Mealybug, Citrus.
Scale, Cottony Maple; European Fruit Lecanium; Putnam; San Jose.
Whitefly, Citrus.

PACHYSANDRA (Spurge)

Mite, Two-spotted and other species (serious when plants are crowded).
Scale, Euonymus (thin, white); Oystershell; San Jose.

PALMETTO (Sabal, Cabbage Palm)

Leaf Skeletonizer, Palm (major pest in Florida).
Scale, Glover. **Whitefly,** Citrus.

PALMS

Aphid, Green Peach; Lantana. **Beetle,** Fuller Rose.
Leaf Skeletonizer (serious; leaves webbed).
Mealybug, Citrus; Ground; Long-tailed; Palm.
Orthezia, Greenhouse.
Scale, Black; Black Thread (sometimes important); Boisduval's; California Red; Chaff; Coconut; Cottony-cushion; Dictyospermum;

Fern; Florida Red; Glover; Greedy; Oleander; Olive Parlatoria; Pineapple; Soft; Tea; Tessellated.
Thrips, Banded Greenhouse; Dracaena; Greenhouse.

You don't have to identify the scale to keep indoor palms washed or syringed off. Oil sprays, with 1½ per cent actual oil, are often used for outdoor palms. Malathion controls crawling stages of many scales and also takes care of mealybugs.

PANDANUS (Screw-pine)
Mealybug, Long-tailed. **Scale,** Yellow.

PANSY (*Viola*)
Aphid, Foxglove; other species. **Beetle,** Flea.
Caterpillar, Yellow Woollybear. **Cutworms.**
Leaf Roller, Red-banded. **Leaf Tier,** Celery.
Mealybug, Solanum. **Mite,** Two-spotted. **Nematode,** Root-knot.
Sawfly, Violet. **Slugs. Sowbugs. Wireworms.**

PAPAYA
Nematode, Root-knot.

PARKINSONIA
Scale, Lesser Snow.

PARSLEY (*Petroselinum*)
Caterpillar, Celeryworm; Cabbage Looper. **Fly,** Carrot Rust.
Leafhopper, Six-spotted. **Leaf Tier,** Celery.
Nematode, Root-knot; Bulb and Stem.
Weevil, Carrot (grubs burrow in stalks).

PARSNIP (*Pastinaca*)
Aphid, Bean (black); Honeysuckle.
Beetle, Asiatic Garden; Carrot; Pale-striped Flea.
Caterpillar, Celeryworm; Yellow Woollybear.
Fly, Carrot Rust (tunnels in roots).
Leaf Miner, Parsnip (blotch mines in lower leaves; green and yellow fly, not described in Chapter V).
Nematode, Bulb and Stem. **Webworm,** Parsnip.

PASSION-FLOWER (*Passiflora*)

Caterpillar, Omnivorous Looper. **Leaf Tier,** Celery.
Mealybug, Citrus; Grape. **Scale,** California Red; Greedy; Purple.

PEA (*Pisum*)

Aphid, Bean; Pea (large green, important); Potato.
Beetle, Bean Leaf; Blister; Imbricated Snout; Pale-striped Flea; Spotted Cucumber; Striped Cucumber; Western Striped Cucumber.
Borer, Lesser Cornstalk.
Bug, Garden Fleahopper; Green Stink; Say Stink.
Caterpillar, Alfalfa; Cabbage Looper; Green Cloverworm; Yellow Woollybear.
Centipede, Garden. **Cricket,** Field.
Earworm, Corn. **Leaf Tier,** Celery.
Maggot, Seed-corn (injures seedlings). **Millipedes.**
Mite, Two-spotted (serious in dry weather; vines dry up).
Moth, Pea (small caterpillars in pods). **Nematode,** Root-knot.
Thrips, Onion; Western Flower. **Webworm,** Beet.
Weevil, Broadbean; Pea (serious). **Whitefly,** Greenhouse.

PEACH (*Prunus persica*)

Aphid, Black Cherry; Black Peach; Green Peach; Hop; Mealy Plum; Rusty Plum.
Beetle, Asiatic Garden; Bumble Flower; Cherry Leaf; Fig; Green June; Japanese (prevalent, serious); Peach Bark; Plum Gouger; Rose Chafer; Rose Leaf Beetle.
Borer, Branch and Twig; California Prionus; Lesser Peach Tree; Pacific Flatheaded; Peach Tree (common, serious; gum at base of trunk); Peach Twig; Shot-hole; Western Peach Tree.
Bug, Boxelder; Green Stink (catfaces fruit); Leaf-footed; Tarnished Plant (new shoots black).
Cankerworms. Casebearer, California.
Caterpillar, Forest Tent; Eastern Tent; Yellow-necked.
Cicada, Periodical. **Cricket,** Black-horned; Snowy Tree.
Curculio, Plum (common cause of wormy fruit).
Earworm, Corn. **Fly,** Mexican Fruit (in Texas).
Leafhopper, Plum. **Leaf Roller,** Oblique-banded; Red-banded.
Mealybug, Citrophilus; Ground.
Mite, Clover; European Red; Two-spotted; other species.

Moth, Codling (wormy fruit); Oriental Fruit (blackens tips of shoots).

Nematode, Root-knot. **Rootworm,** Strawberry.

Sawfly, Cherry Fruit (worms in fruit).

Scale, Cottony-cushion; Cottony Maple; Cottony Peach; European Fruit Lecanium; Florida Wax; Forbes; Grape; Howard; Italian Pear; Peach; San Jose (common, serious); Scurfy; Soft; Terrapin; Walnut; White Peach.

Thrips, Pear; Western Flower. **Treehopper,** Buffalo.

Webworm, Fall.

Peach spray schedules are timed primarily for control of diseases, leaf curl, brown rot, sometimes scab. A dormant spray of liquid lime-sulfur, 1 to 10 dilution, takes care of San Jose scale as well as leaf curl. Lead arsenate is included in the shuck-split spray for plum curculio but it must be safened with lime (for 10 gallons wettable sulfur spray, containing not less than ¼ pound actual sulfur, add ½ cup lead arsenate and 2 cups hydrated lime; repeat in 10 days). In July DDT can be used in place of lead arsenate (½ cup 50 per cent wettable powder to 10 gallons of sulfur spray) for control of Oriental fruit moth and Japanese beetle. It is also possible to use a "single-package" spray but consult your own state experiment station for the latest schedule. Peach Tree and Lesser Peach Tree Borers are important; see under Borers for control.

PEANUT (*Arachis hypogea*)

Armyworm, Fall.

Beetle, Corn Billbug; Elongate Flea; Pale-striped Flea; Spotted Cucumber; White-fringed.

Borer, Lesser Cornstalk.

Caterpillar, Velvetbean (serious in Gulf states); Yellow Wollybear.

Earworm, Corn.

Leafhopper, Potato (causes peanut "pouts"); Southern Garden.

Leaf Miner, Locust.

Nematode, Root-knot (special peanut strain); Sting.

Thrips, Tobacco (terminal buds black).

PEAR (*Pyrus*)

Aphid, Apple Grain; Clover; Cowpea; Rosy Apple; Woolly Apple; Woolly Pear.

Beetle, Fig; Green June; Pale-striped Flea; Rose Chafer; Rose Leaf; Syneta Leaf.

Borer, Apple Bark; Branch and Twig; Brown Wood; Carpenterworm; Flatheaded Apple Tree; Pacific Flatheaded; Pigeon Tremex; Roundheaded Apple Tree; Shot-hole; Sinuate Pear.

Bud Moth, Eye-spotted.

Bug, Apple Red; Pear Plant; Tarnished Plant.

Casebearer, California; Cigar.

Caterpillar, Eastern Tent; Forest Tent; Red-humped; Yellow-necked.

Cricket, Snowy Tree.   **Curculio,** Apple; Plum; Quince (wormy fruit).

Earworm, Corn.   **Fly,** Cherry Fruit; Mexican Fruit.

Leaf Crumpler.   Leaf Miner, Unspotted Tentiform.

Leaf Roller, Fruit Tree; Oblique-banded.

Mealybug, Citrophilus; Grape.   **Midge,** Pear (maggots in fruit).

Mite, Clover; European Red; Pear Leaf Blister (dark blisters in leaves).

Moth, Codling; Brown-tail; Leopard; Oriental Fruit; Western Tussock; White-lined Sphinx; White-marked Tussock.

Psyllid, Pear Psylla (leaves and fruit black; defoliation).

Sawfly, Pear-slug (leaves skeletonized).

Scale, Barnacle; Black; Calico; Cottony-cushion; Cottony Maple; European Fruit Lecanium; Olive Parlatoria; Oystershell; Peach; Rose; San Jose; Scurfy; Soft; Walnut; White Peach.

Termites.   Thrips, Pear (blossoms appear burned).

Weevil, New York.

The apple spray schedule is usually used for pears, but the pear leaf blister mite and pear psylla may require special treatment.

PECAN (*Carya*)

Aphid, Black Pecan; Hickory; Pecan Phylloxera.   **Beetle,** June.

Borer, Dogwood; Flatheaded Apple Tree; Pecan; Pecan Carpenterworm; Shot-hole; Twig Girdler; Twig Pruner.

Bud Moth, Pecan.   **Bug,** Leaf-footed; Southern Green Stink.

Casebearer, Pecan; Pecan Leaf; Pecan Nut.

Caterpillar, Hickory Horned Devil; Hickory Shuckworm (most serious pest); Omnivorous Looper; Walnut.

Curculio, Hickory-nut; Hickory Shoot (not described in Chapter V).

Mite, Hickory; Avocado Red.

Scale, Camphor; Cottony-cushion; European Fruit Lecanium; Greedy; Obscure; Purple; San Jose.

Spittlebug, Pecan.
Webworm, Fall.   **Weevil,** Pecan (worms in nuts, serious).

PELARGONIUM (see Geranium)

PENSTEMON (Beard-tongue)
Aphid, Foxglove; Crescent-marked Lily.
Beetle, Fuller Rose.   **Butterfly,** Checker Spot.

PENTAS
Caterpillar, Orange Tortrix.

PEONY (*Paeonia*)
Ants (usually present on buds, not injurious except by spreading disease spores).
Beetle, Japanese (occasional); Rose Chafer (tan, on flowers, common); Rose Leaf.
Bug, Four-lined Plant (small tan circles in leaves); Tarnished Plant.
Curculio, Rose.   **Nematode,** Root-knot (plants stunted).
Scale, Oystershell; San Jose (often present when old stalks are not cut down in autumn).
Thrips, Flower; Greenhouse (petals turn brown, common).

PEPPER (*Capsicum*)
Aphid, Green Peach; Melon; Potato.
Beetle, Asiatic Garden; Blister; Colorado Potato; Potato Flea; Rose Chafer; Spotted Cucumber.
Bug, Garden Fleahopper; Leaf-footed Plant; Pumpkin.
Cutworms.   Earworm, Corn.   **Hornworm,** Tobacco; Tomato.
Leafhopper, Beet.   **Leaf Miner,** Serpentine.
Maggot, Pepper (common cause of fruit decay).
Mite, Broad; Cyclamen; Two-spotted.
Orthezia, Greenhouse.   **Psyllid,** Tomato.
Weevil, Pepper (grubs in fruit).   **Whitefly,** Greenhouse.

PEPPER-TREE (*Schinus molle*)
Caterpillar, Omnivorous Looper.   **Mealybug,** Citrophilus.
Scale, Black (common); Barnacle; Fern; Greedy; Hemispherical; Lesser Snow; Oleander.
Thrips, Citrus.

PERIWINKLE (see Myrtle)

PERSIMMON (*Diospyros*)

Beetle, Fuller Rose.

Borer, Persimmon Root; Flatheaded Apple Tree.

Caterpillar, Hickory Horned Devil; Red-humped; Variable Oak Leaf.

Mealybug, Citrus.

Scale, Barnacle; Black; Camphor; European Fruit Lecanium; Green Shield; Putnam; San Jose; White Peach.

Thrips, Greenhouse. **Whitefly,** Citrus.

PETUNIA

Beetle, Asiatic Garden; Colorado Potato; Potato Flea (tiny shot-holes in leaves); Spotted Cucumber.

Bug, Garden Fleahopper; Tarnished Plant.

Caterpillar, Yellow Woollybear. **Grasshoppers.**

Hornworm, Tobacco, Tomato. **Leafhopper,** Six-spotted.

Mealybug, Ground. **Mite,** Tomato Russet (transmits mosaic); Two-spotted.

Moth, White-lined Sphinx. **Orthezia,** Greenhouse (scalelike).

PHACELIA (California Bluebell)

Aphid, Leaf-curling Plum.

PHLOX

Beetle, Asiatic Garden; Black Blister; Golden Tortoise; June; Potato Flea.

Borer, Stalk.

Bug, Four-lined Plant; Phlox Plant (oval, reddish orange; deforms buds).

Earworm, Corn. **Leafhopper,** Six-spotted.

Mite, Two-spotted (very common, leaves yellow, webby).

Nematode, Bulb and Stem (plants deformed, stems twisted).

Scale, Black; Soft. **Wireworms.**

PHYSOSTEGIA (False Dragonhead)

Aphid, Foxglove.

PINE (*Pinus*)

Aphid, Monterey Pine; Pine Bark (white fluffs on bark); Pine Leaf.

Bagworm.

Beetle, Black Turpentine; Mountain Pine; Pine Engraver; Northeastern Sawyer; Pine Colaspis; Red Turpentine; Southern Pine; Southwestern Pine; Western Pine; White-pine Cone.

Bird, Yellow-bellied Sapsucker (holes around trunk).

Borer, Cedar Tree; Broad-necked Root; Brown Wood; Fir Flatheaded.

Budworm, Spruce. **Butterfly,** Pine. **Caterpillar,** Hemlock Looper.

Leaf Miner, Lodgepole Needle; Pine Needle.

Mealybug, Comstock; Cypress; Golden. **Midge,** Monterey Pine.

Mite, Spruce Spider (needles look grayish or webby).

Moth, Cypress Tip; European Pine Shoot (common on ornamentals, tip yellow, crooked); Gypsy; Imperial; Nantucket Pine; Pandora; Pine Tube; Pitch Twig; Sequoia Pitch; White-pine Shoot; Zimmerman Pine.

Sawfly, European Pine (serious, denudes branches); Introduced Pine; Jack-pine; Loblolly Pine; Lodgepole Pine; Monterey Pine; Redheaded Pine; Balsam Fir; White-pine.

Scale, Barnacle; Cottony-cushion; Florida Wax; Hemlock; Pine Needle (white, pear-shaped, common); Pine Tortoise; Red-pine.

Spittlebug, Pine; Saratoga.

Webworm, Pine; Pine False (needles webbed together).

Weevil, Deodar; Monterey Pine; Pales; White-pine (leader dies back).

A dormant spray of oil or lime-sulfur for scales and spraying with DDT or lead arsenate for sawfly larvae takes care of many problems. Use lindane for bark aphids; remove tips infested with shoot moths.

PINEAPPLE (*Ananas*)

Mealybug, Pineapple. **Nematode,** Root-knot. **Scale,** Pineapple.

PITTOSPORUM

Aphids. Mealybugs.

Scale, Camellia; Black; Cottony-cushion (very common, white fluted sacs and black sooty mold); Florida Wax; Greedy; Lesser Snow; Soft.

PLUM (*Prunus*)

Aphid, Black Peach; Green Peach; Hop; Leaf-curling Plum; Mealy Plum; Rusty Plum; Thistle; Waterlily.

Beetle, Fuller Rose; Grape Flea; Green June; Japanese (especially on ornamental plums); Plum Gouger; Rose Leaf; Syneta Leaf.

Borer, California Prionus; Flatheaded Apple Tree; Lesser Peach;

Pacific Flatheaded; Peach Tree; Peach Twig; Shot-hole; Western Peach.

Bud Moth, Eye-spotted. **Bug,** Boxelder; Harlequin.

Cankerworm, Fall; Spring. **Casebearer,** California; Cigar.

Caterpillar, California Tent; Eastern Tent; Forest Tent; Red-humped; Yellow-necked.

Cricket, Snowy Tree. **Curculio,** Plum (important; wormy fruit).

Fly, Black Cherry Fruit; Mexican Fruit.

Leaf Crumpler. Leafhopper, Grape; Plum.

Leaf Roller, Fruit Tree; Oblique-banded; Red-banded.

Leaf Skeletonizer, Apple. **Maggot,** Apple.

Mealybug, Citrophilus; Ground; Long-tailed.

Mite, Clover; European Red; Pacific.

Moth, Artichoke Plume; Brown-tail; Codling; Leopard; Western Tussock; White-lined Sphinx; White-marked Tussock.

Sawfly, Cherry Fruit; Pear-slug; Plum Web-spinning.

Scale, Black; Cottony Maple; European Fruit Lecanium (brown, convex); Florida Wax; Forbes; Howard; Italian Pear; Lecanium; Obscure; Olive Parlatoria; Peach; Putnam; San Jose; Soft; Terrapin; Walnut; White Peach.

Thrips, Pear; Western Flower.

For plums as for peaches the schedule is primarily for the control of brown rot, a fungus disease, with lead arsenate and lime added for plum curculio. Methoxychlor can be substituted in some cases. Do not use lead arsenate on ornamental plums to control Japanese beetles; it may injure severely, with partial or complete defoliation.

PLUMBAGO (Leadwort)

Beetle, Fuller Rose. **Mealybug,** Citrus.

POINSETTIA

Aphids, Root (woolly, white, at roots).

Mealybug, Citrus; Long-tailed.

Scale, Cottony-cushion; Oleander (yellow); Soft (brown).

POMEGRANATE (*Punica granatum*)

Bug, Western Leaf-footed.

Scale, Black; Citricola; Cottony-cushion; Florida Wax; Greedy; Mining; Olive Parlatoria.

Thrips, Citrus; Greenhouse. **Whitefly,** Citrus.

POPLAR, ASPEN, COTTONWOOD
(*Populus*)

Aphid, Poplar Petiole Gall; Poplar Vagabond; other species.

Beetle, Alder Flea; Cottonwood Leaf; Goldsmith; June; Imported Willow Leaf.

Borer, Broad-necked; Bronze Birch; California Prionus; Carpenter-worm; Cottonwood; Flatheaded Apple Tree; Pacific Flatheaded; Pigeon Tremex; Poplar (large beetle, swollen scars); Poplar and Willow (small beetle, may girdle trees).

Butterfly, Mourning-cloak (spiny elm caterpillar).

Caterpillar, Eastern Tent; Forest Tent; Great Basin Tent; Poplar Tent; Red-humped; Saddled Prominent.

Leafhopper, Poplar. **Leaf Miner,** Cottonwood.

Leaf Roller, Fruit Tree; Oblique-banded. **Mealybug,** Comstock.

Moth, Cecropia; Hornet; Io; Leopard; Oriental; Polyphemus; Rusty Tussock; Satin; White-marked Tussock.

Sawfly, Elm; Poplar; Willow.

Scale, Black; Cottony Maple; European Fruit Lecanium; Greedy; Lecanium; Oystershell; San Jose; Soft; Terrapin; Walnut; Willow.

Wasp, Giant Hornet. **Webworm,** Fall. **Weevil,** Willow Flea.

POPPY (*Papaver*)

Aphid, Bean (black, frequent); Green Peach; Melon.

Beetle, Rose Chafer. **Bug,** Four-lined Plant; Tarnished Plant.

Leafhopper, Six-spotted. **Mealybug,** Grape.

PORTULACA

Moth, White-lined Sphinx.

POTATO (*Solanum tuberosum*)

Aphid, Buckthorn; Foxglove; Green Peach; Myrtle (not described in Chapter V); Potato.

Armyworm, Fall; Southern; Yellow-striped.

Beetle, Ash-gray Blister; Banded Flea; Black Blister; Carrot; Colorado Potato (convex striped beetle devours foliage); Eggplant Flea; Eggplant Tortoise; Imbricated Snout; Margined Blister; Pale-striped Flea; Potato Flea (tiny, black, minute holes in leaves); Spotted Blister; Spotted Cucumber; Strawberry Leaf; Striped Blister; Striped Cucumber; Three-lined Potato; Tobacco Flea; Tuber Flea; Western Potato Flea; Western Spotted Cucumber; Western Striped Cucumber; White-fringed.

Borer, European Corn; Potato Stalk; Potato Tuberworm; Stalk.

Bug, Cotton Fleahopper; Eggplant Lace; False Chinch; Four-lined Plant; Garden Fleahopper; Harlequin; Leaf-footed; Pumpkin; Rapid Plant; Say Stink; Southern Green Stink; Tarnished Plant; Western Plant.

Caterpillar, Cabbage Looper; Yellow Woollybear; Zebra.

Centipede, Garden.

Cricket, Changa; Jerusalem; Northern Mole; Southern Mole.

Cutworm, Black; Dingy; Glassy; Pale Western; Spotted; Variegated.

Earwig, European. **Earworm,** Corn.

Grasshopper, Clear-winged; Differential; Lesser Migratory; Red-legged; Two-striped.

Hornworm, Tobacco; Tomato.

Leafhopper, Arid; Beet; Clover; Intermountain (not described in Chapter V); Potato (very injurious, rolls and burns leaves); Southern Garden; Six-spotted; Western Potato.

Leaf Miner, Serpentine. **Maggot,** Seed-corn; Seed Potato.

Mealybug, Apple; Citrus; Citrophilus; Grape; Solanum.

Millipedes. Mite, Tomato Russet. **Moth,** White-lined Sphinx.

Nematode, Golden (serious); Root-knot. **Psyllid,** Potato.

Slug, Gray Garden; Spotted Garden. **Springtail,** Garden.

Thrips, Bean; Onion; Tobacco.

Webworm, Beet; Garden. **Weevil,** Vegetable.

Whitefly, Greenhouse; Iris.

Wireworm, Corn; Eastern Field; Gulf; Pacific Coast; Prairie Grain; Sugar-beet; Wheat.

DDT usually takes care of the more important potato pests, such as Colorado potato beetle, potato flea beetle, and potato leafhopper.

POTENTILLA (Cinquefoil)
Weevil, Strawberry Root.

PRICKLY ASH (*Xanthoxylum americanum*)
Scale, European Fruit Lecanium; Florida Wax; Howard.

PRIMROSE (*Primula*)
Aphid, Cowpea; Corn Root; Foxglove; Green Peach.

Beetle, Fuller Rose (leaves chewed in from margin); Potato Flea; Steel-blue Flea; Strawberry Flea.

Mealybug, Long-tailed; Yucca.

Mite, Two-spotted (foliage always turns yellow in summer).

Nematode, Bulb and Stem. Slugs (large holes in leaves, common).

Weevil, Black Vine (grubs work on roots). Whitefly, Greenhouse.

PRIVET (*Ligustrum*)

Aphid, Privet. Beetle, Sweetpotato Leaf.

Leaf Miner, Lilac; Privet. Mealybug, Citrophilus; Ground.

Mite, Privet (leaves dusty). Planthopper.

Scale, Black; California Red; Camphor; Japanese; Mining; Olive Parlatoria; San Jose; White Peach.

Thrips, Privet (common, serious, leaves grayish).

Whitefly, Greenhouse (very common in southern gardens).

PRUNE (see Plum)

PUMPKIN (*Cucurbita*)

Aphid, Melon; Potato; other species.

Beetle, Blister; Potato Flea; Squash; Striped Cucumber; Western Striped Cucumber.

Borer, Squash. Bug, Garden Fleahopper; Squash.

Caterpillar, Melonworm; Yellow Woollybear. Earworm, Corn.

Mealybug, Citrus. Nematode, Root-knot.

See Squash for other pests.

PYRACANTHA (Firethorn)

Aphid, Apple.

Bug, Hawthorn Lace (leaves stippled gray, black specks on underside; common, worse in South).

Scale, Greedy; Olive Parlatoria.

Webworm (leaves and twigs webbed together; prevalent in Southwest).

QUINCE (*Cydonia*)

Aphid, Apple; Apple Grain; Clover; Woolly Apple.

Beetle, Grape Flea; Japanese (serious).

Caterpillar, Eastern Tent; Forest Tent; Yellow-necked.

Curculio, Apple; Quince (wormy fruit).

Fly, Mexican Fruit (in Texas).

Leaf Crumpler. Leaf Miner, Unspotted Tentiform.

Leaf Roller, Fruit Tree. **Leaf Skeletonizer,** Apple.

Moth, Oriental Fruit (important); Codling; Rusty Tussock; White-marked Tussock.

Sawfly, Pear-slug.

Scale, Barnacle; California Red; Cottony-cushion; Cottony Maple; European Fruit Lecanium; Forbes; Greedy; Oystershell; Putnam; San Jose; Scurfy.

Treehopper, Buffalo. **Weevil,** Apple Flea.

A spray schedule for quinces can be adapted from one given for apples. Japanese beetles may be a problem in midsummer.

RADISH (*Raphanus sativus*)

Aphid, Cabbage; Green Peach; Turnip.

Beetle, Black Blister; Pale-striped Flea; Potato Flea; Red Turnip; Sinuate Striped Flea; Striped Blister; Western Black Flea; Western Striped Flea.

Caterpillar, Cabbage Looper; Imported Cabbageworm; Yellow Woolly-bear.

Centipede, Garden. **Curculio,** Cabbage. **Leaf Miner,** Serpentine.

Maggot, Cabbage (seedling wilt); Seed-corn. **Moth,** Diamondback.

Springtail, Garden. **Weevil,** Vegetable. **Wireworms.**

See Cabbage for other pests.

RASPBERRY (*Rubus*)

Aphid, Raspberry (may transmit mosaic).

Beetle, Alfalfa Snout; Argus Tortoise; Fuller Rose; Green June; Imbricated Snout; Japanese (serious); Rose Chafer; Rose Leaf.

Borer, Flatheaded Apple Tree; Raspberry Cane; Raspberry Root; Red-necked Cane; Rose Stem Girdler.

Bug, Negro (bad taste to berries).

Caterpillar, Green Cloverworm; Orange Tortrix; Yellow Woollybear.

Cricket, Black-horned Tree.

Fruitworm, Raspberry (beetles injure buds; larvae tunnel fruit).

Leafhopper, Grape. **Leaf Roller,** Fruit Tree; Strawberry.

Maggot, Raspberry Cane (tips die back).

Mite, Clover; Two-spotted. **Moth,** Strawberry Crown.

Sawfly, Raspberry. **Scale,** Latania; Oystershell; Rose; Scurfy; Soft.

Spittlebug, Strawberry. **Weevil,** Black Vine; Strawberry Root.

Whitefly, Glacial.

So far as possible cut out infested canes. Use rotenone for Japanese beetles when berries are ripening.

REDBUD, JUDAS TREE (*Cercis*)

Caterpillar, California Tent. **Leaf Folder,** Grape.
Scale, Greedy; Oleander; Terrapin.
Treehopper, Two-marked. **Whitefly,** Greenhouse.

REDWOOD (*Sequoia*)

Borer, Cedar Tree. **Mealybug,** Citrus; Cypress; Yucca.
Moth, Sequoia Pitch. **Scale,** Greedy; Oleander.

RETINOSPORA (*Chamaecyparis*)

Aphid, Arborvitae. **Weevil,** Black Vine.

RHODODENDRON

Aphid, Rhododendron. **Beetle,** Asiatic Garden; Pitted Ambrosia.
Borer, Azalea Stem; Broad-necked Root; Rhododendron (common; holes in trunk).
Bug, Rhododendron Lace (leaves yellowed, stippled white or gray, rusty flecks on undersurface; prevalent).
Mealybug, Taxus. **Midge,** Rhododendron. **Mites.**
Scale, Azalea Bark; Oleander; Rhododendron.
Thrips, Greenhouse; Madrona; Onion.
Wasp, Giant Hornet. **Whitefly,** Rhododendron.
Lace bugs and borers are most important.

RHUBARB (*Rheum*)

Beetle, Alfalfa Snout; Potato Flea; Japanese.
Borer, European Corn; Stalk.
Caterpillar, Yellow Woollybear. **Curculio,** Rhubarb (important).
Leafhopper, Potato. **Mealybug,** Citrus. **Scale,** Black.

ROSE (*Rosa*)

Aphid, Green Peach; Melon; Potato (pink and green); Rose.
Bee, Carpenter (in pith); Leaf-cutter.
Beetle, Asiatic Garden; Fuller Rose; Goldsmith; Grape Colaspis; Japanese (serious, eats flowers and foliage); June; Oriental; Rose Chafer (tan, on flowers); Rose Leaf; Spotted Cucumber; Strawberry Leaf.

Borer, Flatheaded Apple Tree; Pacific Flatheaded; Pigeon Tremex; Raspberry Cane; Red-necked Cane; Rose Stem Girdler.

Budworm, Rose.

Bug, Four-lined Plant; Harlequin; Tarnished Plant.

Cankerworms (occasional).

Caterpillar, Eastern Tent; Forest Tent; Orange Tortrix; Red-humped.

Earwig, European. **Earworm,** Corn. **Fruitworm,** Green.

Gall, Mossy Rose; Rose Root. **Grasshoppers.**

Leafhopper, Apple (foliage white) ; Potato (brown margins on leaves) ; Red-banded; Rose (coarse white stippling) ; Virginia-creeper; White Apple.

Leaf Roller, Oblique-banded. **Leaf Tier,** Celery.

Maggot, Raspberry Cane. **Mealybugs.**

Midge, Rose (small buds turn black; occasional, but serious).

Mite, Two-spotted; other species (leaves turn yellow, gray, drop).

Nematode, Root-knot (small galls on roots).

Sawfly, Curled Rose; Rose-slug (leaves skeletonized) ; Bristly Rose.

Scale, Black; California Red; Camphor; Cottony Maple; European Fruit Lecanium; Florida Red; Greedy; Green Shield; Latania; Olive; Oystershell; Peach; Rose (round, white) ; San Jose; Soft; Walnut.

Thrips, Florida Flower; Flower (buds ball, petals turn brown) ; Greenhouse; Onion (flowers streaked) ; Tobacco; Western Flower.

Treehopper, Buffalo (curved slits in bark).

Walkingstick, Northern. **Webworm,** Fall.

Weevil, Imported Long-horned. **Whitefly,** Greenhouse.

Control of rose pests starts with a dormant spray for rose scale, preferably with lime-sulfur, and then weekly all summer a combination spray or dust containing lead arsenate or DDT or methoxychlor for rose-slugs and beetles; rotenone and pyrethrum or malathion or nicotine for aphids; lindane or malathion for thrips; and Aramite or malathion for mites. DDT is best for leafhoppers and rose midge but will increase mites.

ROSE ACACIA (*Robinia hispida*)

Aphid, Bean; Cowpea. **Butterfly,** Silver-spotted Skipper.

ROSE-OF-SHARON (*Hibiscus syriacus*)

Aphid, Cowpea (dark, numerous at tips of branches) ; Melon.

Beetle, Japanese (on foliage and flowers). **Scale,** Black.

ROYAL POINCIANA (*Poinciana regia*)
Scale, Lesser Snow.

RUBBER PLANT (*Ficus elastica*)
Mealybug, Long-tailed.
Scale, Black; Cyanophyllum; Florida Red; Oleander; Soft.
Thrips, Banded Greenhouse; Dracaena; Greenhouse.

RUDBECKIA (Coneflower)
Aphid, Goldenglow (red); Crescent-marked Lily.
Leafhopper, Six-spotted.

RUTABAGA (see Turnip)

SAGE, BLACK, WHITE (*Audibertia*)
Mealybug, Yucca. **Scale,** Olive Parlatoria; Greedy.
Whitefly, Glacial; Greenhouse; Iridescent.

SAGE, SCARLET, BLUE (*Salvia*)
Aphid, Foxglove. **Beetle,** Asiatic Garden. **Borer,** Stalk.
Bug, Tarnished Plant. **Caterpillar,** Yellow Woollybear.
Leafhopper, Grape. **Leaf Tier,** Celery. **Mites. Nematode,** Fern.
Orthezia, Greenhouse. **Whitefly,** Greenhouse.

SALSIFY (*Tragopogon*)
Bug, Tarnished Plant. **Caterpillar,** Yellow Woollybear.

SAPODILLA (*Sapota*)
Scale, Florida Wax; Green Shield; Lesser Snow.

SASSAFRAS
Beetle, Japanese (numerous on foliage).
Caterpillar, Hickory Horned Devil.
Moth, Io; Polyphemus; Promethea. **Scale,** Oystershell; San Jose.

SCABIOSA
Beetle, Fuller Rose. **Leafhopper,** Six-spotted.

SCHIZANTHUS (Butterfly-flower)
Leafhopper, Six-spotted.

SEA-GRAPE (*Coccolobis uvifera*)
Scale, Florida Wax; Green Shield.

SEDUM
Aphid, Green Peach; Melon; Sedum. Scale, Greedy.

SENECIO
Butterfly, Painted Beauty.

SHADBUSH, SERVICEBERRY, JUNEBERRY (*Amelanchier*)
Aphid, Woolly Elm.
Borer, Lesser Peach; Apple Bark; Roundheaded Apple Tree; Shot-hole.
Curculio, Apple. Leaf Miner, Shadbush.
Mite, Pear Leaf Blister. Moth, Gypsy.
Sawfly, Pear-slug. Scale, Oystershell. Webworm, Fall.

SHALLOT (*Allium*)
Fly, Lesser Bulb.

SHEPHERDIA
Aphid, Oleaster-thistle.

SILVER LACE VINE (*Polygonum aubertii*)
Aphid, Corn Root. Beetle, Flea; Japanese.

SILVER TREE (*Leucadendron argenteum*)
Scale, Greedy.

SILVER-VINE (*Actinidia polygama*)
Orthezia, Greenhouse. Scale, San Jose.
Cats are very fond of this vine. It may need protection.

SMILAX (see Asparagus Fern)

SMOKETREE (*Cotinus*)
Leaf Roller, Oblique-banded. Scale, San Jose.

SNAPDRAGON (*Antirrhinum*)

Aphid, Green Peach; Melon.   **Beetle,** Asiatic Garden.   **Borer,** Stalk.
Budworm, Rose; Verbena.
Bug, Snapdragon Lace; Four-lined Plant; Red-and-Black Stink; Tarnished Plant.
Caterpillar, Yellow Woollybear.   **Centipede,** Garden.
Leaf Tier, Celery.   **Mite,** Cyclamen; Two-spotted.
Moth, Snapdragon Plume.   **Nematode,** Root-knot.   **Slugs.**

SNOWBALL (see Viburnum)

SNOWBERRY (*Symphoricarpos*)

Aphid, Honeysuckle; Crescent-marked Lily; Snowberry.
Moth, Snowberry Clearwing.   **Scale,** San Jose.   **Whitefly,** Glacial.

SNOWDROP (*Galanthus*)

Fly, Narcissus Bulb.   **Nematode,** Bulb.

SOAPBERRY (*Sapindus*)

Aphid, Ceanothus.

SOURBERRY (*Rhus integrifolia*)

Scale, Hemispherical.

SOYBEAN (*Glycine max*)

Beetle, Bean Leaf; Blister; Japanese (makes lace of foliage); Mexican Bean (not so serious as on other beans).
Caterpillar, Green Cloverworm; Velvetbean (may defoliate in South).
Curculio, Clover Root.   **Grasshopper,** Red-legged.   **Leaf Miner,** Locust.
Webworm, Garden.   **Whitefly,** Greenhouse.

SPANISH NEEDLE (see Yucca)

SPINACH (*Spinacia*)

Aphid, Bean; Green Peach; Melon.   **Armyworms.**
Beetle, Beet Leaf; Blister; Potato Flea; Spinach Flea (small holes in leaves).
Caterpillar, Cabbage Looper.   **Cutworms.**   **Grasshoppers.**
Leaf Miner, Serpentine; Spinach (tan blotches in leaves, common).

Leaf Tier, Celery.   **Maggot,** Seed-corn.
Springtail, Garden.   **Webworm,** Beet.

S P I R E A (*Spiraea*)

Aphid, Spirea (green, common).
Caterpillar, Saddled Prominent.   **Leaf Roller,** Oblique-banded.
Mites.   Nematode, Root-knot.
Scale, Cottony Maple; Oystershell; Spirea.   **Weevil,** Black Vine.

S P R U C E (*Picea*)

Aphid, Cooley Spruce Gall (galls at end of twigs of blue spruce);
   Eastern Spruce Gall (galls at base of Norway spruce twigs); Pine
   Leaf; Spruce.
Beetle, Black Turpentine; Douglas-fir Engraver; Eastern Spruce;
   Engelmann Spruce; Northeastern Sawyer; Pine Engraver; Red Tur-
   pentine; Southern Pine; White-pine Cone.
Borer, Fir Flatheaded; Hemlock.
Budworm, Spruce (needles webbed together; serious pest).
Leaf Miner, Spruce Needle (webs needles together).
Mite, Spruce Spider (common and injurious, needles gray, webby).
Moth, Spruce Epizeuxis; Gypsy; Imperial.
Sawfly, Balsam Fir; European Spruce.
Scale, Pine Needle; Spruce Bud.   **Spittlebug,** Pine.
Weevil, Pales; White-pine.

S Q U A S H (*Cucurbita maxima*)

Aphid, Melon (common, curls leaves); Potato; other species.
Beetle, Imbricated Snout; Spotted Cucumber; Squash; Striped Cu-
   cumber; Tobacco Flea; Western Striped Cucumber.
Borer, Squash Vine (common, serious; vines wilt, die).
Bug, Harlequin; Southern Squash; Squash (flat, brown, vines may
   die).
Caterpillar, Melonworm; Pickleworm; Yellow Woollybear.
Earworm, Corn.   **Leafhopper,** Beet.   **Nematode,** Root-knot.
Springtail, Garden.   **Thrips,** Onion; Western Flower.
Whitefly, Greenhouse (often abundant).
   Many squash varieties are sensitive to sulfur and DDT.

S Q U I L L (*Scilla*)

Aphid, Tulip Bulb.

STOCK (*Mathiola*)

Aphids.

Beetle, Striped Flea; Western Black Flea; Western Striped Flea.

Mealybug, Mexican.   **Moth,** Diamondback.

Springtail, Garden.   **Weevil,** Imported Long-horned.

STRAWBERRY (*Fragaria*)

Ant, Fire.   **Aphid,** Melon; Strawberry; Strawberry Root.

Beetle, Alfalfa Snout; Darkling; Fuller Rose; Japanese; June; Pale-striped Flea; Rose Chafer; Rose Leaf; Strawberry Flea; Strawberry Leaf; Ten-lined June.

Borer, Strawberry Crown.

Bug, Leaf-footed; Negro; Pameras (hard berries); Tarnished Plant.

Caterpillar, Green Cloverworm.   **Cricket,** Field; Northern Mole; Southern Mole.

Curculio, Cowpea.   **Earwig,** European.

Fruitworm, Strawberry.   **Leaf Miner,** Strawberry Crown.

Leaf Roller, Oblique-banded; Strawberry Leaf; Western Strawberry Leaf.

Leaf Tier, Celery.   **Mealybug,** Grape.

Millipedes.   **Mite,** Cyclamen (crown mite, serious); Two-spotted.

Moth, Strawberry Crown.   **Nematode,** Root-knot; Strawberry Bud.

Rootworm, Strawberry.   **Sawfly,** Strawberry.

Scale, Rose; San Jose; Soft.   **Spittlebug,** Strawberry.

Webworm, Garden.

Weevil, Black Vine (grubs on roots); Strawberry (buds injured); Strawberry Root.

Whitefly, Strawberry.

Buy certified strawberry plants and start with clean stock.

STRAWFLOWER (*Helichrysum bracteatum*)

Leafhopper, Six-spotted.

STRELITZIA (Bird-of-Paradise)

Mealybug, Citrus; Long-tailed.   **Scale,** Greedy.

SUGARBERRY (*Rhus ovata*)

Thrips, Toyon.

SUMAC (*Rhus*)

Aphid, Sumac. **Beetle,** Potato Flea. **Borer, Currant.**
Caterpillar, Hickory Horned Devil. **Leaf Roller,** Oblique-banded.
Mites. Psyllid, Sumac (dark with white fringe).
Scale, Cottony Maple; Hemispherical; Lesser Snow; San Jose.

SUNFLOWER (*Helianthus*)

Aphid, Dogwood; Hop; Leaf-curling Plum; Melon; Potato.
Beetle, Carrot; Pale-striped Flea; Potato Flea; Western Striped Cucumber.
Bug, Four-lined Plant; Harlequin; Pumpkin; Say Stink; Southern Green Stink; Tarnished Plant.
Butterfly, Painted Lady. **Caterpillar,** Yellow Woollybear.
Earworm, Corn. **Leaf Roller,** Oblique-banded.
Maggot, Sunflower (stems may break over). **Mealybug,** Citrophilus.
Scale, Cottony-cushion.

SWEET GUM (*Liquidambar*)

Bagworm. Caterpillar, Forest Tent.
Moth, Azalea Sphinx; Luna; Polyphemus; Promethea.
Scale, Cottony-cushion; Walnut.

SWEET OLIVE, TEA OLIVE (*Osmanthus fragrans*)

Scale, Camphor; Chaff.

SWEET PEA (*Lathyrus odoratus*)

Aphid, Corn Root; Pea; Potato. **Beetle,** Spotted Cucumber.
Bug, Four-lined Plant; Tarnished Plant.
Centipede, Garden. **Cutworms. Earworm,** Corn.
Leaf Miner, Serpentine. **Leaf Tier,** Celery.
Mite, Two-spotted (leaves yellow, mealy; common).
Moth, Pea. **Nematode,** Root-knot.
Sowbugs. Thrips, Onion; Western Flower.

SWEETPOTATO (*Ipomoea batatas*)

Aphid, Potato. **Armyworm,** Fall; Southern; Striped.
Beetle, Argus Tortoise; Blister; Sweetpotato Flea; Sweetpotato Leaf; Two-striped Tortoise; White-fringed.
Bug, Garden Fleahopper. **Caterpillar,** Yellow Woollybear.

Leafhopper, Bean. **Leaf Roller,** Sweetpotato. **Maggot,** Seed-corn.
Thrips, Banded Greenhouse. **Weevil,** Sweetpotato. **Whiteflies.**

SWEET WILLIAM (*Dianthus*)

Leafhopper, Six-spotted. **Mites.**

SYCAMORE, LONDON and ORIENTAL PLANE (*Platanus*)

Aphid, Hickory; Sycamore. **Bagworm.**
Borer, Flatheaded Apple Tree; Pacific Flatheaded; Pigeon Tremex.
Bug, Sycamore Lace (common, leaves white); Sycamore Plant.
Caterpillar, Hickory Horned Devil; Omnivorous Looper; Puss.
Mite, Southern Red; other species.
Moth, Imperial; Io; Oriental; Sycamore Tussock; White-marked Tussock.
Scale, Black; Cottony Maple; Grape; Oystershell; Sycamore (serious on Oriental plane); Terrapin.
Treehopper, Two-marked. **Webworm,** Fall. **Whitefly,** Mulberry.

SYNGONIUM

Thrips, Greenhouse.

TAMARISK (*Tamarix*)

Scale, Latania; Oystershell.

TANGERINE (see Citrus)

TAXUS (see Yew)

TEA (*Thea sinensis*)

Scale, Barnacle; California Red; Florida Wax; Green Shield.

TECOMA

Caterpillar, Omnivorous Looper.

THISTLE, GLOBE THISTLE (*Cirsium, Echinops*)

Aphid, Oleaster-thistle; Bean; Melon; Thistle.
Bug, Four-lined Plant; Leaf-footed.
Butterfly, Painted Beauty; Painted Lady.
Leaf Roller, Oblique-banded. **Leaf Tier,** Celery.

THORN (see Hawthorn)

THUNBERGIA (Clockvine)
Scale, Lesser Snow.

THYME (*Thymus*)
Mealybug, Ground.

TOMATILLO (*Physalis*)
Mite, Tomato Russet.

TOMATO (*Lycopersicon*)
Aphid, Green Peach; Potato (both common).
Armyworm, Fall; Semi-tropical.
Beetle, Blister; Colorado Potato; Darkling Ground; Fig; Pale-striped Flea; Potato Flea (common after setting out, minute holes in leaves) ; Spotted Cucumber; Tobacco Flea; Western Potato Flea.
Borer, Potato Tuberworm; Stalk.
Bug, One-spot Stink; Eggplant Lace; Garden Fleahopper; **Green** Stink; Leaf-footed; Pumpkin.
Caterpillar, Cabbage Looper; Tomato Pinworm.
Centipede, Garden. **Cricket,** Field.
Cutworms (frequently cut off young plants).
Earworm, Corn (tomato fruitworm).
Hornworm, Tobacco; Tomato (large green caterpillars devour leaves).
Leafhopper, Beet. **Millipedes.**
Mite, Cyclamen; Tomato Russet; Two-spotted.
Moth, White-lined Sphinx (hornworm caterpillar).
Psyllid, Tomato (plants deformed, appear diseased).
Slugs. Springtail, Garden.
Thrips, Banded Greenhouse; Flower; Onion; Western Flower.
Whitefly, Greenhouse (tiny white "moths" on underside of leaves).

Tomato pests vary in different sections. Flea beetles and cutworms are rather general spring problems.

TOYON (see California Christmasberry)

TRUMPET CREEPER or VINE (*Campsis*)
Planthopper, Mealy Flata.
Scale, Olive Parlatoria. **Whitefly,** Citrus.

TUBEROSE (*Polianthes tuberosa*)
Nematode, Root-knot.

TULIP (*Tulipa*)
Aphid, Green Peach; Tulip Bulb. **Fly,** Lesser Bulb; Narcissus Bulb.
Millipedes. Mite, Bulb; Two-spotted.
Nematode, Bulb (plants twisted and deformed). **Wireworms.**

TULIPTREE (*Liriodendron*)
Aphid, Tuliptree (green, secreting much honeydew, followed by sooty
  mold).
Beetle, June. **Moth,** Promethea.
Scale, Oystershell; Tuliptree; Willow.

TUNG-OIL-TREE (*Aleurites fordii*)
Scale, Olive Parlatoria.

TUPELO, SOUR-GUM (*Nyssa sylvatica*)
Leaf Miner, Tupelo (cuts pieces from leaves).
Moth, Azalea Sphinx (not described in Chapter V). **Scale,** San Jose.

TURQUOISE VINE (*Ampelopsis brevipeduncu-lata*)
Beetle, Japanese (very fond of this vine).

TURNIP (*Brassica rapa*)
Aphid, Cabbage; Potato; Turnip (grayish, often serious).
Beetle, Asiatic Garden; Pale-striped Flea; Red Turnip; Sinuate-striped
  Flea; Striped Blister; Western Black Flea; Western Striped Flea.
Bug, Green Stink; Harlequin; Tarnished Plant.
Caterpillar, Cabbage Looper; Imported Cabbageworm; Yellow
  Woollybear.
Curculio, Cabbage. **Leaf Miner,** Serpentine.
Maggot, Cabbage (seedlings wilt); Seed-corn.
Millipedes. Moth, Diamondback; White-lined Sphinx.
Weevil, Vegetable.

UMBRELLA PLANT (*Cyperus*)
Mealybug, Citrus; Long-tailed. **Thrips,** Citrus. **Whitefly,** Citrus.

UMBRELLA TREE (*Magnolia acuminata*)
Scale, Greedy; Oleander. **Thrips,** Citrus. **Whitefly,** Citrus.

VELVETBEAN (*Stizolobium*)
Beetle, White-fringed. **Caterpillar,** Velvetbean.

VERBENA
Aphid, Foxglove; Green Peach; Melon. **Beetle,** Gray Blister.
Bud Moth, Verbena (bores in new shoots).
Bug, Snapdragon Lace; Tarnished Plant.
Caterpillar, Omnivorous Looper; Yellow Woollybear.
Leaf Cutter, Morning-glory.
Leaf Miner, Verbena (light blotches in leaves, very common).
Leaf Roller, Oblique-banded. **Mite,** Broad; Cyclamen; Two-spotted.
Nematode, Fern (brown areas in leaves).
Orthezia, Greenhouse. **Scale,** Cottony-cushion.
Thrips, Flower; Greenhouse. **Whitefly,** Greenhouse.

VERONICA
Butterfly, Checker Spot.

VIBURNUM (Snowball and other types)
Aphid, Bean; Currant; Grapevine; Ivy; Snowball (prevalent on old-fashioned snowball, curling new leaves).
Beetle, Asiatic Garden; Potato Flea.
Borer, Dogwood Twig. **Bug,** Tarnished Plant.
Hornworms. Mites. Planthopper, Mealy Flata.
Scale, Chaff; Cottony-cushion; Cottony Maple; Olive Parlatoria; Oystershell; San Jose; Putnam.
Thrips, Flower; Greenhouse. **Whitefly,** Citrus.
Viburnum carlesi may be injured by some chemicals, especially sulfur and DDT.

VIOLET (*Viola*)
Aphid, Foxglove; Red Violet; Green Peach; Violet.
Beetle, Potato Flea. **Caterpillar,** Omnivorous Looper.
Leaf Tier, Celery. **Mealybug,** Citrus. **Midge,** Violet Gall.
Mite, Cyclamen; Two-spotted (very prevalent; leaves yellow).
Nematode, Fern; Root-knot.
Sawfly, Violet (blue-black larvae feed at night).

Slugs (common, large holes in leaves).
Avoid nicotine on violets; they are sometimes injured by it.

VIRGINIA CREEPER (*Parthenocissus quinquefolia*)
Aphid, Rusty Plum.
Beetle, Grape Flea; Japanese (new leaves chewed to lace); Rose Chafer.
Butterfly, Eight-spotted Forester. **Caterpillar,** Yellow Woollybear. **Hornworms.**
Leafhopper, Grape; Three-banded; Virginia-creeper (foliage grayish). **Mites. Moth,** Achemon Sphinx.
Scale, Cottony Maple; Olive Parlatoria; Oystershell; Peach; San Jose.

WALLFLOWER (*Cheiranthus*)
Aphid, Crescent-marked Lily.
Beetle, Red Turnip; Western Striped Flea. **Moth,** Diamondback.

WALNUT (*Juglans*)
Aphid, Hickory; Walnut. **Beetle,** Hickory Bark; Strawberry Leaf.
Borer, Brown Wood; California Prionus; Painted Hickory; Tiger Hickory; Twig Pruner.
Bug, Walnut Lace.
Caterpillar, Walnut (black with white hairs); Hickory Horned Devil; Omnivorous Looper; Orange Tortrix; Red-humped; Yellow-necked.
Curculio, Black Walnut; Butternut.
Fly, Walnut Husk. **Leaf Roller,** Fruit Tree.
Mealybug, Citrophilus; Grape.
Mite, European Red; Platani; Southern Red; Walnut Blister.
Moth, Codling (serious on Pacific coast); Hickory Tussock; Luna; Western Tussock.
Rootworm, Strawberry. **Sawfly,** Butternut Woollyworm.
Scale, Black; California Red; Calico; Citricola; Cottony-cushion; Greedy; Oystershell; Putnam; Scurfy; Walnut; White Peach.
Termites. Webworm, Fall.

WANDERING JEW (*Tradescantia*)
Caterpillar, Orange Tortrix.
Leaf Cutter, Morning-glory. **Leaf Tier,** Celery.
Mealybug, Citrus. **Nematode,** Root-knot. **Scale,** Chaff.

WATERCRESS (*Nasturtium officinale*)

Aphid, Bean; Spinach. **Beetle,** Watercress Leaf; Flea.
Moth, Diamondback. **Sowbug.**

WATERLILY (*Nymphaea*)

Aphid, Corn Leaf; Waterlily. **Beetle,** Waterlily.
Midge, False, Leaf-mining. **Leaf Cutter,** Waterlily.

WATERMELON (*Citrullus vulgaris*)

Aphid, Melon (common, serious).
Beetle, Potato Flea; Squash; Spotted Cucumber; Striped Cucumber.
Caterpillar, Melonworm; Pickleworm. **Cricket,** Camel.
Leaf Miner, Serpentine. **Millipedes.**
Scale, Black; California Red. **Wireworms.**
See Melon for other possible pests.

WEIGELA

Bug, Four-lined Plant. **Mealybug,** Comstock.

WILLOW (*Salix*)

Aphid, Hickory. **Bagworm.**
Beetle, Alder Flea; Cottonwood Leaf; Imported Willow Leaf (skele-
tonizes leaves, small, metallic blue; common); Japanese (makes
leaves into lace); June; Rose Leaf; Willow Flea.
Borer, Bronze Birch; Brown Wood; Carpenterworm; Cottonwood;
Flatheaded Apple Tree; Pacific Flatheaded; Poplar and Willow
(may be serious).
Butterfly, Mourning-cloak. **Casebearer,** California.
Caterpillar, California Tent; Eastern Tent; Forest Tent; Hemlock
Looper; Omnivorous Looper; Orange Tortrix; Poplar Tent Maker;
Red-humped; Walnut.
Leaf Roller, Fruit Tree. **Mite,** Platani.
Moth, Brown-tail; Buck; Cecropia; Gypsy; Hornet; Io; Leopard
(borer); Luna; Oriental; Rusty Tussock; Satin; White-marked
Tussock.
Nematode, Root-knot. **Sawfly,** Poplar; Willow.
Scale, Black; California Red; Cottony-cushion; Cottony Maple; Euro-
pean Fruit; Greedy; Lecanium; Obscure; Oystershell; Putnam; Soft;
Terrapin; Willow.
Thrips, Citrus; Pear. **Treehopper,** Two-marked.
Wasp, Giant Hornet. **Weevil,** Willow Flea.

WISTERIA (*Wistaria*)

Beetle, Sweetpotato Leaf.   Butterfly, Silver-spotted Skipper.
Mealybug, Japanese.   Planthopper, Mealy Flata.
Scale, Lesser Snow; Mining; Peach.
Webworm, Fall.   Weevil, Black Vine.

WITCH-HAZEL (*Hamamelis*)

Caterpillar, Saddled Prominent.   Gall, Witch-hazel Cone; other galls.

YAM VINE (*Dioscorea*)

Whitefly, Cloudy-winged.

YEW (*Taxus*)

Mealybug, Taxus (white bodies covering main trunk and branches);
  Grape.
Mites.   Scale, Cottony Taxus; California Red; Oleander; Purple.
Termites.   Weevil, Black Vine (grubs at roots; plants die).

YUCCA

Aphids.   Borer, Stalk.   Bug, Yucca Plant.
Mealybug, Citrus; Yucca.   Mites.
Moth, Yucca (effects pollination).
Scale, California Red; Oleander; Oystershell.   Thrips, Flower.

ZINNIA

Aphid, Bean.
Beetle, Asiatic Garden; Blister; Flea; Japanese (serious); Spotted
  Cucumber.
Borer, Stalk.   Bug, Four-lined Plant; Tarnished Plant.
Leaf Cutter, Morning-glory.   Leafhopper, Red-banded; Six-spotted.
Mealybug, Long-tailed.
Mite, Broad; Cyclamen; Two-spotted.   Thrips, Composite.

LIST OF AGRICULTURAL EXPERIMENT STATIONS IN THE UNITED STATES

Alabama: *Auburn*
Alaska: *Palmer*
Arizona: *Tucson*
Arkansas: *Fayetteville*
California: *Berkeley* 4
Colorado: *Fort Collins*
Connecticut:*New Haven* 4 (State Station)
   Storrs (Storrs Station)
Delaware, *Newark*
Florida: *Gainesville*
Georgia: *Athens*
   Experiment (State Station)
   Tifton (Coastal Plain Station)
Hawaii: *Honolulu*
Idaho: *Moscow*
Illinois: *Urbana*
Indiana: *Lafayette*
Iowa: *Ames*
Kansas: *Manhattan*
Kentucky: *Lexington* 29
Louisiana: *Baton Rouge* 3
Maine: *Orono*
Maryland: *College Park*
Massachusetts: *Amherst*
Michigan: *East Lansing*
Minnesota: *St. Paul*
Mississippi: *State College*
Missouri: *Columbia*
Montana: *Bozeman*
Nebraska: *Lincoln* 1
Nevada: *Reno*
New Hampshire: *Durham*

New Jersey: *New Brunswick*
New Mexico: *State College*
New York: *Geneva* (State Station)
   Ithaca (Cornell University)
North Carolina: *Raleigh*
North Dakota: *Fargo*
Ohio: *Wooster* (State Station)
   Columbus (Ohio State University)
Oklahoma: *Stillwater*
Oregon: *Corvallis*
Pennsylvania: *State College*
Puerto Rico: *Rio Piedras*
Rhode Island: *Kingston*
South Carolina: *Clemson*
South Dakota: *Brookings*
Tennessee: *Knoxville* 7
Texas: *College Station*
Utah: *Logan*
Vermont: *Burlington*
Virginia: *Blacksburg* (College Station)
   Norfolk (Truck Experiment Station)
Washington: *Pullman* (College Station)
   Puyallup (Western Washington Experiment Station)
West Virginia: *Morgantown*
Wisconsin: *Madison*
Wyoming: *Laramie*

GLOSSARY

Abdomen. The third, posterior division of the insect's body, usually composed of 10 or 11 segments, and with no functional legs in the adult stage.

Aerosol. An atomized fluid with very small particles, usually appearing as a fog or smoke.

Alternate Host. A second type of plant required for the completion of the life cycle of an insect.

Antenna (pl., *antennae*). Paired segmented appendages, borne one on each side of the head, sometimes called "feelers."

Anus. The posterior opening of the alimentary tract.

Apterous. Wingless.

Beak. The protruding mouth-part structures of a sucking insect; proboscis.

Bilateral Symmetry. With parts arranged more or less symmetrically on either side of a median vertical plane.

Brood. Individuals which hatch from the eggs laid by one mother, or individuals which hatch and normally mature at about the same time.

Caterpillar. Immature form, larva, of a moth, butterfly, or sawfly, having cylindrical body, well-developed head, thoracic legs, and abdominal prolegs.

Cephalothorax. United head and thorax, found in the Arachnida and Crustacea.

Cercus (pl., *cerci*). One of a pair of appendages at the end of the abdomen.

Chitin. A colorless, nitrogenous substance occurring in the outer layer of the body wall of arthropods.

Chrysalis (pl., *chrysalids*). The pupa of a butterfly.

Clypeus. A hardened plate on the lower part of the face, just above the labrum or upper lip.

Cocoon. A silken case inside which the pupa is formed.

Compatible. A material that can be used with another without counteracting or changing its effect.

Compound Eye. An eye composed of many individual elements, each represented externally by a facet.

Contact Poison. One which is effective on contact, as contrasted with a poison that must be swallowed.

Corium. The elongate, usually thickened, basal portion of the front wing, found in the order Hemiptera.

Cornicle. One of a pair of dorsal tubes on the posterior part of the abdomen of aphids, secreting a waxy liquid.

Coxa (pl., *coxae*). The basal segment of the leg, by which it is joined to the body.

Crawler. The active first instar of a scale insect.

Crotchets. Hooked spines at tip of prolegs of caterpillars.

Deuteronymph. The third instar of a mite.

Diluent. Inert material used in the preparation of a spray or dust.

Dormant. Inactive, usually in winter; the term is applied either to the host plant or the insect.

Dorsal. Pertaining to the back or upper side.

Dust. A finely divided or pulverized powder, applied dry.

Elytra (pl.). The thickened, leathery, or horny front wings of beetles, occasionally other insects.

Emergence. The act of an adult insect leaving the pupal case or last nymphal skin.

Exoskeleton. A skeleton or supporting structure on the outside of the body.

Exuviae (always used in plural). The cast skins of an arthropod.

Femur (pl., *femora*). The third leg segment, between the trochanter and the tibia.

Filiform. Hairlike or threadlike.

Frass. Sawdust or wood fragments, made by a wood-boring insect, mixed with excrement.

Furcula. The forked springing apparatus of the Collembola, springtails.

Gall. Abnormal growth of plant tissues caused by stimulus of an animal or another plant.

Gaster. Rounded part of the abdomen of an ant.

Grub. Immature form, larva, of a beetle, with thick body, well-developed head, thoracic legs but no prolegs.

Halter (pl., *halteres*). A small, knobbed structure in place of the hind wings in the order Diptera, flies.

Head. The anterior body region, bearing eyes, antennae, and mouth parts.

Hibernation. A period of suspended animation in animals during seasonal low temperatures.

Honeydew. A sweet substance discharged from the anus of aphids, mealybugs, scales, and whiteflies.

Host Plant. Plant attacked by, or supporting, insects or diseases.

Hyperparasite. A parasite whose host is another parasite.

Inactivated. Made inactive or inefficient.

Instar. The form of an insect between successive molts. The first instar is the stage between hatching and the first molt.

Integument. The outer covering of the body.

Labium. The lower lip.

Labrum. The upper lip, just under the clypeus.

Larva (pl., *larvae*). Immature form of an insect having complete metamorphosis. The name is also given to the 6-legged first instar of mites (Acarina).

Maggot. A legless wormlike larva, without a well-developed head; immature stage of Diptera, flies.

Mandibles. The first or anterior pair of jaws.

Maxillae (sing., *maxilla*). The second pair of jaws, immediately posterior to the mandibles.

Mesothorax. The middle or second segment of the thorax.

Metamorphosis. Change in form during development.

Metatarsus (pl., *metatarsi*). The basal segment of the tarsus.

Metathorax. The third or posterior segment of the thorax.

Molt. A process of shedding the skin.

Nocturnal. Active at night, flying or feeding.

Nymph. The immature stage of an insect with incomplete metamorphosis, one that does not have a pupal stage; also the 8-legged immature stage of Acarina.

Ocellus (pl., *ocelli*). The simple eye of an insect or other arthropod.

Order. Subdivisions of a class, containing a group of related families.

Oviparous. Reproducing by laying eggs.

Ovipositor. Specialized organ in the female for depositing eggs.

Ovisac. An egg sac, conspicuous in mealybugs and some scale insects.

Palpus (pl., *palpi*). A segmented process borne by the maxillae or labium.

Parasite. An animal that lives in or on the body of another living animal, at least during part of its life cycle. Also, a plant living on or in another plant.

Parthenogenesis. Reproduction by development of unfertilized eggs.

Pedicel. The "waist" or stem of the abdomen (between thorax and gaster) in ants; also second segment of the antenna.

Phylum (pl., *phyla*). One of the major divisions of the animal kingdom.

Posterior. Hind or rear.

Predator. An animal which attacks and feeds on another animal.

Proboscis. Extended beaklike mouth parts.

Proleg. One of the fleshy "false" abdominal legs of a caterpillar.

Prothorax. First segment of the thorax.

Protonymph. Second instar of a mite.

Pulvillus (pl., *pulvilli*). A soft pad or lobe beneath each tarsal claw.

Pupa (pl., *pupae*). Stage between the larva and adult in insects with complete metamorphosis; non-feeding, usually inactive.

Puparium (pl., *puparia*). The thickened, hardened last larval skin in which the pupa is formed in the Diptera or flies.

Pupate. Transform to a pupa.

Scavenger. An animal that feeds on dead plants or animals, or decaying material.

Segment. A subdivision of the body or an appendage between joints.

Seta (pl., *setae*). A bristle.

Species. A group of individuals similar in structure and physiology, capable of interbreeding and producing fertile offspring, and differing in structure or physiology from other such groups.

Spinneret. Organ used by certain insects in making silk or spinning webs.

Spiracle. A breathing pore, external opening of the tracheal system.

Spray. A liquid dispersed in fine drops.

Stem Mother. Female aphid giving birth to living young without fertilization.

Stipe. A short stalk or support.

Striate. With grooves or depressed lines.

Systemic Insecticides. Compounds which, applied to soil or foliage, are absorbed by the plant, rendering the sap toxic to certain insects.

Tarsus (pl., *tarsi*). The part of the leg beyond the tibia, consisting of 1 or more segments, bearing at the apex claws and pulvilli of the insect "foot."

Tegmina. Hard fore wings of grasshoppers.

Thorax. The body region behind the head, bearing legs and wings.

Tibia (pl., *tibiae*). The fourth segment of the leg, between the femur and the tarsus.

Tolerance. The amount of a spray or dust that can be left as residue on harvested fruits or vegetables without danger when they are used as food.

Trachea (pl., *tracheae*). A spirally ringed internal elastic air tube in insects, part of the respiratory system.

Trap Crop. A crop, usually planted in advance, to lure insects so they can be destroyed before attacking the desired crop.

Triungulin. The first instar larva of a blister beetle.

Trochanter. The second segment of the leg, between the coxa and the femur.

Tubercle. A small rounded or knoblike protuberance.

Vector. A carrier of disease-producing fungi, bacteria, or viruses.

Vein. A thickened line in the wing.

Ventral. Pertaining to the lower side of the body.

Viviparous. Giving birth to living young, not egg-laying.

SELECTED BIBLIOGRAPHY

The purpose of the new *Gardener's Bug Book* remains the same as that of the original manual: to collect, correlate, and condense between two covers much scattered information on garden pests. I acknowledge a great debt to the authors of many books, circulars, and articles. Listed below are some of the well-thumbed books in my plant doctor library that may also be useful to you. I have regretfully omitted many of the books listed in the first edition either because they are no longer in print or because their outmoded control measures might be more confusing than helpful. Their place has been taken by more recent publications, but even these are somewhat out of date in the light of our rapidly advancing knowledge.

In addition to continually acquiring books, I receive regularly, and at least scan, many scientific, technical, and popular publications, among them: *Journal of Economic Entomology: Bulletin of the Entomological Society of America; Cooperative Economic Insect Report* (issued by Plant Pest Control Branch, Agricultural Research Service, U. S. Department of Agriculture) ; *Plant Disease Reporter,* which covers work on nematodes (issued by Plant Disease Epidemics and Identification Section, Agricultural Research Service, U. S. Department of Agriculture); *Agricultural Chemicals; N.A.C. News and Pesticide Review* (National Agricultural Chemicals Association); *Biological Abstracts; A.I.B.S. Bulletin* (American Institute of Biological Sciences) ; *Science: New Jersey Agriculture* (Agricultural Experiment Station, Rutgers); *Farm Research* (New York Agricultural Experiment Station); *Frontiers of Plant Science* (Connecticut Agricultural Experiment Station) ; *Arborist's News; Annual Proceedings of National Shade Tree Conference; The Shade Tree* (New Jersey Federation of Shade Tree Commissions); *Trees Magazine; American Fruit Grower* (which has excellent charts of chemical compatibility and a description of a different fruit pest each month) ; *Farm Journal; Florists Exchange; Under Glass; Garden Facts for Garden Leaders* (issued by Federal

Extension Service, U. S. Department of Agriculture); *Plants & Gardens* (Brooklyn Botanic Garden); *The Garden Journal* (New York Botanical Garden); *The National Gardener* (National Council of State Garden Clubs); publications from nearly all the state garden clubs; *Home Acres* (Women's National Farm and Garden Association); *American Home; Better Homes and Gardens; Flower Grower; Horticulture; Pacific Gardens and Homes; Popular Gardening; American Camellia Quarterly* and *Yearbook; American Rose Magazine* and *Annual;* and *The Gladiolus Magazine.* I also receive news letters from several chemical companies and make use of innumerable bulletins, circulars, and spray schedules from many state experiment stations and the U. S. Department of Agriculture. Too few gardeners realize how much information is available free from local county agents or state experiment stations, or, for a few cents, from the Superintendent of Documents, U. S. Government Printing Office, Washington 25, D.C., nor how much help the local public library can be along this line.

American Society for Horticultural Science and the National Fertilizer Association. *The Care and Feeding of Garden Plants.* 184 pp., 70 illus. The National Fertilizer Association, Washington 5, D.C., 1954.

> An important book, distinguishing, by color photographs, between mineral deficiencies or effects of improper temperature and injury by mites, nematodes, etc.

Borror, Donald J. and Dwight M. Delong. *An Introduction to the Study of Insects.* 1030 pp. Rinehart and Company, New York, 1954.

> A fine textbook, not too complicated for the serious gardener.

Brues, Charles T., A. L. Melander, and Frank M. Carpenter. *Classification of Insects.* Bulletin of the Museum of Comparative Zoology at Harvard College, Vol. 108. 917 pp. Cambridge, Mass., 1954.

Clausen, Lucy W. *Insect Fact and Folklore.* 194 pp., 30 illus. The Macmillan Company, New York, 1954.

> Fascinating bits of information and legend.

Craighead, F. C. *Insect Enemies of Eastern Forests.* U. S. Department of Agriculture Misc. Publ. 657. 679 pp., 197 illus. U. S. Goverment Printing Office, Washington 25, D.C., 1950.

> There are many excellent photographs of insects that are garden as well as forest pests.

Dimock, A. W. *The Gardener's ABC of Pest and Disease.* 191 pp. M. Barrows and Company, Inc., New York, 1953.

Dodge, Bernard O. and Harold W. Rickett. *Diseases and Pests of Ornamental Plants.* 638 pp., 201 illus. The Ronald Press Company, New York, Rev. 1948.

> The first large-scale attempt to bring together information on diseases and pests of a large number of ornamentals grown in greenhouses and outdoors.

Eadie, W. Robert. *Animal Control in Field, Farm, and Forest.* 257 pp. The Macmillan Company, New York, 1954.

> Good summary of heretofore scattered information on control of wild animals that disturb gardeners as well as farmers.

Entoma: A Directory of Insect and Plant Pest Control. 10th ed. 1953–54. Entomological Society of America, Washington 5, D.C.

Essig, E. O. *Insects of Western North America.* 1035 pp., 766 illus. The Macmillan Company, New York, 1926.

> I can't conceive of gardening in the West without this book, which is still in print though we eagerly look forward to a promised new edition.

Felt, Ephraim Porter. *Plant Galls and Gall Makers.* 364 pp., 344 figs., 41 pls. Comstock Publishing Company, Inc., Ithaca, N.Y., 1940.

> For those really interested in the queer malformations caused by insects.

Fenska, Richard R. *The New Tree Experts Manual.* 238 pp. A. T. De La Mare Company, Inc., New York, 1954.

> Condensed, useful information by a practical tree man.

Fernald, H. T. and Harold H. Shepard. *Applied Entomology.* 5th ed. 385 pp., 269 illus. McGraw-Hill Book Company, Inc., N.Y., 1955.

> Selected pests in the various insect orders discussed in clear detail.

Frear, Donald E. H. *Chemistry of the Pesticides.* 3rd rev. ed. 469 pp. D. Van Nostrand Company, Inc., New York, 1955.

———. *Pesticide Handbook.* 7th ed. 208 pp. College Science Publishers, State College, Pa., 1955.

> An alphabetical list of more than 6000 trade-named pesticides with information on their active ingredients and manufacturers; a decidedly useful tool. Send order to Pesticide Handbook, P.O. Box 798, State College, Pa.

Garman, Philip and J. F. Townsend. *Control of Apple Insects.* Connecticut Agricultural Experiment Station Bulletin 552. 84 pp., 71 illus. New Haven, Conn., 1952.

> Practically a book, with many excellent illustrations.

Hough, Walter S. and A. Freeman Mason. *Spraying, Dusting and*

Fumigating of Plants. 726 pp., 241 illus. The Macmillan Company, New York, 1951.

> Modern version of an old stand-by, with detailed information on chemicals and equipment, seed treatment, spraying operations, good keys for diagnosis of fruit and vegetable troubles.

Keen, F. P. *Insect Enemies of Western Forests.* U. S. Department of Agriculture Misc. Publ. 273. Rev. 280 pp., 111 illus. U. S. Government Printing Office, Washington 25, D.C., 1952.

Klots, Alexander B. *A Field Guide to the Butterflies of North America, east of the Great Plains.* Houghton Mifflin Company, Boston, 1951.

Leach, Julian Gilbert. *Insect Transmission of Plant Diseases.* 615 pp., 238 illus. McGraw-Hill Book Company, Inc., New York, 1940.

> Not too technical for the serious gardener, this book presents clearly the part insects play as vectors of plant disease and shows how they themselves can cause disease symptoms.

Lutz, Frank E. *Field Book of Insects.* 510 pp., 100 pls. G. P. Putnam's Sons, New York, 1935.

> Standard handbook for every budding entomologist.

Matheson, Robert. *Entomology for Introductory Courses.* 600 pp., 500 illus. Comstock Publishing Company, Inc., Ithaca, N.Y., 1944.

> A very readable textbook on insects and their relation to man.

Metcalf, C. L. and W. P. Flint, rev. by R. L. Metcalf. *Destructive and Useful Insects.* 3rd ed. 1071 pp., 584 illus. McGraw-Hill Book Company, Inc., New York, 1951.

> In its various editions, this has been my bible for plant doctoring and writing, and I probably owe more to it than to any other book in my library.

Newcomer, E. J. *Orchard Insects of the Pacific Northwest and their Control.* U. S. Department of Agriculture Circ. 270. 63 pp., 70 illus. U. S. Government Printing Office, Washington 25, D.C., Rev. 1950.

New England Section, Society of American Foresters. *Important Tree Pests of the Northeast.* 2nd ed. 191 pp., 82 illus. Evans Printing Company, Concord, N.H., 1952.

Palmer, Miriam A. *Aphids of the Rocky Mountain Region.* 452 pp., 8 pls., in color, 455 figs. Thomas Say Foundation. Vol. V. 1952.

> For the entomologist; aphids common over a much wider area than the Rocky Mountains are included.

Palmer, Ralph S. *The Mammal Guide.* 384 pp., 40 pls., in color. Doubleday & Company, Inc., Garden City, N.Y., 1954.

> Very helpful in identification of animal pests.

Peairs, Leonard Marion. *Insect Pests of Farm, Garden and Orchard.* 4th ed. 540 pp., 648 illus. John Wiley & Sons, Inc., New York, 1941.
    Good descriptions and photographs of vegetable and fruit insects.

Pirone, P. P. *Maintenance of Shade and Ornamental Trees.* 2nd ed. 436 pp., 173 illus. Oxford University Press, New York, 1948.
    Equally good for the tree expert and the homeowner who employs one.

――――. *Modern Gardening.* 371 pp. Simon and Schuster, New York, 1952.
    Numerous lists of pesticides, with trade names; 500 garden questions answered.

Pyenson, Louis L. *Elements of Plant Protection.* 538 pp., 226 illus. John Wiley & Sons, Inc., New York, 1951.
    A textbook, but good for gardeners who want basic information on types of pests, including mammals and birds.

Quayle, J. J. *Insects of Citrus and Other Subtropical Fruits.* 583 pp., 377 illus. Comstock Publishing Company, Inc., Ithaca, N.Y., 1941.
    Detailed life histories, lists of food plants, and excellent photographs to help you if you garden in California or the South.

Reed, L. B. and S. P. Doolittle. *Insects and Diseases of Vegetables in the Home Garden.* 64 pp., 4 color pls., figs. U. S. Department of Agriculture Home and Garden Bulletin 46. U. S. Government Printing Office, Washington 25, D.C., 1955.

Ries, Victor H. *The Gardener's Trouble Shooter.* 320 pp., 59 illus. Sheridan House, Inc., N.Y., 1952.
    About 300 plants and their problems treated alphabetically by a professor who spends much of his time answering gardeners' questions.

Standen, Anthony. *Insect Invaders.* 228 pp., 56 pls. Houghton Mifflin Company, Boston, 1943.
    Read this to know how much trouble insects have caused in this country.

Swain, Ralph B. *The Insect Guide.* 261 pp., 48 color pls. Doubleday & Company, Inc., Garden City, New York, 1948, 1952.
    Brief descriptions of orders and families with fine examples in color; a very useful introduction to insects for both the layman and the student.

Teale, Edwin Way. *Near Horizons: The Story of an Insect Garden.* Dodd, Mead & Company, Inc., New York, 1942.

――――. *The Boys' Book of Insects.* 237 pp., 55 illus. The Blakiston Co., Philadelphia, 1943.

Teale, Edwin Way, Editor. *Green Treasury: A Journey through the World's Great Nature Writing*. Dodd, Mead & Company, Inc., New York, 1952.

———, Editor. *The Insect World of J. Henri Fabre*. Dodd, Mead & Company, Inc., New York, 1949.

Any book by Teale is a delight and his photographs are superb.

U. S. Department of Agriculture. *Insects*. The Yearbook of Agriculture, 1952. 780 pp., 72 color pls. U. S. Government Printing Office, Washington 25, D.C., 1952.

Weigel, C. A. and L. G. Baumhofer. *Handbook on Insect Enemies of Flowers and Shrubs*. U. S. Department of Agriculture Misc. Publ. 626. 115 pp., 170 illus. U. S. Government Printing Office, Washington 25, D.C., 1948.

Westcott, Cynthia. *Garden Enemies*. 261 pp., 66 illus. D. Van Nostrand Company, Inc., New York, 1953.

Diagrammatic sketches for recognition of enemies; charts listing enemy, damage, and control; dictionary of pesticides.

———. *The Plant Doctor*. 231 pp., 40 illus. J. B. Lippincott Company, Philadelphia, 3rd ed. 1950, 1953.

First published in 1937 as a calendar of pest control for the Northeast, later enlarged to cover other sections of the country.

——— and Peter K. Nelson, editors. *Handbook on Pests and Diseases*. 96 pp., 150 photographs. Brooklyn Botanic Garden, Brooklyn 25, N.Y., 1955.

Easy to read articles by twelve specialists, well illustrated.

Wheeler, W. M. *Ants: Their Structure, Development and Behavior*. Columbia University Press, New York, 1910.

The standard treatise on ants, perhaps available at your public library.

This very brief listing includes none of the books on single plants, African violets, azaleas, lilies, roses, etc. (not even my own *Anyone Can Grow Roses*), which contain information on their specific problems. Nor does it include the hundreds of state and U.S.D.A. bulletins and circulars on pests of special crops, peaches, peanuts, pecans, potatoes etc., etc., etc., and the bulletins on special groups of pests, ants, nematodes, slugs, wireworms, etc. Do visit your public library, ask to see the bulletins available, and then order for your private library those that interest you.

INDEX

Boldface numerals indicate line drawings; plate numbers refer to color illustrations.